CW00404732

"Contemporary debates over such central g[...]
versity and food security often come dow[...]
often the role of natural resources is ignored or masked [...]
from various sides of the political spectrum.

Are We Running Out? addresses this gap with a factually rich, dispassionate analysis that seeks to answer a simple question. What is the current state of professional knowledge about different types of resources? Avoiding the easy answers, Bryan weaves together ideas from a host of disciplines. The result is something unique: a magisterial survey of the global environmental conundrum which humanity has created for itself.

No reader can come away from these pages without having gained a richer sense of this conundrum. Nor can they remain unmoved by Bryan's urgent call to action."

Mark Lovewell

Interim editor, *Literary Review of Canada*, marklovewell.com

"As a species we have an unlimited capacity for ignoring uncomfortable truths. Anyone who reads Ingrid Bryan's thoroughly researched and wise book will no longer be able to deny that we are facing a global crisis of sustainability for human life on this planet. We owe her a debt of gratitude for laying it out so clearly and in such a compelling way."

Margaret MacMillan

Warden of St Anthony's College, Oxford University

"Ingrid Bryan's timely new book addresses a central question for a world dependent on natural resources: *Are we running out?* Professor Bryan explores this question as it relates to fossil fuels and minerals, biodiversity, fresh water, agriculture, ocean resources, and the world's forests. The author's expertise in natural resource economics unifies a wide-ranging comprehensive discussion that draws on insights from a broad array of disciplines. This book is essential reading for those seeking information on the natural resources that future generations will inherit and on policy directions that can lead to better outcomes."

Robert Deacon

Professor Emeritus of Economics, University of California, Santa Barbara

Are We Running Out?

The Sustainability of the World's Resources

Ingrid Bryan

Sustainability Press

Library and Archives Canada Cataloguing in Publication
Bryan, Ingrid A., author
    Are we running out? : the sustainability of the world's resources /
Ingrid Bryan.

Includes bibliographical refrences and index.
ISBN 978-0-9947845-0-6 (paperback)

    1. Natural resources—Management. 2. Sustainable development.
3. Human ecology. 4. Environmental economics. I. Title.
HC79.E5B79 2015   333.7   C2015-905085-5

Editing by Arlene Prunkl
Book cover design by Julie Hawkins
Text design by Fiona Raven

First Printing, September 2015
Printed in the USA

Published by Sustainability Press

www.sustainabilitypress.com

For my grandchildren, Tristan and Imogen.

O mother earth,
ocean-girdled
and mountain-breasted,
pardon me for trampling on you.

(Text from a Sanskrit prayer)

Contents

Preface

THIS BOOK is about the importance of natural resources in the twenty-first century, how they affect living standards in both rich and poor countries, and the consequences of natural resource degradation. Always an avid environmentalist, following the birth of my grandchildren I began to become increasingly worried about the legacy my generation is leaving for future generations. After retiring as a professor of economics at Ryerson University in Toronto, I decided to follow my interests and write a book about the role of resources in the past and present, examining whether our current use is sustainable into the future. During my career I taught both environmental and resource economics courses, and like most such courses, their focus was very narrow; I was convinced there was an important story to tell for larger audiences. But I found no books that were comprehensive, and none that would appeal to readers not versed in an academic discipline such as economics. To be sure, many books deal with specific resources, but few treat resources as a whole. In my view, this is important because no resource can be examined in isolation—everything is interconnected. Lomborg's optimistic book, *The Sceptical Environmentalist: Measuring the Real State of the World* is extensive but is widely regarded as biased because of the selective use of data. My book gives a comprehensive, objective, up-to-date account of our use of resources ranging from non-renewable resources (minerals and fossil fuels) to renewable resources (biodiversity, forests, water, soils, fisheries, and other ocean resources). In each case, I set current use in a historical context and analyze whether it is sustainable, and if not, how it can be made sustainable for the benefit of future generations. Having spent the last decade immersed in the resource literature, I now believe that the resource situation is so precarious that it is our moral duty to be informed and to do all we can to influence our governments to take appropriate action. I hope this book can help. Rapid changes in technology have alleviated the immediate pressure on most non-renewable resources, but the situation is serious for renewable resources. In addition to the critical, overarching problem of climate change, areas of particular concern are the state of agricultural resources, fresh water resources, ocean resources, and the precarious situation of biodiversity.

Chapter 1 provides the context for the rest of the book by discussing the role and importance of natural resources in the past and present development of modern economies and what we can learn from history. The concept of sustainability is explored, with examples of unsustainable resource use. The chapter explains why some resource-rich countries remain poor (the "resource curse") and what measures countries can take to profit from their natural resource endowments. It concludes with a discussion of the often-debated notion that lack of resources and competition for resources are likely to lead to future resource wars.

The following chapters analyse the situation of individual resources. In Chapter 2, I explain how commodity markets operate and the reasons behind large fluctuations of metals and minerals prices. The chapter explores the present use and availability of metals and minerals, ranging from the common metals such as copper and iron ore to the less common ones such as rare earth minerals and lithium, now very important in the manufacture of some consumer electronics and electric cars. Mineral depletion and the sustainability of mining are discussed, and the environmental record of the mining industry is assessed as well as the problems of recycling, with particular emphasis on the recycling of ships and electronic wastes.

Chapter 3 is devoted to the availability and use of fossil fuels, which provide the foundation for the prosperity of industrial countries. This chapter examines energy use since the Industrial Revolution, including the early search for sources of lighting that resulted in the near extinction of whales because of the demand for whale oil. The chapter traces the development of OPEC and analyzes the reasons behind the large fluctuations in the price of oil and their repercussions on the world economy. The development of non-conventional oil, such as oil from the Alberta oil sands and shale oil, is discussed in some detail, as is the situation for coal and natural gas in view of newly discovered deposits of shale gas.

Any discussion of the sustainability of fossil fuels must include the extremely contentious and complicated topic of climate change. Chapter 4 includes a concise account of the known history of climate change, dating back thousands of years, as well as the history of the science. The current evidence for global warming is examined along with costs and benefits of mitigation and the various measures that can be employed such as carbon taxes, cap-and-trade policies, and geoengineering solutions.

Chapter 5 also discusses methods of reducing carbon dioxide in the atmosphere, but this time by examining the prospects for developing carbon-free energy. It surveys the costs and benefits of a whole range of possible alternatives, including the prospects for nuclear energy following the Fukushima Daiichi disaster. It also assesses whether renewable resources can replace fossil fuels.

Chapter 6 is the first in a series of chapters dealing with the state of renewable resources. Evidence shows that the earth's biodiversity is in danger, and some biologists claim we are currently experiencing a sixth species extinction. In this chapter, I explain the meaning of biodiversity, how it is measured, what recent data indicate, and why we should be concerned. The chapter surveys estimates of the economic value of biodiversity and ecosystem services. It includes an examination of the effectiveness of international conventions such as the Biodiversity Convention, the Convention for the Regulation of Whaling, and The Convention on International Trade in Endangered Species (CITES).

Chapter 7 continues the discussion of biodiversity by concentrating on the importance of forests. Apart from providing us with wood and habitats for wildlife, forests critically influence climate change by acting as carbon sinks. How do we balance the ecological need for intact forests with the commercial need for wood? The chapter examines the evolution of attitudes to forests and forestry and the state of the world's forests with particular attention to the causes of deforestation. It also evaluates the debate about best logging practices, moves toward forest certification, and the implications of the REDD+ program.

The problem of growing food for a predicted 2050 population of over nine billion people is addressed in Chapter 8 in light of strong evidence that modern industrialized agriculture is not sustainable. The chapter discusses various proposals for making agriculture more environmentally friendly and the need for more agricultural research and investments, particularly in Africa. A section is devoted to the advantages and disadvantages of GM crops. The problem of price instability of agricultural products is discussed, and the chapter concludes with an examination of food security and how it might be achieved.

Water is the focus of Chapter 9—one of the most critical current global resource issues of today. In most of the world it is a critical issue because of massive failures in water management, ranging from the adverse environmental effects of irrigation and industrial contamination to the lack of water treatment facilities, leading to a scarcity of potable water. Economic approaches to water management are discussed as well as the likelihood of conflicts relating to water rights as water sources often straddle international borders.

Nowhere is the "tragedy of the commons" as obvious as in the mismanagement of the oceans, and Chapter 10 highlights the problems of maintaining the ecology of the oceans in the face of increased pollution, overharvesting of fish resources, increased exploitation of mineral and oil and gas resources, and the threat posed to oceans by climate change. Many of the world's fisheries are near total collapse, and this chapter examines the reasons along with what can be done to save fish stocks and viable marine ecosystems. The development of aquaculture is discussed as one of many possible solutions to declining fish stocks. The chapter also examines the regulatory framework for ocean resources under the "the Law of the Sea" process.

The final chapter focuses on how the current unsustainable situation of resource use arose, emphasizing the role of explosive population growth and the implications of humans transforming earth into a totally human-dominated planet—the Anthropocene. It examines the question whether a mechanism exists that guarantees the earth will heal itself, and if not, what measures can be taken to avert catastrophe. It emphasizes the need to decrease resource use in rich countries, enabling poor countries to increase their resource use in order to grow and prosper.

In writing such a wide-ranging book over so many years, I am indebted to many experts who offered constructive comments on individual chapters. They are in alphabetical order: Michael Bardecki, professor of geography, Ryerson University, and reviewer for the IPCC (climate); Robert Deacon, professor of economics, UCSB (forestry and biodiversity); Evan Fraser, associate professor of geography and Canada research chair, University of Guelph (agriculture); David Griffith, former general secretary of the International Council for Exploration of the Sea (fisheries); Shashi Kant, professor of forestry, University of Toronto (forestry); Conrad Pilditch, associate professor of ocean biology , Faculty of Science and Engineering, University of Waikato (biodiversity and oceans); Anthony Price, associate professor of environmental sciences, University of Toronto (water). My husband, Rorke Bryan, professor emeritus of geography and forestry, University of Toronto, greatly enhanced my understanding of soils and desert environments and the larger issue of forest conservation. We spent many hours over the years discussing environmental and resource issues. Our daughter, Karin Bryan, associate professor of oceanography, University of Waikato, contributed to my understanding of ocean circulation.

I am particularly indebted to Mark Lovewell, formerly associate professor of economics, Ryerson University, and the current editor of the *Literary Review of Canada*, who read the whole manuscript and offered encouragement and support over the years. David Pettersson read and commented on the chapter on fossil fuels; our son Feargus Bryan, an environmentalist and a sailor, pointed out flaws in the oceans chapter; and my late brother-in-law Maurice Bryan, also an environmentalist, gave constructive comments on the climate chapter. I could not have written this book without full access to the Ryerson library and its electronic journal collection. My editor Arlene Prunkl greatly improved and polished the manuscript and assisted in the tedious work of reference checking. I am also very grateful for the excellent work of my book designer Fiona Raven and my cover designer Julie Hawkins.

1

The Importance of Natural Resources

The importance of natural resources and their influence on history and culture. The "resource curse" and the impact of resources on economic development. The sustainability of resource use. Examples of unsustainable resource use: depletion and resource collapse. Resource scarcity and resource wars. Concluding remarks.

URBAN DWELLERS IN RICH COUNTRIES typically do not regard the natural environment as being of much consequence in their daily lives because most consume goods and services that seem to have no connection with natural resources. This book will show this is not true—the state of the natural environment has an enormous effect on our lives through the air we breathe, the water we drink, and the goods we consume. The environment also has a direct impact on the billions of people living in developing countries whose existence still depends on their ability to live off the land or the sea. This book is an examination of the state of the world's resources, their importance, and the extent to which current resource policies are appropriate to ensure resources are exploited sustainably for the maximum benefit of the people who depend on them, both today and in the future.

A natural resource occurs naturally in the environment and can be exploited for the benefit of humans. *Biotic* resources are obtained from processes in the biosphere. Examples are forests, animals, including fish, and even fossil fuels

1

formed by decaying organic matter. *Abiotic* resources are derived from non-organic materials such as metals, minerals, and water. A more familiar division of resources is into *renewable* and *non-renewable* resources. Renewable resources can be replenished naturally such as air, water, fish, and biodiversity, while non-renewable resources are replenished on a geological timescale—too slowly (millions of years) to be of any consequence for humans. Examples are metals, minerals, and fossil fuels. This difference has implications for resource policy. In the case of renewable resources, sustainability would dictate that resources are not exploited beyond their replacement level, while for non-renewable resources the issue is more complex because any extraction, by definition, cannot ensure sustainability.

The importance of a resource for local economies is determined by the need for survival, the dictates of the markets, or the whims of governments. A resource will not be exploited if there is no demand for it or no technology to exploit it.[1] The next section will give a few illustrations of how resources have shaped history and cultures, and how quickly a country's fortune can change if the market for its resources disappears. A discussion will follow of the benefits to a country of being endowed with valuable resources. In some cases resource-rich countries remain desperately poor—for example, the Democratic Republic of the Congo—while in other cases they benefit enormously—for example, Norway. Then the issue of the importance of sustainability will be addressed with some illustrations of what can happen if a resource is not sustainably managed, if there is a danger of resource wars, and what lessons can be drawn for resource management in modern times.

The importance of natural resources and their influence on history and culture

Life would not be possible without natural resources such as air, water, soils, and biodiversity, but resources have also played a significant role in shaping the world's political, economic, and social environments. The first civilizations developed in the Middle East because of a natural environment conducive to agriculture. Europeans colonized much of the Americas and Australia in search of land and other resources with little or no regard for the rights of indigenous peoples to use their own land. Energy resources in particular have had a huge effect in the development of modern industrial society. The Industrial Revolution was made possible because of abundant coal, and today's industry developed based on the premise of continued access to cheap oil. Much of world politics today is focused on the strategic significance of fossil fuels and the impact of their use on the atmosphere, a topic that is discussed in Chapter 4.

The need for resources laid the foundations for trade. Trade allows people to acquire goods they cannot make or find themselves, increasing living standards by introducing variety and comfort into people's daily lives. Trade also makes it possible for people to survive in cities without being directly involved in food production. The search for goods to be traded has been guided by complex interplays of basic needs, culture and fashion, and politics and economics, and has had a substantial impact on history and culture. A good illustration is salt.[2] Given human physiology, salt is absolutely essential for survival. Early hunters and gatherers received their salt from eating meat, but agriculturalists had to include salt as supplement to their diet while providing it to their domesticated animals. As well, salt was important for food preservation.

While salt can be found almost everywhere in the world, it is not necessarily very accessible and thus a salt trade developed early. Many settlements were built near salt deposits, and many ancient roads were built to facilitate the transportation of salt. For example, the *Via Salaria* ("salt road") dates from the fifth century BC and connected Ostia, the outport for Rome, with the Sabine Hills before continuing to the Adriatic Sea.[3] Because of its commercial importance, the Romans and Venetians used salt to pay *salaries*, and a salt tax was an easy way to raise money for wars and other ventures. The French tax on salt—*la gabelle*—was first introduced during the thirteenth century and was so resented by the population that it became a powerful symbol of injustice. It was abolished in 1790 following the French Revolution, was briefly reinstated by Napoleon, and stayed on the books until 1945.[4]

Salt also played a part in many ancient customs.[5] For example, it was thought to be an aphrodisiac (the word *salacious* comes from the Romans, who called a man in love *salax*—in a salted state), and in several cultures the sprinkling of salt has long been used in wedding ceremonies. For some, salt also has a religious significance. In Judaism, salt is the symbol of God's eternal covenant with Israel, and both in Islam and Judaism, friendship and loyalty are sealed with salt. In Christianity, the Catholic Church uses not only holy water but also *sal sapientia* (holy salt—the salt of wisdom). In Japanese, Haitian, Jewish, and Muslim cultures, it is believed that salt protects against evil spirits.

Its economic and political significance continued to modern times. Most famously, salt played a pivotal role in Mahatma Gandhi's non-violent struggle for Indian independence.[6] In 1930, he was looking for a just cause that could increase the following for his movement toward independence, and he found it in salt. Under British law, Indians could not produce or sell salt; instead, they were required to buy their salt from British-owned salt factories at a very high price. The high price hit the poor particularly hard, and Gandhi decided to try to break the monopoly by organizing a march to the sea at Dandi. When he and his followers reached the sea, they managed to separate some salt crystals from the mud and urged every Indian to do the same. Thousands of Indians were jailed, including Gandhi—a notorious illustration of British injustice that served as a catalyst for India's independence movement.

While historically the need for salt laid the foundations for local and regional trade, the trade in many other commodities necessitated the building of long-distance links between political entities and cultures in different parts of the globe. The best example is the trade in spices, which are another essential part of food flavouring and preservation. The search for spices led to the discovery of the sea route from Europe to the Indian Ocean as well as to the European discovery of North America. The spice trade is thought to predate the Roman Empire, and it is not unlikely that spices were transported over large distances as early as 3000 BC.[7] During the Middle Ages, Europe's ruling classes developed a liking for spicy food, which to some may seem excessive. Pepper, cloves, cinnamon, and nutmeg were used in large quantities in preparing both meat and fruit dishes as well as drinks. According to the ancient Greek physician Hippocrates, a person's health was determined by the four fluids (humours) in the body (blood, yellow bile, black bile, and phlegm); an imbalance of these would throw the person's bodily functions out of kilter, and it was believed that spices were essential in maintaining the necessary bodily balance. The wealthier the household, the greater was the use of spices. Not only was the food prepared with spices, but spice platters were presented at the table to allow diners to add even more. According to one household account book from the later Middle Ages, a banquet for forty required one pound of columbine powder (derived from the plant *aquilegia*), half a pound of ground cinnamon, a quarter pound of cloves, an eighth of a pound of pepper, and an equal amount of nutmeg and bay leaves.[8]

For most of recorded history, spices were used in Europe, but initially their origin was shrouded in mystery. It was sometimes said that pepper grew like a bamboo forest on a plain near Paradise. Ginger and cinnamon, according to some accounts, had been carried by the Nile from Paradise and were collected by Egyptian fishermen casting nets into the floodwaters of the Nile.[9] The smell of spices was commonly believed to have spread from Paradise over the human world; therefore, spices were a tangible link to Paradise.[10] In reality, the much coveted mace and nutmeg come from the same fruit (*Myristica fragrans*), which could be found only on the tiny Banda Islands, approximately eight hundred kilometres north of Darwin, Australia. Cloves also came from the same general area (the Moluccas) and were as highly prized in China as in Europe. Both the Banda Islands and the Moluccas are often referred to as the Spice Islands. Pepper, cinnamon, and camphor came from India. Spices were first transported by Arab middlemen to Syria and Egypt, using the ancient Silk Road, and were then loaded on ships destined for Venice. Some were re-exported to northern Europe via alpine passes.

The spice trade was highly profitable for the Italian merchants, who used their earnings to build luxurious palaces and to commission great works of art. Demand for spices continued to increase through to the end of the Middle Ages, when their use spread among the middle classes. The increased demand, combined with the cumbersome transportation network and increased customs duties imposed by new rulers in Asia Minor and Egypt, caused a thirtyfold increase in prices, which in turn precipitated a race for different transportation routes and ships that could carry more cargo.[11] The focus was on finding a sea route to India and the Spice Islands, inspiring the voyages of exploration by Columbus, who "discovered" America in 1492 (believing he had reached India), and Vasco da Gama, who found the sea route around the tip of Africa to India in 1498, securing a monopoly of the spice trade for the Portuguese. Portugal and Spain were the dominant sea powers at the time and, to avoid conflict, the 1494 Treaty of Tordesilla established that Spain had the rights to all new lands to the west of a line of longitude situated one hundred leagues (345 miles) west of the Cape Verde islands and Portugal to all new lands east. This is why Brazil is Portuguese speaking while the rest of South America is Spanish speaking. Magellan's westerly journey in search of another route to the Moluccas was financed by Spain to challenge the Portuguese dominance of the eastern sea route around Africa. Even though Magellan himself was killed in the Philippines, the journey was a success as his flagship *Victoria*, one of the original five ships, returned to Spain in 1521 after having completed the first circumnavigation of the earth. This proved without doubt that there was another continent between Europe and Asia. The quest for other routes to the Spice Islands also led to the search for the Northeast and Northwest Passages. Jacques Cartier's travels from 1534 to 1542 seeking the Northwest Passage resulted in the first settlement around the St. Lawrence River in Canada. By this time, the European discovery of the Americas and the plentiful supplies of gold and silver that the Spanish conquest of Central and South America had provided were leading to a shift of emphasis from spices to precious metals and other commodities.

While the search for spices led to lasting changes in the world as it was then known, the quest for other commodities also had huge impacts on the newly discovered regions, particularly on its original inhabitants. An example is the trade in brazilwood, which led to the naming of Brazil.[12] Pau Brasil, a powder made from a tree found in Asia, had a ready market in Europe because its red colour was used to make red die for red velvet clothing, fashionable and highly valued during the Renaissance. The early explorers found an abundance of the Pernambuco tree (*Caesalpinia echinata*) in the Amazon forest, which was an even better source of the red dye and which also provided wood for bows of string instruments. However, harvesting the trees required a large amount of physical labour in cutting and transporting the trees to the coast. It is likely that as many as six million people lived in Brazil in 1500, but the native Indian population had no interest in hard labour or in the goods the Europeans offered as payment. Enslavement did not help either, as the natives who were enslaved made it clear they would prefer to die rather than cut trees for the whites. The only solution was to bring in a vast number of slaves from Africa. But slaves were expensive, and the earnings from the Pernambuco trade were not sufficient. Thus a more profitable commodity was introduced: sugar. After the introduction of sugar plantations, which drove the native population farther and farther into the interior, the ready supply of wood dwindled and timber production declined. The tree is now so rare that it is on the endangered species list.

Another example of how consumer demand for fashionable products influenced the development of a country is the trade in beaver pelts and the exploration of Canada. The fashion for broad-brimmed felt hats developed during the latter part of the sixteenth century.[13] The felt hats were made from beaver fur by removing the fur from the skin and mixing it with stiffeners and adhesives such as mercury—a process that often ended up poisoning the hat makers (which led to the expression "mad as a hatter"). Beavers in Europe became increasingly rare, and some of the ships carrying cod from Newfoundland started bringing back beaver pelts as well, especially once traders realized the abundance of the Canadian beaver (*Castor canadensis*). A beaver pelt has two layers, an outer shield of guard hair and an inner layer of soft undercoating known as *castor gras*. It was the castor gras that was desirable, and it was most easily obtained from beaver coats worn by the Indians as the guard hairs had been worn off. But the European search for raw beaver pelts intensified following the French discovery of the felting process, which made it possible to make hats of different shapes from the raw furs.

French traders established a trading post near Quebec City in 1608, and the French government established a monopoly. When beavers were extirpated from the immediate area around the St. Lawrence, the search for new supplies pushed both traders and Indians farther and farther north and west on to the Precambrian Shield, following the habitat of the beaver. Meanwhile, the Hudson's Bay Company, formed by the British in 1670, was given rights to all the lands surrounding the rivers that drain into Hudson Bay (Rupert's Land). It did not surrender this land to Canada until 1869—two years after Canada became an independent country. In the early years of the fur trade, Indian corn, Indian methods of making buffalo meat into pemmican, and Indian-designed birch-bark canoes were essential. The Indians demanded European goods in return for the pelts—in particular, guns and alcohol. The impact of European culture on the native population was, as is most often the case, destructive. The Indian tribes were decimated by disease and warfare, and consequently it became necessary to introduce European transportation, personnel, and food supplies. Meanwhile, the fur trade was responsible for both the economic and political dominance first by the French and later by the British in the northern regions of the continent. However, fashions changed, and by the 1850s most hats in Europe and North America were made from silk and other materials, and the market for pelts collapsed. By this time, the fur trade had left its indelible mark both on the native populations and on the shape of a new country, Canada.

Changes in demand not only affect the market for a resource but also competition from other sources of the same material or from changes in technology that make the original resource obsolete. The impacts of such changes on local populations were often long-lasting. Two examples are rubber and guano (bird excrement). Rubber, which is the latex from the rubber tree (*Hevea brasiliensis*), was known by the Mayas and the Aztecs because of its unusual qualities of durability and elasticity—qualities that were also noted by the Europeans. However, natural rubber was too weather sensitive to be of much use, since boots and other products made from rubber would turn rock hard in the winter and melt in the summer. After a solvent was found and the process of vulcanization was discovered by Charles Goodyear in 1839, the demand for natural rubber increased rapidly because of the popularity of waterproof coats, bicycles, and pneumatic tires. As with the sourcing of Pernambuco, collection of the latex was labour intensive because the trees were isolated and spread over large areas. The Amazonian settlers did not have access to slaves, partly because they did not have the money to invest in slaves and partly because the location of the rubber trees was too far away from the slave routes. Again, the impact on the native population was devastating. Renewed attempts to enslave the local population met with limited success.[14] The pace of production in the Amazonian jungle could not increase quickly enough to meet demand, so prices soared. The rubber boom brought some temporary wealth into the Amazon, an example of which is the famed opera house in the city of Manaus, completed in 1896 with roofing tiles from Alsace, furniture from Paris, and marble and light fixtures from Italy.

Enslavement in the interest of rubber production was more successful in the Congo. King Leopold of Belgium, who had made the Congo into his own fiefdom, rapidly realized that the gum vines (*Landolphia owariensis*), which covered nearly half of the equatorial forest, could be made very profitable if they were exploited quickly for rubber to supply the booming market.[15] He went about the business in a ruthless manner, using forced labour. Belgian soldiers surrounded villages and took women and children hostages, and they were not to be released until the men had collected a certain amount of rubber. Any resistance was crushed by massacring the villagers—hands severed from the bodies were shown to prove how many had been killed. Millions of people, amounting to half the population, died. Outrage grew in Europe about conditions in the Congo, thanks to the dedicated effort of Edmond Morel, a British shipping company employee, who devoted a decade of his life to exposing the king and his barbaric practices, and the situation improved after Leopold's death in 1909. The rubber boom in Amazonia and in the Congo came to an end after a British trader managed to get hold of rubber seeds, which were smuggled to Malaya and colonies in the East Indies. Production now took place in large plantations, putting naturally harvested rubber at a significant cost disadvantage. After 1912, Amazonian and African rubber could no longer compete with rubber from plantations.[16] The development of synthetic rubber, particularly during and after World War II, led to further declines in the market for natural rubber, which at present has only approximately 40 percent of the rubber market, mostly from plantations.

Guano is an example of another resource that made a brief but significant appearance on the world trade scene.[17] It had been known since Greek and Roman times that the application of manure to agricultural land led to increased crop yields. Usually the manure was local, but the discovery of large deposits of guano on the Chincha Islands off the coast of Peru led to a highly profitable trade between Peru and Europe between 1808 and 1880.[18] The link between nitrogen and plant growth was discovered by German chemist Justus von

Liebig in 1843, a discovery that boosted demand for guano.* England, in particular, wanted nitrogen fertilizer to grow turnips (rutabagas), regarded as an essential part of the four-field rotation system introduced by "Turnip" Townshend in the early part of the eighteenth century.[19] Nearly 4.5 million tonnes of guano was shipped to England between 1840 and 1880. The British had a monopoly on the guano trade, with guano in such demand that the US Congress passed the Guano Islands Act in 1856.[20] The act allowed any citizen of the United States to claim any uninhabited island with guano deposits. Under this law, the United States laid claim to sixty or so uninhabited islands in the Caribbean and the Pacific—claims that were later rescinded. The guano trade declined after 1880 following depletion of the deposits and the discovery of large

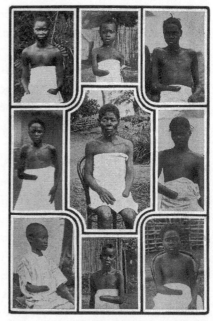

Figure 1.1. Images of Congolese natives who had their arms severed by Belgian officials as punishment for failure to collect enough rubber. Source: Wikimedia Commons.

deposits of nitrates—known as saltpeter ($NaNO_3$)—in the coastal areas of Peru, Bolivia, and Chile. The value of the deposits was comparable to the current value of oil deposits in the Persian Gulf, and disputes over these led to the War of the Pacific (1879–1883), when Peru and Bolivia lost the nitrate fields to Chile.[21] Bolivia also lost its access to the sea, still a bone of great contention between Chile and Bolivia.[22] At the peak of the saltpeter trade in 1928, 3.1 million tonnes were exported. The mining of saltpeter declined in importance following competition from ammonium, produced as a by-product from a coal coking process, and the discovery by the German chemist Fritz Haber of the technology to produce nitrates through the processing of atmospheric nitrogen shortly before World War I.[23]

---

*Pure nitrogen (N) is an atmospheric gas that cannot be directly used by plants (with the exception of legumes). Instead plants get the necessary nitrogen through various water soluble compounds in the form of nitrates (NO_3) and ammonium (NH_4) found in manure.

The history of cocoa illustrates another set of the problems associated with resources: the instability of commodity markets and the repercussions on populations if they are entirely reliant on one commodity for their livelihoods. Originally the cocoa tree grew naturally in the rainforests of southern Mexico and Central America. Its fruit, the cocoa bean (particularly the criollo bean), was much prized by the Maya and Olmec civilizations, who made it into a drink. Cocoa was also prized as a luxury item and was used in religious ceremonies.[24] Following the Spanish conquest of the Aztecs and colonization of Mexico and Central America in the sixteenth century, cocoa became popular first in Spain and later in the rest of Europe mainly because of its supposed medicinal benefits. But a large market did not develop until the Dutchman Coenraad van Houten developed a technology for extracting cocoa powder from the beans in 1828. The cultivation of cocoa trees spread to Indonesia and West Africa. Greater demand for tropical products, including cocoa, increased West Africa's strategic importance, and following a conference in Berlin in 1885, West Africa was divided among the colonial powers. The British claimed Nigeria and the Gold Coast (today Ghana), and the French, the Ivory Coast (Côte d'Ivoire).

In trying to expand cocoa production, the French found that the locals did not want to work on plantations, particularly given the very low pay. Consequently, France introduced a poll tax, forcing Africans to work so they could earn enough money to pay the tax.

At this point, the history of cocoa merges with the story of one of the most ill-starred figures of African history, Félix Houphouët. Originally a successful cocoa farmer on the Ivory Coast, Houphouët, like most other farmers, found it difficult to compete with the French colonial landowners, particularly after the French brought in a pricing scheme that favoured French producers. He became involved in politics as a communist, attempting to reverse these discriminatory policies, and in 1945 became the first African elected to the French parliament. After the lifting of wartime wage and price controls in major countries, global commodity prices plummeted, including the price of cocoa, affecting the livelihoods of cocoa farmers all over the world. In Côte d'Ivoire, rioting ensued, threatening France's colonial administration all over West Africa. Houphouët renounced his previous connections to the Communist party in return for a French promise of preferential treatment of cocoa and coffee imported from Côte d'Ivoire. When the country became independent in 1960, Houphouët, under a newly adopted surname, Houphouët-Boigny, became its first president. He was a dictator, but initially he used his powers well, turning the country's economy into the strongest in West Africa. He promoted full-scale conversion

Figure 1.2. The cathedral built by Houphouët-Boigny in Côte d'Ivoire with money earned from cocoa production. Source: Wikimedia Commons.

of farmland into cocoa plantations. Europeans were encouraged to invest, and the 1960s saw large-scale developments of luxury resorts in the coastal areas with an impressive infrastructure, including lavish touches such as a skating rink in the coastal city of Abidjan.

But Côte d'Ivoire's wealth still depended almost completely on cocoa. Houphouët-Boigny guaranteed his country's farmers a fixed price for cocoa beans. If the market price dropped below its guaranteed value, the government paid farmers the difference, borrowing heavily from European banks to do so. Cocoa prices were as high as US$5,500 per tonne in the mid-1970s but started to drop toward the end of the decade. In the mid-1980s, oversupply led to further decreases in cocoa prices, which coincided with the start of the building of a huge cathedral to commemorate the president, rivalling St. Peter's cathedral in the Vatican in size. The cathedral's construction was finished in 1989 at a cost of US$300 million (and was consecrated by Pope John Paul II in 1990), but by 1987 the national debt had increased to US$4.5 billion, forcing Houphouët-Boigny to declare the country insolvent. For two years he blocked all cocoa shipments out of the country while negotiating a secret deal with the French government whereby Côte d'Ivoire received a large cash grant in exchange for selling all its cocoa production to two French companies. In 1989, the International Monetary Fund and the World Bank stepped in to try to sort out the failing economy. As a condition for receiving a loan, the country had to agree to liberalize cocoa production and remove the guaranteed floor prices. This resulted in rapidly falling prices that dropped even further when Asian countries entered the cocoa market. Since Houphouët-Boigny's death in 1993, Côte d'Ivoire has gone from crisis to crisis. In 1999 his successor, Henri Bédié, was toppled in a military coup. The brutal civil war that followed caused the country to split into two factions. A peace accord was signed in 2007 between the two warring sides with the possibility of free elections, but renewed hostilities led to another civil war 2010–11. The poisoned legacy of Houphouët-Boigny, including the country's overreliance on cocoa as its single cash crop, is far from over.

These examples raise the question of whether resource trade can generate sufficient income for the economy of a country to grow and prosper. The markets for resources appear to be very fickle, where the demand for one resource can suddenly decline and for another increase, often generating major upheavals in national economies. The world has experienced many resource booms in non-renewable resources such as metals and minerals and fossil fuels, including the most recent one that came to an end 2012–2013. Many resource-rich countries such as the Democratic Republic of the Congo appear to be mired in internal strife and remain desperately poor. The benefits of increased resource prices appear to be fleeting and in general do not appear to trickle down to local populations in resource-rich countries. Why?

The "resource curse" and the impact of resources on economic development

Following World War II, the world saw an unprecedented expansion in the economies of industrialized countries, while most of the resource-based developing countries lagged behind. The gap in per-capita income levels between high-income and low- to middle-income countries widened in the postwar period, and much effort has been devoted to finding an explanation. First, there was considerable interest in possible links between raw-material prices and poor economic growth. The famous Argentine economist Raul Prebisch pointed out that over time, real (inflation-adjusted) raw-material prices had declined, and countries that rely on exports of raw materials had become increasingly impoverished compared with other countries, as their export earnings could not keep up with the increasing cost of imports of manufactured products.[25] He and others argued that long-term decline in raw-material prices occurs because the demand for primary commodities expands at a slower rate than incomes and the demand for manufactured products at a faster rate.[26] This is also true at the individual level because when people become richer, the proportion of income spent on food declines and that spent on other products increases—this is known as Engel's Law. Therefore, as a result of expanding incomes, raw-material prices do not increase at the same rate as the prices of manufactured products. The only solution Prebisch saw was for a country to implement policies to decrease the reliance on international trade and resources, using tariffs and export taxes as a means to encourage local manufacturing. This was an inward-looking strategy, and in most cases (for example, in Argentina, some African countries, and initially in Canada) did not work well, as it encouraged the establishment of inefficient, high-cost local industries with powerful political lobbies with a vested interest in continued protection.[27]

Another possible explanation for the poor performance of raw-material-producing countries is the well-known volatility of commodity prices. Oil and gas prices are particularly unstable, closely followed by the prices of copper, coffee, and cocoa.[28] If a country is dependent on the export of raw materials, the resource boom-and-bust cycle can be disruptive and costly—note the example of Côte d'Ivoire. In good times people and capital move into the resource sector, and in bad times they either become unemployed or leave the sector. Boom periods encourage overinvestment, inappropriate risk taking, and heavy borrowing. The bust often leads to banking crises and budget cuts that weigh particularly heavily on poor people. Postwar attempts to insulate countries from the vagaries of the market included commodity stabilization schemes supported by the United Nations.[29] These failed because they relied on price supports that could not be maintained as they were too costly. Invariably, support prices were set at too high a level, encouraging overproduction and requiring governments to buy any surplus to stop prices from dropping, as happened in Côte d'Ivoire. Interference with global markets fell out of fashion in the last decades of the twentieth century, and it was believed that trade liberalization held the key to economic growth and development. Some countries benefited (the "Asian Tigers"), while others fell even further behind, despite receiving generous development aid. This generated renewed curiosity about the role of resources in development.

In 1997, two economists, Sachs and Warner, published an influential study that statistically linked natural resource abundance and poor economic growth.[30] Because of difficulties in finding a variable that describes natural resource abundance, they correlated the share of natural resource exports in total exports with the growth rate of GDP (gross domestic product), controlling for other possible influences on GDP. The results of their analysis showed that an increase in natural resource intensity in exports led to a reduction in the GDP growth rate—that is, an abundance of natural resources led to slower growth. They argued that, almost without exception, today's resource-abundant countries have stagnated compared with other countries. This finding created quite a stir in development circles and was interpreted to mean that the presence of natural resources was unlikely to lead to economic development for many poor countries (the "resource curse"). A vast number of statistical studies followed, confirming the same trends: high resource dependency is associated with low levels of GDP per capita, a low savings rate, high degrees of rural poverty, and a higher proportion of the population living in fragile environments.[31] Many attempts were made in trying to explain why this would be the case, some emphasizing economic factors such as the Dutch disease, and political and institutional factors.

The Dutch disease is a term describing the ailments that beset the Dutch economy after the 1959 discovery of natural gas in the Dutch region of economic influence in the North Sea. The argument is as follows: a quickly expanding resource sector driven by resource exports will lead to an increase in the exchange rate that will make it difficult for other export industries to remain competitive. Workers will move into the rapidly expanding resource sector in search of higher wages, making it even more difficult for other sectors of the economy to survive, as they either have to match the higher wages or lose workers. For these reasons other sectors may contract, and if these sectors are high-growth sectors, the country's economic growth will stagnate. Unemployment will increase if more workers are laid off from the now uncompetitive export industries than can be hired by the resource sector.

However, the Dutch disease did not describe the situation in many poor countries where the resource sector was dominant. More recent studies confirm that the resource curse can be mainly attributed to political and institutional factors.[32] For example, resource exports could fail to generate economic growth because expansion of the resource sector often encourages bribery and corruption, involving attempts by people or groups to obtain more of the rich resource revenues—the recent case involving the giant engineering firm SNC-Lavalin comes to mind, where alleged bribes were paid to officials in Libya, Nigeria, Uganda, Mozambique, and Bangladesh.[33] This sort of activity is unproductive, and takes resources away from the productive sectors. An interesting illustration is an analysis of corruption in the small island nation of São Tomé and Príncipe following the discovery of oil some twenty years ago.[34] Statistical analysis showed convincingly that corruption increased following the increase in oil revenues. No such trend was found in the neighbouring nation of Cape Verde, where no oil had been discovered. The two countries were similar in size, colonial history, and history following independence.

Another factor is that resource revenues may discourage governments from establishing a fair tax system. Governments need revenue to provide basic government services, and in the absence of resource revenues, their only option is to tax the population. In return for paying taxes, people demand accountability to ensure government revenue is well spent—a process that establishes a political relationship between the population and the governing body. In resource-rich countries, the need to tax is less, resulting in a broken political relationship between rulers and subjects. Bad governments become difficult to get rid of as they can often buy off opponents with resource revenues and can afford to maintain armies to subjugate any revolt. An example is the reputed wealth that Colonel Muammar al-Gaddafi of Libya had stashed away, allowing him to keep a permanent army of mercenaries. There were also allegations that cash from Chinese and Zimbabwean diamond companies allowed Robert Mugabe, president of Zimbabwe, to manipulate the results of the 2013 election in his favour.[35] Non-democratic countries tend to make little progress toward democracy if they have a resource windfall.[36]

Yet others have pointed out that the presence of particular resources in a country or a region often leads to conditions that promote income inequality, a situation not conducive to economic growth.[37] For example, climate and soils in parts of Latin America and the Caribbean were perfect for producing sugar, particularly if the producers could rely on slave labour. Only big landlords could afford the infrastructure required to run big slave plantations. As a result, the population was split into two groups: fabulously wealthy sugar producers and destitute slaves. When the newly independent countries developed their own political and social institutions, the rich landlords made sure they were favoured, and the slaves, of course, had no say. Even after abolition, institutions that protected elites and restricted the participation of a large part of the population remained in place. The inescapable conclusion is that countries with strong institutions are more likely to benefit from a resource windfall compared with countries with poor institutions.[38]

A final explanation for the resource curse is globalization.[39] Until the early part of the twentieth century, the primary means for countries to attain military and economic superiority was through the expansion of territory and agriculture. This was followed by a new trend in which growth and development became largely determined by the ability and expertise to explore and develop fossil fuels, minerals, and iron ore, necessary for fighting the two world wars. Increased globalization meant that the required resources could be imported, and of critical importance was the ability to use them productively. Since resource-rich poor countries often lacked the ability to develop and integrate the resource sector into the economy, they specialized in supplying the rest of the world with raw materials. The resource sector typically became an island unto itself with little connection to the rest of the economy—and the resource curse manifested itself. Either the profits from the harvesting of the resource were too small to generate surplus capital to invest in education, infrastructure, or manufacturing; or, if the profits were large—for example, in the case of some minerals—they were invested in unsustainable exploitation of the resource with no connection or linkage to the rest of the economy or were frittered away through corruption. The expansion of arable land and agriculture was still a necessary outlet for the poor, but because of rapid population growth, the expansion usually took place on poor and marginal lands, which made it impossible for the settlers to improve their living standards. Indeed according to the World Bank, the population in poor countries living on fragile lands has doubled since 1950.[40] Fragile lands are upland areas, deforested lands, and drylands that suffer from low agricultural productivity. Resource economist Edward Barbier argues that the resource curse goes beyond oil and gas and mineral resources: "The problem of underdevelopment, and particularly the lack of economic opportunities among the world's poorest people, may be inextricably linked to the poor management of land and natural resources in the *natural* world."[41]

It is clear, then, that the link between resources and living standards is extremely complex and depends on the interplay of history, institutions, and government policies. Many countries have profited from resources—most notably the United States, Canada, Norway, Australia, Chile, China, Botswana, Indonesia, Brazil, and Malaysia. The United States is an excellent example of a country that benefited greatly from an abundance of mineral resources. Between 1879 and 1914, the mineral intensity of US exports increased at the same time as the economy grew substantially and the United States became a leader in manufacturing. At the end of the period, the United States had the largest global share of production of the major minerals (lead, copper, iron ore, nickel, silver, and zinc, to name a few), larger than its global share of mineral resources themselves. This standing was achieved through an accommodating legal regime and investment in government-sponsored research and education. There were also large-scale investments in transportation and infrastructure and in exploration and improvements in the technologies of extraction. The United States Geological Survey (USGS), established in 1879, is regarded as the most ambitious government science project of the nineteenth century, and mining engineering and metallurgy departments were set up at the major universities. Several major breakthroughs occurred in research in copper mining and refining, including the application of the Bessemer process to copper refining and the introduction of electrolysis to the final refining process, which allowed almost all the copper to be extracted even from low-grade ore. In summary, the United States was so successful because it developed industries that supported the mining sector. The mining sector was, and still is, at the cutting edge of knowledge development. [42]

Oil played a similar role in the Norwegian economy. Norway is the tenth-largest oil exporter and is ranked number one on the Human Development Index.[43] Oil was not discovered in the North Sea until 1969, and the Norwegians signalled their clear intention of being full participants in developing the resource. The country was able to transfer its traditional engineering skills in shipbuilding to adapting drilling technologies and exploration to the challenging North Sea conditions. As well, substantial investments were made in the training of petroleum engineers and in setting up a Norwegian oil company, *Statoil*. The newfound oil also led to the creation of an export industry centred on deepwater drilling platforms, a technology that subsequently became essential in many offshore oil developments around the world. State oil revenues above a certain level are put aside in a special fund from which money can be released only in keeping with future wealth and needs. The money is kept in dollars to minimize any effects on the Norwegian krone, thereby avoiding the Dutch disease.

Botswana, an African country, is another model for resource development. The first president of Botswana, Seretse Khama, implemented a series of policies in the late 1960s, focusing on the potential wealth of diamonds. The mining was controlled by De Beers, but instead of nationalizing the mines, Khama insisted that a proportion of the revenues accrued to Botswana through a joint venture between the government of Botswana and De Beers (Debswana). A national fund for mineral wealth was created in the 1990s to assist in financing national priorities, ranked according to their rate of return. The agreement with De Beers is mutually beneficial: if diamond prices increase, Botswana gets more revenue. De Beers, on the other hand, benefits from knowing that its assets will not be arbitrarily seized and therefore reinvests some of the profits in the mines.

Botswana also insisted that the diamonds be mined slowly, matching the capacity of the country to absorb the revenue for use in sensible projects. Because of its track record of handling its resource revenue and in dealing with foreign companies, Botswana has been able to negotiate successfully with De Beers to develop local diamond-cutting and -polishing businesses.

What conclusions can be drawn from the preceding discussion of the resource curse? How can it be avoided? Apart from policies promoting democracy and good governance, a case can be made for transparency in the management of resource revenues. Transparency would expose the size of the revenue base and thus prevent it from being squandered by the government in paying bribes or spending it on inappropriate projects. One such movement advocating transparency is called Publish What You Pay—an attempt to make oil and mining companies reveal their royalty payments or fee payments to governments and to make governments reveal what they earn.[44] The movement was launched by George Soros in 2002 following a report in 1999 of the complicity of oil and financial companies in plundering state assets during the Angolan civil war. Another initiative—the Extractive Industries Transparency Initiative—was launched in 2003 under the British government of Tony Blair.[45] Under the initiative, countries can apply for a validation, committing themselves to abide by certain principles of transparency. Companies are encouraged to sign up for compliance. So far, forty-two of the world's largest multinationals have signed up, including the major oil companies. Another attempt was made jointly by the International Monetary Fund and the World Bank to reach an agreement on how to best deal with resource revenues. Sadly, an agreement was not achieved, not surprisingly because of resistance from many resource-rich countries that interpreted any imposed rules as an intrusion on their own sovereignty. An example of the barriers to reform and the naïveté of officials was the World Bank funding of an oil pipeline from the impoverished country of Chad to Cameroon on the coast.[46] A condition of the funding was that a proportion of the oil revenue was to be put aside in a transparent "future generations fund" and the remainder spent on health and education. Unfortunately, after the pipeline was built, the Chad government bypassed the agreement by declaring a state of emergency under which the president could spend the funds in whatever ways he desired. The funds were used for the military, causing the World Bank to withdraw from the project.

Yet another approach was pioneered by Paul Collier in collaboration with other economists at the Natural Resource Charter.[47] It has the backing of the IMF, the World Bank, and the African Development Bank, but it does not receive any funding. It consists of a set of voluntary principles to guide the use of natural resources for maximum benefit to the citizens of a country. One of the key recommendations is to use natural resource revenue for investments, as the lack of investment capital appears to be one of the main barriers to economic growth and development.

The sustainability of resource use

The preceding section showed that resource exploitation is not likely to benefit a country unless it is supported by open and democratic institutions and appropriate government policies. It is also important to develop the resource sustainably. The concept of sustainability emerged out of fear of resource scarcity, which dates back at least to Thomas Malthus, who in 1798 argued that the world faced a crisis as population expanded at an exponential rate while food production could only increase linearly. Malthus presumed that technological progress in producing food was too slow and the gains from more intensive cultivation were too limited to overcome this basic dichotomy, so that in time the relative supply of food would fall, finally resulting in at best a subsistence standard of living for the majority of people.[48]

Malthus's theory was based on conditions prevalent before the Industrial Revolution. The world then was caught in a Malthusian trap in which the average person in 1800 in all likelihood was no better off than the average person one hundred thousand years ago.[49] However, the Malthusian trap disappeared after the Industrial Revolution because of advances in agricultural technologies, including the discovery of artificial fertilizers and the decline in fertility rates (number of children born per woman) that has occurred in the centuries since he made his prediction. But the spectre of mass starvation was raised again in 1968 by Paul Ehrlich in his book *The Population Bomb*.[50] The book's first sentence is dramatic: "The battle to feed humanity is over. In the course of the 1970s the world will experience starvation of tragic—hundreds of millions of people will starve to death."[51] This did not happen. According to the World Food Summit, the proportion of people starving fell from 35 percent in 1970 to 18 percent in 1996, largely due to the widespread introduction of new seed varieties (the Green Revolution) as well as applications of irrigation and fertilizer. Whether this trend will continue is discussed in detail in Chapter 8.

Not only have there been concerns about the adequacy of agricultural resources but also of mineral resources. For example, the depletion of Britain's coal supplies became an issue during the nineteenth century, and the adequacy of US mineral supplies was another issue following World War II.[52] The warnings about imminent resource shortages made by the Club of Rome—a global think tank—in the 1972 book *The Limits to Growth* were more dramatic, as its publication preceded the oil crisis of 1973.[53] The book, which sold twelve million copies, predicted that unless a concerted global initiative was organized to economize immediately on non-renewable resources—particularly fossil fuels—and to stop all economic growth, the world would run out of resources in the middle of this century, resulting in living standards much lower than those prevailing in the early 1970s. The Club arrived at this gloomy prediction from computer simulations. The oil crisis of 1973, when temporary shortages of gas led to long lineups at gas stations, seemed to confirm the gravity of the situation. As 2050 is not yet here, we do not know whether its prediction will come true, but its model was wrong for the same reason as those of Malthus and Ehrlich: it did not allow for technological progress and the power of the price mechanism in encouraging conservation of and substitution between scarce and more abundant resources.[54] The lesson from Malthus, Ehrlich, and the Club of Rome seems clear: prophecies of imminent dire shortages of resources need to be evaluated carefully.

The debate about resources becoming scarcer led to a famous wager between Paul Ehrlich and Julian Simon, an economist who was confident in the ability of technology and market signals to counteract any threat of shortages of natural resources. In 1980, Simon asked Ehrlich to pick a thousand dollars' worth of any five metals. Ehrlich picked copper, nickel, chrome, tin, and tungsten. If in 1990 the inflation-adjusted market prices of these metals were higher than in 1980, Ehrlich would win; if they were less, Simon would win. The winner would pay the loser the difference in the value. Ehrlich lost and had to mail Simon a cheque for $576.07. Both Simon and Ehrlich were proposing a new bet, but were unable to agree on the criteria before Simon's death in 1997.[55] With the exception of a brief period from the Second World War to the 1980s, real (inflation-adjusted) mineral prices decreased during the twentieth century. One of the reasons was that technology made it possible to use far fewer mineral resources in production than was previously necessary, causing the mineral resource production intensity to decrease substantially. Fossil-fuel prices also decreased. However, the early years of the new millennium saw a commodity boom with large price increases that were attributed to the rapid development and entry to the world markets of emerging economies such as China and India. Many saw the boom as a sign that old-fashioned resource scarcity has finally manifested itself, a topic that will be examined further in Chapters 2 and 3.

In the late 1970s and early '80s, concern shifted from the future availability of non-renewable resources to the quality of renewable resources and the sustainability of the environment, triggered by a series of natural disasters such as drought in the Sahel region of Africa and deforestation of the Amazonian rainforest as well as increased awareness of water and air pollution. In response, the United Nations General Assembly established the World Commission on Environment and Development in 1983 (known as the Brundtland Commission after its chair, Gro Harlem Brundtland, who was then prime minister of Norway). The gist of the commission's report, *Our Common Future*, was that development cannot be separated from the environment; therefore, all countries must adopt a different approach to development, integrating production with conservation and enhancement of natural resources.[56] The recommended approach included both equitable access and an adequate livelihood for all. The emphasis was on "sustainable development" defined as "development that meets the needs of the present without compromising the ability of future generations to meet their own needs."[57] Unlike the report of the Club of Rome, the commissioners did not call for the halting of economic growth. The rejection of the need to stop all growth ensured that the report was acceptable to governments and NGOs, and the word *sustainability* became a buzzword. Governments in industrialized countries began to make efforts to ensure that their policies were sustainable. But this new focus begged a key question: what does *sustainability* really mean?

There are many interpretations, depending on the context in which the word is used. In general, the sustainability of resource use has not figured prominently in the discipline of economics and thus neither in the economic statistics used to measure how the economy is performing, because until recently the scale of human activity was not large enough for scarcity and sustainability to be an issue. It is interesting to note that when the father of modern economics, Adam Smith, wrote *The Wealth of Nations* in 1776, the world population was probably around eight hundred million—it is now seven billion. Resources are still lumped in with land as a means of production and therefore enter our most common statistic, GDP, only to the extent that they are used in producing marketable goods and services. The current national accounts thus give little indication of the importance of resources in a country's economy. Ecosystem services rendered by forests and biodiversity are not included because they do not have a price.[58] GDP includes a measure of the depreciation of machinery and equipment (an estimate of the wear and tear of man-made capital), but there is no such measure of any depreciation of the natural resource base. This could produce bizarre distortions; for example, if for one year a country cut down all its forests for timber and pumped all its oil wells dry, GDP in that particular year would increase.[59]

Traditionally, the only important means of production in the economy are considered to be labour and capital (machinery and equipment), and capital is considered to be a near-perfect substitute for resources. For example, we can invest in more efficient furnaces and better insulation to reduce energy use, thus making energy and man-made capital substitutable for each other. In theory, we will never run out of copper because with increased shortages and hence higher prices, we will exploit previously uneconomical copper deposits, we will develop substitutes (e.g., fibre optics in cables), we will recycle, and we will become more efficient in our use of copper. Similarly, we will never run out of oil because when oil becomes scarce, its price will increase, which means we will use less, and we will use it more efficiently. We will develop new energy resources, and it is assumed that the working of the price mechanism will guarantee that the transition to a new energy regime will take place smoothly—again, at least in theory.

However, mainstream economists agree that the price mechanism cannot solve all problems of scarcity and allocate resources efficiently. One reason is that the market fails to take into account the cost to the environment of economic activities (*negative externalities*) and in some cases the benefits of activities (*positive externalities*), and the other is that many resources, including the environmental services offered to us by the atmosphere, the oceans, water resources, tropical and boreal forests, soils, wetlands, and biodiversity in general do not have a price. Many of these are "open-access resources" with little or no control over who can use them. These types of resources are critical for our survival—they have an impact on the quality of the air we breathe and the water we drink and on nature's capacity to grow things for our immediate survival. Overwhelming evidence that these resources have been adversely affected by human activity has led to concern that we are running out. Economists' solutions to these problems include putting a price on externalities such as pollution and assigning values and property rights to open-access resources. These are complicated topics that will be discussed throughout the book.

The presumed interchangeability of capital and natural resources brings us back to the notion of sustainability. If indeed capital and natural resources are perfect substitutes, the depletion of some particular resource is not especially worrying provided increases take place in other forms of capital—for example, machinery and equipment or infrastructure—that can be used by future generations.[60] We can become better off in the future, but the products we consume and the inputs we use in production will not necessarily be the same. Technological advances, substitutions, and government policies that ensure environmental resources are priced properly would result in sustainable growth and development. This view is often labelled as *weak sustainability*.[61]

However, the notion of unlimited substitutability that is implied in weak sustainability is absurd because some resources do not have substitutes. Moral obligations to future generations require us to protect some natural resources that are critical to life support and to prevent pollution from increasing beyond irreversible limits—this is *strong sustainability*. Renewable resources (e.g., fisheries, clean air, and clean water) must not be used up faster than they can be renewed, and the depletion of non-renewable resources should be compensated for by investing in renewable resources. For example, depletion of fossil fuels should be offset by investment in the production of wind and solar energy.[62] The fact that we know so little about the future means we should also err on the side of caution ("the precautionary principle"). The complexity of natural systems and the limits of the human brain mean that we might not be able to devise appropriate policies and technologies to deal with environmental degradation until it is too late.[63]

Examples of unsustainable resource use: depletion and resource collapse

It is not difficult to find examples of unsustainable exploitation of animal populations: classic cases include cod, buffalo, and the passenger pigeon. The case of cod provides a recent example of unsustainable resource use. When John Cabot returned from Newfoundland in 1497, he and his crew were full of tales of waters so teeming with codfish that if you submerged a bucket, you pulled it up full of fish.[64] Because cod contains virtually no fat, it could easily be dried and stored, with or without salt, and therefore could be transported over large distances. In Europe, the demand for cod was bolstered by religious laws, which mandated the eating of fish on Fridays and during the Christian period of observance known as Lent. Portuguese and Basque fishermen had early control over the fisheries, and many fishing ports in Newfoundland have names from that period (e.g., Port aux Basques). The other sources for cod were the North Sea and the waters around Iceland, most of which were controlled by the Hanseatic League.[65] By the middle of the sixteenth century, 60 percent of the fish eaten in Europe was cured cod caught either off Iceland or Newfoundland. Cod also had a strategic value as food during the long sea voyages to the New World. Cured cod was later used to purchase slaves in West Africa and to feed the slaves on the sugar plantations in the West Indies. It was cheap and high in protein. As a legacy from this period, consumption of salted cod is still part of West Indian culture.

Newfoundland was a British dominion until 1948, when it voted by a narrow margin to join Canada. Its culture had developed around cod and fishing, and the livelihoods of the majority of the population were closely tied to the industry. At the time of Confederation, local fishermen dominated the inshore fisheries, while foreign fishing fleets dominated the lucrative fisheries off the Grand Banks. In 1977, Canada declared a two-hundred-mile territorial limit to provide control over most of the Grand Banks. The intention was to make the fisheries more profitable for Newfoundlanders. Conservation of the fish stocks was not seen as an issue as the catches seemed to be large, thanks to the use of efficient fishing equipment that was partly subsidized by the Canadian government. Meanwhile, the foreign fishing fleets continued to ply the waters beyond the two-hundred-mile limit. Nobody recognized until it was too late that the cod stocks were in fact declining drastically. In 1992, the Canadian Ministry of Fisheries and Oceans announced a two-year fishing moratorium, which has never been lifted. Once it was clear that the cod population would not recover, the whole culture built around the cod in Newfoundland—a culture that dates back over five centuries—began to disintegrate. At the same time, the even older Icelandic cod fisheries still continue. Facing the same situation as Newfoundland, Iceland declared a two-hundred-mile territorial limit in 1975. However, in contrast with Canada, Icelanders used their control to conserve the fisheries rather than treat the cod as an inexhaustible resource. As the Icelandic counterexample shows, resource depletion need not be an irreversible trend; government policy, implemented quickly enough, can make a major difference.

But in other cases government policy has done very little, and in some cases governments have actually promoted resource depletion. The most notable example is the case of North American bison. At the end of the eighteenth century, it is estimated that between thirty and seventy million bison populated the Prairies. The bison were an integral part of the culture of the Plains Indians, who used the meat for food and the hides for clothing and in the construction of teepees. Because of the behaviour of the bison herds, they were easy to hunt by herding and driving them over cliffs, where they fell to their deaths. With the arrival of European settlers to the Prairies during the latter part of the nineteenth century, the bison were doomed when settlers, adventurers, and thrill seekers indiscriminately slaughtered millions of them, aided and abetted

Figure 1.3. Bison skulls waiting to be processed for fertilizer around 1870. An example of the indiscriminate killing of bison, which almost led to their extinction. Source: Burton Historical Collection, Detroit Public Library, Wikimedia Commons.

by the US Army. Passengers on Canadian Pacific trains used to shoot bison for entertainment on the long journey across the Prairies. The Army's role was based on the government's realization that the killing of bison would make it easier to defeat the Plains Indians, a barrier to European settlements. By the 1890s only about 350 bison remained, and while the bison population has since increased, the culture of the Plains Indians was effectively wiped out.

In some cases, overharvesting of an animal species can lead to its outright extinction. A telling example is the disappearance of the passenger pigeons. Accounts of early settlers describe continuous streams of huge flocks of birds flying overhead for an entire day. The total number of passenger pigeons has been estimated at five billion, far outnumbering any other bird species.[66] The birds were so plentiful they could be knocked out of trees with a stick and caught by Indians using large nets, a practice the settlers imitated. They proved to be a cheap and nutritious food source for the rapidly growing urban populations in the eastern United States, and a huge number of pigeons were brought to the markets in boxcars. For example, in 1869, 7.5 million birds were shipped out of Van Buren County in Michigan. Young pigeons in particular were reputedly delicious. The cull was so great that caught pigeons were used for many other purposes as well: animal feed, fertilizer, even target practice. Clearly, hunting on this scale was not sustainable. By 1900 the population was decimated, and the last surviving bird died in captivity in a Cincinnati zoo in 1914.

Today there is increased concern about resource collapse. Not only are we facing the collapse of individual animal populations such as black rhinos, mountain gorillas, and Amur leopards, but also of natural systems. We do not have to pay for services such as the natural purification of water through wetlands, the reduction and storage of carbon dioxide through forests, the natural breakdown of waste products, crop pollination, and genetic diversity. Exploitation of traditional resources typically has an impact on these critical resources, ranging from the effect of mining on water quality downstream to the general impact of carbon dioxide emissions on climate. It is not possible to find substitutes for many of these resources that are critical to our survival. One attempt to realistically value the condition of some of these resources was a recent joint study by the World Resources Institute, the World Bank, the United Nations Development Programme, and the United Nations Environmental Programme to determine the capacity of ecosystems to provide services such as water quantity and quality, biodiversity, carbon storage, and shoreline protection.[67] The study included five ecosystems (agricultural, forest, coastal, freshwater, and grassland) and eight types of services, giving a total of forty combinations (e.g., biodiversity and agricultural systems; carbon storage and grasslands). Out of the twenty-four combinations the study's authors were able to assess, six were found to be in good condition, twelve in fair condition, five in poor condition, and one in bad condition. The capacity of most of the ecosystems was declining, confirming the increased scarcity of critical resources. Another approach to assessment involves the concept of "planetary boundaries", which defines safe operating space for nine measures of the environment including freshwater use, ocean acidification, biodiversity loss, ozone depletion, climate change, land use, chemical pollution, atmospheric aerosol, and interference with the nitrogen and phosphorus cycles (Figure 1.4). If human activity exceeds any of these boundaries, or tipping points, we are running the risk of irreversible and sudden environmental change. According to this approach, we have already exceeded three out of nine critical planetary boundaries—atmospheric carbon dioxide, biodiversity loss, and our tampering with the nitrogen cycle—and we are close to exceeding others.[68]

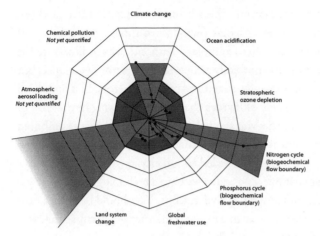

Figure 1.4. Planetary boundaries. The lightly shaded polygon shows the safe planetary boundaries for the nine measures, and the darkly shaded areas show the current measures. Source: Johan Rockström et al., "Planetary Boundaries: Exploring the Safe Operating Space for Humanity," Ecology and Society 14, no. 2 (2009): 32.

Malthusian thought has returned. What happens if we exceed the earth's ability to support us? This has rekindled interest in factors behind the collapse of early civilizations and what we can learn.[69] Jared Diamond, in his 2005 book *Collapse: How Societies Choose to Fail or Succeed*, gives vivid historical illustrations of unsustainable resource exploitation resulting in resource collapse, and therefore social collapse, on Easter Island, Greenland (the Norse settlement in the early Middle Ages), Central America (the rise and the fall of the Mayas), southwestern United States (the Anasazi), and other areas.[70] In the case of Easter Island, known for its famous statues, he argued that the decline of a formerly advanced civilization was caused by resource degradation. The transportation and the raising of the statues required technology involving logs, ropes made of tree bark, and the coordinated efforts of many people. But the mania for statues and the accompanying demand for trees required for their erection led to the total deforestation of the island. As materials to make the canoes that were necessary for fishing disappeared, islanders soon exhausted the wild animal population as a food resource. With decreased crop yields because of soil erosion and absence of firewood, the population resorted to tribal wars and cannibalism. Historians have estimated that the resulting population decline on the island was in the order of 90 percent. However, other researchers claim that Diamond's analysis was not correct. Evidence indicates that when the first Europeans arrived in 1722, the island was still thriving, and collapse did not come until the late 1870s when only a hundred or so of the population were left.[71] Why? Because for a hundred years following the European discovery, the island was raided by slave traders, colonists, and whalers, with devastating effects on the indigenous population. The advanced civilization declined not because the inhabitants destroyed their own environment, but because of attacks from outsiders. In the other examples Diamond uses to illustrate his thesis, resource degradation was probably a contributing factor in collapse, but other causes included climate change, social and political factors, invasions, and pandemics—it was the interplay of factors that was important. In the case of the ninth century collapse of the Mayan civilization, a drier climate combined with rapid rates of deforestation for agriculture and wood fuel to create the lime for the building of the large temples led to soil erosion and crop failures.[72] Societal collapse is not inevitable, and today we have a technological sophistication that makes us different from older civilizations. We should be able to deal with any imminent resource scarcity in a rational manner—a premise that will be discussed in the final chapter of this book.

Resource scarcity and resource wars

It is also possible a link could exist between resource scarcity and societal collapse via resource wars. For example, Michael Klare, in his controversial book *Resource Wars*, argues that international conflicts over resources will inevitably arise because of the continued rapid expansion of global resource demand led by China and India, the development of shortages of many minerals, and the proliferation of potential disputes over ownership and control of contested areas.[73] He claims this will be a lethal mix that will play out in the future.

Wars and aggression seem to be an integral part of human existence, and world history is riddled with human migrations, conquests, empires, and colonies. From their origins in East Africa, humans had probably spread to all of Africa about 150,000 years ago, left Africa 70,000 years ago, and spread across Asia, Australia, and Europe 40,000 years ago. These early migrations are believed to have been driven by a search for resources as climatic change and population pressures made it necessary to move into new areas. The behaviour of hunter-gatherers should offer some insight into the role of aggression in human nature, as the hunter-gatherer period accounts for 99.5 percent of human existence. The anthropologist Azar Gat and others have studied current and past hunter-gatherers, providing research that suggests they engaged in wars and other forms of aggression.[74] Ancient male hunter-gatherers were more likely to die violently than modern foragers, but even modern foragers are far more likely to die from homicide than males in high-income countries. The reason is Darwinian: resources such as food and water are selection forces guaranteeing survival. In common with other animals, humans need to maximize reproduction, a need that was historically kept in check by resource scarcity. Aggression was one way of acquiring more resources and therefore more reproductive success. For agriculturalists, the main resource was land, and if the land was capable of producing a surplus, population expanded, which in turn required more land, forcing people to move into new areas to survive through peaceful or not so peaceful means.

Examples of conquests and colonizations in historic times were the early Mediterranean colonies established by the Phoenicians around 1000 BC and the Greeks around 800 BC, which were later conquered by the Romans. Following and coinciding with the decline of the Roman Empire, a succession of barbarian invasions between 300 and 700 AD heralded the Dark Ages and to a large extent wiped out many of the cultural achievements of the Romans. The Huns, the Visigoths, the Ostrogoths, the Langobards, the Angles, and the Germanic tribes were all looking for better places to live. Later, they were followed by the Vikings, the Mongols, the Tartars, and the Arabs. In many cases, the main impetus was a search for trading opportunities; in other cases, power. Most invaders eventually integrated with the local populations, and periods of peace and stability followed. Some conquered peoples never forgot: the Basques, the Catalans, the Welsh, the Scots, the Irish, the Kurds, the Armenians, and the Tibetans, to name a few; for others independence was a romantic dream.

The last expansion of empires in the form of colonialism started in the fifteenth century, with the European powers establishing outposts in the rest of the world, and continued to the second half of the twentieth century.[75] Colonialism was different from previous territorial expansions: rather than involving the conquest of nearby states, it instead involved administering territories far away with little in common with the mother country. There was little or no desire to integrate with the native populations, which were thought to be inferior to the European races. The Spaniards were largely motivated by the quest for treasure and conquered large parts of South America. The Portuguese were explorers and traders, colonizing parts of Africa and South America. However, in Asia, the Portuguese could not resort to conquests as they did not have the military resources to subdue the often huge local populations. They thus had to find other means of gaining trading opportunities by building strategic forts controlling key sea passages such as Macao and Goa. The English and the Dutch were also in pursuit of trade, supporting their merchants, who were in search of profits. The Dutch East India Company, the English-controlled East India Company, and the Hudson's Bay Company had immense power—if anything stood in their way they asked their governments for help, and their governments usually obliged by using military power if necessary. Bit by bit the British acquired India, Canada, Australia, New Zealand, parts of Burma, and smaller territories of strategic importance such as Gibraltar, Hong Kong, Cape Town and Singapore (but lost the United States). Starting in the 1860s all of Africa with the exception of Ethiopia and Liberia was colonized by Europeans. The Italians occupied Ethiopia in 1936 but were driven out during the Second World War by the English, and Ethiopia regained its freedom in 1941. With the exception of King Leopold's actions in the Congo, the African land grab was not as much a quest for resources as strategic quests for land, as the African resources were largely unknown.

After World War II, empires crumbled, and over one hundred new states emerged. The inhabitants treasured their new freedom and expected prosperity to arrive when the colonial yoke was thrown off, but unfortunately it did not happen. The former mother countries prospered while the new countries did not, with some exceptions (for example Singapore and Taiwan). Another major war seemed a distinct possibility during the height of the cold war, but after the fall of the Soviet Union in 1991, the danger subsided. The cold war was a conflict over ideologies, and after it was over, American foreign policy, under President Clinton, reverted to an emphasis on economic dominance.

While human aggression has been a recurring feature of history, few international wars have been fought exclusively over resources, and the incidence of international wars has declined, while the incidence of civil wars has increased. The link between wars and resources can go both ways. Wars can be caused by the desire or need to acquire resources, or an abundance of marketable resources can lead to disputes over control of resource revenues, as discussed above. The first argument is Malthusian in nature—population pressures lead to resource scarcity and in turn to conflicts over diminishing resources. The other argument is that resource revenues provide a ready source of cash for rebels or for unscrupulous governments to spend on military adventures with little need for electoral approval, creating situations that can lead to more reckless foreign policies.

Even though it is easy to blame the need for resources on wars, the roots of war are complex, and to blame it on one cause is simplistic. Nevertheless, the War of the Pacific (1879–1884) was caused by a dispute over the valuable nitrate deposits in the Atacama desert in South America, and the iron-ore-rich Lorraine region was the centre for military engagements in three wars: the Franco-Prussian War (1870–71), World War I, and World War II. When Hitler came to power, he claimed that Germany needed *Lebensraum* (living space), which could be gained only through expansion of its territories and a return of Germany's lost African colonies.[76] A contributing factor was that Germany had never been well supplied with minerals (apart from coal and potash) and had lost its access to iron ore in Lorraine in the Franco-Prussian War, and the collapse of world trade following the Great Depression reduced the ability to access raw materials through trade. Germany's subsequent occupation of the Rhineland, Austria, and Czechoslovakia relieved the rearmament industry's mineral shortages that had allegedly prevented Germany from becoming a great power. The Japanese invasion of northern China and Manchuria in 1937 was also partly caused by the need for raw materials, as Japan had very few and was largely unable to import materials from many parts of the world. Northern China and Manchuria had coal, iron ore, and magnesium, all necessary for the steel industry. Other examples of resource-driven actions are the USSR annexation of the nickel-rich Finnish Petsamo region on the Barents Sea in 1939 and the French reluctance to grant oil-rich Algeria independence, which led to the 1954–62 Algerian war.[77]

At present, oil is the ultimate resource of strategic importance. Arguably, no other resource in world history has played the same role in influencing world politics. In particular, the oil-rich Middle East has remained an area of political unrest since the end of the World War II, fuelled by the founding of the State of Israel in 1948 and the postwar US dominance of the oil industry. A partial list of conflicts in which oil was central includes the CIA removal of the democratically elected government of Mohammed Mossadeq in Iran following the nationalization of the Anglo-Iranian Oil Company in 1951; the Arab-Israeli War of 1973 that led to an oil embargo against the United States and its allies, causing the 1973 energy crisis; the Iran-Iraq War of 1980–1988, in which Saddam Hussein started hostilities by invading oil-rich Iran, taking advantage of Iran's perceived weakness because of internal unrest following the Iranian revolution; the Iraq invasion of Kuwait in 1990, caused by disputes over financial debt and oil production in fields spanning the two countries; and arguably the Iraq War of 2003–2011. The justification for the Iraq War was to find and destroy weapons of mass destruction despite the fact that there was no record that any existed. The removal of the odious Saddam Hussein from control over oil-rich Iraq seems to be a more likely reason for the war, as Iraq has the second-largest oil reserves in the Middle East after Saudi Arabia, and furthermore, they were largely untapped.[78] Alan Greenspan, former US Federal Reserve chairman, wrote in his memoir that "the Iraq War is largely about oil."[79]

Oil has also played a role in civil wars. Many recent oil discoveries are in countries such as Chad, Mauritania, Azerbaijan, Kazakhstan, Cambodia, and East Timor—none known for their stable and democratic governments. Oil-producing developing countries are twice as likely to suffer from insurgencies as non-oil-producing countries.[80] Even though rebels may find it difficult to lay their hands on oil, as oil extraction requires skill and technology, they can still benefit from oil resources by demanding bribes from oil companies or by kidnapping employees and demanding ransom. In some cases, oil is lootable. For example, in Nigeria crude oil is siphoned off by rebels in the delta area and loaded onto barges hiding in the mangrove forests on the shore. It is estimated that up to 10 percent of total oil production in Nigeria "disappears" in this fashion.[81] There are also increased incidences of piracy on the high seas, where pirates seize whole oil tankers. Oil wealth can also encourage separatism—oil and gas are often found and produced in areas removed from power, where the local population often does not benefit from the oil discoveries because most of the oil revenue goes to the central government, and few jobs are created for locals, who have to bear many of the environmental costs. Rebels in undeveloped oil-rich areas often demand funding from prospective oil producers in return for concessions in case the rebellion succeeds. Examples of oil-induced rebellions can be found in Bolivia, Indonesia, Iran, Iraq, Nigeria, and the former Sudan.[82]

However, the causes of conflicts are many. Two hundred and fifty-four armed conflicts have occurred since the end of World War II. In 2013 alone there were thirty-three conflicts, all fought within states, but several were internationalized by the involvement of foreign troops; this has been the predominant pattern since the Second World War.[83] In the early twentieth century, most wars were international and most of the casualties were soldiers. Today, most wars are civil wars and most casualties are civilians. Why the change? Paul Collier and his associates at Oxford University spent years using statistical analysis to try to sort out the underlying reasons behind civil wars, with fascinating findings.[84] First, civil wars are mainly fought in poor countries. Countries that have a high per-capita income growth are at less risk of violent conflict than those whose incomes do not grow at all. The poorest one-sixth of the world's people endure four-fifths of the civil wars. The researchers found that when income per person doubles, the risk of civil war decreases by 50 percent. Why? It is possible that with growth, there is some feeling of hope in the country, and people can be persuaded to cooperate for the common good, but it may also mean that growth allows a government to employ more advanced security services. Second, colonial history does not statistically explain the incidence of war. It does not matter whether the country was a former British colony, French colony, or any other country's colony; nor does the amount of time elapsed since the former colony became independent matter. In some cases decolonizing had disastrous consequences, and in others it did not. Ethiopia and Liberia were never colonies but suffered devastating civil wars. Third, a previous civil war greatly increases the probability of having another; the risk decreases with the lapse of time since the last war. War feeds on itself, as nobody wants to invest in factories or employment opportunities in war zones, and skilled people flee. Fourth, resources have an impact on the probability of a civil war occurring. Using several alternative measures of resources and controlling for other variables, Collier and his associates found that dependence on natural resources increases the risk of civil war. A country in which resource exports make up 10 percent of GDP has an 11 percent probability of being at war. If resource exports make up 30 percent of GDP, the probability increases to 33 percent. However, the link is not clearcut because an abundance of natural resources (such as oil in Saudi Arabia), is associated with a decline in the probability of violence. Rich countries can afford sophisticated security and to buy off opponents.

The findings of Collier et al. generated huge interest, and other studies followed. Many historians argued that the models did not adequately incorporate the historical legacy. While the link between low incomes, slow economic growth, and civil war seems solid, the link between resources and civil war is not clear-cut—some subsequent studies found a link, while others did not.[85] If there is a link, it may work via institutions. While most countries harbour disaffected groups, if they are democracies with relatively equal income distributions, the disagreements can usually be solved in a peaceful manner. On the other hand, where states are weak and income distributions are highly unequal, the presence of lootable resources may provide an easy way to riches for some, providing the financing to address grievances with violent means.[86] An easy source of income for insurgents, particularly if they are readily available, are resources such as alluvial diamonds and timber or easily extractable minerals such as tin and coltan. Illegally obtained ivory and drugs like opium and cocaine also fund rebel movements. Some economists now argue that perhaps the main reason many poor countries have failed to get richer is that they have suffered too many costly civil wars.[87]

The international community can take measures to discourage the use of resource revenues to fuel civil war and bloodshed. In 2000 there were six diamond-producing states engaged in civil war, and in 2006 there were none. A United Nations–led effort to sever the link between diamonds and civil war clearly bore fruit, starting with sanctions in 1998 against diamond producers involved in conflict, followed by the Kimberley Process in 2002, which required major diamond traders to certify that their diamonds did not come from rebel groups. As a result, the funding for rebel groups dried up and civil wars in Angola, Sierra Leone, and Liberia stopped. The United States has been instrumental in trying to control the flow of so-called *conflict minerals* through the Dodd-Frank Wall Street Reform and Consumer Protection Act of 2010 that requires companies to disclose their usage of conflict minerals (coltan, tin, gold, and tungsten) that originate in central Africa.[88] The law came into effect in 2014.

To do the same with oil will be far more difficult. Because of the critical importance of oil in the world economy, oil-producing countries have more bargaining power and sanctions are less of a threat. Possible solutions include more transparency among oil importers (such as Nigeria's Publish What You Pump campaign[89]) and a ban on buying oil from insurgents. The various proposals discussed above, such as the Extractive Industries Transparency Initiative, would also help, as well as schemes to help new oil-producing countries to manage oil revenues for the benefit of their people. It will not be easy.

In conclusion, resources and resource revenues are not the only explanation for or even the most important factors behind civil wars. All conflicts are about resources and their distribution at a superficial level, but they are also about identity and basic needs, rights, and grievances, and we do not have a firm understanding of which factor is the trigger for violence and how they feed on each other.[90] It is probably true to conclude that each conflict is unique.

Is Michael Klare right in his warnings about the likelihood of future resource wars? Results of recent economic modelling support the link between resources and international wars. The economist Daron Acemoglu and his colleagues have demonstrated that the probability of war between a resource rich and a resource poor country is high if the demand for a particular resource is relatively price insensitive (for example oil), and if the resource is becoming depleted.[91] There are enormous challenges and dangers to world peace. Gwynne Dyer, in his book *Climate Wars*, claims that the future will be dire if the world fails to deal with climate change because failing to do so will make parts of the world uninhabitable due to rising sea levels and climate-induced water scarcity. Large numbers of refugees will attempt to migrate to less affected areas, where they will not be welcomed with open arms; instead, he sees increased use of military force or other measures such as security corridors to keep them out.[92] Indeed, a contributing factor to the Syrian civil war may well have been the 2007–2010 drought that caused the migration of 1.5 million Syrians into cities.[93] A second danger is that dwindling water resources will lead to international conflicts over shared river basins.[94] The Jordan River, the Nile, the headwaters of the Euphrates and Tigris, and rivers in Southeast Asia come to mind. A third danger is more frequent disputes over resources whose ownership is not truly delineated—an example is the current dispute over ownership of the islands in the South China Sea and areas in the Arctic[95]—and a fourth that overpopulation in general will put such a strain on resources that wars are inevitable. There is also fear that escalating food prices will lead to riots and possibly civil wars. Food price increases in 2009 did indeed lead to rioting in several countries, scenarios that may well be repeated if climate change and land degradation lead to decreased agricultural production. A detailed discussion of our ability to feed the growing world population is provided in Chapter 8.

Concluding remarks

Have the historical illustrations in this chapter any relevance for today? What can we learn from the past? The first lesson is fundamental and obvious: resource neglect can lead to the destruction of livelihoods and cultures. Some of our indicators show that many of the ecosystems critical for our own survival are nearing collapse, and we ignore the sustainability of our resource use at our own peril. Our critical resources appear to be in danger, and scarcity is a real problem, lending credibility to the whole notion of "running out of resources." The challenge is to put a value on the services of nature, to understand how natural systems are maintained and created, and to implement policies that ensure sustainability.

A second lesson is that resource extraction has usually only been achieved through ruthless exploitation or suppression of indigenous people, a situation not uncommon even in modern societies, particularly if there are unsettled land claims. In fairness, this has become a sensitive issue for today's mining companies, and because of pressures from NGOs, they are attempting to address the problems. A third lesson is that the importance of a particular resource changes over time, something we need to remember in view of our current dependence on oil and the extent to which fossil fuels currently govern our lives.

The concept of (strong) sustainability is an integral feature of this book. We have to aim for both ecological and economic sustainability in our use of both non-renewable and renewable resources. The exploitation of non-renewable resources must be managed to provide long-term benefits for the countries that own them, which means governments must ensure that resource revenues are transparent and used for the benefit of people, both of current and future generations. Governments should also promote policies of diversification and policies that support industries related to the resource in question. Of critical importance is the development of a knowledge base focused on the specific conditions of resource extraction in the country. It is also important to set aside a significant proportion of the resource revenue for future use, with the proceeds spent on national priorities. Renewable resources should be exploited only at a level that guarantees renewal—easy in theory but difficult in practice, as will become obvious in the latter part of the book. It is imperative to protect our natural resources that are critical to life support such as air, fresh water, and the oceans. The next two chapters will focus on the management of non-renewable resources.

2

The Sustainability of Mineral Resources

Factors determining demand and supply of minerals. The markets for minerals. Common metals: iron ore and ferro-alloy metals. Common metals: aluminum, magnesium, titanium, manganese, and silicon. Base metals. Less common metals. Rare earth minerals. The special case of gold and silver. Diamonds. Other important minerals: fluorspar, graphite, phosphate, and potash. Environmental impacts of the mining industry. Recycling. Mineral depletion and sustainability.

THE HISTORY OF METALS provides a fascinating insight into the ingenuity of humans in exploiting the earth's resources for their own benefit. Metals have been employed for a very long time, possibly for over nine thousand years—the oldest-known metal object is a copper pendant found in northern Iraq dating from 8700 BC.[96] Gold has been used for approximately six thousand years, and silver, lead, tin, iron, and mercury have been used for well over two thousand years. [97]

It is not surprising that these seven metals were the first to be utilized as they can be found in metallic form in nature (*native metals*) and do not require a complicated refining process. For example, a gold nugget does not need any further processing to be shaped directly into its intended use. Gold and silver were used for jewellery and coins, copper and iron for tools, and lead for containers and piping. Tin was worked with copper to form bronze that was more suitable than copper for making weapons and farm implements; it was harder and could take and retain a sharp edge. The making of bronze was in fact an early example of the use of metallurgy following the discovery that the combination of the two metals (90 percent copper and 10 percent tin) was stronger than the metals themselves. Mercury was used for medicinal purposes and to dissolve gold and silver for use in plating. Iron is less easily extracted from ore bodies, and it is believed that the first usable iron came from meteorites, in which it often occurs in a relatively pure metallic form. Another easily accessible source of iron was found in bogs and swamps (*bog iron* is formed by a natural chemical process), and there is some evidence that the Vikings settled where deposits of bog iron were found.[98] The Hittites, who inhabited Turkey from the eighteenth century BC, are thought to have discovered a basic steel-making technology around 1300 BC by melting iron ore over charcoal (adding carbon), making the iron stronger, which expanded its use greatly, particularly for weapons.[99] Bronze was initially the favoured metal for making tools because the melting point was lower than iron, but iron was more common than copper and tin and was also more easily forged into objects following the discovery of iron-smelting and -smithing technology.

Until the seventeenth century, only twelve metals were known. These included arsenic, zinc, bismuth, antimony, and platinum in addition to the seven metals known since antiquity.[100] Even today, there are just eighty-six known metals. While some metals such as gold have always been valued because they do not corrode, others (especially iron, copper, tin, and lead) are valuable because they are malleable, and still others are important as alloying elements. Rapid changes in technology and metallurgy during the twentieth century led to numerous new applications of metals such as the use of copper in conducting electricity, lighter metals such as aluminum in airplanes, and non-corrosive compounds such as steel both in transportation and building. New products such as cell phones, LED (light-emitting diode) lighting, fuel cells and batteries for electric cars, medical technologies, and wind and solar technologies have driven the search for and the use of previously obscure metals and minerals with desirable properties relating to electrical conductivity, catalytic efficiency, or melting point.* One example

---

*A mineral is any solid inorganic substance that can be mined; for example, clay, limestone, asbestos, potash, diamonds, and hematite (a type of iron ore). Minerals can be metallic or non-metallic, and metallic minerals can be made into metals that can be shaped and conduct electricity. Coal, on the other hand, is not a mineral as it is formed from decayed plants and animals, and is therefore organic. The precise definition of what is a mineral is open to debate.

of a previously little-known mineral is coltan (columbite-tantalite), mined in Africa as well as Australia and Canada. Its refined form (tantalum) is essential for the manufacture of cell phones, computers, jet engines, airbags, and various types of capacitors. It became notorious a few years ago in the Democratic Republic of the Congo, where a significant proportion of global coltan deposits are found in an area inhabited by the increasingly rare mountain gorilla. Mining in this region takes place on a small scale with no environmental controls and has had predictable effects on the gorilla population, which has decreased by 90 percent. The high profits from extraction also made coltan a conflict mineral that helped to fuel the Congolese civil war—a classic example of lack of regulations and weak government leading to a form of the resource curse as described in the preceding chapter.[101]

Another unfamiliar metal is indium, which was only discovered in the 1920s and is a by-product of zinc mining. Its use in the manufacture of liquid crystal displays (LCDs) for computers and televisions led to a large increase in demand, with prices soaring from US$94/kg in 2002 to a record approaching $1,000/kg in 2005, a peak which has not been reached since.[102] Photovoltaic cells employ silicon, cadmium, gallium, selenium, and tellurium; electric cars require neodymium and lithium; and solar panels require gallium, selenium, and tellurium. Automobile catalytic converters cannot be made without the platinum group metals and rare earth minerals, which are so scarce that China, their main producer, imposed a decade-long limit on their exports. New high-speed trains require cobalt and samarium and the new aircrafts, rhenium.[103]

However, even in today's world economy with its apparent reliance on sophisticated electronic products, the most important raw material in volume terms is cement—followed by aluminum, iron ore, and copper. Cement is a chemical binder made from limestone and clay that is mixed with sand and gravel to form concrete. This basic technology was discovered by the Romans, who used burnt lime and volcanic ash in house building, and the technology gave the cement the desirable property of hardening under water, which made it possible to construct harbours and lighthouses. However, this knowledge was lost during the Middle Ages, and the mortar used in building Europe's monumental cathedrals was not of the same high quality and has led to problems in maintenance. It was not until the early part of the eighteenth century that it was rediscovered by English inventor Joseph Aspdin, who discovered that better cement could be made by subjecting limestone and clay to high temperatures. The cement was named Portland cement because it resembled the popular Portland stone used in buildings. Modern cement is mainly a combination of lime and silica with gypsum added to control the speed at which the concrete sets. Cement production is energy intensive as the materials are subjected to very high temperatures in kilns, forming *clinker*, which is then crushed and pulverized.[104] The components necessary for making cement are readily found all over the world; thus little of this product is traded across borders.

Apart from cement, modern society is totally dependent on four common metals: iron (together with manganese) for steel-making, aluminium for transportation, copper for electrical transmission, and lead for batteries. Other important metals are chromium and nickel used in steel production, zinc for preventing corrosion, and tin which is essential in modern electronics.

Following the surge in commodity prices in the first decade of 2000, prospecting for new mineral deposits became a lucrative occupation in many parts of the world, and international mining companies invested heavily in West Africa (Gabon, Guinea, Niger) and Mongolia. Many countries benefited greatly from mining and its related activities, but in other countries the benefits of mining did not spread to the general population—a good example of the resource curse, discussed in the last chapter. Table 2.1 gives information on the ten largest mineral producers measured by value of production in 2012. It is interesting to note that despite the large expansion in the value of production between 2000 and

Table 2.1. Value of mineral production, 10 largest producers, 2012

Country	Value of mineral production, 2010 (billions of $US)	% change in value of production 2000–2012	Value of mineral production % of GDP	Value of mineral exports as % of merchandise exports
China	123.1	10,613	1.5	1.5
Australia	108.5	563	7.1	57.3
Brazil	65.9	745	2.9	17.3
Russian Fed.	53.0	390	2.6	9.6
Chile	42.1	301	15.8	61.6
United States	41.8	270	0.3	7.7
South Africa	38.5	203	10.1	38.8
Canada	32.7	314	1.8	12.8
India	26.8	824	1.4	11.4
Peru	25.1	434	13.0	60.1

Source: International Council on Mining and Metals, *The Role of Mining in National Economies*, London, 2014, Table 1. http://www.icmm.com/document/7950.

2012, the mining sector was of only minor importance in terms of its contribution to most of these countries' GDP, with the exception of Chile, where the contribution was over 15 percent. The role of mining was far more important for some developing countries. The sector accounted for 57.5 percent of GDP for Mauritania, 34.7 percent for Papua New Guinea, and 52.9 percent for Mongolia.

Mining's contribution to world trade is small compared with that of other sectors. In 2010, for example, mining products represented 4.6 percent of the value of world exports, fuels 15.8 percent, agricultural products 9.2 percent, and manufactured products 67.1 percent.[105] However, for some countries mining exports are a significant source of foreign exchange, employment, and foreign direct investments. While mineral exports constituted between 1.5 percent and 61.6 percent for the ten largest producers in 2012, they accounted for 91.6 percent of total exports for Botswana, 81.5 percent for the Democratic Republic of the Congo, and 74.6 percent for Mongolia. For a few countries revenue from mining makes up a large proportion of government revenue: Botswana (44.6 percent), Democratic Republic of the Congo (25.3 percent), and Papua New Guinea (22.9 percent).[106]

The previous chapter discussed the issue of the sustainability of a resource in the wider sense. For mining to be sustainable, resource revenues collected by national governments must invested for the benefit of future generations—the resource curse has to be avoided—and the environmental impact of extraction must be minimized.[107] As was noted, this is often not the case. In many parts of the world, the mining sector contributes little to the present and future welfare of a country, and some resource-rich countries are still desperately poor, leading to increased pressure on the mining industry for transparency and accountability. This chapter continues the discussion of the world's resources by focusing on current and future availability of mineral resources. In doing so, it is critical to understand the markets for minerals and the role of prices in determining availability. The first section examines markets both in general and for particular minerals. The chapter continues with an account of the environmental record of the mining industry and a discussion of the risks of depletion—that is, does the world face an imminent shortage of minerals?

Factors determining demand and supply of minerals

The importance of minerals in the world's economies and in global trade is determined by basic economic factors governing demand and supply, as well as technology and government trade and environmental policies. The demand for any mineral is determined by the demand for the goods that require the mineral for their manufacture. It is obvious that if manufacturing does not require a mineral's use, it will not be mined. The amount demanded is, of course, strongly affected by the price of the mineral itself. If the price of a mineral increases, and if there are cheaper substitutes, the use of the mineral will usually decrease, at least over time.

Technology is also important. For example, even though the manufacture of computers and televisions with liquid crystal displays (LCD) requires indium, the amount needed is minute and represents a very small share of the total cost and therefore demand may not be very price sensitive. Changes in technology have resulted in diminished raw-material use per unit of production and changes in the composition of raw materials employed. Bridges and cars use less steel because the steel produced is now stronger. Aluminum cans are thinner, requiring less metal, and plastics and ceramics and so-called composites have replaced heavier metals in many products. For example, ceramics are used in car engines and carbon fibres in racing-car bodies, bicycles, fishing rods, and baseball bats. Raw-material use per unit of production declined by 50 percent during the twentieth century partly because of these changes in the composition of raw materials and partly because of a general shift in production toward services and away from heavy industry in industrialized countries. Health, education, and personal and financial services, for example, account for a larger proportion of GDP in rich countries than in poor countries. However, this trend toward a reduction in raw materials per unit of world output appears to have come to a (temporary?) halt because of the growing role of China in the world economy. Massive industrial expansion in China meant that China's copper and aluminum use per $1,000 of GDP was 1.8 and 4.1 kilograms for the period of 2007–09, while the corresponding figures for the world as a whole were 0.4 and 0.7 kilograms, resulting in a reversal of the long-term downward trend of metal consumption per unit of global GDP.[108]

Health and safety concerns and government regulations also affect the demand for minerals. Examples are the health concerns surrounding asbestos and mercury, which led to a large drop in demand in developed countries. A European Union ban on the use of asbestos became effective in 2005, and many jurisdictions have banned the use of mercury in thermometers and barometers.

The supply of minerals ultimately depends on their occurrence in the earth's crust. However, even more important factors are market prices, costs of production, the possibilities of recycling, technology, political conditions, and the accessibility of financial instruments to spread risks. If the market price of a

Figure 2.1. The Bingham Canyon Mine in Utah. The copper mine was opened in 1906 and is still one of the world's largest open-pit mines. Source: Wikimedia Commons.

mineral increases, producers will respond over time by increasing production, but the increase of production depends on production costs. These are influenced by the costs of extraction and refining which in turn are determined by technology, the purity and chemical composition of the mineral deposits, the cost of labour and machinery, and the tax and royalty regime.

Copper is an interesting example of the impact of technological change on supply. At the end of the nineteenth century, the American engineer Daniel Jackling discovered the benefits of shifting from selective underground mining to mass mining (open-pit mining). This allowed the full utilization of low-grade ore bodies without cost increases. In the early part of the twentieth century, the average grade of copper ore was 4 percent, by the 1920s, it had fallen to 2 percent, and in 2006, 45 percent of copper was extracted from ore bodies with a concentration of 0.5 percent.[109] Other examples of changes in technology that have greatly benefited the mining industry include uses of more efficient mining machinery, improved chemicals and explosives, and remote-sensing imagery technology that makes it easier to uncover new deposits of minerals

Figure 2.2. New mining technology often involves very large equipment. Bagger 288, a mobile strip-mining machine, is the world's largest land vehicle. Source: http://commons. wikimedia.org/wiki/File%3ABagger-garzweiler.jpg.

in remote regions. In other cases technology is a limiting factor. For example, metals such as copper, lead, zinc, and nickel are found in readily available silicate minerals, but these minerals cannot be easily concentrated into volumes that can be processed into metals because the chemical bonds are too strong to be easily broken into component parts. Hence these metals are mined only from mineral deposits containing sulphur or oxygen, which make them more

Figure 2.3. Mining in developing countries often happens on a very small scale and often involves children. The picture shows mining of cassiterite and wolframite in the Congo. Source: http://commons.wikimedia.org/wiki/File:Child_labor,_Artisanal_Mining_in_ Kailo_Congo.jpg.

easily extractable.[110] Aluminium was once as costly as gold until the process of separating aluminium from its oxide using electricity rather than chemicals was discovered in the 1880s. Today, the prices of tantalum, titanium, neodymium, and tungsten are high because of a very expensive extraction process, a situation that may change rapidly because of the development of a new promising technology.[111]

Government regulations also affect the supply of minerals. Environmental regulations and health and safety regulations increase the cost of mining operations, creating an adverse effect on supply. Some governments may also impose specific requirements on hiring local labour and buying local products, which may or may not lead to higher costs, and others (such as Bolivia) do not allow foreign mining companies to operate mines. Recently, Chinese export restrictions of a whole range of minerals adversely affected their supply on world markets—a development that will be analyzed in detail in the latter part of this chapter.

The markets for minerals

Commodities markets in general are unregulated, and information is often not easily available to investors. No legal ban exists on insider trading.[112] The markets are also relatively small, dominated by few participants, and political events in one country can have a large impact on commodities markets. For example, strikes in Chilean copper mines in 2006 had an effect on copper prices, and stricter mining regulations in Indonesia increased tin prices.[113] Markets are also volatile because supplies are not responsive in the short run to price increases due to the long lead times between exploration and production. For example, in a 1995 study of fifty-four mining deposits around the Pacific Rim, the average time from the initial exploration to the first drill hole for base metals was fourteen years, and for gold, twenty-two years. It then took another 13.5 years to begin production for base metals and seven years for gold—that is almost thirty years between exploration and mining.[114] This means that any short-term changes in demand result in large fluctuations in prices of metals and minerals.

Before the 2000–2011 commodities boom, global commodities booms occurred roughly every twenty to thirty years. The previous bull market for oil came to an end in 1981, for sugar in 1973, and for gold in 1979. The 1970s-era bull market was caused by political events, the most important being the Arab-Israeli War of 1973. The ensuing decades of declining or stable commodities prices ended after the bursting of the dot-com bubble in 2000, when many

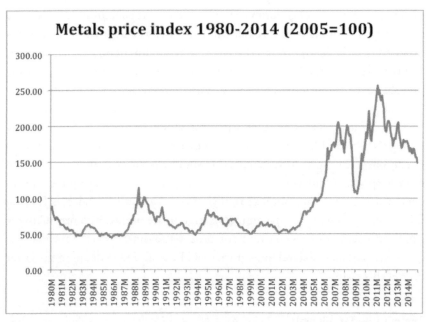

Figure 2.4. Metals price index (2005 = 100). The index includes copper, aluminum, iron ore, tin, nickel, zinc, lead, and uranium price indices. The graph shows clearly how relatively stable prices started to escalate around 2003. Source: The International Monetary Fund. http://www.imf.org/external/np/res/commod/index.aspx.

wealth-holders began searching out fresh investment opportunities in commodities. The emergence of China and India, with their relatively underdeveloped infrastructures, led to increased demand for raw materials and rapidly rising prices. When a country first becomes industrialized, economic growth is materials and labour intensive because roads, factories, and ports have to be built. This is usually followed by urban development with the building of houses, offices, and shops, followed by increased demand for home and domestic needs such as kitchen appliances and furniture, all of which need materials. For example, between 2000 and 2008, the Chinese GDP grew at an annual rate of 10 percent, while at the same time the Chinese demand for steel grew at an annual rate of 16 percent, aluminum at 20 percent, copper at 13 percent, and nickel at 23 percent, resulting in a situation where China accounted for one-third of the world's steel and aluminum consumption and one-quarter of the copper and nickel.[115] Figure 2.4 shows price increases during the recent boom.

Because of these prolonged price increases, many analysts have argued that the recent boom was a *supercycle.* According to Alan Heap of Citygroup Global

Markets, a commodity supercycle occurs when the prices of a range of commodities move in tandem.[116] A typical cycle has an upswing of ten to thirty-five years, and the complete cycle lasts ten to seventy years. He argues that the cycle is driven by industrialization and urbanization of a major country. For example, one supercycle started in the late 1800s and lasted until the early 1900s, driven by the industrialization of the United States. The second supercycle, which started at the end of World War II and lasted until 1975, was caused by the postwar reconstruction in Europe and the industrialization of Japan. Heap claims that a third cycle began around 2000, caused by the industrialization of China. The supercycle hypothesis has received support from the results of recent statistical studies.[117]

In a bull market, money is available to invest in new facilities, which in the long run increases supply and brings down prices. Little investment seems to have taken place in mining infrastructure during the latest bull market for several reasons. One is the long lead time between exploration and production referred to above. Furthermore, when prices of many materials increase at the same time, all affected producers will have an incentive to open new mines and expand production, resulting in a scramble to hire new engineers and other skilled personnel and to buy new machinery. This is likely to lead to capacity constraints with shortages, and as a result the opening of new mines is often postponed.[118] It was also reported that many of the big mining companies used their cash for mergers and acquisitions during the last boom period, which rarely results in improvements in infrastructure or opening of new mines.[119] Table 2.2 shows prices and price increases from 2007 to 2011 for some of the more important metals and minerals.

The commodities boom came to a temporary halt in 2008 following crashes in both equity and housing markets in the United States but prices quickly resumed their upward climb, but in 2012–2013, the boom came to an end following slower growth in the Chinese economy.

Common metals: iron ore and ferro-alloy metals

Table 2.2 summarizes the salient statistics of today's mineral production. Iron ore, aluminum, copper, zinc, and lead are the most important metals in terms of volume produced, and most of these have been known and used for a very long time. Iron is the third most abundant metal after silicon and aluminum—5.6 percent of the world's crust consists of iron.[120] The mining of iron first developed in the Middle East about 1300 BC. Because iron ore was worked by heating the

Table 2.2. World mineral production, reserves, reserve-production ratios, the share in reserves of the two largest sources, and prices (2014)

	2014 world production	2014 world reserves	Reserve-to-production ratio*	Country (% share of total reserves)	2014 average price USs/kg	Price change (%) 2010–2014
Antimony (tonnes)	160,000	1,800,000	11	China (53) Russia (35)	9.50	+7
Bauxite and alumina (thousand tonnes)	234,000	28,000,000	118	Guinea (25) Australia (21)	0.03	No change
Beryllium (tonnes)	270	Not available		Main producers: United States, China	448	−0
Cadmium (tonnes)	22,200	Traces in zinc ores		Main producers: China and South Korea	1.94	−50
Cement (million tonnes)	4,180	Abundant		China	0.09	+7
Chromium (thousand tonnes)	29,000	>480,000	>17	Kazakhstan (48) South Africa (42)	0.22	+5
Cobalt (tonnes)	112,000	7,200,000	64	D.R.Congo (47) Australia (15)	0.03	+31
Copper (thousand tonnes)	18,700	700,000	38	Chile (30) Australia (13)	7.08	−7
Fluorspar (thousand tonnes)	6,850	240,000	35	South Africa (17) Mexico (13)	0.35	+20
Gallium (tonnes)	440	Traces in bauxite and zinc ores		Main producers: China, Germany	362	−40

*Reserves refer to proven reserves, and the reserve-to-production ratio is a rough estimate of the number of years the reserves could last, given current production. The table does not include estimates for total resources—deposits that are likely to be there but have not yet been delineated. For this reason the reserve-production ratio is not a reliable guide to future scarcity. For example, in 1970, world copper resources were estimated to contain 1.6 billion tons of copper, and reserves were estimated to 280 million tonnes. Meanwhile, 400 million tonnes of copper have been produced, but by 2011 the world copper reserves had increased to 690 million tons (from Appendix C, Mineral Commodities Summaries, USGS).

	2014 world production	2014 world reserves	Reserve-to-production ratio*	Country (% share of total reserves)	2014 average price US$/kg	Price change (%) 2010–2014
Germanium (kg)	165,000	Traces in zinc, lead, and copper ores		Main producers: China, Russia	1,900	+58
Gold (tonnes)	2,860	55,000	19	Australia (18) South Africa (11)	10,830	+3
Graphite (thousand tonnes)	1,170	110,000	94	China (50) Brazil (36)	1.54	+114
Indium (tonnes)	820	Traces in zinc ores		Main producers: China and Korea	735	+30
Crude iron ore (million tonnes)	3,220	190,000	59	Australia (28) Brazil (16)	0.10	+2
Lead (thousand tonnes)	5,460	87,000	16	Australia (40) China (17)	1.89	−13
Lithium (tonnes)	36,000	13,500,000	375	Chile (55) China (27)	6.60	+27
Magnesium (thousand tonnes)	907	abundant	Not estimated	Main producer: China	2.50	−14
Manganese (thousand tonnes)	18,000	570,000	32	South Africa (26) Ukraine (24)	0.01	−30
Mercury (tonnes)	1,850	600,000	320	Mexico (29) China (22)	54	+72
Molybdenum (tonnes)	266,000	11,000,000	38	China (39) US (24)	26.90	−23
Nickel (tonnes)	2,400,000	81,000,000	34	Australia (23) New Caledonia (15)	0.02	−22
Niobium (columbite) (tonnes)	59,000	>4,300,000	>73	Brazil (95) Canada (5)	42	+11

Continues on next page

Table 2.2, continued

	2014 world production	2014 world reserves	Reserve-to-production ratio*	Country (% share of total reserves	2014 average price US$/kg	Price change (%) 2010–2014
Palladium and platinum (kg)	351,000	66,000,000	188	South Africa (90)	26,684 (palladium)	+57
Phosphate rock (thousand tonnes)	220,000	67,000,000	304	Morocco and Western Sahara (75) China (6)	0.09	+17
Potash (thousand tonnes)	35,000	>13,500,000	>353	Canada (46) Russia (35)	0.73	+16
Rare earth minerals (tonnes)	110,000	130,000,000	1181	China (42) Brazil (17)	4.50 (cerium oxide)	-92
Rhenium (kgs)	48,800	2,500,000	51	Chile (52) US (16)	3,000	−36
Silicon (thousand tonnes)	7,680	abundant	Not estimated	Main producer: China	2.66 (silicon metal)	−14
Silver (tonnes)	26,100	530,000	20	Peru (19) Poland (16) Australia (16)	611.18	−6
Tantalum (tonnes)	1,200	>100,000	>83	Brazil (67) Australia (33)	242	+104
Tin (tonnes)	296,000	4,800,000	16	China (31) Indonesia (17)	21.56	+6
Titanium (thousand metric tons)	7,450	770,000	103	China (29) Australia (17)	0.16 (ilmenite)	+120
Tungsten (tonnes)	82,400	3,300,000	40	China (58) Canada (9)	0.35	+91
Vanadium (tonnes)	60,000	14,000,000	233	China (36) Russia (36)	12.76	−10
Zinc (thousand tonnes)	13,300	230,000	17	Australia (27) China (19)	2.16	+1

Source: Calculated from information in the US Geological Survey, *Mineral Commodities Summaries, 2015*. The prices listed are approximate. Cement is listed because its main component is limestone, a commonly occurring mineral.

ore in charcoal fires, the lack of trees for fuel often limited production. In the early 1700s, the British discovered how to use coke produced from its abundant coal resources for iron making, thereby setting in motion the Industrial Revolution. Today, fully 98 percent of iron mined is used for steel production and the remainder for construction, for making pigment, and for several other specialized purposes. China is the world's largest producer and consumer of iron ore, and increased Chinese demand resulted in a substantial increase in ore prices during the first decade of the twenty-first century. Recycling is very important, as it takes less energy to use scrap steel rather than crude iron for making new steel. In the United States, the auto industry is the main source of scrap steel with a 140 percent recycling rate (i.e., industry recycles more steel than is used in domestic auto production). The corresponding figures for appliances and steel cans are 90 percent and 66 percent. Approximately 98 percent of construction materials are also recycled.[121]

The ferro-alloy metals, which include chromium, nickel, vanadium, cobalt, molybdenum, and tungsten, play an important role in steel-making, so their prices are linked to the price of steel. Chromium was initially used in the tanning industry and for the making of dyes. Its major use today is in stainless-steel production for cars, household products, and kitchen appliances as it resists corrosion. It is regarded as a critically important metal by the United States because of its use in aircraft engines, military vehicles, and weapons. Following the rapid expansion of the steel industry in China, the prices of ferrochrome reached an all-time high in 2008 but have since dropped because of weakened steel demand.[122] Another metal essential for steel production is nickel, which is resistant to corrosion and oxidization. This is the reason stainless steel has a nickel content of between 8 and 10 percent. Its early use was for household utensils in a nickel-silver alloy, and later it was used as an addition to copper in coins to make them harder (a five-cent coin is still called a nickel in North America). Nickel-alloy steels are used in aircraft and trucks to enhance reliability and strength, and nickel has found a new use in nickel-metal hydride batteries for gasoline-electric hybrid cars. It occurs as sulphide deposits in Sudbury in Canada and in the big Russian Norilsk mine, and as lateritic deposits in Cuba, New Caledonia, and Indonesia.[123]

Even a very small presence of vanadium increases strength and temperature resistance in steel, making it important for the aerospace industry, while electric-car makers are experimenting with vanadium-lithium batteries. These newer type of batteries also require cobalt, another superalloy that also has magnetic properties, making it essential for many electronic products. Molybdenum is used for gun barrels, ranging from artillery pieces to pistols, and tungsten (also known as wolframite), a very heavy metal with a high melting point, is used as an alloy, but its main use is in the preparation of drill bits, cutting edges, and electric light bulbs. It is also employed as a non-toxic substitute for lead—for example, in fishing floats. The price of tungsten quadrupled in 2005 when China ceased exporting because of domestic supply concerns,[124] and prices remained fairly high through 2013 because of continuing demand for drill bits in oil and gas exploration. New applications have also been found for tungsten in cellular phones and LED screens. Under the Dodd-Frank Wall Street Reform and Consumer Protection Act in the United States, tungsten is listed together with coltan, cassiterite (a mineral containing tin), and gold as a conflict mineral from the Democratic Republic of the Congo and neighbouring countries.[125] This act requires electronics companies to verify where these minerals come from.

Common metals: aluminum, magnesium, titanium, manganese, and silicon

Other common metals include aluminum, magnesium, titanium, manganese, and silicon. Even though aluminum is abundant in clay minerals all over the world, no commercially viable process exists to extract it from this source. Instead, aluminum is produced from bauxite ores, which are heavily weathered claylike deposits typically found in tropical countries. The largest producers of bauxite are in Australia, Brazil, China, and Guinea.[126] Bauxite is processed into alumina, which in turn has to be converted to aluminum metal by electrolysis. For this reason, the production of aluminum metal is extremely energy intensive, and refining tends to be located near locations with low energy costs. The largest aluminum producers are China, Russia, Canada, and the United States. The metal has found many uses because of its conductivity, lightness, and resistance to weathering such as in the manufacture of cars, airplanes, drink cans, and high-power transmission lines. Fuel-efficiency regulations have in general favoured the use of aluminum in car production because of its low weight.

As is the case for aluminum, the production of magnesium, titanium, and silicon is very energy intensive, so even though the ores are abundant, the prices of these metals are relatively high. Magnesium can be extracted from seawater and brine and is therefore abundant. Its largest producer is China. Because it is heat resistant, the main use of magnesium is for lining for furnaces, incinerators, and kilns. Much of the demand is closely linked to the steel industry, and magnesium is also used in making aluminum alloys. Supply, on the other hand, is linked to energy prices because of the energy-intensive refining process.

Titanium is used as a strengthening agent in alloys used in aircraft bodies and sports equipment as it is four times more resistant to corrosion than stainless steel and has twice the strength-to-weight ratio of steel.[127] Titanium oxide is used for white pigment in paint, plastics, and rubber. Traces of the mineral can be found in most types of rocks, but commercially viable deposits are less common. The largest producers are Australia, South Africa, and Canada. Manganese, another important metal used in steel production, is locally abundant in several countries, including South Africa and the Ukraine, and in small nodules on the ocean floor. Silicon has many uses; the most important is in making aluminum and aluminum alloys, but it is also employed in glass and ceramics, semiconductors, and solar cells. The largest producers of silicon metal are China, Brazil, and Norway. Even though silicon is abundant, there are few producers of high-grade silicon suitable for semiconductors.

Base metals

The mining community refers to base metals as the main commercial non-ferrous metals (excluding precious metals). These are copper, lead, zinc, tin, mercury, and cadmium. Copper is the most important base metal because of its widespread use, and copper prices are often taken as a leading indicator of where the world economy is heading. As mentioned previously, copper has been used for millennia, but following the introduction of electricity, copper's applications expanded greatly because of its high conductivity. Approximately 40 percent of copper is used in electrical and electronic applications and in construction (for plumbing, roofing, and decoration). Many of today's electrical motors rely on copper wiring, with new hybrid cars requiring 50 percent more copper than conventional cars.[128] It is relatively scarce in the earth's crust but can be found on the ocean floor in the form of nodules that also contain manganese, iron, nickel, cobalt, and zinc. Lead, another base metal that has been used for thousands of years has a low melting point that makes it relatively easy to fashion into a variety of products. At one stage it was commonly used for piping, particularly for water, and for paints, pigments, and cosmetics as well as an additive to gasoline. Unfortunately, it was also found to be highly toxic, particularly for children, so its use is now constrained. Today 70 percent of its use is as a component in lead-acid batteries for motor vehicles. It is also used for radioactive shields and as a weight because of its high density.[129] Lead's largest producers are China and Australia, though the recycling rate is high, with 97 percent of lead used in batteries coming from recycled sources. Lead and zinc—the primary use of which is still for galvanizing—are often paired as both metals commonly occur together in nature.

Tin is another ancient metal. Traditionally it has been used as an alloying agent in making bronze in a process that combines copper with tin and in making pewter, which combines tin and lead. Bronze is still used in the manufacture of automobiles and aircraft. However, the main use of tin today is in cans and containers, replacing lead, while a tin and indium alloy is used as coating for flat-panelled plasma and LCD screens. Increased demand for tin has led to large price increases for the ore cassiterite, a tin oxide mineral. Officially, the largest producers of cassiterite are China, Indonesia, and Peru. Unofficially, the Democratic Republic of the Congo is the source of 10 to 15 percent of the ore, and the country possesses one-third of the world's deposits. The ore is often mined under appalling conditions under the scrutiny of Congolese soldiers who pocket much of the profits—the reason it became listed as a conflict mineral.[130] In response to public outcry, the Congolese government ordered a temporary closing of the mines in 2011.

Mercury and cadmium were once major metals, but because of environmental concerns and the risk of poisoning, the use of both is being phased out. At one point in history, mercury poisoning was a common problem. For example, in the story *Alice's Adventures in Wonderland*, mercury poisoning is the ailment from which the Mad Hatter is suffering—a nod to the common practice of coating the fur used for making hats with mercury to make it easier to work. During Roman times, mercury was used in gold mining, a practice continuing today in small mining operations in developing countries that is a source of serious water contamination. Until recently, mercury was widely used as an amalgam by dentists in fixing teeth as well as in batteries and thermometers. Matters changed once the toxic properties of mercury were fully understood, particularly for infants and fetuses. In the late 1950s, a major environmental disaster in Minamata, Japan, involved mercury pollution, with people dying from various neurological symptoms. Over two thousand people were affected. The symptoms, which became known as the "Minamata disease," resulted from the release by a chemical company of waste water contaminated with highly toxic methyl mercury into Minamata's harbour; it was ingested by fish, which were then eaten by the local population. A similar though less severe case occurred in Ontario, Canada, with another chemical company releasing water contaminated with mercury into the Wabagon-English River system with adverse health effects on members of the Grassy Narrows and White Dog First Nations. Today mercury is used as an agent to separate chlorine from caustic soda and in button-type batteries, fireworks, and skin-lightening creams. Despite efforts at reduced use, mercury is still entering the atmosphere and water bodies through coal-fired generating stations and through small-scale gold mining; these two uses now account for 35 percent of total mercury pollution. Apparently, coal naturally absorbs metals such as mercury and cadmium present in the groundwater. These pollutants are released into the atmosphere when the coal is burned, and find their way into rivers, lakes, and the oceans, where mercury is transformed into the methyl mercury that is subsequently ingested by bacteria and enters the food chain. As a result, mercury levels among fish eaters in the United States are four times higher than among those who do not eat fish.[131]

In response to the heightened concern about mercury, most uses are being phased out through legislation by national governments.[132] International negotiations led to a binding United Nations treaty in 2013: the Minamata Convention on Mercury.[133] It was agreed to ban the trade and production of certain products containing mercury and to install filters and scrubbers on new coal-fired generating stations as well as to reduce emissions from existing plants. The treaty also contained measures to reduce the use of mercury in gold mining—but not a ban. Cadmium has a similar history. A by-product of zinc mining, most of its early use was in paints and in rechargeable nickel-cadmium batteries. Cadmium can cause anemia and various bone disorders, and acute poisoning can be fatal.[134]

Less common metals

Table 2.2 lists the prices and occurrences of some of the more unusual metals now in demand because of their use in new and emerging technologies. These include antimony, niobium (formerly called columbium), tantalum, germanium, beryllium, gallium, indium, lithium, and the platinum group metals. Some are used because of high conductivity (e.g., tantalum) in cell phones, pagers, and personal computers, and while others, because of their high melting points, are useful for brakes, ceramics, and telecommunications (tantalum, beryllium, and germanium). Antimony has traditionally been used as an alloy for lead and tin and in lead-acid batteries. Recent demand for antimony has been created for its use in flame retardants and microcapacitors. Eighty-nine percent of production comes from China, and following the closing of some of its mines allegedly for environmental reasons, supply shortages have resulted in price increases, but new mines are set to open in Australia, Canada, and Laos. Niobium is a hard element used in carbon steels and superalloys because of the strength it adds. The main producers are Brazil and Canada. The largest producers of tantalum are Australia, Brazil, and Mozambique. Rwanda and the Congo have significant reserves of niobium/tantalum (coltan). Germanium is quite a common metal with semiconductor properties but its use is limited because of its toxicity. Its use also extends to night-vision enhancement devices.[135] Beryllium, with its high melting point, is used in the manufacture of friction brakes, in telecommunications, and in ceramics. Gallium, a relatively common metal occurring in a form that makes economic extraction difficult, is mainly a by-product of bauxite mining. Gallium arsenide can convert electricity directly into light and is employed in making LEDS, an electronic light source that uses less energy than either incandescent or fluorescent light sources. Indium, a relatively rare metal, is currently a by-product of zinc mining. It was first used in the manufacture of aircraft engines during World War II, but today its major application is in LCD screens, and new developments in solar technology are expected to increase demand. The largest producer is China, which controls 73 percent of the market and which has recently restricted exports of the metal. Other sources of indium are in Canada, Japan, and Russia.

Another metal used in electronics is lithium, the lightest of all metals. Lithium-ion batteries have a higher power density than conventional batteries and are suitable for use in electric cars, cell phones, and laptop computers. The demand for lithium is expected to triple within fifteen years, causing some (unfounded) concern that the world's lithium deposits are not large enough to meet expected demand for electric-car batteries.[136] Lithium can either be mined from some types of pegmatite and sedimentary rock or extracted from brine, which is a cheaper and more abundant source. Deposits occurring in Argentina and Chile are currently mined, but it is believed that up to 70 percent of the world's reserves are on the salt plains of Bolivia. The Bolivian government has so far refused to allow foreign investors into its mining sector, and it mostly extracts the deposits on a very small scale, using primitive technology. First a hole is dug on the salt pan; the hole fills with water from an underground lake. The water evaporates and the lithium, which is lighter than water, rises to the surface, where it can be skimmed off.[137] However, a large-scale plant opened in 2013, but it is not clear how much lithium it is capable of producing without access to better technology and foreign capital.[138] The government claims that it is now open to foreign investment, provided 60 percent of profits accrue to Bolivia. There have been preliminary negotiations with South Korea and China.

Besides platinum, the platinum group of metals contains palladium, rhodium, iridium, ruthenium, and osmium, with platinum and palladium most commonly used. These metals, which always occur together and are thus usually lumped together, have the desirable properties of high melting points, corrosion resistance, superior electrical conductivity, and catalytic capabilities. Long before European contact, the Indians in South America had learned to use platinum, but the conquering Spaniards saw no use for it and even forbade its importation as they did not want to debase silver. Today, the main uses for platinum group metals are in jet engines, in portable electric devices, and as catalysts for air pollution equipment. Platinum and palladium prices, set twice a day on the London Platinum and Palladium Market Fixings, are largely determined by demand by the auto industry, which shifts its use between the two metals depending on the price.[139] Commercial development of fuel cells in cars may further increase the demand for palladium as it can absorb hydrogen at a rate of nine hundred times its volume. The prices of platinum, palladium, and rhodium are volatile because of the relatively few sources of supply. South Africa, at 77 percent of world production, is the most important source for platinum, followed by Russia at 14 percent, while Russia dominates the market for palladium at 41 percent compared with South Africa's share of 38 percent.[140] The mines in South Africa are particularly prone to strikes. New mines have opened up in Zimbabwe, but their continued operations may be in doubt because of political factors.

Rare earth minerals

In a relatively short time, rare earth minerals have gone from being a curiosity in the periodic table to a multimillion-dollar market. Rare earth elements are scandium, yttrium, and the so-called lanthanides (elements 57 to 71 in the periodic table).[†] They have an interesting history, originating in an old mine at Ytterby in the Stockholm archipelago in Sweden.[141] The mine was opened during the seventeenth century, mining quartz (SiO_2) used in nearby iron mines, and later feldspar for a newly opened porcelain factory. In 1787, the amateur geologist Arrhenius, while working at Ytterby, noticed an unusually heavy stone, which he sent off for analysis to Johan Gadolin at the Åbo Academi in Finland. Gadolin realized that the sample contained a new mineral, later named gadolinium. Other rare earth minerals were discovered during the eighteenth century, including yttrium, ytterbium, erbium, and terbium, all named

---

[†]The lanthanides are lanthanum, cerium, praseodymium, neodymium, promethium, samarium, europium, gadolinium, terbium, dysprosium, holmium, erbium, thulium, ytterbium, and lutetium.

after the Ytterby mine. The first commercial use of the minerals occurred in Austria with the manufacture of mantles for gas lights from a mix of different lanthanide oxides.[142] Some are not rare at all but do not necessarily occur in minable concentrations. Cerium is the twenty-fifth most abundant element in the earth's crust, while thulium and lutetium are very rare.[143] All are typically found in clay minerals; the dominant supplier of these is China. However, Japanese researchers claim that they have found huge deposits in the deep sea mud in the Pacific Ocean at depths of 3500 to 6,000 metres—1,000 times larger than deposits on dry land.[144] Whether it is possible to exploit such deposits in the near future is doubtful because of complexities of operating on the ocean bed; for further discussion, see Chapter 10.

Today, the most important of the rare earth elements are praseodymium, neodymium, terbium, and dysprosium, which have special magnetic properties used in the manufacture of hybrid automobiles—each Toyota Prius requires several kilos of neodymium—iPhones, Blackberries, catalytic converters, magnets, rechargeable batteries, and wind turbines. Terbium is also utilized as a green phosphor for flat TV and computer screens, LCDs, and plasma screens. According to 2014 estimates by the US Geological Survey, 65 percent of rare earth minerals are used as chemical catalysts, 21 percent in metallurgical applications, 14 percent in petroleum refining, 19 percent in catalytic converters, 9 percent in glass and ceramics, and the remainder for computer monitors, magnets, and pharmaceuticals.[145]

The leading producer of rare earth minerals between the 1960s and 1980s was Molycorp, an American company that mined deposits of bastnaesite in the Mojave Desert in California. Bastnaesite—named after another Swedish mine, Bastnäs—contains cerium, lanthanide, and yttrium. The mine was forced to cease processing in 1998 following an environmental spill, closing in 2002 because it could no longer compete with China.[146] Cerium is radioactive, and lax environmental regulation combined with low labour costs quickly made China the leading producer, accounting for 95 to 97 percent of total production.[147] Since the closing of the Molycorp mine, China has totally dominated rare earth mineral production, and the mine Bayan Obo in Inner Mongolia currently provides most of the world's supplies.

The Chinese recognized the strategic importance of rare earth minerals and since 1999 implemented policies to discourage their export through the use of increasingly restrictive export quotas as well as export taxes in an effort to encourage foreigners to buy the finished products (e.g., magnets or hybrid engines) rather than the raw material.[148] China claimed it was restricting production in order to control the adverse environmental effects of the mining, which include contaminated water and heavy air pollution. It was also believed that China is building strategic stockpiles of the minerals; consequently, prices skyrocketed. For example, between July 2010 and February 2011, the value of a ton of rare earth exports from China rose from US$14,045 to US$109,036. In response to rising prices, other countries such as Japan and South Korea also stockpiled the material, and the United States considered putting rare earth minerals on its list of strategic minerals partly because of their military use in global-positioning guidance control systems.[149] However, in a typical boom and bust scenario, prices quickly dropped when more mines came on stream in Canada, South Africa and Kazakhstan, and demand moderated when manufacturers in response to higher prices economized on their use of rare earth minerals or switched to equivalent metals.[150] China's share of the global market dropped from 95 percent to 70 percent.

The special case of gold and silver

Gold has been used from ancient times as money, jewellery, and as a display of conspicuous consumption.[151] Even today, gold seems to promise instant riches and often leads to an irrational obsession that manifests in periodic gold rushes. For example, gold was discovered in California in 1848 and led to an influx of several hundred thousand people—known as the forty-niners—all hoping to become rich. The discovery of gold in 1896 on the Klondike River in the vicinity of the Arctic Circle in the Yukon Territory of Canada led to a similar mania, though not quite on the same scale. A major metropolis, Dawson City, grew up around these finds. For twelve months (July 1898 to July 1899) this remote city in the middle of northern Canada had a telephone service, electricity, a movie theatre (only three years after the motion picture had been invented), fashions from Paris, three hospitals, seventy physicians, and a population of approximately forty thousand.[152] In 1899 came the news of a new find in Nome, Alaska, and most of the miners left Dawson City for Alaska.

The history of gold mining is full of colourful stories of fraud and attempts at fraud, with many examples of prospectors falsifying their claims of major finds by adding gold obtained from other sources to their samples (called *salting*). One of the most notorious examples is the story of Bre-X Minerals, a minor Canadian mining company that in 1995 announced that its site in Busang, Indonesia, contained large quantities of gold—up to 8 percent of the world's gold reserves. Following the announcement, the stock price went from a few

Figure 2.5. Gold diggers on their way to Dawson City, passing through the Chilcoot Pass. Credit: Wikimedia Commons.

cents to $286.50. In 1997, after the company's chief geologist jumped (or was pushed) from a helicopter over the Borneo jungle, the stock collapsed when it became known that the assaying samples had been salted with outside gold, including shavings from gold jewellery. It became the biggest stock scandal in Canadian history and the biggest mining scandal ever.[153]

Gold does not corrode. It is so indestructible that it is often found in streambeds, where the flowing water washes away lighter sand grains and leaves behind what is known as placer gold. The gold rushes in California and the Klondike were started by finds of placer gold, and the huge gold deposits at Witwatersrand in South Africa were ancient placer deposits. Because of its stability, gold is unique among metals as so little appears to have been lost over time: less than 10 percent of the gold ever mined has been lost. Typically, almost 80 percent of the gold traded on the market goes into jewellery making, with a minor use in electronics. The largest producers are South Africa, the United States, Australia, and China.

Gold is different from most other metals in that it is not only desirable for its use in manufacturing, but also for its role as a financial asset. During periods of financial turbulence, more gold is bought as an investment because it is reputed to hold its value in times of turmoil. For centuries, gold was used as money both in coins and as a backing for currencies (the gold standard). Between 1934 and 1967, the price of gold was set at US$35 per ounce, and under the rules of the International Monetary Fund, each of the Fund's member countries had to hold a certain amount of gold in currency reserves. At this constant price, not much gold was mined. But because of an excess of US dollars, the artificially low price of gold could not be maintained, and the gold price was set free in 1967. Remnants of the gold standard did not disappear until 1971, when the US Federal Reserve severed the last symbolic tie to gold by no longer promising to exchange US dollars for gold. Today gold's market price is fixed twice a day by five members of the London Bullion Market Association. In 1980, the price reached a peak of US$800 per ounce. After this, there followed a period of relative stability, with gold trading between US$250 and $500 per ounce. But in 2009, in response to global financial turmoil and the weakening of the US dollar, the gold price climbed to over $1,200 per ounce and continued rallying in 2011 because of concerns about the future of the euro, and gold reached a price peak of over $1,900 per ounce. The price has since plummeted due to better stock market performance in the United States and signs of more robust recovery of the US economy.

The price of gold is influenced not only by market demand and supply but also by how much gold is bought and sold by the central banks, which are believed to hold 18 percent of the available gold. To keep currency reserves in the form of gold does not earn any return (unless the price of gold is increasing); thus it may be in the banks' interest to trade gold for interest-bearing assets. Since 1999, the amount of gold sold by central banks has been controlled by an agreement among participating countries not to sell more than a specific amount of the metal to keep the price from dropping too quickly. However, by 2009 the increases in gold prices and record-low interest rates earned on other assets meant that central banks were no longer selling gold; instead, many countries—including Russia, China, and many OPEC countries—switched to buying gold in order to decrease the proportion of their reserves held in US dollars, the value of which had been falling rapidly on foreign exchange markets.[154] The International Monetary Fund has also entered the market as a potential supplier of gold. The IMF, which since its inception has held gold as part of its currency reserves, adopted a new income model in 2008 that included a provision to generate funds needed to assist poor countries from gold sales, either to central banks or, if this did not generate sufficient funds, to the commercial market. In November 2009, the central bank of India announced that it had bought two hundred tons of gold from the International Monetary Fund, which sent the price even higher, a sign that the markets interpreted the sale as an indication of increased demand rather than increased supply.[155] Such price volatility will likely continue as long as there is uncertainty in world markets.

Similar to gold, silver is traded both as a commodity and as a financial asset. It too was employed for centuries as money. The 1545 discovery of silver by the Spaniards at Potosi in Bolivia heralded the start of truly global trade in the sense of integrating the American continents into the existing trade networks. Not only did silver flow to Europe, it also flowed to China, which held approximately one-quarter of the world's population, and events in China meant ramifications for the commerce of the rest of the world.[156] China had used a paper currency since the eleventh century, but printing too much currency had made it almost worthless, and by the early sixteenth century silver had become the currency of choice. The introduction of a new tax system in which taxes had to be paid in silver also helped to consolidate its importance. As silver prices increased in China, large profits were earned from exports to the Chinese markets. Spanish America was the source for most of the silver trade with the remainder coming from Japan.

During the sixteenth century, the influx of vast amounts of silver led to price inflation in China and in Europe. By the seventeenth century, the Mexican peso was the dominant currency, prized for its pure silver content and consistent weight. Not only was it circulated in Europe but also in China and India. The decline in its significance happened in the nineteenth century with the introduction of gold as the basis of currencies. Most importantly, the British pound sterling was switched to a gold standard in 1821.[157] The importance of gold as money was secured by the major gold finds during the nineteenth century in California and later in Australia, which left the world awash in gold and led to an unprecedented expansion of world trade.

Apart from jewellery, one of the main uses of silver has been in developing photographic films. The decline in the use of traditional film cameras coincided with increased use of silver in high-quality photographic paper; thus the switch to digital cameras did not have a large impact on the demand for silver. The metal is also used as a backing in mirrors and, because of its high conductivity, in batteries and electronics. New applications of silver are developing in medicine, for dressing wounds, and as an addition to clothing material for the control of body heat and odour. Its largest producers are Peru, Mexico, China, and the United States.

Like gold, silver has been touched by scandal. Following a spike in gold prices in 1979, the price of silver rose almost tenfold.[158] This rise had nothing to do with normal market forces. Instead, two wealthy Texan brothers, Nelson Bunker Hunt and William Herbert Hunt, had decided to corner the silver market, and together with several wealthy Arabs they bought in excess of two hundred million ounces of silver, which was equivalent to half of the world's supply. The bubble they created burst following intervention of the Federal Reserve and a change in trading rules. In 1980, the price dropped from US$50 to $10 per ounce, resulting in huge losses for investors, including the Hunt brothers.[159]

Diamonds

Diamonds are abrasives and are the densest form of carbon, used in jewellery and in industry for drilling, grinding, and cutting. They are formed under high pressures at depths of 150 kilometres and can reach the surface through pipe-like vents (*kimberlites*), which are exceedingly rare, but diamonds also occur in placer deposits. Diamonds were used in India a few thousand years ago, and it seems likely they were also known in China. Christian Europe did not approve of diamonds because of their use as amulets, and they were also difficult to obtain because Arab traders restricted their entry to Europe. In the late Middle Ages, a diamond-cutting industry was established in Holland. The popularity of cut diamonds started to spread among the rich, and they were occasionally used in wedding rings. Diamond wedding or engagement rings did not become fashionable until the famous diamond producer De Beers started to market them through cinema advertising in the 1940s with the slogan "Diamonds are the girl's best friend."

De Beers was founded by Cecil Rhodes and his partner C.D. Rudd in 1880, who bought up the existing diamond producers in the Kimberly region of South Africa. It grew to become the largest diamond company in the world, and in its heyday controlled 90 percent of the global diamond trade. For decades it operated an effective monopoly and by controlling supply was able to keep a firm control over the prices. Its influence then waned following diamond discoveries in Russia, Australia, Canada, and other parts of Africa. General Electric in the United States was the first to develop a process for making synthetic diamonds, using graphite and subjecting it to high pressure. Today, 90 percent of industrial diamonds are synthetic.[160]

Conflict diamonds or *blood diamonds* became an issue after the devastating civil wars in Angola in the 1990s, and later in Côte d'Ivoire, the Democratic Republic of the Congo, Sierra Leone, and Angola, where rebel groups used the revenue from diamond sales to pay for their military efforts. The conflict in Angola led to a resolution in 1999 by the UN Security Council to enforce sanctions on diamond sales by the rebel group Unita. This led to an attempt to stem the flow of illegal diamonds through the Kimberly Process Certification Scheme, which requires participants to certify that any shipment of rough diamonds is free from conflict diamonds.[161] Forty-five countries are part of the scheme that includes all diamond producers.

Other important minerals: fluorspar, graphite, phosphate, and potash

Fluorspar, a feedstock to the chemical industry, is used in the fluoridation of water and toothpaste, in making Teflon coating, in the manufacture of some refrigerants and pesticides, and in the processing of aluminum and uranium. It is by no means rare—the US Geological Survey states that the resources are "enormous." China, the world's largest producer, imposed export restrictions allegedly for environmental reasons, and as a result prices doubled between 2007 and 2011. The United States filed a formal complaint against China with the World Trade Organization on grounds that the restrictions were against WTO rules; it won the complaint in 2011 and the restrictions were lifted.[162] Graphite, which is a form of carbon, has traditionally been used in the manufacture of break-linings, foundry operations, and steel-making, but recently demand has surged because of its use in lithium-ion batteries, lap-tops, and cell-phones. Each electric car battery requires approximate 50 kg graphite.[163] China, the largest producer, has closed several mines because of excessive water and air pollution. As a result, prices doubled between 2010 and 2014. Phosphate rock and potash—sources of potassium—are of critical importance as fertilizers for agriculture. China is the largest producer of phosphate and Canada of potash. However, the largest deposits of phosphate are found in the tiny area known as the Western Sahara—a disputed territory because of the rich deposits. When Spain abandoned the territory in 1975, it ceded sovereignty to Mauritania and Morocco without any input from the local population, which sought independence under the rebel group Polisario Front.[164] Morocco gradually seized the Mauritanian part during the next fifteen years. A war of independence was fought against Morocco, and following a ceasefire in 1991 it was agreed that a United Nations–supervised referendum would be held in 1998, but this never happened. Morocco continues to export phosphate from the territory and has granted offshore oil exploration licenses to American and Irish companies, much to the outrage of the international community. Currently the Polisario operates through an unofficial government (the Sahrawi Arab Democratic Republic) which is backed by Algeria. The United Nations recognizes the Western Sahara as a non-self-governing territory.

Environmental impacts of the mining industry

Despite occasional popular panics, the case of minerals seems to confirm that depletion of non-renewable resources does not constitute a major problem: we will not run out in the near or distant future. Many of the supply shortages are temporary and are political in nature. Ownership is usually clear, and the self-interest of the owner encourages efficient use of the resource. If a shortage of a mineral does arise, prospective users either recycle, find other minerals that work just as well, or are forced to economize in the face of supply-induced higher prices.

However, the performance of the mining industry does cause considerable problems, both from an environmental and a social perspective.[165] Waste disposal and access to land often populated by indigenous peoples are the key problems facing the industry. As shown in Chapter 1, the negative impact of resource extraction on indigenous people has a long history. Clashes between mining companies and indigenous populations occur regularly in many parts of the world, including Canada, Australia, Peru, and Ecuador. These clashes usually involve unsettled land claims, lack of consultation, or concerns over environmental effects of mining operations. Adverse environmental impacts of mining include erosion due to deforestation, the development of sinkholes, loss of biodiversity, air pollution, and contamination of ground and surface water. Copper, zinc, and lead mining are known to be particularly problematic and so is open-pit mining.[166] Smelting releases nitrous oxides, particulates, and sulphur dioxide (SO_2) into the environment—all significant sources of air pollution, and in the case of SO_2, acid rain. The wastes from mining operations in the form of tailings are substantial, usually regarded as the largest environmental challenge faced by the industry. For example, copper mining generates ninety-nine tonnes of waste for each tonne of copper produced, and the ratio for gold mining is even worse. It is estimated that because of the shift to lower-quality ores, three times as much material is needed per unit of ore compared with a century ago.[167] Usually the tailings are contained by dams that sometimes leak toxins and break, releasing the waste into the environment.[168] The wastes contain sulphides and often noxious metals such as cadmium, mercury, and arsenic—common by-products of gold mining. If the oxidized tailings come in contact with air, they form sulphuric acid (acid mine drainage), leading to further water contamination. If the mines are located anywhere near the sea, the preferred solution is to pump the tailings into the sea as the mining companies feel that this minimizes the environmental damage—a contentious claim to say the least, as so little is known about the impact of toxic wastes on the marine environment.[169]

The mining industry has had its share of environmental disasters involving tailings, mostly but not exclusively in developing countries. The most notorious are the Ok Tedi disaster in Papua New Guinea and the Philippine spill involving the Marcopper Mining Company. The Ok Tedi disaster involved a copper mine operated at the headwaters of the Ok Tedi River by BHP Billiton in cooperation with the Papua New Guinea government and Inmet Mining Corporation, a Canadian company.[170] Starting in the 1980s, the mine discharged approximately eighty million tons of tailings per year into the river, affecting the fifty thousand people who lived in the villages downstream. The tailings raised the riverbed and caused flooding in the surrounding area, leaving contaminated mud on previously fertile plains and damaging close to thirteen hundred square kilometres. The affected communities sued BHP Billiton, which settled out of court, paying over $28 million in compensation in the late 1990s.The Marcopper mining disaster occurred in 1996 in the province of Marinduque in the Philippines.[171] The Marcopper Mining Company, a subsidiary of Placer Dome, had been operating a copper mine since the 1970s, closing an old pit and cementing it for use as a tailing pond for mine waste. In 1995, seepage was discovered and the concrete ruptured, discharging tailings into the Boac River system. In total, 1.6 million cubic metres of tailings were released, inundating the lowlands and destroying crops. The river was left dead. In 2005, the provincial government of Marinduque sued Marcopper's parent company, Placer Dome, for $100 million in damages in a Nevada court. After its takeover of Placer Dome, Barrick Gold inherited the lawsuit, which has not been settled. The court dismissed the case in 2007 on the grounds that the court was not the appropriate judicial venue, but the court of appeal ruled in 2009 that the case should not have been dismissed.

Gold mining is particularly hazardous to the environment, especially in rainforest areas such as the Amazon, where there are alluvial gold deposits. To find and exploit the deposits, prospectors and miners have to cut down trees, causing a large amount of deforestation. Mercury is used to amalgamate the gold, and even though most of the mercury is recycled, some of it ends up in the river. This is particularly true for small operations that on average release 1.32 kilogram of mercury into the river for every kilogram of gold produced.[172] Cyanide, another highly toxic compound, is also used in gold mining to help separate the gold from the surrounding ore. In 1995, four billion litres of water contaminated with cyanide was accidentally released into the Essequibo River in Guyana from a tailings pond from a gold mine operated by Golden Star Resources of Denver and Cambior of Montreal. This caused widespread die-offs of fish and plants and contaminated the soil around the river. Another cyanide-rich pond overflowed in Romania in 2000, and the contamination spread throughout the Danube catchment in Hungary and Serbia. This time public outrage was such that the mining industry realized something had to be done. Following a joint workshop sponsored by the United Nations Environmental Programme (UNEP) and the International Council on Metals and the Environment, a voluntary international code for the management of cyanide in gold mines was negotiated. In 2005, the code received its first fourteen signatories, which included the major gold-mining companies. The purpose of the International Cyanide Management Code for the Manufacture, Transport and Use of Cyanide in the Production of Gold is to reduce exposure of workers and communities, limit releases, and improve response mechanisms to accidental spills.[173] The International Cyanide Management Institute runs a certification process in which the companies are audited for compliance every three years.

Because of the highly publicized environmental spills and disputes between mining companies and local populations, particularly in South America, the mining industry has not received good press. In 1999, in preparation for the 2002 World Summit on Sustainable Development, nine CEOs of the metals and mining industry launched the Global Mining Initiative, the purpose of which was to examine the whole issue of mining and sustainability. This led to the creation of a new industry group, the International Council on Mining and Metals, consisting of the CEOs of the major mining companies "committed to the responsible production of metals and minerals."[174] The council adopted ten voluntary guiding principles concerning sustainable development, human rights, preservation of biodiversity, health and safety, and the environment—all motherhood issues. In 2008, the council committed the participating companies to third-party certification of the implementation of its principles. It is probably true to say that the environmental record of the big multinational mining companies is better than the many small artisanal mining operations found in parts of Africa and South America, which are dangerous both to the environment

Table 2.3. Energy requirements of using primary ores and recycled metals (tetrajoules/ 100,000 tonnes)

Material	Primary metal ores	Recycled metals	Energy savings from using recycled metals
Aluminum	4700	240	4460
Copper	1690	630	1060
Ferrous	1400	1170	230
Lead	1000	13	987
Nickel	2064	186	1878
Tin	1820	20	1800
Zinc	2400	1800	600

Source: Sue Grimes, John Donaldson, and Gabriel Cebrian Gomez, *Report on the Environmental Benefits of Recycling*, Commissioned by the Bureau of International Recycling, 2008. http://www.bir.org/assets/Documents/publications/brochures/BIR_CO2_report.pdf.

and the people involved. Developing countries are reluctant to regulate these mines because they provide a necessary livelihood for many poor people.

Recycling

Recycling of materials increases their availability over time and avoids the environmental costs associated with mining. In particular, producing metals from recycled materials requires considerably less energy than extracting metals from virgin ores. Table 2.3 shows the energy requirements and savings from recycling for the more common metals with the largest gain in aluminum production.

However, a recent study of sixty metals indicated that only eighteen achieved an end-of-life recycling rate (i.e. percentage of metal in discards) of more than 50 percent, and thirty-four metals had a recycling rate of less than 1 percent.[175] Lead is the most recycled metal (80 percent) and others with high rates are aluminium, cobalt, chromium, copper, gold, iron, manganese, niobium, nickel, palladium, platinum, rhenium, rhodium, silver, tin, titanium, and zinc. Steel production in particular uses a large proportion of scrap steel as an input. Despite the substantial energy savings, recycling is not cheap because collecting and separating the scrap is costly, and the sources for scrap materials are often concentrated in urban areas while the production facilities are near the sources of the virgin materials. Most of the rare earth metals are seldom recycled as they occur in minute quantities in many electronic goods.

In many cases, recycling is not done under environmentally sound conditions. Unfortunately, the really hazardous recycling is taking place in poor countries where environmental and labour regulations are lax and labour is cheap. For example, 80 percent of the recycling of large ships (ship breaking) is not done in dry docks but on the beaches of Southeast Asia like Alang in India and the Bangladeshi port city of Chittagong under appalling conditions, releasing asbestos, PCBs, lead, and other noxious substances, endangering both workers and the environment. Ships are made largely of steel that, if recycled, is suitable for the manufacture of simple steel products. Between two hundred and six hundred

Figure 2.6. Ship breaking on a beach near Chittagong, Bangladesh. Source: Wikimedia Commons.

ships per year are taken apart on the beaches. The ship-breaking technology is primitive and inexpensive, relying on cheap labour and suitable beaches with high tidal ranges. Shipyards are located near the beach. The ship is first anchored off the beach, and as much as possible of the material is taken off at low tide. Then the ship is refloated and beached at high tide, and an army of workers with no better tools than crowbars and flashlights pulls the ships apart. In a submission to the International Maritime Organization (IMO), India claimed that the beaching method is cost effective and environmentally sound. However, another submission by Greenpeace to the IMO painted a far different picture:

> The assertion that running aground ageing ships with fragile hulls, laden with fuel and oil residues and with hulls known to be covered in heavy-metal-laden paints including extremely toxic TBT[‡] (which this body has outlawed) and then allowing these massive vessels to be cut by hand and sectioned without access to cranes and heavy-lifting equipment is environmentally superior is surprising. The assertion that a method that involves dropping cut sections

---

[‡]TBT paints are anti-fouling paints containing tributyltin, which is highly toxic to the environment.

containing hazardous substances into the sea where they are then grindingly winched ashore, and where all activities are conducted in conditions where, when accidents occur or fires break out, one is unable to quickly evacuate or bring aid to the fallen workers, or to quell fires due to the lack of access [to] emergency equipment is environmentally superior is also surprising, to say the least. These are in fact assertions that defy science, norms of occupational safety and health law, coastal zone management law and hazardous waste facility siting laws, to name but a few . . . if one is willing to discount the externalities incurred both in terms of human health and the environment one might be able to make the case that beaching is more cost effective. But the externalities that would have to be overlooked include the destruction of the intertidal ecosystem, pollution of the sea, loss of fisheries and most devastating, loss of invaluable life and limb."[176]

Ship breaking falls under an international convention that covers the movement of hazardous materials across borders. The Basel Convention on the Control of Transboundary Movements of Hazardous Wastes and Their Disposal came into force in 1992 following several widely publicized cases of shiploads of toxic wastes having been dumped in developing countries. It is a United Nations treaty and is administered under UNEP. The convention does not ban trade in hazardous waste if both parties agree and if both parties are signatories to the convention. While a ban on exports to Antarctica is in place, there is only limited control on other exports. Waste exports cannot occur unless a competent authority in the receiving country gives written consent. All parties have to implement a tracking system and adopt the definition of what constitutes hazardous wastes. There is no enforcement mechanism. Many environmental groups were unhappy that the convention did not totally ban the export of waste to poor countries and pushed through an amendment to the convention in 1995 prohibiting export from the EU and OECD countries to countries not members of these organizations. The amendment (the Basel Ban Amendment) was never ratified because of opposition from some industrialized countries. However, 2011 brought an acceptable compromise, allowing the Basel Ban Amendment to come into force for those countries that want to join.

It was affirmed by a conference of the parties to the convention in 2004 that the Basel Convention applied to ship breaking, but there were loopholes. For example a ship could be sold to a party that later decided to have it decommissioned and broken up, in which case it would not fall under the convention. Massive lobbying from NGOs for safer practices in the disposal of ships led to yet another convention—the Hong Kong International Convention for the Safe and Environmentally Sound Recycling of Ships (Hong Kong Convention)—which was signed in May 2009 after more than five years of negotiation but is not yet ratified. The convention requires each ship to carry an inventory of any hazardous material at all times, which must be surrendered to the recycling facilities when the ship is ready to be dismantled. The facilities must equip their workers with protective gear and have equipment and procedures for the disposal of hazardous materials as well as procedures in place in case of emergencies. However, the convention does not specify the methods for the recycling, which of course means there is no guarantee it will be done in an environmentally sustainable manner. Much to the dismay of environmentalists, the convention does not ban the grounding and dismantling of ships on beaches. Nor does the convention cover military and government-operated vessels, vessels only used for domestic voyages, and vessels below five hundred gross tons,** which means that even if it is ratified it will only cover half of the world's shipping.[177] The shipping companies, allying themselves with the cheap registry countries such as Panama and Liberia, argued against costly regulations that would adversely affect the industry, particularly given the glut of ships after the 2008–09 recession and a new requirement that all tankers must be double hulled by 2015.

In common with other international conventions, the Hong Kong Convention will come into force after receiving the requisite number of signatures. Ratification requires the approval of fifteen states controlling over 40 percent of the world's shipping tonnage as well as the major ship-breaking nations: China, Turkey, Pakistan, India, and Bangladesh. The latter requirement is thought to be the most problematic, and at this writing in 2015, the convention has not received the necessary signatures. A report by the European Union recommends the creation of a fund financed by the shipping industry to cover the additional cost of recycling in environmentally sustainable facilities using dry docks instead of beaching. This would encourage more facilities to be developed in industrialized countries.[178]

The recycling and disposal of electronic waste has also become a contentious issue following the publicity surrounding disposal sites in several developing countries including India, China, and Ghana. It is estimated that every year, approximately fifty million tonnes of electronic waste makes its way to dumps in the developing world, which is becoming the West's digital dumping ground.[179] Rapid advances in technology mean that computers, televisions, and

---

**Gross tons are measures of a ship's internal capacity.

cell phones are discarded every three to five years for something new. In particular, the switch from older cathode ray tube technology for display screens to LCD or plasma screens led to a substantial disposal problem because recycling is expensive. In some cases, old electronic equipment is being repaired and resold in poor countries or dismantled to recover some of the raw materials such as heavy and scarce metals. For example, an average of 115,000 tonnes of used computers and 472,000 tonnes of televisions were imported annually into Nigeria between 2005 and 2010.[180] Often the work of dismantling is done by children, exposing them to lead, cadmium, beryllium, PCBS, and often mercury. In other cases the material is burned, melting the plastics and less desirable metals and leaving the valuable metals behind. Burning releases toxic substances such as dioxin into the air and may also contaminate the water table and create toxic runoff. Cathode ray tubes are particularly problematic because they contain a large amount of lead, and if they end up in landfills the lead contaminates the groundwater.[181] Trade in electronic waste has flourished following stricter environmental regulations in rich countries. It is illegal under the Basel Convention if it is strictly waste but not illegal if the shipments contain products that can be used after they are repaired. The Basel Ban Amendment is expected to be ratified, in which case the situation may improve. Recycling technology is also improving. For example, a Japanese company, Dowa Holdings, has built a major recycling facility for electronic goods in Kosaka, Japan, where electronic products are melted into a giant stew from which metals such as indium, silver, gold, neodymium, and antimony can be extracted. The company also hopes to develop a technology for extracting the rare earth minerals.[182]

An obvious solution to the trade in electronic waste is to include the cost of recycling and disposal in the price of the product. This would create an incentive for producers to design their products in such a way that recycling becomes easier. European Union rules that came into force in 2005 require each member country to set up collection systems financed by the producers of electronic items. Producers are required to collect, recover, and recycle waste in an environmentally responsible manner. The aim was to create facilities capable of handling four kilograms of waste per person. This directive did not have the desired results. Three years later it was estimated that only one-third of waste was recycled; the remainder ended up in landfills or was exported to poor countries. New rules came into force in 2012 requiring member states to collect 45 percent of the average weight of electrical and electronic equipment by 2016 and 65 percent by 2019.[183] Many US states and Canadian provinces have also introduced recycling laws for electronic waste.

Figure 2.7. The infamous dump at Agbogbloshie, Ghana. Imported scrap televisions and computers that could not be repaired get deposited and burned. Source: Wikimedia Commons.

Mineral depletion and sustainability

Chapter 1 showed that concerns regularly surface about the scarcity of minerals, but usually these are unfounded. Following the large price increases of minerals during the first decade of the twenty-first century, the possibility of mineral depletion reemerged as an issue among policy-makers, and as is often the case, opinion is split. The pessimists point out that we cannot create more mineral deposits; the deposits are there and have been there since time immemorial. The soothsayers tell us not to worry. Scarcity, if it occurs, will manifest itself in higher prices; higher prices will force us to economize, to recycle, to discover new technologies, or to switch to substitutes. It will also become economical to exploit lower-grade deposits. The soothsayers also argue that recent price increases are the sign of yet another typical raw-material cycle: a booming world economy, which leads to increased demand for raw materials and increased prices of raw materials. This in turn results in increased exploration for new deposits and the opening of new mines in the long run. The high prices of raw materials will choke the economic boom and prices will come down again. After a while, new mines and deposits will come on stream, further depressing prices until the next boom starts. When prices are low, there will be underinvestment in new capacity and in research. As will be discussed in the next chapter, oil is a good example of this never-ending cycle.

What about minerals that are regarded as particularly important for manufacturing or national security? The future supply of a mineral depends on geological availability, the technology of extraction and refining, the environmental and social effects of extraction and refining, government policies relating to the environment and trade, and other economic factors. Can the mineral be produced at a cost that is economically viable? The long-term real costs of mineral products are likely to continue to increase because of declining ore grades, smaller deposit sites, the need to go underground, challenging mineralogy, and remoteness. If the mining company has to pay all the environmental costs associated with its extraction, the cost of the mineral may be so high that no demand will exist for the end product and thus no demand for the mineral. In the shorter term, critical supply disruptions resulting in price spikes could occur if the mining industry is highly concentrated, in which case a strike in a mine or restrictive trade policies could lead to severe repercussions on world supply. Problems could also arise if production is close to capacity and an unexpected increase in demand occurs. Some minerals are extracted only as a by-product of the mining of another mineral, which could also create problems in assuring adequate supplies, because it will be the demand for the main mineral that will determine the viability of the mining operation. For example, indium is a by-product of zinc mining, gallium of bauxite mining, and rhenium (used in memory chips for satellites and military hardware) of molybdenum mining, which in turn is a by-product of copper mining. The lack of technology for recycling could be an additional problem in ensuring adequate future supplies.

In 2006, The US Geological Survey and the National Mining Association set up the Committee on Critical Mineral Impacts on the US Economy to examine whether future problems could be in store for the US economy if supply disruptions occurred. In its 2008 report, the committee concentrated on eleven minerals and mineral groups: copper, gallium, indium, lithium, manganese, niobium, platinum group metals, rare earth elements, tantalum, titanium, and vanadium.[184] Of these, the committee deemed rare earths, indium, platinum group metals, manganese, and niobium the most critical because of the difficulty in finding substitutes and the risks of supply disruptions caused by political factors, though the committee did not specify these in any detail. As noted above, manganese is an abundant mineral, but 80 percent of manganese originates in South Africa, which the committee probably regarded as unstable. Indium and most of the rare earths come from China and were at the time of the report subject to Chinese export restrictions.

The European Commission—the executive arm of the European Union—also looked into future critical minerals.[185] According to its definition, critical minerals are those that might experience supply shortages that would have larger impacts on the economy than other minerals. The commission identified two types of risks: supply risks and environmental risks. The supply risks depend on the political and economic stability of the producing countries, how many producers are involved, and the possibilities for substitution and recycling. The environmental risk means serious measures a country might have to take to protect its own environment, which could lead to supply disruptions of the raw material in question. On the basis of the needs of emerging technologies (such as micro capacitors, permanent magnets, thin-layer photovoltaics, new medical technologies, seawater desalinations, and battery technologies), the commission identified the raw materials in Table 2.4 as critical.

Table 2.4. Critical minerals listed by the European Commission

Mineral	Emerging technologies	Major producing countries
Antimony	Microcapacitors, flame retardant	China, Bolivia, South Africa
Beryllium	Telecommunications, aerospace, defence	US, China
Cobalt	Superalloys, batteries, synthetic fuels	Democratic Republic of the Congo
Fluorspar	Processing of aluminum and uranium; water fluoridation	China
Gallium	LED lights, solar cells, thin-layer photovoltaics	China
Germanium	Fibre optic cables; optical technologies	China
Graphite	Break lines, batteries, refractory applications	China
Indium*	LCDs for electronics	China
Magnesium	Castings, wrought products and alloys	China
Niobium*	Superalloys, aerospace, microcapacitors	Brazil
Platinum metals*	Automotive catalysts, fuel cells	South Africa, Russia
Rare earths*	Cell phones, hybrid cars, batteries, LCD screens	China
Tantalum	Microcapacitors, medical technologies	Democratic Republic of the Congo
Tungsten	Automotive, aerospace, lighting	China

Note: The starred raw materials are also classified as critical by the United States—but note the absence of manganese. Source: European Commission, *Critical Materials for the EU*. Report of the Ad-hoc Working Group on defining critical raw materials, 2010. http://ec.europa.eu/enterprise/policies/raw-materials/files/docs/report-b_en.pdf, and US Geological Survey, *Mineral Commodities Summaries 2011*.

Tables 2.4 and 2.2 indicate that supply shortages are more likely to arise from domestic and trade policies than real shortages of available materials. Cheap labour and lax environmental regulations made it possible for China to dominate production of certain minerals including rare earths, an advantage it has capitalized on. It appears that the Chinese stranglehold have loosened because of the opening of new mines in other countries, escalating labour costs, stricter environmental regulations, and possibly political pressure following the successful World Trade Organization challenge in 2009 of Chinese export restrictions on bauxite, coke, magnesium, fluorspar, manganese, silica carbide, silicon metals, yellow phosphorus, and zinc. Another successful trade challenge was launched in 2012 involving Chinese export restrictions on tungsten, molybdenum, as well as seventeen rare earth minerals.[186]

In conclusion, the answer to the question of whether we should worry about mineral depletion is that the world is unlikely to run out of minerals in the foreseeable future. However, local and temporary shortages may be an issue for reasons explained above. It is also critically important for countries—many of which are poor—to exploit their minerals in a sustainable manner and to avoid the resource curse. Even though mining and resource extraction provide much-needed employment in many parts of the world, unless the mining companies are required to adopt effective environmental safeguards and unless revenue generated for the state is used to invest in projects for the long-term benefit of its citizens, mining is not sustainable.

3

How the World Came to Be Dependent on Fossil Fuels

The evolution of energy use. The rise of oil. The emergence of
OPEC. *Are we running out of oil? The Alberta oil sands. Growth*
in oil demand. Natural gas. Coal. Fossil fuels and sustainability.

THE FIRST CHAPTER gave examples of how resources shaped history and cultures, but in terms of overall significance, none can match our current dependence on fossil fuels. Modern economies rely on oil, gas, and coal for transportation; for feedstock for the production of plastics, fertilizers, lubricants, and paints in the chemical industry; for heating and cooling of our homes; and to provide the power for mining and manufacturing. While some electricity is generated from hydro and nuclear power, more than 60 percent comes from coal and natural gas. Modern intensive agriculture is totally dependent on fossil fuels both for fertilizer and for draft power. If we went back to using horses in agriculture in North America, we would require ten times as many horses as we used in 1900, and twice the arable land in the United States for growing food for the animals, together with a vast number of people to feed and care for them.[187] Developed countries cannot function without electricity for lighting, for powering communications systems and appliances from computers to refrigerators, and in the future we may need electricity to run our cars. Fossil fuels have

77

given us low-cost transportation, which has been the driver of globalization, allowing goods from low wage countries to compete with goods produced in industrialized countries, and allowing inhabitants of cold climates to eat fresh produce the year around. The security and adequacy of energy supplies is one of the most important issues in the world today. Add to this mix the warming of the world's climates, attributed by the overwhelming majority of scientists to the burning of fossil fuels, and oil has probably become the most important, controversial resource in world history.

In understanding energy, it is helpful to divide the world's energy system into primary energy that is supplied by nature, and secondary energy that is man-made. Primary energy resources include wood, oil, gas, coal, hydro, biomass, wind energy, geothermal power, solar energy, and uranium. Figure 3.1 shows the expansion of energy consumption by source since 1900, when the main primary energy source was coal. Table 3.1 shows the world's primary energy shares in 1973—the pivotal year of the energy crisis—and 2012. The 2012 data indicate that less than one-third of the world's energy is derived from oil, more than one-quarter from coal, and one-fifth from natural gas. It is interesting to note how the composition of our energy use changes in response to economic and political factors, shifting from dominance by coal to the current situation. Since 1973, the prices of coal and natural gas have not kept up with the price of oil, and as a result the share of oil has decreased and the shares of coal and natural gas have increased—a trend that is expected to continue.[188] Because of the large decline in the share of oil, the total share of fossil fuels decreased from 87 to 82 percent, with most of the slack taken up by nuclear energy and only a minute fraction made up of renewables such as solar and wind.

Table 3.1. World primary energy shares, 1973 and 2012 (percentage of total)

	1973	2012
Oil	46.2	31.4
Coal	24.4	29.0
Natural gas	16.0	21.3
Nuclear	0.9	4.8
Hydro	1.8	2.4
Biofuels, waste	10.6	10.0
Geothermal, solar, wind	0.1	1.1

Source: International Energy Agency, *Key World Energy Statistics, 2014*.

Secondary energy is man-made energy that includes gasoline, kerosene, diesel, heavy heating oil, propane, electricity, and hydrogen. Hydrogen is produced by separating the hydrogen from the oxygen in water molecules either using fossil fuels combined with steam, or from water using a process that

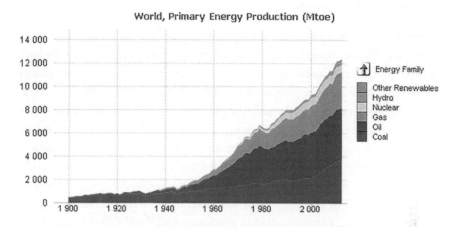

Figure 3.1. World primary energy production, 1900–2013. Source: The Shift Project. http://www.tsp-data-portal.org/Energy-Production-Statistics. Note: Mtoe = million tonnes of oil equivalent.

relies on electricity. Though at present it is used primarily to upgrade heavy oil and to make ammonium-based fertilizer, hydrogen is seen by many as the clean fuel of the future. Table 3.2 shows that electricity is mainly generated from coal-fired power plants (40.4 percent in 2012) followed by natural gas, hydro, coal, and nuclear power.[189] Only 5.6 percent is generated by renewable energy resources such as thermal, wind and solar. In 1973, coal was also the main source of electricity (38.3 percent) followed by oil and hydro. The main shift in electricity generation has been from oil and hydro to coal, natural gas and nuclear, a change again dictated by market conditions.

Table 3.2. Electricity generation by fuel, 1973 and 2012 (percentage of total)

	1973	2012
Coal	38.3	40.4
Oil	24.7	5.0
Natural gas	12.1	22.5
Nuclear	3.3	10.9
Hydro	21.0	16.2
Other	0.6	5.6

Source: International Energy Agency, *Key World Energy Statistics, 2014.*

Secondary energy is the source for all the services we need to run a modern society, such as lighting, transportation, communications, cooking, heating, power for machinery in industry, agriculture, and resource extraction. This chapter will examine the history of energy services, the current production and consumption of fossil fuels, and the sustainability of our current energy use.

The evolution of energy use

In common with other animals, early humans had to rely on their own muscles for power. The first use of other energy came with the ability to control fires induced by lightning, allowing people to cook their food and to keep warm, and later to clear land for agriculture. Various types of biomass in the form of wood, wood residue, plant materials, and dung have been used over the centuries for heat, lighting, or power. It is interesting to note that buffalo dung (often called buffalo wood) was essential for the survival of early settlers on the Prairies as late as during the nineteenth century, and dung is still commonly used as fuel in rural areas of Africa and parts of Asia.[190] Water power was well known to the Romans, and by the end of the Roman era the vertical water wheel was used to power mills that crushed grain, tanned leather, made cotton cloth, and helped in iron-making. During the medieval period in Europe and other parts of the world, water wheels became relatively common, used for milling, metallurgy, and paper-making until they were replaced by water turbines and steam power during the nineteenth century. They laid the foundations for the Industrial Revolution in providing continuous and reliable power. For example, a water-powered machine capable of manufacturing two hundred thousand nails per day decreased the cost of nails by 90 percent during the early part of the nineteenth century.[191]

Wind power involving sail propulsion was probably first employed by the Egyptians approximately 3000 BC followed by the Polynesians around 1200 BC. The first known reference to windmills dates to 947 AD, when the Arab traveller Al-Masudi claimed he saw windmills powering irrigation systems in Seistan (eastern Iran).[192] Windmills were not as common as water mills—except in dry areas—and were mainly used for milling grain and pumping water for irrigation. They reached their peak usage during the middle of the nineteenth century, after which they could no longer compete with steam power.

The development of steam power is associated with coal. The Chinese, during the Han dynasty (206 BC–220 AD), employed coal as a fuel for iron production, and some evidence exists that the Romans were also familiar with the use of coal, but in Europe coal mining did not start until the Middle Ages. The overexploitation of forests for fuel wood on a large part of the continent encouraged the use of coal, particularly in England where coal production increased from two million tonnes in 1650 to ten million at the end of the seventeenth century.[193] Increased coal production required deeper mines, which created engineering challenges since seepage caused deeper pits to become filled with water that had to be pumped out. The race was on to develop more powerful pumps.

The invention by Thomas Savery of a simple steam pump in 1698 resulted in a series of technological advances that made it possible to extract water from the coal mines to prevent flooding, but the most important invention was the first steam engine, patented by James Watt in 1769. This engine and later refinements made factory production possible as the power supply was reliable. Large cities grew up in England, continental Europe, and later North America, all dependent on abundant coal supplies. The first steamboat, the *Clermont*, was launched in 1807 and the first locomotive in 1804, heralding an Industrial Revolution almost totally dependent on coal. The negative effects of coal burning were as well known then as they are to this day. The air in industrial cities was filthy, thick with soot from the coal-burning plants, reminiscent of the present-day situation in many Chinese cities, and even then people were concerned about the health hazards. There were reports in the *British Medical Journal* of the increased mortality in London and Glasgow following periods of smog in 1873 and 1879. The smog was caused by a combination of temperature inversion and coal smoke laden with sulphur dioxide.[194] "After a fog the nostrils are like chimneys, and are lined with a layer of black smut. The expectoration is black from the amount of carbon arrested in the mucus of the air passages. For a day or two after exposure to a smut-laden atmosphere, black phlegm is brought up."[195] The death toll, mainly from bronchitis, was in the thousands and continued through the first part of the twentieth century. Not until after the great smog of 1952, which killed twelve thousand people, were serious pollution control measures introduced in the 1956 Clean Air Act.[196] The act established smoke-free areas, introduced diesel trains in place of steam trains, and gave incentives to people to shift from using dirty coal for heating to cleaner fuels such as electricity, gas, and smokeless coal.

Adequate sources of power were obviously necessary in launching the Industrial Revolution, but sources of illumination were also critical. The Romans used oil lamps fuelled by olive oil, and for centuries the only types of lighting available were crude candles, lanterns, and flares that did not provide much illumination. Candles were made from any type of fat or oil derived from plant, fish, or other animals. When the early settlers came to North America, they noted that the indigenous populations hunted whales and seals, using their oils to preserve hides to make clothing and for cooking. The settlers discovered that candles made from whale oil were far superior to those made from tallow rendered from beef or mutton fat. Whale-oil candles gave better illumination, and the smell was much more bearable. Any whale could be used, but the sperm whale was particularly sought after, because the best lighting came from *spermaceti*, a wax derived from the head of the sperm whale. By the beginning of the eighteenth century, the demand for whales set off a whale rush that took larger and larger ships much farther afield. The ships were fitted with facilities to render the fat on board, which meant the ships could remain at sea for years as there was no need to butcher the whales on shore. Trading in spermaceti even led to the first oil cartel, the United Company of Spermaceti Candlers, which tried to control wildly fluctuating prices by setting a ceiling price for spermaceti and a floor price for candles.[197] Members of the cartel also made provisions to go into whaling themselves if the price of spermaceti exceeded the ceiling price. Like most cartels, this one failed as it was unable to control all the players in the market. Soon the emphasis shifted from the waxy spermaceti used to make candles to whale oil. This oil could be burned in specially designed lamps that provided better illumination. For almost a hundred years between 1750 and 1850, whale oil was the most common source of lighting.[198]

Other uses for whales included perfume from ambergris found in the intestines and baleen found in the mouths of most whales that was made into corsets, umbrella ribs, skirt hoops, and carriage springs. By 1846, the US whaling fleet had 735 ships, 80 percent of the world total.[199] Each year the fleet brought back four to five million gallons of sperm oil, six to ten million gallons of train oil (from the right whale) and 1.6 to 5.6 million pounds of bone. Overharvesting meant increasing effort was required to secure a steady supply, and prices went up. In 1825 the price of train oil was $0.35 per gallon; in 1855 it was $0.95.[200] Profit margins were small, and many voyages did not cover costs. Sealers were also involved in the hunt for oil and particularly treasured elephant seals. By the 1830s the world's seal stocks had been seriously depleted and the trade declined. Not only did the search for whale oil have a disastrous impact on whale and seal populations but also on tortoises from the Galapagos Islands. It was discovered that tortoises could live for long stretches without food and water, and could therefore be stored live on ships to provide the crew with a source of fresh meat during long sea journeys. It is estimated that up to fifteen thousand tortoises were taken, almost wiping out the islands' entire population.

For a while whaling was helped by the demands of fashion, which dictated that women should wear corsets requiring baleen found in all whales except sperm whales. The price of whalebone soared from $0.32 per pound in 1870 to $5 by the end of the century.[201] However, even this market crashed within a few years as spring steel began to be used for corsets, and the introduction of motorized transport decreased the demand for whalebone horsewhips and wagon suspensions. The invention of margarine created another demand for whale blubber, which postponed the inevitable decline in demand for whale products, but only temporarily. Whalers and sealers scoured the oceans for prey, continuing the slaughter, using big factory ships. The last American whaler left its port in 1924; it could no longer compete with the European whalers facing increased labour costs and decreased demand for whale products.[202] European whaling continued in the Antarctic during the two world wars following the discovery of yet another use for whales: the oil could be used to manufacture nitroglycerine for munitions. Limited whaling still goes on today in Japan, Iceland, and Norway but elicits much controversy and relatively small profits.

The supply of whale oil was insufficient—too expensive—for street lighting; instead, street lamps were fuelled by coal gas produced by carbonizing coal, a dirty process involving boiling a slurry of coal and capturing the gas, which was then transported in underground pipes. This technology, developed at the end of the eighteenth century, was a common form of fuel for street lighting both in Europe and North America. Alcohol blends and camphene (a liquid similar to turpentine) were also used as a source of lighting during the 1850s.[203]

In 1849, the Canadian geologist Abraham Gesner managed to distill bituminous tar into coal oil, which he named kerosene.[204] It was as clean burning as whale oil, and it could be used to fuel the same oil lamps. It was cheap, durable, and the supply was reliable, particularly following the discovery that it could be made from rock oil (petroleum) found in Pennsylvania and from oil found in Lambton County in Ontario, Canada, where the first successful oil well was drilled in 1858. By the end of the 1850s, thirty kerosene-making plants had been established worldwide, and the market for whale oil for lighting had collapsed. Kerosene was so cheap that it was within reach of most people. In 1856, the price of sperm oil was $1.77 per gallon; by 1896 the price had dropped to $0.40 because of competition from kerosene, which cost $0.59 per gallon in 1865, and just $0.07 in 1895. By the 1880s, Thomas Edison's invention of the electric light bulb signalled the end of the dominance of both kerosene and coal gas for lighting.

The rise of oil

At the end of the nineteenth century, one fossil fuel dominated power supplies: coal. The steam engine was run on coal as were all trains and ships that criss-crossed continents and oceans. Both Britain and the United States had ample coal supplies. However, coal as a ship fuel had its limitations, particularly for navies. Refuelling had to be done in ports, and keeping the steam engines going required much manpower to shovel coal into the burners. In the lead-up to the World War I, a strategic decision was made to convert the British Navy from using coal to oil.[205] Oil had the advantage of allowing refuelling at sea, which reduced downtime in ports. Oil was also more fuel efficient than coal, did not deteriorate, and freed up navy personnel, who no longer were required to handle coal. The decision to convert to oil was made despite the fact that Britain had no secure oil supplies. Standard Oil, owned by the American Rockefeller family, controlled most of the supplies that were used almost entirely to make kerosene.

Oil became a strategic commodity. During World War I, Britain had managed to establish control over oil supplies in Russia, Romania, Trinidad, Persia, and Mesopotamia (modern-day Iraq), but continuing shortages of oil created a problem until the United States with its ample oil supplies entered the war. In the postwar period, the scramble for control over the world's oil supplies continued, particularly in Mesopotamia. The British managed to outmanoeuvre the French and the Americans, and by 1928 had control over 75 percent of oil supplies outside the United States. The British oil company, Shell, established in the latter part of the nineteenth century, soon rivalled Standard Oil in power, having merged in 1906 with a Dutch company to become Royal Dutch/Shell, while Standard Oil had been broken up into smaller companies under US anti-trust laws in 1911. Still, the British government was so worried about its lack of control over oil prices that it purchased majority interest in the Anglo-Persian Oil Company that became British Petroleum (BP). A state-owned oil company was not the American way, and the United States had to use other tactics to regain the control it had previously exerted with the Standard Oil monopoly. Standard Oil of New Jersey (later Exxon) and Socony Vacuum (later Mobile Oil) managed to get a foothold in the Middle East by buying a 20 percent interest in the Turkish Petroleum Company in 1922, which became the Iraq Petroleum Company. This company was jointly owned by a French consortium, Exxon and Mobil, Anglo-Persian, Royal Dutch Shell, and an Armenian businessman named Calouste Gulbenkian. The participants agreed under the so-called Red-Line Agreement not to compete with one another within what is now the Middle East, including the Arabian Peninsula, Turkey, Israel, Jordan, Syria, and Iraq. No such restrictions faced Standard Oil of California (later Chevron), which established a presence in Bahrain. Increased oil production from the Baku and other fields in the Soviet Union created oversupply and falling prices in the markets. In response, the executives of Royal Dutch Shell, Standard Oil of New Jersey, and the Anglo-Persian Oil Company met secretly at Achnacarry Castle in northern England in 1928, and between periods of grouse hunting, agreed to limit production and fix prices. Each was allocated a quota based on market shares in 1928, resulting in Middle East oil production being held back.[206]

The emergence of OPEC

While Britain faced a setback due to backing the Hashemite kings in their dispute with the later victorious Wahabi tribes of Saudi Arabia's Ibn Saud in the 1930s, an increased share of world oil reserves fell under the United States' control: from less than 15 percent at the end of the 1920s to over 45 percent in the early 1950s. At that time, most American oil consumed was domestic in origin, but in subsequent decades, US reliance on foreign oil continued growing, from 10 percent in 1970 to 65 percent in 2004.[207]

As more oil was discovered in the Middle East, cutthroat competition caused falling prices (and increased oil consumption). Oil-producing US states tried to shield their own producers from cheap Middle Eastern oil by imposing production quotas known as pro-rationing, which kept domestic prices artificially high. The increased importance of oil in the world economy consolidated the power of the international oil companies, known as the Seven Sisters: Standard Oil of New Jersey (currently Exxon), Royal Dutch/Shell, the British Anglo-Persian Oil Company (currently BP), Standard Oil of New York (currently Mobil), Texaco, Standard Oil of California (currently Chevron), and Gulf Oil.[208] Increased resentment of the multinationals among the oil-producing countries led to attempts to gain an increased share of profits. The first such attempt originated in Venezuela in 1938. Following a threat to nationalize its oil concessions, Venezuela received a larger share of profits—in 1945 this share became 50 percent.[209] After Venezuela's success, gaining 50 percent of profits became the goal for many oil-producing countries. Saudi Arabia demanded concessions from the American-based multinationals, and in response the United States agreed to hand over large amounts of money to the Saudi government. Iran, under the democratically elected government of Mossadeq, unsuccessfully tried to negotiate with British Petroleum for a fifty–fifty split in profits, and when the negotiations collapsed, the government seized the assets of BP. The company did not gain another foothold in Iran until a military coup restored Mohammad Reza Shah Palavi to power in 1953.

At the end of the 1950s, the situation for American oil became so precarious that President Eisenhower imposed an import quota system to protect the domestic oil industry, resulting in a considerable price premium for domestic oil (US prices were $3.18 per barrel compared with $1.30 in the rest of the world).[210]

Almost immediately, in 1960, other oil-producing countries responded with an attempt to increase prices by establishing the Organization of the Petroleum Exporting Countries (OPEC). The initial participating countries were Iran, Iraq, Kuwait, Saudi Arabia, and Venezuela, joined later by Qatar, Indonesia, Libya, United Arab Emirates, Algeria, Nigeria, and Angola. Ecuador and Gabon were members for twenty years, but both left the organization in the early 1990s.[211]

The purpose of OPEC is to operate as a cartel. According to its statutes, one of its primary missions "is to devise ways and means of ensuring the stabilization of prices in international oil markets with a view to eliminating harmful and unnecessary fluctuations."[212] For a cartel to be successful in maintaining prices, three conditions must be present. First, the demand for the product must be fairly price insensitive (price inelastic). For example, even if a cartel has a 100 percent control of output, if there are close substitutes, the cartel will be unable to increase prices as consumers will switch to the substitute product. Second, a cartel can maintain prices only by controlling output, so cartel members must agree on individual quota allocations. Third, the cartel must have an effective policing mechanism to catch cheaters since it is in the interest of each member to exceed its quota and thereby increase its own profit at the expense of other members. In the case of OPEC, the first condition was certainly present; the second and third were not. The cartel, in common with other commodity cartels, suffered from overproduction. OPEC's allocation of quotas was politically sensitive due to the different interests and objectives of participating countries. As a result, little headway was made in raising prices during the 1960s. But soon a new set of political dynamics took over.

In 1969, Colonel Gaddafi seized power in Libya, bringing a far more aggressive stance to OPEC. He argued for an immediate increase in the posted oil prices agreed on by the members and a cutback in production. Libya reduced production by eight hundred thousand barrels per day. A break in a pipeline from the Arabian Peninsula to Syria further reduced the flow of oil by five hundred thousand barrels per day, allowing OPEC to increase prices from $1.80 per barrel to $2.24 per barrel in 1971 with provisions for further price increases. In October 1973, during the Jewish holiday of Yom Kippur, Egypt attacked Israel. When the expected victory did not seem imminent, the Arab countries decided to use oil as a weapon. Arabian members of OPEC led by Saudi Arabia vowed to decrease production by 5 percent each month until Israel withdrew from occupied Arab land. Saudi Arabia not only cut production but also put an embargo on oil exports to the United States and the major oil market in Rotterdam, Holland. The cut in production could not have come at a worse time for consuming countries, as a buoyant world economy had increased the demand for oil and resulted in very low inventories and shortages of oil in some markets.

The effects of this strategic move were immediate, with residents of oil-consuming countries queuing at the gas pumps, fostering a belief that a real shortage of oil existed—for some, an indication that the world was running out of resources, confirming the predictions of the Club of Rome in the book *The Limits to Growth*. People believed that the end of oil was near. Faced with cutbacks, the industrialized countries failed to put up a common front. No attempts were made at rationing, which could have spread the available inventories over time, nor were serious efforts made to pool resources. Oil companies flocked to the Rotterdam spot market to try to build up inventories.[213] Spot prices soared, convincing OPEC that further increases in posted prices were possible. The posted price of Arabian light oil rocketed from $3.00 per barrel in early October, 1973, to $11.65 in January, 1974—a previously unimaginable increase.

An energy conference was hastily convened in Washington in 1974, focusing on the problems of energy security for the participating countries that included Canada, the United States, Western Europe, and Japan. The outcome was an International Energy Treaty, requiring the participating countries to hold emergency oil stocks equivalent to at least ninety days of oil net imports. The International Energy Agency was established under the treaty in 1974.[214] The main function of the agency was and is to ensure energy security by helping countries to coordinate a collective response to major disruptions in the oil market through the release of these emergency stocks. Other actions could include policies to restrain demand, to switch to other fuels, to increase production or to share resources in a coordinated fashion. Since its inception, the agency has taken on a major role as a source of energy statistics and forecasts and acts a forum for dialogue between energy-producing and -consuming nations.[215]

The trebling of oil prices in such a short time led to double-digit inflation in most industrialized countries and a global recession, the worst since the Great Depression of the 1930s. This economic slump led to a decrease in energy demand as the demand for energy is closely related to incomes. Faced with higher prices, consumers cut back on oil use while producers started to tap previously uneconomical sources, including those in the North Sea and Alaska. If it had not been for Saudi Arabia's willingness to cut production, a surplus of oil would have driven prices down again. As it was, prices fell in real inflation-adjusted terms. But this too had an effect. By 1978, demand was again increasing as the world economy began to expand and lower real prices made their way to consumers. In the late 1970s, Saudi Arabia's hold over OPEC

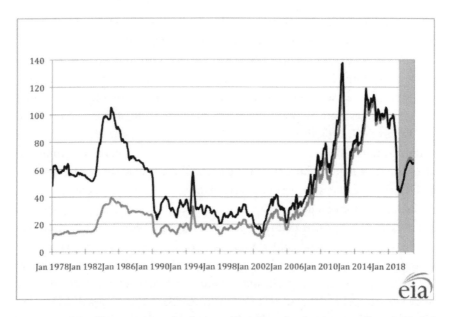

Figure 3.2. Monthly nominal and inflation-adjusted crude oil prices in $/barrel, United States, 1974–2015 (2015 = 100). The upper line follows nominal prices, the lower follows inflation-adjusted prices. The shaded area includes forecasted prices. Source: Energy Information Agency, Short-Term Energy Outlook, April 2015.

declined. Keeping OPEC in line meant having enough spare capacity to expand production if prices went too high, but there were signs that the capacity of Saudi Arabia to increase production was waning. Expanding demand with lagging increases in supply set the stage for another market circus, this one started in Iran by a strike of oil workers in the winter of 1978–1979, followed by the fall of the Shah. When Iran's oil fields opened again, they were operating at low capacity. OPEC had met in December 1978 and agreed that oil prices in the coming year should increase from $12.70 to $14.54, but by the summer of 1979 shortages were such that a new OPEC conference was called at which the Saudis agreed to increase the price immediately to $18.

Despite small increases in world production in 1979, buyers continued to stockpile, again turning to the Rotterdam spot market where the spot price soon reached $45 per barrel, indicating to OPEC that the posted price increase had been too modest. In a repeat of history, posted prices leapfrogged in disarray. Saudi Arabia tried to stabilize prices, announcing in December 1979 its target price of $24, but at another OPEC conference later that same month, Libya announced an increase in price to \$29.40 and Iran to \$28.50. With the outbreak of the Iran-Iraq War came fears of disruptions of oil supplies. Further price increases were announced but not implemented as another glut materialized. In the early 1980s, prices began to fall due to increased production in Alaska, the North Sea and Mexico as well as reduced demand for oil caused by several factors, including another recession induced by high oil prices. Residents of consuming countries had also begun to respond to higher oil prices by buying smaller cars and insulating their homes. Governments implemented policies forcing auto manufacturers to build cars with better fuel economy. Electricity generation shifted from oil to coal and nuclear power. An entire infrastructure for the use of natural gas was developed, including liquefied natural gas tankers and pipelines for transportation of natural gas.

During the 1980s, the price of oil dropped both in inflation-adjusted and nominal terms (Figure 3.2). The first Gulf war in 1990–1991 led to a small spike, followed by more price drops during the Asian crisis beginning in the summer of 1997. Venezuela disagreed with its allocated quotas within OPEC and decided to ignore them and produce at its maximum rate, increasing its oil production by 40 percent between 1992 and 1998, which contributed to a further glut on the oil markets.[216] Prices were close to \$12 per barrel. In 1998, Hugo Chavez was elected president of Venezuela, with ambitious plans for costly social reforms that could be financed only if oil revenues were increased. He began revitalizing OPEC. The result was an agreement in 2000 to adhere strictly to agreed-on quotas in an effort to keep the oil price within a range of \$22 to \$28 dollars per barrel. The new pact was successful, and prices started to increase. Asian countries began to recover from the recession, and the demand for oil was increasing, and by September, prices had reached \$37 per barrel. Following Chavez's re-election in 2000, opposition to his reign increased in Venezuela, culminating in a general strike in 2002 during which oil production plummeted and contributing to a shortage on the world market. Political problems in Nigeria, the world's eighth-largest oil producer, made the supply situation worse. In 2005, Hurricanes Katrina and Hugo temporarily eliminated 30 percent of US oil production by damaging rigs and refineries. The US invasion of Iraq in 2003 and the subsequent war had its own impact on oil supplies. In July 2008, the price hit a record high of \$145 per barrel due to the continuing uncertainties created by the Iraq War as well as the demand pressures created by the rapid growth of China and India. For example, oil consumption in China almost doubled between 2000 and 2009 and in India by 50 percent. Many commentators saw the high price of oil as an indication that world supplies

Table 3.3. World oil consumption 2000 and 2013 (000's daily barrels, percentages of total, percentage change)

Region	Consumption (2000)	Share of total (%)	Consumption (2013)	Share of total (%)	Change 2013 over 2000 (%)
North America	23,674	30.9	23,292	24.5	−1.6
South and Central America	4,866	6.4	6,775	4.4	39.2
Europe and Eurasia	19,682	25.7	18,645	21.0	−5.3
Middle East	5,021	6.6	8,526	9.2	69.8
Africa	2,439	3.2	3,624	3.2	48.5
(China)	(4,706)	(6.1)	(10,756)	(12.1)	128.6
(India)	(2,261)	(3.0)	(3,727)	(4.2)	64.8
Asia Pacific	21,136	27.6	30,470	33.3	44.2
Total world	**76.605**		**91,331**		

Source: *BP Statistical Review of World Energy, June 2011* and *June 2014.*

of oil were finally being exhausted. Then history repeated itself yet again with high oil prices contributing to another world recession (often called the Great Recession because of its severity), causing prices to fall in 2009.[217] However, prices did not fall for long, and by early 2012 they had exceeded $100 per barrel because of continued increases in consumption in India and China as well as uncertainties about the political situation in Iran.

In the summer of 2014—contrary to expectations of most industry analysts— another glut appeared and prices started to fall rapidly. By January, 2015 they were down to $46 per barrel. There were many reasons. First, oil consumption in Europe and North America had been declining (Table 3.3) because of low income growth and a decade of rising oil prices, and there was evidence that the Chinese economy was slowing which would result in lower growth in demand. Second, oil production in Libya, in Canada, and in the United States increased substantially.[218] It has been known for a long time that a large oil-bearing formation (Bakken) spans the Dakotas, Montana, Saskatchewan, and Manitoba. A new technology widely used to unlock shale gas—a combination of horizontal drilling and hydraulic fracturing—was successfully applied to oil deposits and, as a result, the Bakken formation yielded four hundred thousand barrels per day in 2010, up from ten thousand in 2005, and reached 3.22 million barrels per day in the fourth quarter of 2013, making the United States the world's largest oil producer—an astounding change in the US energy situation.[219] In view of the rapid falling prices it was expected that OPEC would agree to production cuts. This did not happen. At the November 2014 meeting the organization decided to keep output at the same level, despite pressures from Venezuela and Iran, and let the market decide the price. It was believed that the decision was taken to maintain OPEC's market share, and to prevent further expansion of oil production from non-conventional sources such as oil sands, shale oil, or deep-sea oil, many of which are only economical at prices above $80.

This brief history shows that the short-term price of oil is determined by basic supply and demand—shortages lead to high prices and gluts to low prices—but changes in supply and demand depend on a complex interplay of technology, political factors, and world economic conditions, many of which are often not foreseen. If short term predictions are difficult, long-term predictions are even more so as they rely on educated guesses of future supply of and demand for oil.

Are we running out of oil?

The long-term supply of oil depends on current proved reserves and undiscovered resources. Table 3.4 shows the location and size of the world's oil reserves. Venezuela has 17.6 percent of the world's oil reserves, followed by Saudi Arabia with 16.1 percent and Canada with 10.6 percent. These estimates include heavy oil and shale oil. However, proved reserve figures are notoriously unreliable as they are based on estimated quantities of oil recoverable given current economic data and operating conditions. In fact, the reserve estimates have consistently increased every year in line with oil consumption.[220] There are several explanations. One is that the data are supplied by private and government sources that may have an interest in either overstating or understating the reserves. OPEC countries are notorious for giving inflated estimates of reserves for the simple reason that reserves determine production quotas,[221] but there are other reasons, including further exploration of existing discoveries, changes in reporting requirements, new production technologies, better understanding of reservoirs, and upward changes in oil prices, making marginal fields commercially viable.[222] Historical data from the United States indicate that, on the average, a well will contain six times as much oil as was first estimated (known as *reserve growth* or *appreciation*). Advances in computer technology have made it possible for geologists to produce 3D seismic mapping, improving the interpretation of underground strata and thus assisting in exploration.[223] The introduction of horizontal drilling has made it possible to recover more of reservoirs of oil and

Table 3.4. World's proved oil reserves, 2013

Country	Reserves (billions of barrels)	Share of total (%)	Reserve-to-production ratio
United States	44.2	2.6	12.1
Canada	174.3	10.3	>100
Mexico	11.1	0.7	10.6
Total North America	**229.6**	**13.6**	**37.4**
Brazil	15.6	0.9	20.2
Ecuador	8.2	0.5	42.6
Venezuela	298.3	17.7	>100
Total South and Central America	**329.6**	**19.5**	**>100**
Kazakhstan	30.0	1.8	46.0
Azerbaijan	7.0	0.4	21.9
Russian Federation	93.0	5.5	23.6
Total Europe and Eurasia	**147.8**	**8.8**	**23.5**
Iran	157.0	9.3	>100
Iraq	150.0	8.9	>100
Saudi Arabia	265.9	15.8	63.2
Total Middle East	**808.5**	**47.9**	**78.1**
Angola	12.7	0.8	19.3
Libya	48.5	2.9	>100
Nigeria	37.1	2.2	43.8
Total Africa	**130.3**	**7.7**	**40.5**
China	18.1	1.1	11.9
India	5.7	0.3	17.5
Vietnam	4.4	0.3	34.5
Total Asia Pacific	**42.1**	**2.5**	**14.0**
Total world	**1687.9**	**100.0**	**58.3**

Source: Adapted from *BP Statistical Review of World Energy, June 2014*. Statistics are included for the three largest oil producers from each region; the reserves include estimates for gas condensates and natural gas liquids, the Alberta oil sands, as well as the heavy oil deposits in Venezuela.

gas through fracking, and the introduction of computer-assisted design and manufacturing has made it possible to construct offshore drilling platforms for use in previously unheard-of depths.

Will we run out of oil in fifty-eight years as the reserve-to-production ratio seems to suggest? This will not happen because scarcity, if it occurs, will lead to higher prices, which in turn will encourage increased use of substitutes for oil, such as natural gas, coal, biofuels, hydrogen, and wind and solar energy. Indeed, changes in energy use are taking place through large-scale investment in shale gas, ethanol, and biofuels as well as wind and solar energy and various types of clean-coal technology. Table 3.1 and Figure 3.1 show how the components of energy use have changed over time. In particular, the share of oil has decreased substantially since 1973, and the shares of the other energy sources have increased in response to price signals. All available evidence indicates that we are not facing an imminent shortage of oil.[224]

However, there have been few new discoveries of conventional oil.[225] The lack of new discoveries is partly caused by the low oil prices in the 1980s and '90s, which discouraged companies from looking for more oil. After the collapse of prices in 1998, the oil industry was reluctant to invest in new capacity out of fear that any price increase would be temporary.[226] Following the large price increases in 2004 and 2005, the industry was unable to respond quickly because many petroleum engineers, geologists, drilling rigs, pipefitters, etc. had left the industry for lack of work, and as a result, costs escalated. The cost of developing an oil field in 2008 was twice as high as in 2004.[227] The other reason is that the easily found oil has already been exploited. Are there large oil fields waiting to be discovered? The most authoritative source is a 2012 study by the US Geological Survey which predicts that approximately 565 billion barrels are yet to be discovered, 75 percent are likely to be in South America and the Caribbean, sub-Saharan Africa, Middle East and North Africa.[228] This is approximately one third of current proved reserves.

A significant share of new discoveries is likely to be in deep water, and in the Arctic which is expected to hold 90 billion barrels (18 percent of the total undiscovered resources), most of it offshore.[229] Increasingly, newly discovered and yet-to-be discovered oil is expensive oil—it is estimated that the average cost of extracting new oil is around $100.[230] Between 2005 and 2009, 41 percent of new oil and gas reserves were discovered offshore, where both exploration and recovery is more costly than on land, and is also environmentally hazardous. Offshore drilling was pioneered off the coast of the United States but did not take off worldwide until the 1973 energy crisis with large discoveries in the North Sea, still in relatively shallow waters. By the early 1990s, drilling had expanded into deepwater, with the first platform in eight hundred metres of water in Brazil. In 2011, Shell completed a well in 2,377 metres of water in the Gulf of Mexico. The large underwater reserves in the Gulf of Mexico are very difficult to recover, and the giant rigs are very vulnerable to hurricanes as shown by the extensive damage to several of them during Hurricane Katrina. In April 2010, an explosion on the Deepwater Horizon Oil rig led to a blowout that caused a massive oil spill, resulting in extensive damage to marine and coastal habitats. So far the spill has cost the oil company British Petroleum $6 billion in compensation to fishing industry workers and others adversely affected, with an additional $7.8 billion to come.[231] A similar blowout in the Arctic would be catastrophic.

Then there is politics. Shell had invested billions in the Sakahlin-II offshore project in the waters near the Siberian coastline in the North Pacific only to face government demands that they sell their interest to Russians because it was alleged that Shell did not meet environmental regulations. Other areas such as Ecuador and Kazakhstan are underexplored because their governments are trying to get a larger share of oil revenue, reducing companies' expected profit. Africa may have promising areas, particularly in Nigeria and South Sudan, but the political situation is such that investment is very risky and therefore costly. Disputes over national jurisdictions may also be a complicating factor, hindering exploration in Arctic waters.

The Alberta oil sands

The Alberta oil-sands deposits and the heavy oil deposits in Venezuela are often seen as creating a buffer against any future shortage of oil. The huge Venezuelan deposits are largely untapped while the Alberta oil-sands are being exploited at an increasing rate. The oil sands are indeed vast, and in the 1970s they were believed to contain the equivalent of one trillion barrels. More recent estimates put a realistic figure of recoverable reserves at 168 billion barrels, still a very large amount.[232] But this oil is not easily recoverable given its resemblance to tar. While the deposits have been known for a long time—Indians used the tar to caulk their canoes, and later it was employed for roofing and paving materials—the problem of separating the oil from the sand was not easily solved. The initial technology was developed in the 1940s by the Alberta Research Council. In early pilot projects, the oily sand was dumped into big flotation tanks filled with warm water. When the slurry was heated, the bitumen rose to the surface and

Figure 3.3. Shell Jackpine oil sands mine. Credit: Julia Kilpatrick and the Pembina Institute.
https://www.flickr.com/photos/pembina/16445992462/in/set-72157650233209937.

Figure 3.4. Tailings dam in Alberta—reputedly the largest man-made structure in the
world. Credit: Jennifer Grant and the Pembina Institute. https://www.flickr.com/photos/
pembina/7159711546/in/album-72157637876932305/.

was skimmed off. A similar process that also requires the addition of chemicals is used today. The remaining sand, water, and minerals are removed and put into tailing ponds (Figure 3.4). On average, two tonnes of oil sands are required for each barrel of bitumen produced. Surface mining has so far affected 500 km^2 of the 140,000 km^2 area of oil-bearing sands. Bitumen is different from ordinary crude oil; it contains less hydrogen and thus has to be upgraded into synthetic oil that involves adding hydrogen and removing impurities.

Not all the sands can be mined from the surface, since approximately 80 percent of the deposits are found underground. The underground bitumen is extracted through so-called in-situ technology. This consists of a process called steam-assisted gravity drainage, which involves drilling two horizontal wells, one above the other. High-pressure steam is injected in the upper well, which melts the bitumen, which in turn collects in the lower well and is then pumped out.

Oil produced from oil sands is expensive because both extraction and processing are very energy intensive. The energy used to heat the bitumen comes from natural gas, which is currently cheaper than oil on an energy-equivalent basis. This is the only reason tar-sands oil is profitable. It is estimated that the extraction process requires one unit of energy for every three units of energy produced, while Middle Eastern oil requires one unit of energy for every one hundred units of energy produced.[233] Some analysts claim that in-situ techniques could utilize the whole of the natural gas supply in western Canada by 2025. Natural gas is cheap in North America because of a regional imbalance of supply and demand. No truly integrated world market in natural gas exists because natural gas is not as easy to transport between continents as is oil; ocean transportation requires first liquefaction and the use of special tankers to transport the liquefied natural gas. Given the huge demands that oil-sands production is putting on the supply of natural gas, cheap gas may not last for long. One proposed solution is the use of nuclear energy.[234] An underground explosion would conveniently create both heat to separate the oil and a cavern to collect it. Alternatively, nuclear power could be used to generate the power used for in-situ recovery. However, the cost of such a proposal is unknown, and given the planning period required for nuclear plants and the political controversy that would surround such a proposal, it is very unlikely that it would be implemented.

While the cost of production includes land reclamation after the site is finished—as required by the Alberta government—other environmental costs are ignored. Extending over a tract of boreal forest as large as Florida, the deposits occupy land that is home to many types of birds and animals, including the increasingly rare woodland caribou. The traditional method of oil-sands extraction involves taking off the entire tree cover and digging. As well as exhibiting an exceedingly high carbon footprint, the process also requires a profligate water use. Producing one barrel of oil from the oil sands requires two to three barrels of water taken from the Athabasca River, representing 76 percent of that river's water allocations. In periods of low rainfall, the limited water flow combined with the high water extraction is likely to have a substantial negative impact on the river ecosystem. The water requirements are even higher for in-situ production where water is drawn from underground saline aquifers whose salt is removed and put in landfills before the water can be used for steam injection. Some of this water is now recycled, which will improve sustainability, but most analysts agree the water use is not sustainable.

The tailings dams, estimated to hold 223 billion gallons of toxic waste, appear even more problematic than previously thought, as the waste seems to take a long time to settle and the dams have an unfortunate tendency to leak. Despite efforts to try to stop birds from settling on the ponds, there are recent heavily publicized cases where birds have landed and died. No government agency in Canada has made a complete assessment of the impact of the tar sands on boreal wetlands and rivers, including the Mackenzie, the second-longest river in North America. A break in one of the tailings dams could have potentially disastrous effects on the entire ecosystem in the Athabasca River, Great Slave Lake—the sixth-largest freshwater lake in the world—and the Mackenzie River system. Ecosystems in Arctic areas do not recover as quickly as in more temperate areas.

Overall, the environmental impacts are substantial, not just from the mining but also from the upgrading facilities that transform bitumen to usable crude oil. Adding hydrogen and removing impurities produces three to four times more nitrogen oxides, sulphur dioxides, particulate matter, and organic compounds than traditional refining.[235]

Industry officials have claimed to have monitored the impact of oil-sands extraction on the Athabasca River system and have found little if any adverse effects. Any pollutants were deemed to have been "natural"—caused by the presence of the oil sands that have always been there. However, in 2009 a major study published by David Schindler and his associates found that water quality had been adversely affected, particularly by the presence of carcinogenic polycyclic aromatic compounds in concentrations potentially toxic to fish.[236] The researchers were able to show that the presence of these compounds was largely caused by airborne particulates derived from the upgrading. A subsequent study showed that the industry released thirteen elements classified as priority pollutants by the US Environmental Protection Agency, including cadmium and mercury.[237] The studies argued that monitoring was inadequate, and a subsequent study by the Royal Society of Canada also recommended improvement in monitoring.[238] Consequently, a new and independent water monitoring system was announced in 2012. In 2014, another study was published showing that official data used in environmental impact assessments underestimate the presence of polycyclic aromatic hydrocarbons in emissions by excluding the indirect emissions from the tailing ponds.[239]

Oil produced from the Alberta oil sands came under increasing scrutiny in 2011 because of two events. One was the proposal for the Keystone XL pipeline delivering bitumen to refineries in the United States, and the other the European Union's fuel quality directive. The Canadian section of the pipeline had already been completed and approval for the American section was expected, particularly as the US Environmental Protection Agency in an environmental impact study stated that provided environmental protection measures were followed, the pipeline would have no significant impact on most resources, including aquifers running under the proposed route. However, environmentalists argued that building the pipeline would undermine any policy for clean energy, as oil-sands oil was the dirtiest transportation fuel available. The *New York Times*, in an editorial published August 21, 2011, agreed that the pipeline should not be approved because of the danger of oil spills along the line "and the fact that the extraction of petroleum from the tar sands creates far more greenhouse gas emissions than conventional production does."[240] For political reasons, President Obama postponed the pipeline decision until 2013, and at the time of this writing (2015), no decision had yet been made. With large amounts of US oil produced from shale deposits, there may no longer be a market in the United States for Canadian oil which makes approval less likely.[241] A proposal to build the Northern Gateway Pipeline to the West Coast in order to get the oil to Asian markets is also mired in controversy, causing some of the companies involved in the oil sands to scale back production.

The labelling of oil sands as dirty oil spread to Europe. The European Union is aiming for a 20 percent reduction in carbon emissions by 2020, and in order to achieve this target, suppliers of transport fuels must reduce their carbon emissions by 6 percent, which is part of the Fuel Quality Directive.[242] The EU proposed to assign a higher emissions value to oil from the Alberta oil sands than oil from other sources, backed by a scientific study demonstrating that Albertan oil has carbon emissions 12 to 40 percent higher, mainly because of higher emissions in extraction and upgrading.[243] This does not include emissions caused by the destruction of peatland habitats during the construction of the open mines, which releases a large amount of carbon.[244] The proposal was narrowly defeated in the European Parliament in December 2014,

The Alberta oil sands can make a significant contribution to the energy picture but at a significant price to the environment. The oil industry claims that the price of oil must exceed $80 per barrel for the sands to be economically viable, assuming there are no carbon taxes or requirements for sequestration or new strict environmental regulations in Alberta and Canada.[245] Much is now transported by rail—a problematic choice as the oil is more flammable than conventional oil and derailments have led to spectacular fires. The most notorious was the 2013 derailment at Lac-Mégantic, which caused forty-seven people to lose their lives.

Growth in oil demand

The question of whether or not we will run out of oil in the foreseeable future does not only depend on oil reserves, technology and political factors, but also on future oil demand. The primary reason for escalating oil prices during the last decade was increasing demand, not only in rapidly growing India and China, but also in oil-producing countries. Table 3.3 shows that between 2000 and 2013, Chinese demand increased by 129 percent and demand in the Middle East by 70 percent, while North American, European, and Eurasian demand was stagnant or declined. The increase in oil prices from $20 per barrel in 2000 to $147 per barrel in 2008 contributed to the severe recession in the industrialized world, which curbed oil demand in rich countries but had little immediate effect in countries outside the Organisation for Economic Co-operation and Development. OECD countries now only account for slightly more than half the world's oil consumption compared with 63 percent ten years earlier.

In China, production of plastics and petrochemicals requires oil, and in India, diesel consumption is soaring because of farm mechanization and rising commercial freight deliveries. However, one of the main drivers of oil demand is increased car ownership in emerging economies, particularly in India and China. In this context, it is important to know that over 60 percent of a barrel of oil ends up as fuel in transportation, a proportion that has increased from 45 percent in 1973.[246] The Chinese auto industry expanded at a rapid rate during the first decade of the millennium, and production surpassed that of the United States in 2009; China now has the largest domestic auto market in the world. Chinese-made cars are cheap because of low labour costs and their use of established technologies and models through joint ventures with Western auto manufacturers.[247] The domestically designed Chery and Geely sell for less than $10,000. However, estimates for 2011 show only sixty-nine vehicles per one thousand people in China compared with 786 in the United States and 588 in Japan, so there is still a huge potential demand.[248] The future demand for cars is highly sensitive to income projections, and, assuming the Chinese economy will continue to expand, most analysts project a continued growth in car production in China by 6 to 11 percent per year, while other analysts claim it is likely to be much higher.[249] Car ownership in India is lagging behind China's but is expected to expand rapidly. The Indian Tata also sells for less than $10,000; its new model, the Tata Nano, sells for $2,500. Many households in developing countries find high car prices more of a deterrent to car ownership than the high price of gas; however, the cheap Nano has not fulfilled its potential because it is seen as a poor man's car and therefore not desirable.

The other main driver of oil demand is that domestic markets in oil-producing countries are now second in size only to the US market. This is not only because these oil-producing countries are rich (in general, rich countries consume more oil per capita than poor countries) and countries like Saudi Arabia are involved in large investments in infrastructure, but also because oil in many of these countries is ridiculously cheap. In 2008—the year when global oil prices peaked—the price of gas at the pump was two cents per litre in Venezuela, ten cents in Iran, fourteen cents in Libya, and sixteen cents in Saudi Arabia, but in Norway, also an oil-producing country, the price was $1.63 per litre (Table 3.5). People in most oil-producing countries appear to feel they have a right to cheap gas. This has caused fuel shortages in Iran, where cheap gas has led to underinvestment in refining capacity with the result that Iran has to import refined petroleum products. In 2007, the Iranian government attempted

Table 3.5. Premium gas prices in 2008, selected countries

Country/region	2008 price of premium gas (US$/litre)
United States	0.56
Canada	0.76
Brazil	1.26
Venezuela	0.02
France	1.52
Germany	1.56
Russian Federation	0.89
Norway	1.63
Iran	0.10
Saudi Arabia	0.16
United Arab Emirates	0.45
China	0.99
India	1.09
Japan	1.42

Data on gas prices from Table 2.5.2 in annual statistics compiled by the *Deutsche Gesellschaft für Technisch Zusammenarbeit.* http://www.gtz.de/de/dokumente/gtz2009-en-ifp-full-version.pdf.

Figure 3.5. A ski resort in Dubai where temperatures outside can reach 40°C. Source: Wikimedia Commons.

to raise the price at the pump but had to back down in the face of riots in the streets. Venezuela is using cheap oil to favour friends and allies such as Cuba and Nicaragua. Even China and India, which are oil-importing countries, are subsidizing their oil. Countries in the Middle East also use cheap oil to produce cheap electricity, which explains such anomalies as a ski resort in Dubai, complete with chairlifts and artificial snow, that allows customers to spend the day skiing when the temperature outside is 40°C.

Increased demand in developing countries and subsidized prices in producing countries acted together to cushion the impact of the 2007–2009 global recession on the demand for oil and therefore on oil prices. Future increases in oil demand is most likely to come from non-OECD countries, most likely from high growth countries in South East Asia, South America and parts of Africa. The International Energy Agency projects a slowing in energy demand to 2040 (but still an increase by 37 percent) because of gains in energy efficiency and changes in the global economy towards less energy-intensive activities.[250] So much depends on what measures, if any, the world is prepared to implement to mitigate climate change—a topic discussed in detail in Chapter 4.

Natural gas

The situation for natural gas is marginally better than for oil with a reserve-to-production ratio about fifty-six years, but it is far more difficult to estimate the reserves of natural gas than to estimate oil reserves. Oil and gas are usually found together, and earlier, natural gas was routinely *flared* (set on fire) as there was no market for it, gas being more difficult to transport and requiring specially built pipelines. Non-conventional gas includes coal-bed methane gas associated with coal, various types of gas trapped in rocks, permafrost, and gas hydrates in the oceans (see Chapter 10) and in deep aquifers. It also includes shale gas. New technology, including the development of horizontal drilling and hydraulic fracturing, has made it possible to commercially exploit gas locked up in shale formations, and as a result estimates of reserves of natural gas have increased substantially. The presence of gas in shale deposits has been known for a long time—indeed, it is likely that the first natural gas well, drilled in 1821 in the United States, was on a shale deposit.[251] However, shale gas is difficult to extract, and it was not until the early part of the twenty-first century that the technology of fracking made shale gas commercially viable. Hydraulic fracturing, used since the 1940s, involves the injection of water, chemicals, and sand under pressure into shale formations, which fractures the underground rock, making it possible for the trapped hydrocarbons to find their way to the well. In combination with horizontal drilling, it has unlocked a vast supply of natural gas. For example, in 2009, potential American natural gas deposits were revised upward by 39 percent.[252]

The largest reserves of natural gas outside the United States are found in Iran, which has 18 percent of total world reserves, followed by Russia and Qatar with 17.6 and 13.4 percent (Table 3.6). Currently gas is used mainly for heating and power generation, but the technology is already in place to power vehicles by compressed natural gas. Of course, natural gas can also be used to generate the electricity to fuel the new generation of electric cars. Natural-gas-powered vehicles require larger tanks compared with conventional vehicles as natural gas only has 60 percent of the energy density of diesel. However, the main problem for the development of gas-powered cars and trucks is the current lack of infrastructure, particularly filling stations.

As already noted, one of the disadvantages of natural gas is that it is more difficult to transport than oil; therefore, so far, there is no natural gas world market, only regional markets in which gas prices can be very volatile. On land, the gas has to be transported by pipelines, which can be very expensive to build. As a consequence, it is sometimes not economical to exploit natural

Table 3.6. Proved reserves of natural gas, 2013

	Trillion cubic metres	Share of total (%)	Reserve-to-production ratio
United States	9.3	5.0	13.6
Canada	2.0	1.1	13.1
Total North America	**11.7**	**6.3**	**13.0**
Venezuela	5.6	3.0	>100
Total S. and Central America	**7.7**	**4.1**	**43.5**
Norway	2.0	1.1	18.8
Russian Federation	31.3	16.8	51.7
Turkmenistan	17.5	9.4	>100
Total Europe and Eurasia	**56.6**	**30.5**	**54.8**
Iran	33.8	18.2	>100
Iraq	3.6	1.9	>100
Qatar	24.7	13.3	>100
Saudi Arabia	8.2	4.4	79.9
United Arab Emirates	6.1	3.3	>100
Total Middle East	**80.3**	**43.2**	**>100**
Algeria	4.5	2.4	57.3
Egypt	1.8	1.0	32.9
Nigeria	5.1	2.7	>100
Total Africa	**14.2**	**7.6**	**69.5**
Australia	3.7	2.0	85.8
China	3.3	1.8	28.0
Indonesia	2.9	1.6	41.5
Total Asia Pacific	**15.2**	**8.2**	**31.1**
Total world	**185.7**	**100**	**55.1**

Source: Adapted from BP *Statistical Review of World Energy, June 2014*.
Note: only countries with reserves larger than 1 percent of global reserves have been included.

gas finds if they are of a relatively small size in remote areas. Natural gas can be shipped between continents in liquefied natural gas (LNG) tankers, which involves converting the gas to a liquid at a temperature of $-162°$c. In the process the gas only takes up 1/600th of its initial volume, which makes shipping more economical. But port areas must have liquefaction facilities from which the gas can be pumped onto the tankers, and the receiving ports have to possess similar facilities to regasify the gas for further transportation in pipelines. The liquefaction takes 10 percent of the energy in the gas and the regasification even more. So far, there is underinvestment in LNG facilities, partly because of a reluctance to build them after several spectacular explosions both in the United States and Algeria.[253] Qatar as a major gas producer has invested heavily in LNG facilities, and among consuming nations, Japan is at the forefront because of its dependence on imports of natural gas. Europe imports one-quarter of its natural gas from Russia, which is now building a pipeline under the Baltic Sea. As a result of the different modes of transportation, three separate markets for gas have emerged: Asia, which mainly relies on LNG, Europe with its own domestic gas, Russian gas delivered by pipeline and some LNG, and North America, totally dependent on pipelines. Different supply-and-demand conditions in each market have caused regional prices to diverge. One-third of market prices are subject to regulation, and many are indexed to oil prices. In 2013, European prices were around $10 per MBtu (MBtu = 1,000 British Thermal Units), Japanese prices were $16 per MBtu, and US prices fluctuated between $3 and $4 per MBtu , reflecting an oversupply in US markets.[254]

The excitement about fracking and its impact on potential gas reserves has been tempered by environmental concerns focusing on water demand and water and air pollution. Fracking requires more drill holes than conventional drilling for gas and uses a large amount of water and chemicals. The fracking of six wells requires 54 to 174 million litres of water, equivalent to 22 to 69 Olympic-sized swimming pools.[255] Chemicals including methanols, diesel, and benzenes are added to the water and mixed with sand before the liquid is pumped into the wellbore. After it has been used, most of the water is contaminated with toxic organic compounds, heavy metals, and natural radioactive material and is returned to the surface (*flowback*). This waste water is often returned to injection wells or municipal sewerage systems. Water that is not recovered remains underground and could contaminate groundwater, but industry analysts downplay this as a problem, arguing that the technology has been used for oil wells for a considerable time with no ill effects, and the fracking usually occurs at depths below groundwater aquifers. Others argue that toxic spills at the surface are more likely to be a hazard. Additional concerns include earth tremors and leakages into the atmosphere of methane—a powerful greenhouse gas—caused by the underground disposal of contaminated flowback water.[256] In response to these and other concerns, the Environmental Protection Agency in the United States has commissioned a major study of the impact of fracking on groundwater.[257] Environmental concerns may lead to tightened regulations and higher costs.

Some analysts claim that the amount of shale gas available is overstated. Industry methods used in estimating recoverable shale-gas reserves may not be reliable as there is limited experience in assessing such reserves. A telling point is that the Energy Information Administration in the United States had to revise its estimates downward in its 2012 Annual Energy Outlook to 482 trillion cubic feet from the 2011 figure of 827 trillion cubic feet.[258] A conventional gas well may produce thirty to forty billion cubic feet, but a shale-gas well only a fraction, meaning that more wells have to be drilled to achieve a given volume of gas. It also appears that production rates drop more rapidly with shale-gas wells than with conventional wells—indeed, in some cases as much as 70 percent of the gas is extracted in the first year.[259] Thus, for shale gas to become a reliable source of gas, new producing wells have to be added continually, which increases the costs of production.

Europe has substantial shale-gas deposits—almost as large as those in the United States, but conditions are not as favourable for exploitation in terms of the legal framework, the nature of the deposits, and the cost of drilling. The European shale deposits tend to be deeper underground and thus more costly to extract. They are also likely to be in more populated areas, which makes obtaining permissions to drill more difficult. Because of lack of competition in the oil-services business in Europe, a single gas well might cost three and a half times more to drill in Europe than in North America.[260]

Coal

In common with oil and gas formations coal deposits are the result of geological processes involving ancient biotic materials. There are different types of coal, ranging from low-grade lignite to anthracite with the highest carbon content and therefore heat value. Coal can be found in abundance in all regions of the world. The United States has 28 percent of the world's reserves, followed by Russia and China (Table 3.7). The US uses more coal per capita than China, but China is the largest consumer in the world, using twice as much as the US and as a result its reserve-to-production ratio is only thirty-one years. In common with other fossil fuels, coal prices increased during the first decade of the 21st century, causing old coal mines to be reopened even in the United Kingdom,

Table 3.7. Proved reserves of coal, 2013

	Million tonnes	Share of total in percent	Reserve-to-production ratio
United States	237,295	26.6	266
Total North America	245,088	27.5	250
Total South and Central America	14,641	1.6	149
Germany	40,548	4.5	213
Kazakhstan	33,600	3.8	293
Russian Federation	157,010	17.6	452
Ukraine	33,873	3.8	384
Total Europe and Eurasia	310,530	34.8	254
South Africa	30,156	3.4	117
Total Middle East and Africa	32,936	3.7	126
Australia	76,400	8.5	160
China	114,500	12.8	31
India	60,600	6.8	100
Total Asia Pacific	288,328	32.3	54
Total world	891,531	100	113

Source: Adapted from *BP Statistical Review of World Energy, June 2014*.
Note: The table includes only countries with more than 1 percent of total world production. The reserves include anthracite, bituminous, sub-bituminous, and lignite coal deposits.

where massive mine closures occurred in the 1980s. However, weakening demand in China and competition from natural gas in the United States led to rapidly falling prices on the world market.

Coal is almost exclusively used for power generation, but there are other uses. The conversion of coal into synthetic petroleum was first accomplished in Germany during the Second World War, when the Germans had limited access to imported petroleum. The technology was improved in South Africa by the national oil company Sasoil during the apartheid years, when oil exports to South Africa were subject to embargoes. Some of these refineries are still in operation. Coal gasification is currently used to produce hydrogen for use in upgrading of oil and for the production of ammonia for fertilizer production.

However, in whatever way we use coal, we cannot get away from the fact that the burning of coal is dirty and coal mining is highly unsafe and has a poor environmental record. Chinese cities are like English cities during the Industrial Revolution in having the most polluted air in the world, mostly due to the heavy use of coal.[261] The World Health Organization estimates that over 355,000 people a year die from air pollution in Southeast Asia alone. Coal-burning plants are also a source of mercury pollution, and are emitting a much larger amount of carbon dioxide, a greenhouse gas, than do natural gas and petroleum plants. Coal-fired plants can be made cleaner by washing the coal before it is burned, by removing the ash through forcing fumes between electrically charred plates, and by fitting scrubbers that remove sulphur dioxides and nitrogen oxides— causes of acid rain. The emerging technology of removing carbon dioxide and pumping it underground will be examined in the next chapter. As for safety, underground coal mining has a scandalous record. It is estimated that since the start of the twentieth century, over one hundred thousand people have died in coal-mining accidents worldwide. Even though fatalities are decreasing, the yearly death toll in Chinese coal mines is still unacceptably high. The fatalities are most often caused by cave-ins and accidental explosions of so-called coal gas (methane). Open-pit mining, or strip mining, is better for miners, but not necessarily for the environment because of the tailings. Most controversial is mountain-removal mining, which means levelling entire mountaintops to expose the coal seams, then dumping the debris into the valleys. This type of mining has polluted almost a thousand kilometres of stream and converted approximately 160,000 hectares of temperate forests in Appalachia into wastelands.[262]

Fossil fuels and sustainability

The question of sustainability of fossil fuels is complex because of the link between the use of fossil fuels and climate change that will be examined in Chapter 4. It is clear that the world is in no immediate danger of running out of oil, gas, or coal, but does that mean that fossil-fuel producing countries have used these resources sustainably in terms of leaving a positive legacy to future generations? The discovery of oil has often been recognized as a mixed blessing, as noted in the discussion in Chapter 1 of the resource curse. The first head of OPEC, the Venezuelan Juan Pablo Pérez Alfonso, is known to have coined the term *the devil's excrement* following the first oil crisis in the 1970s, saying, "I call petroleum the devil's excrement. It brings trouble . . . . Look at this *locura*—waste, corruption, consumption, and our public services falling apart. And debt, debt we shall have for years."[263] More often than not, oil as a resource is not used sustainably. Venezuela has amassed over six hundred billion dollars of oil revenue since the 1970s, but real income per head has not increased. Like many of the oil-producing countries, Venezuela embarked on a policy of huge public spending during the boom years of the 1970s, incurring large internal and external debts it could not service after the collapse in oil prices in the 1980s.[264] Venezuela was the world's fourth-biggest oil exporter at the time, with oil accounting for 80 percent of export revenue. In a classic case of the Dutch disease, the oil revenue pushed up the value of the currency (the bolívar), making any other exports uncompetitive. This led to a drop in bond ratings and therefore large increases in real interest rates, which crippled the economy for the next decades. The poor suffered badly. Hugo Chavez was elected president in 1998 with a mandate to help the poor through social programs and state-led industrial development; he used oil revenue to implement ambitious social programs. Part of his strategy was to increase control over the national oil company Petróleas de Venezuela S.A. (PDVSA) by making his own political appointments to its board. He siphoned millions out of the company, which deprived it of necessary capital for investments and, as a result, the double-digit growth of the oil sector disappeared. Oil production was cut and the country has now moved from being the fourth-largest oil producer to the tenth-largest. Half of the oil is sold at subsidized prices to domestic consumers and foreign allies. Most of the oil revenue has been spent on nationalization and on social programs. But his anti-business stance led to a substantial decline in private-sector activity, causing the economy to become even more dependent on oil exports, which now account for 92 percent of export revenue. Private capital has fled the country, making it difficult to develop the huge shale-oil deposits in the country. To finance social spending, Venezuela has borrowed massively from China, loans that are repaid in oil shipments. Many economic analysts maintain that the situation is unsustainable.[265]

Other oil-producing countries have probably been more successful than Venezuela, though, in general, oil-producing countries have grown less rapidly than other countries. Whether they could have done better still is open to question. Between 1970 and 1980, the price of oil increased tenfold, which led to binge spending, particularly in Middle Eastern oil-producing countries. Saudi Arabia's spending increased 50 percent per year between 1974 and 1979, resulting in inflation in excess of 15 percent per year. Real per-capita GNP rose eightfold between 1970 and 1980, but with little information on income distribution, we do not know the extent to which the money was spread through society.[266] While incomes grew in an unsustainable fashion, the economy diversified too slowly. During the 1990s, per-capita income levels halved from the peak level.

Following the decline in oil prices in 2008, most of the Gulf states undertook massive new investments in their own countries.[267] Worried about the spreading unrest in the Middle East in 2011, many Arab countries announced generous measures to spread the wealth. For example, Kuwait offered $4,000 for each citizen and free food for fourteen months, Bahrain proposed to give $2,500 to each family and Saudi Arabia a 15 percent pay increase for public-sector workers. Fuel subsidies account for 7.5 percent of GDP in North Africa and the Middle East. Most of the Arab states have also initiated massive infrastructure projects. The oil-producing countries can afford it—the others cannot.

In general, lack of diversification is a serious problem, and compared with other regions, productivity and investments are underperforming. Manufacturing exports of the entire Arab world are lower than those of Israel and the Philippines, which are far less populous countries.[268] The lack of rights for women is notorious, with negative effects on education, culture, and social development. The United Arab Emirates, which has only a small percentage of total Gulf reserves, seems to have been more successful in diversifying its economy than some of the other Arab states. Before oil there was a pearl industry, and the area had been a trading centre for millennia—at one time it was known as the "pirate coast." Dubai, the most populated of the seven Emirates, has been particularly successful in becoming a financial hub and has also successfully developed high-end tourism, partly because of some spectacular architecture. It has the world's first seven-star hotel, the much photographed Burj al-Arab, where guests arrive by helicopter and where the smallest room is 170 square metres. Abu Dhabi, another of the Emirates, has established itself as a centre for diabetes research and for research into renewable energy.

The lack of diversification exacerbates the huge problem facing the Arab world of creating employment for an increasingly young population that is expected to grow by 40 percent over the next couple of decades. One in four young people is out of work in the region, and the employment rate is the lowest in the world.[269] Oil extraction by itself generates few jobs. For example, before the fall of Gaddafi, 60 percent of Libya's GDP was generated by oil while only 3 percent of its population was employed. It is not helpful to shower the population with gifts if there is nothing useful for them to do. Many citizens are well educated but not necessarily for the needs of the job market. Their only prospects are often to join a bloated and inefficient civil service, where it takes connections and often bribes to land a job. It is not surprising that the unrest in Arab countries in 2011 was to a large extent led by disaffected young people, and it is perhaps no coincidence that a high proportion of the Al Qaeda terrorists came from affluent homes. Many of the oil-producing countries are aware of the problems, but it appears that every time oil prices increase the incentives for serious reform decrease.

But oil can also be an engine of growth. It became a leading sector of development in the United States during the nineteenth and early twentieth centuries, repeating the successful development of the minerals sector. Even though the oil deposits in the United States were modest by international standards, it became a world leader in petroleum production through technology and research.[270] There were early technological improvements in drilling and a tremendous expansion in knowledge of oil geology. The US Geological Survey and newly established university departments of petroleum engineering played major roles. The discovery of oil in Norway played a similar role in the Norwegian economy, and, as explained in Chapter 1, Norway was able to avoid the resource curse by diversifying its economy and investing some of the oil revenue into a sovereign wealth fund.

History has shown the extent to which economic factors, technological change, and political forces drive the choice of energy and the extent to which switches can be made from one source to another. This is something to keep in mind in predicting the future. It is also clear that most countries do not exploit their fossil fuels in a sustainable fashion in terms of implementing environmental safeguards and ensuring that future generations will benefit from the resource. History is full of examples of unsustainable use of energy resources, from wood to whales to the current use of fossil fuels. However, no discussion of the sustainability of fossil fuels is complete without an analysis of their carbon content and the impact of carbon emissions on climates, oceans, and biodiversity, a topic that will be covered in the next chapter.

4

Fossil Fuels and Climate Change

*The historical record of changing climates. The theory of
climate change: the history and the evidence. The costs
and benefits of strategies to deal with climate change.
Mitigation policies. Carbon pricing. Regulations. Barriers
to reaching international agreements on limiting emissions.
Potential geoengineering solutions. The way ahead.*

CLIMATE CHANGE has emerged as one of the most pressing and controversial issues of our time, with believers pitted against non-believers in a
never-ending battle over who is right. Most of the earlier discussions centred
on the increase in average temperatures (global warming), but the issue is not
restricted to temperature but also encompasses changes in rainfall patterns,
extreme weather, the oceans, and ecosystems. Believers, backed by an overwhelming majority of scientists, argue that the world is warming; it is caused by the
burning of fossil fuels, and unless we do something about it now, our children
and grandchildren must live with consequences that may be catastrophic. For
most of this group, climate change is the inevitable result of a failure of resource
management, in the sense that the cost to the environment of greenhouse gas
emissions has not been included in consumption or production decisions made
by individuals, producers, or governments, mainly because they were not aware
of the dangers until recently. Non-believers, also known as skeptics or deniers,

fall into three categories. One group believes warming does not occur at all, and another believes warming is taking place but no scientific consensus can been reached on what is causing it because the science has not been settled and warming could easily be occurring due to factors beyond our control such as sunspots or cosmic dust. A third category believes the increase in greenhouse gas emissions is too small to have a significant impact on warming. The non-believers support their claims by scouring the scientific literature for papers showing that warming is not occurring, and if it is, it is not man-made. Others bring in religion. For example, conservative Republican US Senator Jim Inhofe invokes the Bible in arguing that only God can change the climate and thus global warming is the greatest hoax ever perpetrated on the American people.[271] Some see climate change as a leftist conspiracy designed to disrupt capitalism.[272] Intense lobbying by corporations, particularly energy companies, against measures to combat climate change may also have had an effect.[273]

This chapter discusses the issues pertaining to climate change by first giving a historical account of the world's climates, followed by an examination of climate science and the various options of dealing with the realities of climate change, including carbon pricing, regulations, and geoengineering.

The historical record of changing climates

Climate change is a natural phenomenon, as the earth's climates have always been in a state of change; sometimes slow, sometimes fast, and sometimes radical. For example, millions of years ago during the era of the dinosaurs, temperatures may have been at least ten degrees* higher than today, and in the last million years, the earth has passed through five glacial periods with much colder temperatures than at present, and with permanent ice covering large areas of the Northern Hemisphere. Between the ice ages, temperatures also fluctuated. After humans evolved in Africa approximately two hundred thousand years ago, they had to adapt to changing living conditions to survive, and it is possible that a change in climate precipitated early human migrations from Africa. Evidence of change from ice cores in Greenland and Antarctica as well as from deep-sea ocean cores indicates that extreme climatic changes were beginning approximately eighty thousand years ago, with periods of heavy rainfall followed by extended droughts in the parts of Africa inhabited by humans.[274] In addition, a cataclysmic eruption of Mount Toba in Indonesia

---

*Degrees refer to the Celsius scale.

seventy-three thousand years ago led to a six-year-long volcanic winter in many parts of the earth during which the sun did not shine because of volcanic dust, an event that very likely caused a global ecological disaster. Possibly in response to these adverse conditions, humans left Africa about fifty to sixty thousand years ago to settle in Asia and Europe. Migrations were easier during the last glacial period because ocean water levels were much lower than today. For example, Indonesia could be reached by land from Asia, and a natural land bridge existed between Siberia and Alaska. It is believed that the Americas were populated twelve to fifteen thousand years ago, with people moving across the land bridge.

The last ice age lasted until twelve thousand years ago, followed by the Middle Holocene or Atlantic period from 6000 to 3000 BC, which exhibited a very benign climate with temperatures two to three degrees higher than today. This period coincided with the transformation of humans from hunter-gatherers to agriculturalists and led to the development of trade and interchange of cultures. The warm and dry climate continued into the Bronze Age, followed by a wet and cool period coinciding with the Iron Age, when even parts of the Sahara Desert were cultivated. Since the first millennium, the climate has also undergone considerable changes. Of particular interest is the warm period between 1000 and 1300 AD when temperatures were about two degrees higher than today, and up to four degrees higher in Arctic regions.[275] This period coincided with the Viking colonization of Greenland. Northern regions were so warm that vines were cultivated in southern Norway and wheat cultivation occurred much farther north in Scandinavia than is currently possible. This warm period led to the blossoming of European civilization, with agricultural improvements and thriving cities.

The good times did not stay. The medieval warm period was followed by the Little Ice Age that lasted until the end of the nineteenth century, a period when glaciers advanced all over the world and areas near the equator suffered from significant drops in rainfall. Rivers in Europe froze regularly in the winter, sometimes

Figure 4.1. River Thames frost fair, 1683–1684 by Thomas Wike. Source: Wikimedia Commons.

all the way to the bottom (Figure 4.1). Vine growing, wheat growing, and olive growing shifted southward. Villages were deserted in Iceland and Norway because people could no longer make a living in the colder climates. A succession of bad harvests led to a severe famine in Europe between 1315 and 1322, followed a few decades later by the Black Death (1346–1352) during which half of Europe's population may have died.[276] The high death toll was likely related to a starvation-weakened population. Climate records in China also indicate that this was a very cold period. The climatic situations in Europe and other continents did not improve during the following centuries. For example, in the seventeenth century, population growth in China came to a halt due to harvest failures and famines. Famine and epidemics were also reported in the Philippines, Indonesia, and Thailand.

The cultural ramifications of the Little Ice Age were many, including the need to blame someone for the bad weather. The idea that famines and other misfortunes happened for no good reason was alien at the time. In people's minds some individuals were at fault. In Europe, the assumed culprits were those who were thought to have sinned against the Almighty; the presumption was that everyone was being punished because of the sins of the select few. In the latter part of the thirteenth century, for example, Jews in many parts of Europe were blamed for the worsening of the climate, which led to pogroms and systematic persecutions in France and the expulsion of Jews from England.[277] A few centuries later, the blame shifted to another group who appeared to be in cahoots with the devil: witches. Following a cold wave in the 1560s, peasants in many areas wanted to root out once and for all the evil personified by witches. As a result, persecutions reached an all-time high. It is estimated that up to fifty thousand women were killed across Europe, usually by burning. Today, most people find it incomprehensible that select groups could be blamed for weather or natural disasters. However, it is interesting to note that as recently as 2010, the American televangelist Pat Robinson declared that the people of earthquake-stricken Haiti were being punished by God because of a supposed pact they had made with the devil to help to throw out the French two hundred years ago.[278] Shiite clerics of Iran have been known to attribute earthquakes to God's punishment for women dressing immodestly.[279]

As this brief survey has shown, the world has seen many upheavals in climates, and the fact that the world is currently warming should not be alarming. However, as will be explained below, the impact of warming climates on the world as a whole could be substantial and cause major economic disruptions because of rising sea levels, increased frequency of severe weather, and adverse implications for agriculture and biodiversity. There is also scientific evidence to show that, this time, climate change is caused by humans, which raises the possibility that it can be halted before major damage has occurred.

The theory of climate change: the history and the evidence

While people have always taken an interest in the causes of weather changes, climate science is relatively recent.[280] At the end of the eighteenth century, it became fashionable for writers and painters to visit the European Alps to describe and paint mountains and glaciers. Some early visitors began to notice that when glaciers receded, they left big boulders behind, giving rise to a highly respected theory that the boulders had been buried inside big icebergs that had been dislodged from glaciers during Noah's flood. However, it did not take long for scientists to make a connection between scratch marks on rock surfaces and huge boulders scattered over landscapes in other parts of Europe, leading to hypotheses of long-gone giant glaciers covering much of the continent. Similar telltale signs were also found in North and South America. More recent scientific findings from ice-core studies in the Antarctic and Greenland show that glacial periods have occurred with considerable regularity. There have been five of them in the last eight hundred thousand years, with the last ending approximately twelve thousand years ago. The question is, why? Could they have been caused by fluctuations in the intensity of the sun, by volcanic activity, by shifts in the earth's plates, or by something in the air itself?

One of the most popular early theories of the causes of the ice ages was continental drift. Newly evolving mountain chains were thought to have blocked prevailing winds or ocean currents and thus changed the climate dramatically. However, this theory was soon discredited because of timing issues. Mountain chains evolved over millions of years while ice ages developed over only hundreds of thousands of years. Others believed that powerful volcanic eruptions could have been the cause, with volcanic ash blocking sunlight for years. Yet others believed that changes in ocean currents could have been contributing factors, as could small changes in earth's orbit around the sun (the Milankovitch cycles). In the early part of the twentieth century, sun-spot theory came into prominence when it was noted that the sun's energy output varied, seemingly in a regular cycle, and it was thought that this cycle offered one method of forecasting longer-term climate changes.

Then the focus of thinking shifted to the air itself. The atmosphere consists of nitrogen (N_2), oxygen (O_2), argon (Ar), carbon dioxide (CO_2), neon (Ne), helium (He), methane CH_4, water vapour, and traces of other gases such as nitrous oxide (N_2O) and ozone (O_3). Nitrogen is the largest component of the atmosphere at 78 percent, followed by oxygen at 21 percent, argon at 0.9 percent and carbon dioxide at 0.04 percent. In the early nineteenth century, French scientist Joseph Fourier proposed that the earth's temperature could be explained by infrared radiation—the process whereby the heated surface of the earth emits infrared heat from the sun into space, and the temperature is determined by the balance of incoming and outgoing radiant energy. In 1859, Irishman John Tyndall discovered that both CH_4 and CO_2 were opaque gases, meaning they were capable of reducing the heat radiation escaping from the atmosphere. It was left to Swedish scientist Svante Arrhenius to propose in 1896 that a sudden influx of CO_2 through, say, a volcanic eruption, would increase the temperature. This in turn would increase the amount of water vapour in the atmosphere (a feedback effect), and thereby lead to more warming—water vapour is even more potent than CO_2 and methane in trapping heat. This became known as the greenhouse effect. Arrhenius followed Scottish scientist James Croll in raising the idea that feedback effects could be crucial in influencing climate. An example is the *albedo* effect, a measure of how strongly an object reflects light. Croll had pointed out that snow-covered regions would reflect more sunlight back into space, which would reinforce cooling. Thanks to the work of these early pioneers, we have known for over 150 years that even though the greenhouse gases make up a tiny percentage of the total atmosphere, they are essential in trapping infrared radiation; if it were not for them, the earth's temperature would drop to −18°c. Greenhouse gases are therefore necessary for our survival, and if they increase the earth will warm.

In the 1930s, people started to notice that the earth was warming, but it was seen as beneficial. The earth was believed to be self-regulating, and few people thought humans could affect the atmosphere. The Second World War spawned an increase in funding for scientific research into climate and weather, as the military began to realize that everything from invasions to the launching of missiles depended on weather conditions. Earlier it was thought that CO_2 could not build up in the atmosphere, as any surplus would be immediately absorbed by the oceans. During the 1960s, it was proven that atmospheric increases could occur, and better instrumentation and techniques made it possible to measure the increases accurately. Ice cores collected from the Arctic and Antarctic ice sheets proved to be a powerful tool in estimating air temperatures thousands of years ago. The cores contain tiny air bubbles that have been locked in since the time the snow and ice was formed. Not only do the air bubbles record the

CO_2 and methane in the atmosphere at the time of their formation, but they also record the presence of certain hydrogen and oxygen isotopes that will give an approximation of the ambient temperature. By the 1970s, evidence was available to show that the world's climate could change rapidly, within a couple of centuries, or even decades.

Following the environmental movement in the 1970s, concerns grew about the impacts of humans on the environment. Large-scale tree-cutting seemed to be related to desertification, contributing to the massive famines experienced in the Sahel and Ethiopia as Africa grew dryer. There were also droughts in the Soviet Union and failures of the monsoon in India. Scientists pointed out that increased air pollution could block off sunlight reaching the earth and create global cooling. This, coupled with a cooling trend that had started in the early 1940s, meant the public did not know what to believe. Was the earth cooling or warming? Scientists were reluctant to take part in the public debate and focused on arguing for additional funding for further studies. High-level discussions took place on how to deal with global cooling, including various types of geoengineering measures such as a proposal to build a dam between Russia and Alaska across the Bering Strait in an attempt to control the amount of cold water entering the Pacific. President Kennedy mentioned the proposal during his presidential campaign; it was also discussed during Richard Nixon's and Gerald Ford's presidencies. Other suggestions included covering the polar ice caps with black foil to reduce solar reflection, sending huge mirrors into orbit to direct more sunlight to the earth, or blowing up undersea mountains using atomic bombs near the Faroe Islands to extend ocean currents into the Arctic. A suggestion was even put forward to melt the polar ice cap with nuclear bombs.[281]

Climate scientists realized that climate research was incredibly complicated and involved cooperation across many disciplines such as oceanography, meteorology, glaciology, geophysics, geography, hydrology, and plant ecology, to name a few. Using increasingly complex computer models, scientists tried to model the earth's climate and make predictions. At the same time, measurements of average global temperatures revealed that the earth was warming. Thanks to the pioneering work of Charles Keeling in the 1960s, measurements of CO_2 concentrations in the atmosphere became more precise and showed that the buildup was continuing (Figure 4.2). The first CO_2 monitoring stations were set up at the mountain top of Mauna Loa in Hawaii in 1956 and at the South Pole in 1957, and others were to follow.[282] A large portion of the CO_2 entering the atmosphere comes from natural causes through the carbon cycle, with the remainder from the burning of fossil fuels, deforestation, and some industrial

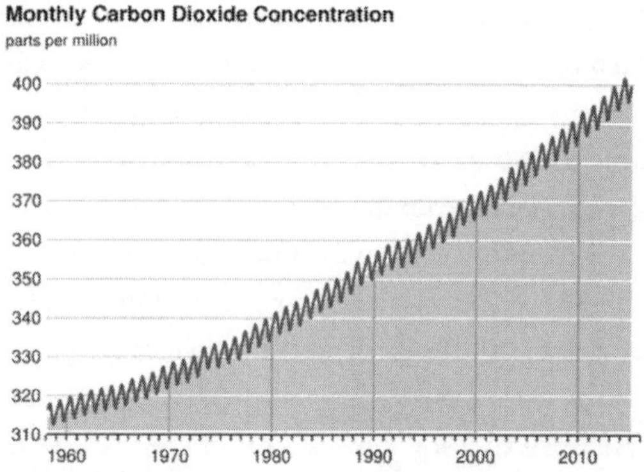

Monthly Carbon Dioxide Concentration
parts per million

Figure 4.2. The Keeling measurements of carbon dioxide concentrations at Mauna Loa, Hawaii. Source: http://scrippsco2.ucsd. edu/

processes such as cement manufacturing. We can tell that the current buildup is caused by humans, partly because it is relatively easy to calculate the amount of carbon emitted in the atmosphere through the burning of fossil fuels, and partly because human-induced carbon emissions can be identified through the use of spectrometry. Carbon has three different isotopes, only one of which is common in emissions from human activity.

As concerns mounted that man-made (anthropogenic) CO2 would have long-term effects on the world's climate, the Intergovernmental Panel on Climate Change (IPCC) was established by the United Nations in 1988 with a mandate to assess all information relevant to understanding the causes of human-induced climate change, its impact, and what could be done for adaptation and mitigation. The panel published five assessment reports, in 1990, 1995, 2001, 2007, and 2013. The first report argued that human activities have increased the buildup of greenhouse gases since the Industrial Revolution by adding CO_2, methane (CH_4), chlorofluorocarbons (CFCs), and nitrous oxide (N_2O) to the atmosphere, of which CO_2 is responsible for more than half of the greenhouse effect.[283] It also highlighted estimates that the stock of CO_2 in the atmosphere had risen from 280 parts per million of volume (ppmv) before the Industrial Revolution to the 1990 level of about 380 ppmv—an increase of 26 percent (Figure 4.2). The increase in the concentration of methane was 115 percent and nitrous oxides 7 percent. Measurable concentrations of CFCs were also found, gases that did not exist prior to the Industrial Revolution. CFCs, methane, and nitrous oxides are more powerful in forcing warming than CO_2—methane is 58 times more effective and CFCs four thousand times more effective. These emissions can be converted to CO_2 equivalents (i.e. the amount of CO_2 that would have had a warming effect equal to the gas in question). The total increase in greenhouse gases since the Industrial Revolution is equal to a 50 percent increase in CO_2 equivalents even though the actual increase in CO_2 was only 26 percent; the remainder was caused by the other gases.

The first report estimated that this increase in concentration of greenhouse gases resulted in an average global temperature increase of approximately half a degree since the Industrial Revolution. Carbon dioxide takes up infrared radiation at a predictable rate, and if CO_2 levels double, it should result in approximately one degree of warming if there are no feedback effects such as increased water vapour created by warming. As well, the impact of soot and aerosols may increase or decrease the rise in temperatures. The temperature change is consistent with the predictions of the climate models, but the report stated the warming could also be caused by natural variation—more research was needed before a definite conclusion could be arrived at. If emissions continued at the current rate, the report predicted the greenhouse gas concentration would double by 2050. The panel concluded that the buildup was primarily caused by the burning of fossil fuels, and to a lesser degree by changes in land use and deforestation—forests absorb carbon dioxide, acting as carbon sinks while they grow. The increase in methane was caused by increases in rice cultivation and livestock agriculture. The increase in nitrous oxides was also attributed to agriculture through the use of fertilizers, while the presence of CFCs was caused by the introduction of refrigerants—a powerful ozone-destroying substance. With accelerating energy use, a doubling of concentrations could be reached as early as 2035, which, according to the models, could result in an increase in average global temperature of more than two degrees. A trebling by the end of the twenty-first century gives a 50 percent chance of a temperature increase of more than five degrees.

The 1990 panel argued that the repercussions could be very serious. The shrinking of glaciers would threaten the water supplies in the Indian subcontinent, China, and South American countries, together containing one-sixth of the world's population. Rising sea levels caused by the melting of polar ice caps could not only inundate small, low-lying islands such as the Maldives but also affect populous countries such as Bangladesh and major cities including London, New York, Tokyo, and Cairo. Global warming is likely to increase rainfall in some areas and decrease it in others, notably in much of Africa with repercussions on food production, while leading to more changeable weather with increased frequency of severe weather. With an increase in global temperatures of two degrees, climatic zones could swiftly move several hundred kilometres toward the poles with many species unable to adapt, particularly on islands and in polar, alpine, and arid regions, resulting in species extinction. The ecology of oceans would also be affected because of acidification caused by increased carbon dioxide uptake. There would be adverse health effects on humans because of heat stress and increased incidence of tropical diseases. The panel predicted that the burden would fall disproportionately on poor countries, partly because they cannot afford to spend money on adaptation and partly because most are located in the tropics or subtropics, where there would be least warming but where the warming would have the most adverse effects on agriculture.

The second and third assessment reports in 1995 and 2001 provided more evidence that the world is indeed warming and that it can be attributed to human (anthropogenic) activity and added more information of the impact of aerosols on climate. The fourth assessment report, published in 2007, held at least one surprise.[284] The long-term trend of declining average CO_2 emissions per unit of energy reversed itself around 2000 and started to increase, probably because of the rapid growth in China, which relies heavily on coal for its energy supplies, and which of course means a more rapid increase in CO_2 concentrations. Some of the models also predicted stronger positive feedback effects of global warming, resulting in higher temperature predictions. For example, a feedback effect previously neglected was that higher ocean temperatures reduce the effectiveness of oceans in absorbing CO_2; thus more of the gas stays in the atmosphere. These models predict a temperature increase of two to 4.5 degrees with a most likely increase of three degrees following a doubling of CO_2. In addition, the report highlighted the following facts, all predicted by climate-change models: in the twelve-year period from 1995 through 2006, eleven of the twelve years were the warmest years on record since 1850; since 1993 sea levels are rising at a faster rate; the average cover of Arctic sea ice is shrinking; and precipitation is increasing in eastern parts of North and South America, northern Europe, and central Asia while decreasing in parts of Africa and southern Asia.

The first part of the fifth assessment report, *The Physical Science Basis*, was released in 2013.[285] The report, based on improved climate models, concluded that "each of the last three decades has been successively warmer at the Earth's surface than any preceding decades since 1850" (p. 3) and "it is extremely likely that more than half of the observed increase in global average surface temperature from 1951 to 2010 was caused by the anthropogenic increase in greenhouse gas concentrations and other anthropogenic forcings together" (p. 15). Since the first report of the IPCC twenty-three years earlier, scientists have become more certain that climate change is occurring and that much of it is anthropogenic. In 1995 the IPCC wrote that warming was *more likely than not* anthropogenic, in 2001 the wording had changed to *likely*, in 2007 to *very likely* and in 2013 *extremely likely*. The 2013 report also confirmed the continued warming and acidification of the oceans, the rise in ocean levels, the decrease in sea ice in the Northern Hemisphere, and the decrease in the size of glaciers. It is predicted that these trends will continue to the end of this century and beyond, with a projected warming at the end of the century (depending on assumed CO_2 concentrations) in the range of 1.5 to 4.5 degrees, which is slightly lower than the projected two to 4.5 degrees in the fourth assessment report. Another prediction is that the global water cycle will change to magnify the differences between dry and wet regions and dry and wet seasons. This will have obvious implications for agriculture.

The IPCC also pointed out that any attempt to keep temperatures within acceptable levels (2 degrees above pre-industrial levels) would require that total carbon emissions must not exceed one trillion tonnes (even less if other climate inducing emissions are included). As of 2011, the world had already emitted 530 billion tonnes, leaving 470 billion tonnes or less. This is the world's carbon budget and the implication is that most fossil fuel reserves must be kept in the ground, rather than burnt.

The international community reacted quickly to the first report. Following the Earth Summit in Rio de Janeiro in 1992, the United Nations Framework Convention on Climate Change was adopted with the objective "to achieve stabilization of greenhouse gas concentrations at a level that would prevent dangerous anthropogenic interference with the climate system."[286] The aim was to reduce greenhouse gases to their 1990 level and protect and enhance carbon sinks, with the main burden falling on developed countries. The convention recognized the special difficulties and needs of developing countries, stating that "developed countries shall provide new additional financial resources to developing countries," and unless such resources were forthcoming, developing countries could not be expected to implement appropriate policies. Following pressure from the oil industry, the convention set no mandatory limits on emissions, nor were there any enforcement provisions. However, the Parties to the Convention committed to keeping national inventories of carbon sinks and of greenhouse gas emissions by sources. The convention was ratified and came into force in 1994 after receiving the required fifty signatures. A Conference of the Parties (COP) would be held at regular intervals to review implementation of the convention.

But the Framework Convention was seen to be too weak to be effective as there were no set targets for emissions reductions. New negotiations were started, resulting in the 1997 Kyoto Protocol that legally bound the developed countries to agreed-on targets to be achieved by 2012.[287] Under this protocol, thirty-seven industrialized countries and members of the European Community agreed to binding targets for emissions of CO_2, CH_4, N_2O, SF_6 (sulfur hexafluoride), and hydrofluorocarbons equivalent to a total reduction of 4.2 percent below the 1990 level. Emissions from developing countries were excluded and so were emissions from airlines and shipping. Included were market-based mechanisms that allowed countries to meet their targets by buying greenhouse gas emissions reductions from countries that did not utilize the emissions permitted under the protocol at a price determined by the market. The protocol went into force in 2005 after Russia finally ratified. The United States signed the protocol but did not ratify because of worries that the proposed measures would be too costly. America also felt the protocol would be ineffective as it did not include the rapidly developing countries, especially India and China.

According to the protocol, the agreed-on targets had to be met by 2012, when Kyoto expired. The purpose of the thirteenth annual COP conference in Bali in December 2007 was to set up a framework to arrive at a new agreement after Kyoto. The deadline passed without consensus mainly because of the intransigence of the United States. After the conference organizer was helped off the stage in tears, the conference was finally saved from total disaster by a delegate from Papua New Guinea, who politely stood and told the United States to get out of the way if it was not prepared to provide any leadership on global warming. In response, the United States signed the final declaration.[288] According to *The Economist* magazine, the conference "produced nothing but a vapid statement of good intentions from which America ensured that all substance was removed."[289] The main achievement of the conference was the establishment of a pilot project to examine ways to stop the destruction of tropical forests. For the first time in climate-change discussions, deforestation, which causes almost 20 percent of all greenhouse gas emissions, entered the agenda in a major way. The participating countries agreed on a range of measures, including an exploration of ways to calculate emissions from deforestation and the encouragement of demonstration projects to address the needs of local and indigenous communities. This laid the groundwork for the REDD program (reducing emissions from deforestation and forest degradation), which will be discussed in detail in Chapter 7. While this was an important step forward, it was clear during and after the conference that the Kyoto Protocol had not been a success, as most countries were unlikely to meet their commitments. However, the public, even in the United States, now seemed to have accepted the danger posed by global warming, to a large degree because the activism of Al Gore, vice president during the Clinton administration. Gore's advocacy as showcased in his documentary *An Inconvenient Truth* earned him the Nobel Peace Prize, which he shared with the Intergovernmental Panel on Climate Change in 2007.

COP 15 took place in December 2009 in Copenhagen. The objective of the Copenhagen conference, which was the fifteenth dealing with climate change, was to develop a new agreement to replace the Kyoto Protocol on its expiry in 2012. This proved far too ambitious, as countries could not agree on anything. Canada was seen to be particularly obstructive, insisting that no agreement would be possible without full participation in emissions reductions by China and India, a position first put forward by the United States under the Bush administration. Canada, under the Liberal government of Jean Chretien, ratified the Kyoto Protocol but did not live up to its commitments. The Conservative government under Stephen Harper distanced itself from the previous commitments, based on its concern that any serious attempt to control emissions would compromise Canada's position as an energy superpower. Canada subsequently withdrew from the Kyoto Protocol—the only country to do so. The conference ended in disarray except for a last-minute accord involving the United States, China, India, South Africa, and Brazil.[290] The Copenhagen Accord achieved a purely political agreement rather than the legally binding instrument that had been hoped for, and it extended the Kyoto Accord to its due date in 2012. With an aim to keep global temperature increases to two degrees—requiring a reduction in emissions of 50 to 85 percent from 2000 levels by 2050—it included a general framework for how countries report their actions and how they could be verified. It also incorporated a commitment by developed countries to provide a total of $30 billion between the years 2010 to 2012 to help poor countries reduce emissions and adapt to climate change, as well as a commitment to work toward raising an additional $100 billion for poor countries by 2020.

One of the reasons behind the failure of reaching an agreement was an event leading up to the conference. Several weeks before the conference, computer hackers managed to get into the data files of the Climate Research Unit at the University of East Anglia, obtaining over a thousand e-mails and other documents relating to climate-change research, which were released over the Internet. The e-mails contained discussions among climate scientists on how to counter the arguments of climate-change skeptics. Quotations from the e-mails, published out of context, seemed to imply that some scientists were trying to cover up evidence that cast doubt on human-induced global warming. The incident created a scandal that threatened to throw scientists and the whole science of climate change into disrepute. Several mistakes were also discovered in the second of the four IPCC assessment reports, including a claim that Himalayan glaciers would disappear by 2035—much earlier than the scientific studies predicted. This claim was apparently based on a report by Greenpeace and not based on scientific evidence. A claim was also made that 55 percent of the Netherlands was at risk of becoming inundated, with the true measure just half of that amount. Within a year the number of people who believed that global warming was occurring dropped by 10 percent in the United States to 33 percent and from 44 percent to 31 percent in the United Kingdom.[291] The number of people in the United States who thought that climate change was a hoax doubled. Because of the timing, the scandal probably influenced the outcome of the December 2009 Copenhagen conference. The United Nations subsequently appointed a group of top-level scientists—the InterAcademy Council, an association of national academies of science—to review how the panel accomplished its work. The review committee of the council was critical of some of the IPCC procedures and recommended more transparency, a clear conflict-of-interest policy, and that the IPCC should adhere to its own procedures and highlight those that were not peer reviewed.[292] All of these recommendations were adopted by the IPCC. The panel also recommended that the chair of the IPCC should serve for only one term and that an executive committee should be established, which also included members from outside the IPCC, but these recommendations were not adopted.

Subsequent conferences also achieved very little. The 2010 Cancun conference of the parties agreed that future global warming should be limited to 2 degrees above the average temperature before the Industrial Revolution which means that emissions should not exceed 450 ppm—in 2014 the world crossed the 400ppm—but there was no agreement how this goal could be achieved. In 2012, at the Doha Conference it was agreed that the Kyoto Protocol be extended to 2020 with a commitment to achieve a new agreement by 2015. In 2014 one of the major roadblocks to an agreement was overcome when the United States and China announced that they had agreed to deep reductions by 2025.[293] It was a first time that China agreed to be part of the process of cutting emissions. The United States agreed to reduce emissions 26–28 percent below their 2005 level by 2025, and China to increase the share of non-fossil fuels in the primary energy demand by 20 percent by 2030.

Even though there is general agreement that warming is occurring, a very small minority of scientists maintains that as the temperature has not increased in the last few years, the warming process has halted contrary to the predictions of climate models. This seems unlikely, as Figure 4.3 clearly shows that while there are substantial yearly fluctuations, the long-term trend is up. As well, while scientists generally agree that greenhouse gases have a significant effect— without them, the earth's climate would be an average of −18°c—some believe that the warming cannot be caused by the buildup of CO_2 as the gas makes up such a small component of the atmosphere.[294] According to this minority group, warming is caused instead by other natural factors such as solar fluctuations. However, no climate model has satisfactorily replicated the warming that has already taken place without including human sources.[295]

Some recent climate models indicate that if the present buildup continues, it will likely lead to a temperature change of over 5°c by 2091, which could result in catastrophic changes.[296] Catastrophic changes can occur if we reach several tipping points such as the collapse of the West Antarctic and Greenland ice sheets, changes in ocean circulation patterns, ocean acidification beyond a certain level, and feedback processes that accelerate warming.[297]

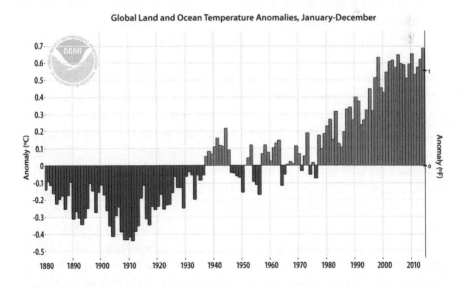

Figure 4.3. Global temperature anomalies 1880–2014, expressed as deviations from the 20th century average. Source: http://www.ncdc.noaa.gov/cag/time-series/global/globe/land_ocean/ytd/12/1880-2014 .

However, Figure 4.3 shows that there is a plateau in the global temperature increase. Air temperatures have not increased significantly between 1998 and 2013. This is a puzzle because approximately one hundred billion tons of carbon were added to the atmosphere between 2000 and 2010—one-quarter of the emissions added since 1750—and the models indicate this should have caused significant warming, a fact that caused consternation among believers and joy among deniers. Several explanations were offered by climate scientists, including the existence of a poorly understood new lag between the amount of carbon dioxide in the atmosphere and warming; that warming was unusually large in the 1990s, which explains the lower-than-expected warming in the first decade of the second millennium; or that the models do not adequately describe how climate responds to higher levels of carbon, as there are many factors we still do not know. Researchers using different models revised the warming predictions downward. For example, in 2013, the UK Met Office Climate Centre revised its predictions from a 0.54°c increase to a 0.43°c increase in average global temperature over the next five years, and the Research Council of Norway published a study projecting an increase in global temperature of 1.9 degrees rather than the IPCC projection of three degrees following a doubling of concentrations, while other researchers have published even lower estimates.[298] As mentioned above, the IPCC *Fifth Assessment Report* also revised downward its estimate of the likely temperature range at the lower end by 0.5 degrees.

Additional studies found convincing explanations for the slowdown, which, if these studies are correct, is only temporary. One explanation is that most temperature records only cover 84 percent of the globe's surface, excluding observations from the desert areas of Africa and the polar regions, where warming is occurring at a very fast rate. The Arctic in particular is warming rapidly—more rapidly than climate models have predicted—and the sea ice is declining. Warming is also rapid in parts of the Antarctic—the Antarctic Peninsula has seen an increase in average temperatures of 2.8 degrees over the last fifty years.[299] Using satellite observations for the reconstruction of temperatures in Arctic regions, the resulting average global temperature increases were consistent with the predictions of climate models.[300] The IPCC *Fifth Assessment Report* pointed to a second explanation that relates to a longer-than-normal solar cycle, unusual volcanic activity, and increases in air pollution, particularly in China. As is well known, aerosols reflect sunlight back into space. When these factors are taken into account, the anomaly between the climate models and observed temperatures largely disappears.[301] A third explanation relates to the impact of warming on the temperature of the oceans, which appear to be warming rapidly. This in turn affects winds and currents, which has resulted in the cooling of the Eastern Pacific Ocean.[302] Another recent study has shown that the Atlantic Ocean is similarly affected.[303]

According to the science, climate change not only affects temperatures but also impacts the oceans through rising levels and acidification. Even though ocean levels have been rising since the last glacial retreat, data indicate that the pace of increase is accelerating, which is consistent both with melting glaciers and warmer sea temperatures as warmer seas have a larger volume. There is also evidence that the average acidity of the oceans is 30 percent higher since the start of the Industrial Revolution because of increased absorption of CO_2.[304] Acidification is likely to have implications for those marine animals and plants (e.g., lobster, corals, and phytoplankton) that require calcium to grow, as extra CO_2 will inhibit the absorption of calcium. This problem is particularly serious in the Arctic for two reasons.[305] One is that cold water takes up more CO_2 than warm water, and the other that rivers supply the Arctic Ocean with a large amount of fresh water, which reduces its ability to neutralize the CO_2.

The evidence is incontrovertible that warming is occurring and most of it is anthropogenic, but opinions differ on what the future will hold, which makes policy formation exceedingly difficult, particularly as a small probability exists that the impact of emissions on future climates will be catastrophic. The precautionary principle is often invoked to justify action on climate change. The principle essentially implies that if a substance or activity is likely to pose a threat to the environment, or to people, action should be taken to prevent it even before there is conclusive scientific proof that it is harmful. For example, Article 15 of the Rio Declaration states[306]:

> In order to protect the environment, the precautionary approach shall be widely applied by States according to their capabilities. Where there are threats of serious or irreversible damage, lack of full scientific certainty shall not be used as a reason for postponing cost-effective measures to prevent environmental degradation.

It has also been adopted as a guiding principle by the European Union. This principle makes common sense but has been criticized on the grounds that even if an action carries a risk to the environment, it could still be justified because some risky actions can have substantial benefits. One analytical approach that can serve as a framework in determining what should be done in combatting climate change is to quantify in dollar terms the total costs and benefits over time of action or inaction under different scenarios—a favoured approach of economists. However, this approach also has its problems.

The costs and benefits of strategies to deal with climate change

Cost-benefit analysis evaluates present and future benefits and costs of an action, and if the benefits are greater than the costs, the action is beneficial. Used for decision making by governments and corporations, cost-benefit analysis takes account of all relevant direct and indirect costs and benefits.[307] What makes the cost-benefit analysis complicated when applied to climate change are the long time horizons. Even if immediate action is taken on climate change, the effects will not be evident for decades because CO_2 remains in the atmosphere for forty to fifty years. The other difficulty is the risk and uncertainty associated with action or inaction. Indeed, in terms of modelling, the economist Martin Weitzman has written that "the economics of climate change is a problem from hell".[308] Most of the standard cost-benefit models estimate that a cost of global warming of two to three degrees would be equivalent to an annual loss of global output ranging from zero to 3 percent of global GDP. The models predicting zero effect on global GDP show that the beneficial effects of warming on some regions such as eastern Europe and Russia outweigh the negative effects on other areas such as Africa.[309] Most models suggest that the benefits of modest mitigation strategies outweigh the costs. The models (usually referred to as integrated assessment models) are incredibly complex, combining economics with geophysical climate dynamics. These models are extremely sensitive to the assumptions made about future climate scenarios, what damages are included, and what interest rates are used in calculations, and they give widely varying estimates of the costs and benefits of action or inaction; therefore, the results are not very useful for policy-makers.[310]

The Economics of Climate Change: the Stern Review, commissioned by the British government, is one of the most controversial in a long series of cost-benefit studies.[311] Published in 2007, the report is both alarming and reassuring. Given the estimates by the IPCC showing that global temperatures may increase more than two to three degrees following a doubling of emissions, the economic cost could be as high as 5 to 10 percent annual loss of global GDP, with losses to developing countries higher. Under some scenarios, the damage to GDP could be as high as 20 percent. These figures are far higher than other economic studies.[312] To achieve a stable climate with warming of two degrees would require a reduction of CO_2 emissions to 80 percent below current levels.

Stabilization of carbon dioxide concentrations at 450 to 550 ppm would require emissions to peak ten to twenty years from now, and then decline by 1 to 3 percent per year. The cost of stabilization is estimated to be 1 percent of global GDP by 2050. Given that the benefits (averting 5 to 10 percent annual loss of GDP) far outweigh the costs (1 percent of GDP), it is obvious that from an economic viewpoint something should be done. To quote Stern:

> The evidence shows that ignoring climate change will eventually damage economic growth. Our actions over the coming few decades could create risks of major disruption to economic and social activity, later in this century and in the next, on a scale similar to those associated with the great wars and the economic depression of the first half of the 20th century. And it will be difficult or impossible to reverse these changes. Tackling climate change is the pro-growth strategy for the longer term, and it can be done in a way that does not cap the aspirations for growth of rich or poor countries. The earlier effective action is taken, the less costly it will be.[313]

Stern's report has been subject to considerable criticism from other economists. The debate is not over whether action is needed; rather, it is over how much action is needed.[314] In particular, the model used in the report has been criticized for attaching too much importance to the future compared with the present, as it uses a very low discount rate, which is the reason the costs of global warming are estimated to be so much higher than in other studies.

Discounting is a method used in finance and economics to compare the value of a dollar today with the value of a dollar, say, one year from now. If given a choice between receiving $1,000 today and $1,000 dollar next year, most people would insist on receiving it today unless they are paid interest as a reward for waiting. At a rate of interest of 10 percent, you would expect to receive $1,100 next year and an additional 10 percent the following year. This works in reverse too. A promise of receiving $1,000 next year is worth $909 (=1000/1.10) today. Add to this the effect of compounding interest rates, and a small amount invested today will be worth a large sum over a multi-year time span. For example, the $1,000 you receive now with interest rates staying at 10 percent will have grown to $2,593 in ten years' time; similarly, $1,000 received ten years from now is only worth $386 dollars in today's money. The higher the interest rate that is chosen for discounting purposes (usually known as the discount rate), the lower is the value of future costs and benefits. If you compare measures that will cost a lot today and that will yield large benefits in the future with those costing a lot today and yielding the same immediate benefits, you are more likely to choose the option leading to immediate benefits. This is a problem in estimating the costs and benefits of dealing with global warming. The immediate costs are large, and the benefits are far in the future.

In discounting, one values the benefits and costs to future generations less than the benefits and costs to current generations. Is that fair? The *Stern Review* did not think so, and used an average discount rate of 1.4 percent, with the result that the costs of global warming to society are much higher than in other studies. The arguments in favour of using high discount rates include the optimistic belief of most economists in continued economic growth. Based on this assumption, future generations will be richer than the current generation; thus it is only fair they should shoulder a more substantial share of the costs of global warming than we do. This argument assumes that the effects of global warming are reversible—it does not matter if we act now or later. But this is not true for most of the impacts of global warming. For example, species extinction cannot be reversed; neither can the melting of the Greenland ice cap if it occurs. A related issue is that we do not know anything about the preferences of coming generations. Most studies use the theoretical construct of a welfare function to evaluate costs and benefits in the future. The welfare function assumes that future generations will have the same likes and dislikes as we do, which is not necessarily true. This creates another element of uncertainty in using economic models. The models can also be criticized for understating the likely effects on humans of climate change as they do not include estimates for the costs of possible climate-induced adaptations and conflicts.[315]

Another question is how to deal with the unlikely but possible event of a climate catastrophe. After all, catastrophes do occur, even though the probability of them occurring is exceedingly small. For example if a climate catastrophe wipes out the human race, the cost of inaction would be infinitely large. Therefore, if a climate catastrophe is certain, it is obvious that the benefits of mitigation are larger than the costs. However, it can be shown mathematically that under some conditions, even if the risk of disaster is small, the expected loss from inaction can be indefinitely large.[316] Even though these conditions are restrictive, we should not ignore the possibility that catastrophe can occur and therefore some action is warranted. How much and what type of action is hotly debated. Should it be voluntary, regulatory, or market based? Should it require action by all countries, and how could any agreement be enforced?

Mitigation policies

While the majority of scientists believes that global warming is occurring, and that the main culprit is the burning of fossil fuels, there is little agreement on what to do. Three options are available. One is adaptation, which means doing nothing except attempting to deal with the effects; a second is mitigation, which involves implementing policies designed to reduce emissions of greenhouse gases through technological improvements, carbon taxes, cap and trade (a form of emissions trading where the total amount of emissions is capped), or regulations; and a third is employment of geoengineering solutions, such as the artificial introduction of more water vapour into the atmosphere, or using "smart" mirrors to deflect sunlight. Each of these policies will be discussed below. The lack of agreement can be explained by several factors. Warmer climates will mainly affect future generations; thus the present generation has to be persuaded to make sacrifices to save coming generations. Another problem is that climate change knows no boundaries, and any agreement must be international, which presents the challenge of balancing competing interests among nations. For example, the interests of oil-producing countries must be balanced against the interests of countries whose coastlines will be affected by rising sea levels. And even if an agreement were to be reached, how could it be enforced? There is no world government to oversee compliance. A third and major problem is that the science of climate change is difficult to understand because the science draws from so many disciplines and the models are so complex. Scientists have not been able to prove with absolute certainty that climate change is caused by the burning of fossil fuels, only that a very high probability of this exists. Of course, this is a feature of science that some find difficult to accept. The 2009 scandals about the handling of data by the Climate Research Unit at England's University of East Anglia have made this problem even more acute. Much of the work by the International Panel on Climate Change was discredited in the eyes of many, with the result that support for climate action plummeted. For example, in November 2008, 71 percent of Americans believed in global warming, while in January 2010, only 57 percent believed it was happening.[317]

In retrospect, the Kyoto Protocol was misguided for three reasons. First, the developing countries were not included, and with the rapid growth of China and India, they are now major emitters; second, the United States did not ratify the agreement and therefore did not commit itself to any policy; and third, while there were penalties for countries that did not fulfill their promises—they would

Table 4.1. Global greenhouse gas emissions by source, 2004

Source	Percent of total
Energy supply	26
Industry	19
Forestry	17
Agriculture	14
Transport	13
Residential and commercial buildings	8
Waste and waste water	3

Source: Adapted from Environmental Protection Agency, Global Emissions by Source, http://www.epa.gov/climatechange/ghgemissions/global.html.

Note: Energy supply refers to emissions from the burning of fossil fuels for electricity and heat; industry to fossil fuels burnt on site for energy and emissions from industrial processes unrelated to energy production; forestry to emissions from deforestation; agriculture to emissions from the management of soils, livestock, rice production and biomass; transport to emissions from road, rail, and marine transport; residential to emissions from on-site energy generation from heating and cooking (excluding electricity; waste and waste water to emissions (methane and nitrous oxides) from landfill, wastewater, and incineration.

be subject to more stringent reductions in the next phase—these penalties were not enforceable. Some countries, such as those in Scandinavia, were serious in their efforts and implemented carbon taxes. The European Union adopted a cap-and-trade policy. Other countries, like Canada, adopted emissions targets but did not put in policies to achieve them.

Mitigation policies should be designed with the information from Table 4.1 in mind. Electricity generation should be targeted, being responsible for the largest proportion of emissions followed by industry. A good policy must encourage a shift from high-carbon emission fuels (coal) to low-emission fuels such as gas or, more importantly, to zero-emission energy resources such as wind, nuclear energy, and solar energy. These will be discussed in Chapter 5 as well as the possibilities of reducing emissions from the transport sector. Policies should also include the protection of forests, as deforestation contributes 17 percent of CO_2 emissions. Chapter 7 analyzes causes of deforestation and the difficulties involved in stopping it. The problems of decreasing emissions by the agriculture sector—another major emitter—are discussed in Chapter 8. Much could be achieved by putting a price on carbon and by eliminating subsidies on fossil fuels, which keep energy prices artificially low. Indeed, a recent study estimated that after tax cost (including environmental costs) of subsidies for petroleum products, electricity, natural gas, and coal reached 5.3 trillion US in 2015, equivalent to 6 percent of global GDP.[318] The largest subsidies accrue to coal, and the largest culprits are China, the United States, and Russia. It is estimated that removal of these subsidies would reduce emissions by 20 percent. Of course, such removal would be very difficult to achieve politically—note the discussion in the previous chapter of the impact of subsidised gas prices and the difficulties in removing the subsidies.

Carbon pricing

There are two options in devising policies to decrease emissions: carbon pricing and regulation. Most economists prefer carbon pricing to regulation because it can be demonstrated that it is a cheaper and more efficient option. The Stern report advocates putting a price on carbon, through a tax, trading permits, or regulation to achieve the equivalent of a carbon price. The logic behind taxation is easy to understand. In economic theory, efficiency requires every product to bear its full cost of production. In a free-market economy, products do not include their full environmental costs as the producer can emit noxious fumes and pollutants without being penalized for doing so—this is an illustration of the failure of markets. Therefore, governments should correct market failure by taxing bad activities (pollution, tobacco smoking, and alcohol consumption) and subsidize good ones (education and research and development). If a producer is faced with a tax equivalent to the cost of pollution, that producer has two options: pay the tax and continue to pollute, or avoid the tax by reducing emissions. The tax must be set at a sufficiently high level to reduce emissions by the desired amount. If the cost to society of emitting a ton of CO_2 is $60, then a tax of $60 per ton should be imposed on carbon emissions. The eminent climate economist William Nordhaus recommends an immediate carbon tax of $25 per tonne to be gradually increased to $160 per tonne by 2050.[319] Such a tax would increase the cost of consumption for the average US household by one percent, the cost of driving by 8 percent and the cost of flying by 6 percent. The government revenue gained from a carbon tax could be used to subsidize the development of green technologies; if the tax is global, the revenue could be used to provide assistance for poor countries in dealing with global warming. Carbon taxes have been introduced in the Scandinavian countries, Ireland, the Netherlands, and the provinces of Quebec, Alberta, and British Columbia in Canada. So far, the taxes have not necessarily been implemented in a very rational way as there are too many exemptions, and in many cases the rates on different fuels do not always reflect their carbon contents.

An alternative method of achieving the same desired reductions is a cap-and-trade system, which involves pollution permits. Such a system was effective in cleaning up sulphur-dioxide emissions in the United States in the 1990s. For example, assume a country wants to reduce carbon emissions from one million tonnes of CO_2 to eight hundred thousand tons of CO_2 per year. It would then issue pollution permits to a total of eight hundred thousand tonnes, and no one would be allowed to emit without a permit. The permits could be allocated according to a formula based on previous emissions, and the holders would be allowed to trade them, or they could be auctioned to the highest bidders. Trade or auction, an essential part of the scheme, can help ensure that emissions are cut in the least costly way. To illustrate, if Produce and Pollute Inc. can cut emissions at a modest cost—for example, $5 per ton of CO_2—while it costs Clean Up Tomorrow Inc. $100 per ton, from society's point of view it would be cheaper if Produce and Pollute did the emissions reductions. If both firms were asked to cut back one ton each, it would cost society $105, while if Produce and Pollute could do all the cutting back, it would only cost $10. A cap-and-trade system would allow Produce and Pollute to sell its pollution permit to Clean Up Tomorrow for, say, $50 and thereby make a profit of $45, while Clean Up Tomorrow would be ahead by $50. The price of the permit would be determined by market forces.

In response to the Kyoto Protocol, in 2005, the EU introduced a cap-and-trade system known as the Emissions Trading Scheme. Dirty industries in all member states were issued with free CO_2 emission permits based on the size of their projected emissions. If they wanted to exceed their permits, they had to buy more. It was expected that the market would set the price of emissions permits at around twenty euros per tonne. However, too many permits were issued because some industries had overstated their future emissions, and not enough industries were included in the scheme. The world recession led to cutbacks in the production of many industries and therefore a decrease in the demand for permits, and for these reasons the price of a carbon permit kept going down, reaching below five euros in spring of 2013.[320] The European Parliament turned down a proposal to rescue the scheme, which involved withdrawing permits for nine hundred million tons that would be reintroduced at a later date when the market had improved. The United Nations carbon-trading scheme also collapsed. Set up under the Kyoto Protocol, it involved industrialized nations paying for projects in developing countries in exchange for tradable Certified Emissions Reduction credits. Following the oversupply of credits in European markets, the market for these credits was destroyed as well. Of course, it can be argued that the low price of carbon means the system is working well because industry reduced its emissions to avoid the cost of paying for pollution permits. On the other hand, the low price of carbon in Europe has led to an increased use of coal, the dirtiest of fuels, and more coal-fired power stations are under construction. Cheap coal is being imported from the United States, where coal prices fell in response to competition from an abundance of natural gas produced by fracking.[321]

Is cap and trade dead? The European experience has not been a success, which probably confirms the opinion of some that cap and trade is a lobbyist's dream come true, as the allocation of pollution permits can be subject to political interference. New Zealand and Australia introduced cap-and-trade policies, but were withdrawn in Australia after the election of a new government. China has launched a pilot project involving seven cities in preparation for a full-fledged scheme expected to be introduced in 2020.

Regulations

Regulating carbon emissions with so-called command-and-control systems is always an option, and is often favoured by politicians because the electorate typically does not want policies that involve higher taxes or that allow companies to avoid cutting back on emissions by paying money. Examples of command-and-control systems include, technology and emissions standards, product bans (e.g., banning incandescent light bulbs and plastic bags), and buy local rules.

Coal is the dirtiest source of fuel and its share of primary energy consumption and electricity generation has increased (Tables 3.1. and 3.2). Forty percent of the world's electricity depends on coal-fired generating stations. Not only does the burning of coal emit twice as much CO_2 per unit of energy as natural gas, but it also spews out particulates, nitrous oxides, sulphur compounds, arsenic, and mercury. As noted in the last chapter, there is plenty of it—not only in China and India, but also in the United States. Indeed, it is the increased use of coal that is responsible for the faster-than-expected buildup of CO_2 during the last decade. The United States uses far more coal per capita than China, and it is the world's largest consumer after China. Half of US electricity is generated by coal.[322] When greenhouse gases first became an issue in the 1990s, it was believed that they could not be removed by any type of scrubbing process similar to that of catalytic converters and desulphurization technologies used for the removal of noxious gases such as SO_2 and N_2O from smokestacks. This is no longer the case.[323] The technology is available to fit new fossil-fuel electricity-generating stations with scrubbers so the CO_2 is bound to or captured by a solvent.[324] Old power stations can be retrofitted, but it is expensive.

After the CO_2 is captured, it has to be prevented from entering the atmosphere by being put into storage either in the oceans or in geological formations. Storage in oceans was initially thought to be a good option as the oceans already store carbon. At depths below eight hundred metres, CO_2 turns to liquid, and at depths below three thousand metres, the liquid becomes heavier than water, which means it sinks. However, the environmental effects of such a scheme are unknown, and concerns have arisen over what such liquid storage would do to deepwater ocean life: if the CO_2 were to react with water, it would make the oceans more acidic. A more promising approach is geocarbon sequestration whereby CO_2 is removed from emissions, pressurized until it becomes liquid, and stored in underground receptacles such as depleted oil and gas reservoirs, old coal seams, or saline aquifers. The storage potential of these options is thought to be very large. Geocarbon sequestration technology has already been used in Norway at the Statoil platform Sleipner in the North Sea.[325] The introduction of a Norwegian carbon tax of $55 per tonne led to a successful initiative by Statoil to avoid the tax by getting rid of the CO_2 by pumping it into saline aquifers. Carbon capture has been introduced in two other places: one in Algeria at a gas well, and another in Weyburn, Saskatchewan, where CO_2 from a coal gasification plant in neighbouring North Dakota is piped into nearby depleted oil wells to increase recovery. This is a common enhanced recovery technique, but what is unusual at Weyburn is that the CO_2 is not pumped out again—it stays. Carbon capture and storage became a technology much in favour with the coal industry and with the Canadian and Alberta governments as it appears to offer a solution to the bad reputation of the Alberta oil sands. By 2009, more than twenty experimental plants were operating.[326]

The International Energy Agency sees CCS as a necessary technology to achieve the 50 percent reduction in carbon emissions by 2050 necessary to limit global warming to 2°C, arguing that it could contribute 20 percent of the reductions. This would require one hundred functioning projects by 2020, and three thousand by 2050.[327] We are nowhere near this goal, and some projects have been cancelled. For example, in 2012, three major energy companies pulled out of a government-subsidized carbon-capture project in Alberta, arguing that it did not make economic sense for them to take part in the absence of a cap-and-trade policy. However, in 2014, a retrofitted coal power station in Saskatchewan became the first commercial carbon-capture facility in the world, expected to capture one million tonnes of CO_2 per year.[328] Most carbon is stored in underground facilities, and some is sold to an oil company for enhanced oil recovery. The costs of CCS involve building a plant for separating and capturing the CO_2, the building of pipelines, and finding suitable storage areas. It is estimated that the capture itself is responsible for up to 70 percent of the costs, as the separation of CO_2 requires 25 to 40 percent of the fuel energy produced by a power plant.[329] One International Energy Agency study estimates that on average, the cost of CO_2 avoided is \$55 per tonne and the estimated impact on electricity costs is 74 percent higher than the costs of a conventional coal-powered station.[330] Apart from the cost, the idea of storing millions of tonnes of compressed gas underground for centuries does not seem realistic. Major leaks could be lethal both to humans and animals as CO_2 is toxic in high concentrations. For example, thousands died in Cameroon following the sudden release of concentrated CO_2 from two lakes in the 1980s.[331] The buildup of gas was caused by volcanic activity under the lakes.

For carbon capture to be a commercially viable option for decreasing emissions, a market must exist for the stored carbon beyond the limited use for enhanced oil recovery. There is now promising research into converting captured CO_2 into commercially usable hydrocarbons that could be used for feedstock in the chemical industry.[332]

California has been at the forefront of legislating auto emissions standards that were then copied by other jurisdictions, partly out of self-interest, as car makers did not want to be excluded from the lucrative California market. However, regulatory standards can easily be thwarted by politics, as exemplified by the preferential treatment of suvs by the US federal government, which lasted until 2007. By 2007, these vehicles made up one-quarter of all new cars sold in North America compared with 2 percent in 1980.[333] The story behind the spectacular rise in the use of suvs goes back to a 1960s trade dispute between the United States and the EU's forerunner, the European Economic Community. After the eec increased tariffs on imports of American frozen chicken, the United States launched a formal complaint against the eec, which was resolved by the gatt dispute-settlement mechanism ruling in favour of the United States.[334] As a result, the American government was allowed to retaliate with tariffs of its own, including a surcharge on French brandy and a 25 percent tariff on light trucks intended to punish German car makers. Under world trade rules, the tariff had to be applied to all light trucks. Once the dispute was settled, the tariff on brandy disappeared, but not the tariff on light trucks. It still exists and is known as the chicken tax.

Given the circumstances, it was clearly in the interest of North American car makers to expand their production of light trucks. Not only were they protected against foreign competition, they were also exempted from fuel-efficiency regulations for cars, based on the logic that a light truck is meant to carry heavy loads and must therefore have a larger engine. One way for car makers to increase their light-truck production was to develop new car models with mass appeal that could be classified in this way; enter sports utility vehicles or suvs. In 1978, Congress enacted a gas tax aimed at vehicles with high gas consumption, but trucks and suvs were exempted. In 1984, Congress lowered the tax deduction for company cars, with suvs exempted; in 1990, a luxury tax on cars worth more than $30,000 was introduced, with suvs exempted.[335] As a result, suvs were extremely profitable and probably saved the North American car industry from bankruptcy. Apart from all the government protection and regulatory exemptions they received, they were cheaper to produce than ordinary cars because their construction is simpler. The body frame of an suv is superimposed on a separate frame, which makes the car much heavier. Standard passenger cars use a more common technology with the underbody and side panels joined in one unit.[336] The profit on a $45,000 Lincoln Navigator was estimated to have been around $15,000. In 2007, the US federal government announced new emission standards that also covered suvs, and the current generation of suvs is smaller and more like ordinary passenger cars in performance.

Many measures have been undertaken to improve energy efficiency for appliances, cars, and homes. However, these efficiency gains do not necessarily translate into comparable decreases in energy consumption because of the so-called *rebound effect*.[337] Lower costs of energy mean that people will demand more. More energy-efficient cars give an incentive to live even farther away from work and use the car more. The money saved by making your house more energy efficient may be used to buy more energy-consuming appliances. However, estimates of the rebound effect for personal transport, heating, and cooling show that the rebound effect is probably less than 30 percent, which means that a 100 percent improvement in energy efficiency will lead to a 70 percent decrease in energy consumption, with 30 percent lost to the rebound effect. Another example of an unintended effect of higher efficiency standards for cars is that the new technology results in higher car prices that in turn leads to higher prices of second-hand cars. When the prices of used cars increase, people are more reluctant to scrap them, resulting in more gas-guzzling cars left on the roads (*used car leakage*).[338]

As well, a consumer movement is building toward buying local products and thereby avoiding the CO_2 emitted in transportation. But this does not necessarily reduce emissions. Sea transport emits by far the lowest amount of CO_2 per tonne per kilometre, followed by train and road. Air transport emits the most. Even so, cut flowers shipped by air from Kenya to Europe emit less CO_2 than cut flowers grown in heated greenhouses in Holland, and locally grown lamb in the United Kingdom does not necessarily create less of a carbon imprint than lamb shipped from New Zealand.[339] It all depends how the local product is produced. For example, are heated greenhouses required? These issues would be made clearer with comprehensive carbon taxes.

Barriers to reaching international agreements on limiting emissions

In summary, many measures can be taken to reduce the use of fossil fuels. Given the urgency of the situation, the difficulty is to get all countries to agree. In Canada and the United States, cities, provinces, and states have been more proactive in dealing with the problem, and in the European Union, most of the member countries have implemented measures. As mentioned earlier, the United States and Canada refused to commit to major international agreements unless China and India also agree to comply with them. This may very well change in view of the 2014 U.S.–China Agreement on climate change where both China and the United States committed themselves to reductions in emissions.[340] The biggest problem with this is how to deal with "free riders." If most countries commit, with expensive measures to reduce emissions, the countries that do not participate can get the benefits without incurring any costs.

One possible penalty for free riders is the use of trade sanctions.[341] With the exception of some agricultural subsidies, members of the World Trade Organization are forbidden to give subsidies to firms, as they would give these firms an unfair advantage in world trade. Under WTO rules, countries are allowed to counter other countries' illegal subsidies with countervailing duties in the form of tariffs. One could then argue that if a country does not introduce measures to combat global warming—for example, through carbon taxes—the firms in that country receive an unfair competitive advantage, equivalent to a subsidy. Therefore, other countries under current WTO rules should be free to penalize imports of the miscreant country by imposing high carbon-related import tariffs.[342] William Nordhaus argues that such tariffs would be exceedingly difficult to administer and therefore proposes across-the-board tariffs on miscreant countries.[343] This would require a change in WTO rules.

The question of how much of the burden in cutting emissions should be shouldered by developing countries is not straightforward. Most of the CO_2 currently in the atmosphere comes from industrialized countries and because of the stability of atmospheric CO_2, it does not disappear quickly. Hence, there is some validity in the argument made by developing countries that industrialized countries put the CO_2 in the atmosphere and so they should deal with it, but the lack of requirements for rapidly growing countries like India and China was one of the major stumbling blocks for a renewal of Kyoto. In general, poor countries have few resources to deal with emissions.

It seems unlikely that any serious reduction in emissions will occur because of the hopeless task of achieving binding international agreements. It was tempting to think, after the success of the Montreal Protocol on Substances that Deplete the Ozone Layer, that a similar accord was within reach for carbon emissions. In the early 1970s, chlorine compounds were discovered to be agents in destroying ozone, but not until 1984 did scientists confirm that the protective ozone layer was thinning in the atmosphere. Destruction of ozone in the upper atmosphere leads to increased exposure to ultraviolet radiation, resulting in increased risk of skin cancer and cataracts in people as well as relatively unknown effects on animals and plants, particularly on the phytoplankton in the Southern Ocean. Chlorofluorocarbons (CFCs) and other chemicals were implicated. These chemicals, developed in the 1930s, had desirable properties. They were non-flammable, non-toxic, and non-reactive with other chemicals, and they were also stable, ideal for use as coolants in refrigerators and air conditioners and as cleaning solvents. Following the discovery of a "hole" in the ozone over the Antarctic in 1985, it became obvious that action was needed, and in 1987 the Montreal Protocol was signed by twenty-four countries; it was entered into force on January 1, 1989.[344] The signatories agreed to reduce their use of CFCs, halons, carbon tetrachloride, and methyl chloroform according to an agreed-on timetable. In 2005, methyl bromide, a commonly used pesticide, was added to the list of chemicals to be phased out. There was a provision for trade sanctions for non-compliant countries. Developing countries were given an easier timetable, and a fund was established under the auspices of the United Nations to assist them in reducing their dependence on the targeted chemicals.

The Montreal Protocol has been a success. According to the latest assessment by the World Meteorological Association, "clear evidence" shows a decrease in the atmosphere of ozone-depleting chemicals and early signs of recovery of the ozone layer. Ozone layers over the Arctic and the Antarctic are no longer decreasing and are expected to increase to 1980 levels before mid-century.[345] However, the assessment raised concern that the replacements for CFCs—HCFCs (hydrochlorofluorocarbons) and HFCs (hydrofluorocarbons)—are powerful greenhouse gases.

The Montreal Protocol succeeded because CFCs can be controlled at relatively low cost, and Kyoto failed because the control of greenhouse gases is very costly. To stabilize emissions at a safe level would require immediate action. A 2015 study published in *Nature* shows that to have a 50 percent chance of achieving the goal to limit warming to 2 degrees Celsius above pre-industrial levels would mean that cumulative carbon emissions 2011–2050 must not exceed 1100 gigatonnes of CO_2.[346] Current reserves of fossil fuels contain approximately three times the allowable amount, which means that 33 percent of oil reserves, 50 percent of gas reserves and 80 percent of coal should be left in the ground. The authors of the study claim that this means there should be no further development of non-conventional and of Arctic resources. The impact of effective carbon reduction policies on the fossil fuel industries would indeed be calamitous adding to the difficulties in getting all countries to agree to cuts. Indeed, the Governor of the Bank of England has warned of the danger to the world economy of a "carbon bubble" leading to a major economic crash if the reserve assets of fossil fuel companies lose their value.[347] Piecemeal measures will not work in handling the world's climates. Given the present evidence, it is possible that sudden changes could quickly warm the world's climates by five degrees, with catastrophic effects on sea levels, agriculture, and biodiversity. Solutions proposed by engineers were previously dismissed on the grounds that they did not deal directly with the problem of emissions, they had unknown consequences, and they were likely to be expensive. But given the urgency and difficulties of reaching any type of comprehensive agreement on emissions, engineering measures should be considered.

Potential geoengineering solutions

As explained above, the world's climate is determined by the balance between the heat reaching the earth through solar radiation and the heat trapped by greenhouse gases. If we cannot come to a binding agreement to reduce greenhouse gases through economic or regulatory measures, the only alternatives (apart from doing nothing) are either to attempt to remove the CO_2 from the atmosphere or to control the amount of solar radiation that reaches the atmosphere. The Royal Society, in its 2009 report *Geoengineering the Climate: Science, Governance and Uncertainty*, outlines five methods of removing CO_2.[348] One is carbon sequestration—the establishment and preservation of carbon sinks—which means either afforestation (the planting of more trees which, when they grow, take up CO_2) or reducing deforestation. This is not usually considered to be geoengineering, but the report includes sequestration for completeness and comparison purposes. The second is the use of biomass for sequestration and as a carbon-neutral energy source. When biomass (e.g., falling trees and branches in the forest) is left to rot, CO_2 is released. This could be prevented by burying the debris in soil, or in the oceans, or by burning it to create biochar (charcoal) in which the CO_2 is more stable. After all, charcoal found on archeological sites has been stable for thousands of years. The *Fifth Assessment* Report promotes bioenergy carbon capture and storage which is growing biomass for sequestration and capturing the CO_2 when it is burnt. A third method is enhancement of natural weathering. Silicate minerals are the most common rocks on earth, and when they weather over time, the silicate reacts with the CO_2 and forms calcium carbonate and another silicate mineral (SiO_2)—a process that could be used to artificially bind the CO_2 by crushing large amounts of silicate rock. The crushed rock could be spread over soil, which would speed up the weathering, or it could be dumped it into oceans. Unfortunately, the take-up rate of CO_2 would be far slower than the rate at which it is added to the atmosphere, and the impact on soil chemistry and agriculture or on oceans is not well understood.[349] It would also involve large, energy-intensive mining operations.

A fourth method is to enhance oceanic take-up of CO_2 through fertilizing the oceans with iron to promote algal growth that, through photosynthesis, would absorb carbon. At the end of their life cycle. the algae would sink to the ocean floor and thereby sequester CO_2. But this method has been subject to many field trials, the results of which show that this is not a realistic option.[350] The CO_2 uptake is highly variable, the amount sequestered is small, and the ecological risks are considerable as the biogeochemistry of the oceans would be altered with unknown effects on ecosystems and fisheries. A final method is to capture CO_2 from the air. While there are pilot projects for removing CO_2 from emissions (carbon capture and sequestration), removal of existing gas from the air is a real challenge, even though there are some current industrial processes that do exactly that. It would involve the development of an industry to remove a cumulative 200 year buildup of emissions. The technology is being developed, but the costs are high. There is also the problem of safe disposal of the captured CO_2.

Air-capture schemes have attracted considerable attention because of financial involvement by some high-profile billionaires like Bill Gates.[351] Current versions of air-capture technology involve variations of forcing an airstream over absorbent material, which catches the CO_2. The material can be layers of Teflon covered with resin or ceramic blocks coated with chemicals that sucks up the CO_2. The captured CO_2 then has to be stored. The technology seems to work but the costs are high: the American Physical Society estimated the cost at $600 to $800 per tonne—considerably higher than carbon capture.[352] David Keith—whose methodology uses cheaper materials and does not require electricity from the grid—thinks it could be done for $150 per ton, which is still higher than carbon markets are likely to pay.[353] The problem, as with CCS technology, is to find a market for the stored CO_2. The Royal Society report concludes that all of these methods address the root cause of the problem of too much CO_2 and should probably be explored, but by themselves they will not solve the problem in a timely manner.

The Royal Society also examined the technology for limiting the amount of solar radiation that reaches the earth, known as solar radiation management. It could be as simple as increasing reflectivity on the ground by painting roofs white, planting crops that are reflective, or putting reflective covers on desert areas. But there are probably not enough roofs on earth to make a significant difference, and reflective crops may have an adverse impact on food production. Covering deserts would have unknown ecological consequences. Other suggestions range from artificially increasing cloud condensation nuclei by spraying saltwater vapour into the air from fleets of ships in order to increase marine cloud reflectivity to placing fifty-five thousand mirrors, each with an area of one hundred square metres, into random orbits around earth. We could also put a giant sun reflector on the moon or add trillions of reflecting disks manufactured from nearby asteroids between the moon and the earth. The costs of these types of futuristic measures would be enormous and probably politically unacceptable, and their impact on the world's climate would not be well understood. Proposals have also been put forward for increasing the ocean's albedo by creating small bubbles—*hydrosols*—that would have the advantage of mimicking natural processes and would not require adding chemicals to the atmospheres.[354] The technology is known, and it involves the expansion of air-saturated water through vortex nozzles. Ocean cargo and passenger ships could be retrofitted with microbubble generators. This technology is reversible and could be used locally to cool ocean temperatures.

We could also tamper directly with the atmosphere. Attempting to control weather has a long history in cloud-seeding, which usually involves adding silver iodide to clouds to promote rain.[355] It has been used with varying success since the 1950s in dry regions ranging from Texas in the United States to Israel, Russia, and Qatar. Most famously it was used around Beijing before the 2008 Olympics to clear the air from air pollution and to ensure that no rain fell during the opening and closing ceremonies.

Paul Crutzen, co-recipient of the 1995 Nobel Prize in Chemistry for work on atmospheric ozone, has suggested that an appropriate response to global warming may be the deliberate introduction of sulphur into the stratosphere, either with balloons or the use of artillery guns.[356] It has been known for some time that air pollution, particularly the emissions of SO_2 and other sulphate particles, helps to form clouds that act to reflect solar radiation back into space, a phenomenon known as cloud albedo. The advantage of using the stratosphere, which is between ten and fifty kilometres above the earth's surface, rather than the troposphere (the lower atmosphere) is that the particles would stay much longer and therefore fewer would be needed. If the sulphur injections were introduced near the equator, the particles would be spread toward the poles by prevailing winds and thus have a maximum impact on climate. It is estimated that the 1991 eruption of Mount Pinatubo in the Philippines had exactly that effect and resulted in a worldwide cooling of 0.5 degrees in the following year. Only a small amount of sulphur (one to two million tons per year, approximately equal to 2 to 4 percent of current sulphur emissions) would achieve the desired results at a relatively modest yearly cost of US$25 to $50 billion. The climatic effect would come within half a year, and the experiment could stop immediately if necessary. Crutzen also suggests that this type of engineering is not the desired option as it would not counter the acidification of the oceans, and there are too many unknowns. But the technology could possibly provide us with an escape route to avoid catastrophe if the climate starts to heat up very rapidly—say, 0.2 degrees per year. It would also have the additional benefit of shielding harmful UV radiation. Thus, cleaning up air pollution makes the atmosphere clearer but adds to warming. It is estimated that a complete cleanup of air pollution would increase warming on most continents by one degree and even more in the Arctic. This creates rather a dilemma for policy-makers. On the one hand, the presence of SO_2 in the atmosphere has been shown to have adverse effects on human health and on ecological systems through acid rain, but on the other hand it decreases global warming.

Other studies confirm that the cost of adding sulphur to the stratosphere compared with the potential benefits is very small. An earlier 1992 Panel on Policy Implications of Greenhouse Warming concluded that adding sulphur to the stratosphere would cost only pennies per tonne of CO_2 emissions reductions.[357] The Canadian scientist David Keith suggests that it may be possible to engineer nanoparticles that would be more effective than sulphate aerosols, and the cost of such a scheme would not be prohibitive.[358] The particles could be designed in such a way that they would not interfere with the ozone layer and be long-lasting, thus avoiding the need for continual replenishment. They could also be designed to move toward the poles, where the warming is most severe, and have minor effects on other parts of the planet. The benefits of such schemes include the control of global warming, the health improvement associated with decreased UV radiation, and the possible beneficial effects on agriculture by maintaining a high CO_2 level. The drawbacks include some destruction of ozone in the upper atmosphere, no solution to the problem of ocean acidification, and that fact that the aerosol injections must be continuously maintained.

There are also many unknown effects.[359] These include the impact on world precipitation patterns, which could adversely affect agriculture; the possible impact of the diffused light on ecosystems; and the possible impact on the El Niño–Southern Oscillation cycle which impacts weather patterns in the east-central Equatorial Pacific with unpredictable effects on climate.[360] There are also possible ecological effects from the effect of sulphates on the acidity of soils and fresh water bodies. Computer simulations show that solar radiation management would have a limited impact on temperatures and could permanently alter regional precipitation and temperature patterns. It would not be able to keep up with increasing temperature and therefore increasing efforts of geoengineering would be required over time. It is not possible to conduct large-scale experiments, and the small-scale experiments that have been suggested have been very controversial. For example, during the autumn of 2011, a group of scientists planned to float a balloon over Norfolk in England and put 150 litres of water into the air.[361] They had to abolish their plans because of mounting opposition from more than fifty organizations. Environmental organizations do not want to promote geoengineering of any kind; they see it as an easy way of avoiding cuts in the use of fossil fuels.

The two approaches to geoengineering—CO_2 capture and solar radiation management—create different problems. CO_2 removal is slow and expensive and, with the exception of iron fertilization of the oceans, has manageable environmental risks. On the other hand, solar radiation management is inexpensive and fast but has unknown environmental risks. The low costs associated with this type of geoengineering mean that any country could employ it without cooperation of other countries, which is clearly a potential problem. Before solar radiation management is employed even as a last resort, many policy issues would have to be sorted out, including the circumstances under which it should be deployed; the desirable temperature to be achieved; compensation, if there are gainers and losers from the policy; and arrangements for financing the whole effort.[362] Regulation is essential as some field research is already taking place.[363] The Royal Society report pointed out that "the greatest challenges to the successful deployment of geoengineering may be the social, ethical, legal and political issues associated with governance, rather than scientific and technical issues."[364] Additional testing is necessary as there are already studies claiming that geoengineering may not be very effective.[365] An international agreement is urgently needed on setting the limits for in-field testing of technologies, as such experiments have transboundary effects. There are many risks involved, including the environmental risk of proceeding, the moral hazard risk—geoengineering may discourage policies to reduce carbon—and risk associated with not doing the necessary research in case the earth is faced with a sudden climate catastrophe.

Iron fertilization of oceans falls under the London Convention on the Prevention of Marine Pollution by Dumping of Wastes and Other Matter and the London Protocol.[366] The International Maritime Organization, which administers the convention and the protocol, ruled that ocean fertilization, if it is not for legitimate scientific research, should not be permitted. This was followed by the call for a moratorium by the 2010 Conference of the Parties of the Biodiversity Convention (COP 10) "until the science is further developed particularly with respect to the risks to the environment and biodiversity in particular."[367] The need for more oversight and perhaps a test ban became clear in 2012 after it was discovered that an American businessman had persuaded the Haida Nation to allow for the dumping of one hundred tonnes of iron sulphate in the waters off the west coast of British Columbia.[368] The Haida Nation was told it would benefit because the iron sulphate would promote growth of algae, which would feed the salmon and thus boost the salmon population, and the businessman who sponsored the experiment believed he could sell carbon credits from the carbon sequestered. Because the science is not yet clear and the market for carbon offsets has collapsed, neither claim could be sustained. In 2010, a conference on climate engineering technologies was convened at Asilomar, California, to establish some principles, in hopes of repeating the success of the famous 1975 Asilomar Conference on Recombinant DNA, which established voluntary guidelines ensuring the safety of biotechnology research.[369] This proved too ambitious, the participants only able to agree to some general principles based on the Oxford Principles promoted by the Oxford Geoengineering Programme. According to these, geoengineering research should be regulated as a public good and must be in the public interest; decisions defining the extent of the public interest should be made with public consultation; all attempts at geoengineering research should be made public and results disseminated openly; there should be independent assessment of any research proposal; and governing arrangements should be clear prior to any actual use of technology.[370] Clearly, the world urgently needs effective rules and regulations governing issues related to geoengineering.

The way ahead

The most important question related to climate change is to decide how to proceed in view of all the uncertainties. Even though the science is not settled around many of the relevant questions, some facts are known. We do know climates can change radically, quickly, and unpredictably. We also know that the earth is currently warming, and significant warming will probably occur in our lifetimes. This is likely to cause the world considerable harm—harm that will disproportionately affect poor countries. People who deny this are ignoring reality or are so committed to their views that they will seize on any occurrence such as an unusual snowfall to deny the danger. In the words of the IPCC, it is extremely likely that current warming is caused by the buildup of CO_2 in the atmosphere, though other factors may be involved, in which case the CO_2 will exacerbate the warming. Therefore, policies aimed at reducing emissions and the use of fossil fuels are basically "no regrets" policies, particularly as they are likely to have beneficial effects apart from reductions in CO_2. These include cleaner air due to lower air pollution, less acid rain, fewer incidents of respiratory diseases and therefore a higher life expectancy, and less ocean acidification.

We take out insurance policies to protect ourselves against the small risk of our houses burning down. The preservation of the earth's ecosystems and our own well-being requires us to buy a similar insurance against severe climate change. Decreases in coal mining and a slowing of the development of non-conventional oil would also have beneficial effects in terms of less destruction of land and waterways. Gradual shifts toward cleaner energy can be encouraged through elimination of all subsidies to consumption and production of fossil fuels in rich and poor countries. Current low fossil fuel prices will encourage the use of more fossil fuels, which is not desirable. The introduction of effective carbon taxes or a cap-and-trade system is an essential part of climate policy as these would increase the price of all products that use fossil fuels in their production. As CO_2 emissions respect no boundaries, all countries should take part, but it now seems clear that a binding international agreement is unlikely. Without such an agreement, the question arises of how to deal with countries that do not implement policies to control emissions. It would be unacceptable to go to war against large emitters. The only other possibility is to employ trade sanctions.

Carbon taxes, cap and trade, elimination of subsidies to fossil fuels, effective regulations, and the halt of deforestation can reduce emissions significantly. However, in the current political climate, carbon pricing seems unlikely to be adopted in most countries. A carbon tax would be more acceptable if the alternative to fossil fuels was cheaper. For this reason, a good policy must include measures to decrease the cost of renewable energy through increased subsidies to energy research and development. Unless there is concerted action now to move toward a carbon-free economy, it is doubtful we will be able to reduce emissions at a level that climate scientists regard as safe. Industry, agriculture, and transportation must change; electricity must be produced from nuclear or renewable energy. If a large-scale shift away from fossil fuels cannot be achieved sufficiently quickly to avoid catastrophe, we should be prepared to consider geo-engineering measures as a last resort—measures that require an international agreement or convention on how they should be used, when they should be used, and who should use them. This will be a difficult task. The next chapter will deal with the prospects of zero-carbon technologies.

5

Nuclear Power, Hydrogen, and Renewable Energy Resources

Nuclear power. Hydrogen. Hydro power. Wind power. Solar energy. Geothermal heat. Biomass. Alternative energy for transportation. Can we get to a zero-carbon economy?

Mitigation of climate change requires a shift from fossil fuels to renewable energy. Because of our existing energy infrastructure is built around the use of fossil fuels, any rapid change is not possible. Switching to natural gas may be a good short-term solution as gas is cleaner than oil and coal, and there appears to be plenty of it, especially following the recent discovery of technology that can be used to extract large amounts of shale gas. But natural gas is not carbon free, and in North America the price is currently so low that it may actually encourage the use of more fossil-fuel-based energy. Moreover, no infrastructure is in place to support the widespread use of natural gas in transportation, and the full environmental effects of the exploitation of shale gas are not yet known. As coal and natural gas are plentiful and cheap, any switch to renewable resources will not occur unless facilitated by government subsidies and by effective carbon pricing. Table 3.1 (Chapter 3) showed that the largest primary energy sources are oil with a share of 31 percent of total energy use, followed by coal at 29 percent, natural gas at 21 percent, nuclear power at 5 percent, and renewables—hydro, biofuels, solar, wind, geothermal—at 14 percent. Such figures show the enormous challenge of raising the current share of renewables and nuclear power from 18 percent to 100 percent, not over centuries, but over decades, especially considering the particular difficulties of developing new technologies in the transport sector. At present, the transportation of people and goods is almost entirely dependent on oil and accounts for approximately 60 percent of total oil use.

Another problem lies in the growth of electricity consumption. While world energy consumption rose at an annual rate of 2.4 percent between 2003 and 2013, electricity consumption increased at 3.0 percent per year—a trend that is expected to continue with increased use of electric cars.[371] While the total consumption of energy per household has been declining in the United States, the electricity needed for appliances, electronics and lighting keeps increasing, and by 2009 it had reached 34.6 percent of total energy demand (compared to 24 percent in 1993) and 67 percent of total electricity demand.[372] Appliances have become more efficient, but the average household has more devices requiring electricity. Power is also consumed by telephone lines, routers, cables, modems, and battery chargers. The faster electronic items become, the more power they consume.

Most electricity is currently generated from hydro and nuclear power, coal, and gas. Table 5.1, which itemizes the sources of electricity in 2012 compared with 1973, shows nuclear power, coal, gas and other sources (renewable and biomass) growing at the expense of oil and hydro power. The challenge is to move from the current situation where only 33 percent of electricity is generated by renewable energy sources and nuclear power, to a situation where they generate 100 percent. The share of renewables is increasing very slowly, reflecting the fact that electricity generation by renewables is expensive compared with generation by coal and natural gas.

A large coal-fired station uses around ten thousand tonnes of coal per day, which, at a price of $75 per ton, results in a daily cost of $750,000. In contrast, electricity generated by wind, solar, geothermal, and hydro power has no fuel costs. Similarly, a nuclear generating station has very low fuel costs because

Table 5.1. World electricity generation by fuel, 1973 and 2012 (percentage of total)

	1973	2012
Nuclear	3.3	10.9
Hydro	21.0	16.2
Natural Gas	12.1	22.5
Oil	24.7	5.0
Coal	38.3	40.4
Renewables	0.6	5.6

Source: International Energy Agency, *Key World Energy Statistics, 2014*. The table is identical to Table 3.2 in Chapter 3.

Table 5.2. Average US comparative electricity generating costs for plants entering service in 2018

Power source	Cents/kilowatt hours	Advantages	Disadvantages
Coal	10–12	Vast supply, inexpensive.	Substantial carbon emissions from power stations. Coal mining hazardous.
Coal with CCS	13.5	Vast supply, expensive, no emissions.	Probably not possible to use the technology on a scale sufficient to make a difference.
Conventional natural gas	6.7	Vast supply, inexpensive, relatively low emissions.	Not emission free.
Natural gas, advanced technologies	6.5–10.4	Vast supply, inexpensive, relatively low emissions.	Not emission free. Possible environmental hazards of fracking.
Natural gas with CCS	9.3	Vast supply, no emissions.	Probably not possible to use the technology on a scale sufficient to make a difference.
Advanced nuclear	10.8	Technology allows for large supply. No emissions.	Potentially costly. Potential radiation hazards associated with waste.
Geothermal	9.0	No emissions.	Scarcity of suitable sites.
Biomass	11.1	Potential reductions in emissions depend on the source.	Can have negative effects on food production and on the environment.
Wind	8.6	No emissions, technology mature, relatively low cost.	Power source intermittent. Negative effects on people if sited near habitation.
Offshore wind	22.1	No emissions, technology mature, relatively high cost.	Power source intermittent.
Solar photovoltaic	14.4	No emissions, technology mature, costs are falling.	Power source intermittent. Power stations require large areas of land.
Solar thermal	26.2	No emissions, technology developing, high costs. Not suitable in cold climates.	Needs a large amount of water. Power stations require large areas of land.
Hydro	9.3	Can be emissions free depending on the siting of dams. New technology associated with freestanding turbines.	Traditional dams are a potential source of greenhouse gases. Can have large, negative environmental and social effects.

Source: US Energy Information Administration, *Levelized Cost of New Generation Resources in the Annual Energy Outlook, 2013*. www.eia.gov/forecasts/aeo/er/electricity_generation.cfm. The listed advantages and disadvantages are a summary of the information provided in this chapter. The technology may be emissions free, while the making of the associated equipment (e.g., reactors, turbines, solar panels) is not.

it needs little uranium to operate. But the capital costs for renewable energy on a large scale are very high; therefore, per-unit costs can only decrease if electricity output is large and reliable. For wind and solar energy, the cost of the backup electricity must also be factored into cost calculations, as no electricity is generated when the sun does not shine or the wind does not blow. For these reasons, cost comparisons are difficult to make. The accepted measure is the *levelized cost of electricity*, defined as the price at which electricity would have to be sold for the generating station to break even over its lifetime. Much of the competitiveness of renewable energy and nuclear power depends on whether there is a carbon tax. Coal-fired stations emit 1.5 to 3.5 tonnes of CO_2 per tonne of coal.[373] A modest carbon tax of $30 per ton of CO_2 would add $45 to $105 per ton to the cost of coal, which could more than double electricity prices from conventional coal-fired stations.[374] Table 5.2 shows levelized cost comparisons for plants expected to enter service in the United States in 2018, assuming no carbon taxes, tax credits or subsidies. These are average levelized costs in the United States and therefore may not be representative for other regions of the world with different local costs and local conditions for generating renewable energy, but most estimates for other countries also show that coal is relatively cheap, wind is almost competitive with coal, nuclear is more expensive than coal, and solar power is (so far) the most expensive alternative.

This chapter examines the advantages and disadvantages of the various non-fossil options of generating electricity, the options for developing emissions-free transportation, and the likelihood that the world can move away from fossil fuels.

Nuclear energy

Nuclear energy must be considered an option in designing a zero-carbon world even though the construction of the plants and the mining of uranium are not emissions free. Nuclear power can be generated either through fusion or fission. The former has yet to be developed for commercial purposes. It involves fusing two light atomic nuclei into one heavy nucleus, which generates an uncontrolled explosion as exemplified by the hydrogen bomb. The problem lies in finding a technology that can harness this huge amount of energy—a task that has so far proven impossible despite years of scientific work. A group of scientists in California claims to be moving closer to creating fusion energy, with the help of extremely powerful lasers that heat a fuel pellet containing hydrogen.[375] This group believes it can build a prototype generating station within a decade. This is not the first time that a "revolutionary" breakthrough has been announced. Even if this group is successful, it will probably be a long time before fusion can be an alternative energy source, as each fuel pellet costs up to $100,000; the costs have to come down to a few cents per pellet for the process to be commercially viable.

Nuclear fission, on the other hand, is a well-known technology. It involves the splitting of a heavy nucleus of uranium (U-235) into two, which sets off a chain reaction generating a large amount of heat. The heat can be used to drive steam turbines to generate electricity. One gram of U-235 packs as much energy as three tonnes of coal.[376] Uranium is a common mineral found in low concentrations in most rocks, soil, and seawater. Large minable deposits occur in Canada, Russia, and Australia, with a current reserve-production ratio of about one hundred years. The mineral has six isotopes, the most common being U-238 (about 99.2 percent of naturally occurring uranium) followed by U-235 (virtually all of the remainder). Uranium used in reactors has to be enriched in a way that separates the isotopes, using technologically advanced gas-centrifuge processes, so that it contains 3 to 4 percent of U-235, and weapons-grade uranium has to be further enriched to reach a U-235 content of 90 percent.

There are five types of nuclear power stations—light-water reactors, heavy-water reactors, gas-cooled reactors, graphite-moderated boiling-water reactors, and fast-breeder reactors—each defined by its embedded technology.[377] Eighty percent of all nuclear stations are light-water reactors using enriched uranium as feedstock, combined with ordinary water. Heavy-water reactors use natural uranium in combination with heavy water (deuterium). Based on technology developed in Canada, these reactors are known as the CANDU (Canada deuterium uranium) reactors, and operate in India, South Korea, Pakistan, and Romania as well as in Canada. Gas-cooled reactors are used only in the United Kingdom, while graphite-moderated boiling-water reactors (including the ill-fated Chernobyl reactor) were developed in Russia. Breeder reactors, which can extract almost all the energy contained in low-grade uranium, were at one time thought to offer a solution to the problem of finding enough high-grade uranium, especially since they can also use reprocessed waste from conventional reactors. However, they are expensive and are problematic because they both use and produce plutonium, a component necessary for the manufacture of nuclear weapons. India, Russia, Japan, and China still have some in operation, but other countries such as France and Germany closed theirs down. CANDU reactors also generate plutonium as a by-product. It is commonly believed that plutonium from a CANDU reactor made it possible for India to build its first nuclear bomb.[378]

Nuclear power plants began to be built in the 1950s. Their number increased steadily until the late 1980s, at which point construction levelled off. It was widely believed that nuclear power offered a cheap, clean, long-term solution to the world's energy problems, with some countries investing heavily in nuclear capacity. In France and Sweden, nuclear power generates 78 and 52 percent of electricity respectively, compared with a world average of 16 percent. But for the last thirty years, there has been little expansion in nuclear capacity. In Sweden, for example, people voted in a 1980 referendum to start decommissioning its nuclear power stations. The main reasons for the halt in construction were increased safety concerns and accelerating capital and operating costs.

Before 1986, the nuclear industry argued that nuclear power had a safety record far more impressive than coal-powered plants, despite a reactor-core near meltdown at the Three Mile Island plant in Harrisburg 1979—an event resulting from a failure of the cooling mechanism. In a core meltdown, the nuclear fuel (either uranium or plutonium) overheats and melts, releasing highly radioactive materials both in the atmosphere and the surrounding groundwater. The nuclear industry argued that nuclear power had never killed anyone, but in 1986 a fatal core meltdown occurred at Chernobyl in Ukraine. Though the official death toll was only thirty-one, unofficial estimates put the real death toll up to a million, counting the longer-term impact on mortality of the people living near the plant.[379] However, this was a gross exaggeration, and twenty-five years later there is still no agreement about how many died, apart from twenty-eight victims of acute radiation syndrome and fifteen cases of fatal thyroid cancer.[380] A survey of medical studies has shown that a large increase occurred in non-fatal thyroid cancer among those exposed to radiation in childhood or adolescence, but no increase could be discerned in other cancers.[381]

Not surprisingly, these accidents caused a general backlash against nuclear power and led to more stringent safety regulations that pushed up the costs of building and operating nuclear stations. But a possible deathblow to nuclear power came in 2011, when a massive earthquake and tsunami hit the east coast of Japan, causing huge fatalities and injuries. The earthquake itself did not damage the Fukushima Daiichi nuclear station, but the fourteen-metre tsunami did (Figure 5.1). As expected, the reactors shut down after the quake hit, leaving the place without electricity. With unexpectedly high waves, the quake-induced tsunami flooded the station and damaged the backup power designed to keep the pumps working to cool the reactors. This led to a full nuclear meltdown of three of the six reactors, which took months to bring under control, and at the time of writing (2015), the plant was still leaking highly radioactive water into the groundwater and the ocean. In retrospect, the meltdown—which in itself caused no fatalities—could have led to a nuclear disaster, probably leading to the full evacuation of Tokyo, had it not been for the dedicated effort of the plant manager and his staff in pouring seawater on the reactors to cool them. The reaction to this latest accident was immediate. Not only did Japan shut down its remaining reactors but so did Germany, which ordered the closing of seven nuclear power plants three days after the accident. This was followed up by an order to close all its plants by 2022. Most other countries with nuclear power ordered increased safety inspections of the plants.

Nuclear plants are expensive to build and to run. The costs of a new nuclear plant include not only the capital cost and the costs of operation maintenance and fuel, but also the cost of decommissioning, which involves dismantling or entombment of the facilities at the end of their life cycle.[382] Depending on the regulatory policies of the government in question, the capital costs are very high—far higher than for coal- and gas-fired stations. Given these high costs, maintaining low per-unit generation costs requires that the reactors operate at

Figure 5.1. The damaged Fukushima Daiichi Reactor Unit 3. Credit: Giovanni Verlini and IEAE, www. flickr.com.

full capacity. At one stage, nuclear power stations were notoriously unreliable with long downtimes. However, between 1990 and 2005 the average capacity factor for nuclear plants increased from 70 to 80 percent with an even larger jump in the United States from 66 to 90 percent.[383] International Energy Agency (IEA) statistics show that by 2007, the costs of nuclear power were only slightly higher than those of coal- or natural-gas-fired stations and that existing reactors could operate profitably. The IEA argues that a carbon tax as low as $10 to $25 per tonne of CO_2 would make nuclear power fully competitive with fossil fuels and that if combined with public acceptance, a $25 carbon tax could raise nuclear power's share in electricity generation from the current 13 percent to 20 percent.[384] After Fukushima, however, this seems unlikely to happen.

Handling nuclear waste, which consists of uranium, fission fragments, and long-lived components, is a real problem.[385] Japan and France reprocess their spent nuclear fuel, which reduces the toxicity and the volume of waste. The reprocessing separates uranium from plutonium, unfortunately creating a ready source of materials for nuclear weapons. The United States and other countries are currently developing a new generation of reactors capable of burning waste—integral fast reactors. The uranium that makes up 95 percent of the waste is similar to the ore found in mines and thus not very hazardous. It can be enriched for further use or even returned to the mines from where it was extracted. About 4 percent of the waste consists of fission fragments that are highly radioactive but lose their radioactivity in a couple of hundred years: this can be contained until no longer dangerous. The most problematic is the remaining 1 percent consisting of plutonium and lesser-known elements such as americium, neptunium, and curium that remain hazardous for well over two hundred thousand years. Only two ways of dealing with this waste are known: either isolating the material or reprocessing it into shorter-lived radioactive materials.

The International Atomic Energy Agency (IAEA) makes a distinction between storage and disposal.[386] Storage, which requires active surveillance and maintenance, is temporary, while disposal is considered permanent. With disposal there is no intention to retrieve the material, and active controls are not necessary. The main waste elements are strontium and cesium that become harmless after about a millennium. Other elements remain dangerous for hundreds of thousands of years. Up to 99 percent of all radioactive waste comes from spent fuel rods. They have to be stored for three to five years in pools of water filled with boric acid, after which they are encased dry in reinforced casts surrounded by suitable materials. It is not easy to guarantee safe storage even for a century, let alone a hundred thousand years, and it is usually agreed that the waste has to be disposed of. Disposal at sea is a possibility, particularly if it can be done at such depth below the ocean floor that the waste is carried to the molten mantel of the earth, where it would be absorbed. However, currently sea disposal is illegal under the United Nations Law of the Sea Convention and so is not considered as an alternative. Space disposal is also possible though regarded as too hazardous because of the potential catastrophic consequences if the launch into space failed. Storage in stable underground geological formations is thought to be the only viable alternative, and is recommended by the IAEA. Only Sweden and Finland are actively involved in setting up such storage sites. The spent fuel rods must first be encapsulated in corrosion-resistant copper, and then be placed under approximately five hundred metres of rock surrounded by bentonite clay to seal the rock should cracks occur. There is now some doubt about the safety of this method after it was pointed out that copper canons from the sunken Swedish galleon WASA showed signs of corrosion after having been on the seabed in an oxygen-free environment for just three hundred years.[387] While the United States was intent on developing a large geological storage facility at the Yucca Mountain in Nevada, the project was halted in 2010 by the Obama administration because of local opposition.

If nuclear waste is buried in bedrock, how can future generations be warned about the danger? This question has generated a great deal of debate, as our generation has no idea what people will be like or what language they will speak, say, fifty thousand years from now. What is the most effective way of communicating danger? Is it through pictures of skulls or screaming faces?[388] Warning signs will not necessarily deter intruders; rather, the signs might entice the curious to start digging—rumours of curses did not stop archeologists from excavating the ancient tombs of the pharaohs. Some argue the best action may be to seal off the containment bunkers without warning signs and assume that if a future civilization finds the bunker it would be advanced enough to be able to identify what it contains. A more primitive civilization would not have the technology to get inside. The plan for the failed Yucca Mountain facility included large markers at its entry with warnings in Arabic, Chinese, English, Spanish, French, and Russian, with pictures as a backup.

Apart from the problematic handling of nuclear wastes, other hazards of nuclear power include the danger of nuclear weapons or waste falling into terrorist hands, and that nuclear power contributes to the proliferation of nuclear weapons. If suicide bombers were to get hold of waste or to acquire spent fuel on its way to reprocessing, they could create a terrifying carnage, spreading the waste over large areas using common explosives. The technology for making nuclear bombs is not very complicated, as became apparent in 1977 when a Princeton undergraduate wrote a term paper on how to make a workable nuclear bomb using information gleaned from academic journals. Plutonium is the main raw material, which can be manufactured from reprocessed wastes from conventional nuclear power stations. One conventional reactor can produce enough raw materials to make 330 pounds of plutonium, enough to make fifteen bombs of Hiroshima strength. The only protection involves very strong safeguards and agreements to control the spread of nuclear weapons.

Heightened concern over the spread of nuclear weapons led to the UN's formation of the International Atomic Energy Agency (IAEA) in 1957 under the rubric "Atoms for Peace."[389] The objective of the IAEA is to promote atomic energy and to ensure that any nuclear assistance provided is not used for military purposes. Years of negotiations resulted in the 1970 Treaty on the Non-Proliferation of Nuclear Weapons. This treaty essentially froze the number of countries with nuclear weapons to China, Russia, United Kingdom, France, and the United States. All other countries were required to forego nuclear weapons and to negotiate safeguard agreements with the IAEA. Following the discovery in 1991 of Iraq's secret nuclear weapons program, there was a call for stronger safeguards. In 1996, the UN General Assembly approved a comprehensive test-ban treaty, and it was now accepted that the IAEA should deal with problems left over from the nuclear arms race such as the storage of radioactive materials from decommissioned nuclear weapons.[390]

But serious problems remain. India, Pakistan, North Korea, and Israel have not signed the Nuclear Non-Proliferation Treaty. The first three countries are known to have nuclear weapons, and Israel is widely believed to possess them. Iran is currently accused of building nuclear weapons, though it maintains that all its nuclear technology is for civilian purposes. It is also likely that Libya and Syria acquired the technology for nuclear warheads. There seems to be a large underground network involved in smuggling technology and nuclear materials.[391] In 2005, US president George W. Bush and the director of IAEA Mohamed ElBaradei jointly proposed that a select number of countries, known as supplier countries, should specialize in both the making of nuclear fuel and the reprocessing and disposal of the spent fuel. Other countries, known as user countries, should then be able to buy all their fuel from the supplier countries and return the spent fuel to the same countries.[392] If this could be agreed to, it would result in a much safer way of handling the fuel, as oversight would be easier and cheaper given the substantial economies that could be gained in building large reprocessing and storage facilities. But the proposal was not approved by US Congress. At a nuclear security summit called by President Obama in 2010, forty-seven participating countries agreed to promote the adoption of nuclear reactors that use low-enriched uranium rather than the highly enriched uranium suitable for weapons. Some countries, including Canada, Mexico, Chile, and the old Soviet republics of Kazakhstan and Ukraine, promised to dispose of weapons-grade uranium following an earlier commitment by the United States and Russia to get rid of sixty-eight tons of weapons-grade plutonium.[393]

Until the Fukushima disaster, interest in nuclear power was briefly revived as a partial solution to climate change. France, the country most heavily reliant on nuclear energy, had a 2011 carbon intensity of 0.167 kilograms of CO_2 per dollar GDP compared with the world average of 0.620 kg.[394] If the world as a whole generated the same proportion of its electricity by nuclear power as France, yearly carbon emissions would be cut by a considerable amount. Currently 435 reactors are operating with an additional 65 under construction, 165 in the planning stage, and another 331 under discussion (Table 5.3). In 2008,

Table 5.3. Number of nuclear reactors operating, under construction, planned, and proposed; 2015

Country	Number of reactors in operation	Number of reactors under construction	Number of reactors on order or planned	Number of reactors proposed
Canada	19	0	2	3
China	26	23	45	142
France	58	1	1	1
India	14	6	22	35
Japan	43	3	9	3
South Korea	24	4	8	0
Russia	34	9	31	18
Sweden	10	0	0	0
Ukraine	15	0	2	11
United Kingdom	16	0	4	9
United States	99	5	5	17
Others	77	14	36	92
World	**435**	**65**	**165**	**331**

Source: Extracted from World Nuclear Power Reactors & Uranium Requirements, www.world-nuclear.org/info/reactors.html.
Note: only countries currently operating ten reactors or more are included.

Britain announced permission for eighteen new nuclear sites. In eastern Europe, Slovakia, Romania, Hungary, Bulgaria, Lithuania, Poland, Latvia, and Estonia have announced plans for expansion, as have India, Russia, and China. China, with twenty-six reactors, has plans to build an additional 187. The American government is offering major subsidies: loan guarantees of up to 80 percent of the building costs, operating subsidies of $125 million per year over eight years, $2.7 billion in research and development, $1.3 billion in decommissioning relief, and a cap on liability in case of an accident.[395] Without subsidies, it is unlikely that any will be built. Except in China, most of the planned expansions were put on hold following the accident.[396]

Hydrogen

"While the fossil-fuel era is entering its sunset years, a new energy regime is being born that has the potential to remake civilization along radical new lines," said Jeremy Rifkin, referring to hydrogen energy.[397] Jules Verne is often cited as the first to realize the alleged potential of hydrogen in solving the world's energy problems. In his book *The Mysterious Island*, he wrote, "I believe that water will one day be employed as fuel, that hydrogen and oxygen which constitute it, used singly or together, will furnish an inexhaustible source of heat and light."[398] These are vastly exaggerated claims. Indeed, it is true that when hydrogen is oxidized, it releases energy and water vapour, and in theory the supply is inexhaustible as it makes up 75 percent of the mass of the universe. But pure hydrogen is not found on earth because it is too light to be held in by gravity. It is therefore a secondary energy source, not a primary energy source like coal or oil. It is usually produced from water at high temperatures using methane, oil, or coal. Less commonly, it can be generated through electrolysis by passing a current between two electrodes in water. Bubbles of oxygen rise from the positive electrode, and hydrogen from the negative electrode.[399] While the use of hydrogen as a fuel is emission free, its production is not, unless the energy used in making it is generated from renewable sources. Most of the hydrogen produced is used for making ammonia for fertilizer production. The other major use is in upgrading heavy oil to lighter compounds through the process of hydrocracking. Before recent health scares about the adverse effects of hydrogenated fats, it was also widely used in the food industry to transform liquid fats into solids, suitable for margarine production.

Hydrogen is often associated with explosions: the hydrogen bomb (H-bomb) and the airship Hindenburg. Compared with atomic bombs, which rely on fission, the hydrogen bomb relies on fusion of two hydrogen isotopes. Because of the large amount of energy released, the bombs are often referred to as thermonuclear bombs. The first was tested in 1952 by the United States, and within a few years all of the five nuclear powers of that era had them. The ill-fated Hindenburg was a dirigible airship designed with an outer aluminum frame filled with hydrogen. It burst into flames in 1937, on its way from Frankfurt, Germany, to New Jersey in the United States. The accident happened just above its planned landing spot, and thirty-five people lost their lives in the spectacular fire. No hydrogen airships have been built since.

Because it is not a source of pollution, hydrogen is promoted as a desirable energy source for power generation and for transport. Considerable excitement has been generated by the development of fuel cells that combine hydrogen and oxygen to generate electricity with higher efficiency than the combustion of plain hydrogen. The use of fuel cells in transportation is more efficient than traditional combustion engines. But while the engines may be efficient, their energy consumption is not, because the manufacture of hydrogen with current technology is extremely wasteful. For example, hydrogen-powered vehicles such as the BMW Hydrogen 7 use 254 kilowatt hours per one hundred kilometres compared with the average fossil-fuel car, which uses eighty kWh, and electric vehicles, which use the six to twenty kWh.[400] Hydrogen buses require 80 to 200 percent more energy than standard diesel buses. Apart from this energy waste, four additional problems remain in using hydrogen for transportation: the high cost of fuel cells; the problem of storage, as the tanks required are three to four times larger than normal fuel tanks; the absence of an infrastructure of fuel stations; and the concern over safety of compressed hydrogen, as it is explosive. If an emissions-free technology becomes available to manufacture hydrogen at low cost, hydrogen could indeed offer a viable solution to the world's energy problems as the cost of fuel cells will likely come down.

Hydro power

Hydroelectrically generated electricity, obtained by conversion of water energy using turbines, is a familiar source of electricity, with the first hydro power plant built in Wisconsin in 1882. Most hydroelectricity is generated from large plants capable of producing seven hundred or more gigawatts (GW) of electricity.[401] Large hydro plants involve dams and reservoirs, while small ones (typically producing less than ten megawatts) usually do not. The capacity utilization of generating stations is on average only 40 to 45 percent, as the flow-through rate of the water and therefore the ability to generate electricity depends on the availability of water. Most hydro developments have taken place in industrialized countries. For example, New Zealand, Norway, Brazil, Switzerland, and Canada rely to a large extent on hydro. In poor countries, such developments have largely been neglected due to the very high capital costs involved. In particular, there is undeveloped hydro potential in Asia and in South America.

The World Bank was a major source of funding for most big hydro dams in developing countries during the latter part of the twentieth century, and as a result was the subject of much criticism because large-scale hydroelectricity was no longer considered to be an environmentally and socially sound investment. For example, the World Bank was initially involved in financing the controversial Three Gorges Dam in China, but it withdrew from the project because of pressures from environmental groups. Economist Kenneth Boulding summarized the issues when he wrote the "Ballad of Ecological Awareness":[402]

> The cost of building dams is always underestimated—
> There's erosion of the delta that the river has created,
> There's fertile soil below the dam that's likely to be looted,
>
> And the tangled mat of forest that has got to be uprooted.
> There's the breaking up of cultures with old haunts and habits loss,
> There's the education program that just doesn't come across,
> And the wasted fruits of progress that are seldom much enjoyed
> By expelled subsistence farmers who are urban unemployed.

Indeed, a study of the impact of large dams in India showed that agricultural production increased but so did poverty.[403] While the actual generation of electricity is emissions free, the flooding and building of dams are not. According to an article in *New Scientist*, the greenhouse emissions from a dam in Brazil were estimated to be more than three and a half times what would have been produced by the equivalent oil-fired generating station.[404] Large amounts of carbon are tied up in trees and plants that are released into the atmosphere when they decay. When a dam is operational, plant materials sink to the bottom, creating methane—a far more powerful greenhouse gas than CO_2—which is released when the water hits the turbines. Because of the changing water levels, there is a continual supply of decaying materials. This is particularly problematic in the tropics, where the reservoirs have high organic-matter content and where temperatures are high both in the water and in sediments, encouraging decomposition and formation of greenhouse gases.[405] The problems with large hydro developments may be solved by a promising new technology involving freestanding underwater turbines that do not require dams—but the absence of dams implies that water supply will be more variable, hence this type of technology may not be suitable to sites where the water flow is very variable.[406] Dams also interfere with fish migration and interrupt the flows of water and sediment so necessary for ecosystem service. However, many environmental issues are not clear-cut. Not all hydro dams are "bad" since they can provide considerable benefits to the local population in terms of employment, adequate irrigation, and food security in the regions. Recent research on the impacts of the siting of dams on biodiversity calls for a more nuanced view.[407] The World Bank has reversed its stance and is now promoting hydro power as a crucial component of low-carbon development.[408]

In theory, a vast amount of energy is locked up in oceans. In Britain, it is estimated that up to 20 percent of energy could come from the sea.[409] Wave energy is of course intermittent. Waves are generated in open water if the wind speed exceeds 0.5 metres per second (m/s). The stronger the wind, the longer it blows, and the larger the expanse of water, the higher will be the waves.[410] Since the prevailing winds are westerlies over the middle latitudes of the Atlantic and the Pacific, there should be considerable potential for wave energy on both the Atlantic coast of western Europe and the Pacific coast of North America. The southern parts of Australia and southern Africa also have potential. At the present time, only a handful of experimental plants are in operation, including the

Figure 5.2. *The Pelamis Wave Power prototype. Source: Wikimedia Commons.*

Pelamis wave-energy collector employed off the coast of Portugal (Figure 5.2). It looks like a giant semi-submerged segmented sea snake with the head placed against the incoming waves. The wave motions drive the electricity generators.

Tidal power can be harnessed by building dams across tidal basins or by employing freestanding tidal-current turbines.[411] Tidal power stations using dams have been in operation for over forty years in China, Russia, and France. The largest of these stations is in the Rance estuary in northern France, built in 1966. The technology is mature and reliable, but building dams is expensive and there may be adverse environmental effects through changes in the flow of tidal currents, which may affect marine life and changes in the water quality in the basins through increased sedimentation and turbidity. Tidal power can also be harnessed by building tidal farms similar to wind farms, where power is generated by ocean currents associated with incoming and outgoing tides. In total, fourteen countries operate wave or tidal power stations, most on a small scale, and most on an experimental basis. Norway and the United Kingdom are the only countries, so far, with operating tidal farms. Compared with wave power, tidal power is predictable while wave power is not. The current has to be a minimum of 2.5 m/s, and many suitable sites exist, for example at Gibraltar, the Strait of Messina, the Bay of Fundy, the Straits of Magellan and the English Channel. However, the technology is not mature and considerable installation challenges remain. Because stresses are much higher due to the higher density of water, the materials used have to be very strong compared with the material used in wind turbines. Political ramifications must also be considered in installing tidal farms in some of the world's main shipping lanes. Tidal power can be generated at half the cost of wave power, but neither tidal nor wave energy is currently competitive with coal, with or without carbon capture and storage.[412]

Wind power

Wind energy has been used for thousands of years in transportation (sailing ships) and for milling and irrigation (windmills). The first wind-driven electric generators were built in the late nineteenth century, but subsequently not much interest was taken in wind power until the energy crisis of the 1970s. This led to large investments in wind turbines, with an annual growth of approximately 30 percent throughout the late 1990s, and investments continue to expand at a high rate. Just five GW in 1995, wind capacity had grown to approximately 319 GW by 2013—a spectacular increase, but the rate of growth appears to be slowing, partly because of increased resistance to expansion in some countries.[413] Twenty-nine countries have active wind-power programs, the early leaders of which were Denmark and Germany. In Denmark, wind power already accounts for almost 22 percent of electricity generation, compared with over 17 percent in Portugal, 16 percent in Spain, and 10 percent in Ireland. However, following an aggressive program of investment in wind power, the leader in terms of total installed capacity is now China, followed by the United States and Germany (Table 5.4).

Table 5.4. Installed solar and wind capacity as a percentage of total world capacity, 2012

Country	Solar voltaic capacity	Wind turbine capacity
Germany	32.6	11.0
Italy	16.2	2.8
United States	7.3	21.2
Spain	4.5	7.9
China	8.3	26.5
Japan	6.9	0.9
Others	24.2	29.7
Total	100	100

Source: BP Statistical Review of World Energy, 2013.

With improved technology and the economies of scale achieved in building larger units, the costs of wind power have declined substantially. In general, offshore winds are stronger; thus many wind turbines are sited at sea. However, capital costs at sea are higher—$4,000 per kW capacity compared with $2,000 per kW onshore—and thus only a small fraction of the total capacity is offshore. Also, offshore turbines suffer breakdowns more often because of the salt corrosion. On the other hand, offshore locations allow turbines to be sited closer to major population centres, which lowers transmission costs. According to Table 5.1, the average cost of planned wind-generated electricity in the United States is 8.6 cents per kWh. However, other sources claim it is only four to seven cents per kWh, making it very competitive with coal-fired plants.[414] As is true for most new technologies, there is a relatively steep learning curve, and it is expected that the cost per kWh may reach three cents per kWh, but any cost calculation is highly sensitive to the average wind speed in an area.

However, the problem with wind power, as with solar power, is that the power source is intermittent. At times, the sun does not shine and the wind does not blow. The full capacity of a wind generator is reached only 20 to 30 percent of the time compared with 90 percent capacity for coal plants. This means backup power is necessary and electricity generation cannot entirely rely on wind power. Advocates argue that if wind farms are located in many different areas, wind will always be present somewhere. In Denmark's case, when winds are excessively strong, cheap surplus electricity is exported to other parts of Europe, but when wind is not blowing, electricity is imported at high prices. If imports are not possible, electricity output from existing nuclear stations or from coal-fired stations would have to be increased to take up the slack, which may not be possible. If hydro power is available, it can be switched on and off with the press of a button, but this is more difficult with nuclear or coal-fired stations. It would not be in the interest of a power company to voluntarily reduce its baseload output to accommodate solar or wind power or to increase the output when the power from the other sources is not forthcoming. Having discarded nuclear power after the Fukushima disaster, Germany is currently building more coal-fired stations to act as a backup for renewables.[415] But this does not make any sense if the main purpose of renewable energy is to decrease emissions.

The alternative is energy storage. For example, storage could involve batteries or pumping water into reservoirs; the water could then be released for power generation when there is no wind.[416] Surplus power can also be applied to make hydrogen, which can be used at a later date to generate electricity or to make compressed air, which can later be released into a turbine. Another suggestion is that electric cars could be used in reverse, taking their power from the grid when plenty of electricity is available and feeding stored electricity back to the grid when power is short. The practical implications are not clear.

While wind power is clean, environmental costs include noise, visual impact, moving shadows, the impact on birds and bats, and possible disturbance to radio, TV, and radar. However, damage to bird populations is negligible compared with damage to birds caused by fossil-fuel installations, high-power transmission lines, high-rise buildings, and by domestic and feral cats.[417] Damage to bat populations appears to be a more serious local issue. In such cases, damage can be minimized if the turbines are turned off at night when the winds are moderate, which is also the time when bats are most active. The noise and the visual impact are probably the most serious concerns. These problems can be largely avoided if wind parks are sited offshore, which involves higher costs of servicing, building, and connecting to the grid. But the visual impact and the noise appear to be difficult to measure objectively. Some people find wind generators attractive; others find them an eyesore. Similarly, the whirring noise affects some more than others, causing "wind turbine syndrome" related to symptoms such as sleep disturbance, headaches, and nausea. One expert panel review concluded in 2009 that no medical evidence exists to show that sounds and vibrations from wind turbines have any adverse physiological effects.[418] More recent studies are not so sanguine. Noise-control bylaws appear to have been drawn up with traffic, industrial, and airline noise in mind, but noise from wind turbines is apparently more aggravating.[419] Audible noise is caused by the changes in amplitude of the blade passing the tower and by the turbulence of wind passing through the blades. These sounds may be amplified if wind turbines are close together. Much of the sound is also at low frequency, which has been shown to be harmful to health. As well, turbines generate inaudible (infrasound) noise, the effects of which are poorly understood.

Surveys in Sweden and the Netherlands have indicated that approximately 20 percent of people who live within a decibel level of 40 to 45 dBA (typically achieved about five hundred metres from a wind turbine) reported the noise as annoying and complained about sleep disturbances.[420] A similar survey in New Zealand indicated that people who lived within two kilometres of a turbine reported a statistically significant lower quality of life and a lower sleep quality than did others.[421] A recommendation drawn from these studies is that wind turbines should be placed at least 1.5 to two kilometres from dwellings—the New Zealand study recommends at least two kilometres. Current regulations are typically five hundred metres. A recent editorial in the *British Medical Journal* argued that in view of the detrimental effect of inadequate sleep on health—particularly children's health—more research is needed.[422]

Solar energy

Solar energy is, of course, the ultimate source of energy for the whole planet. There is a difference between active solar energy and passive solar energy, which has been used for generations. A passive system involves constructing houses in such a way that the intake of solar radiation is maximized in cold climates and minimized in hot climates. The ability to achieve this depends on the aspect of the site, vegetation, and wind patterns. Active solar energy can be of two types: thermal and photovoltaic. Solar thermal energy is a mature technology for generating hot water, which involves rooftop collectors with a circulating water system that is heated and pumped into the house. It is also possible to generate electricity through solar thermal heat, called concentrated solar power. This technology is only at the developmental stage but appears to be capable of generating electricity at a cost of approximately fifteen to thirty-five cents per kWh with a potential of reaching 7.5 cents by 2050.[423] Sunlight is concentrated by mirrors, and the heat generates steam, driving electricity-generating turbines. It also offers a potential for energy storage if the solar heat is applied to sodium chloride, which keeps its heat for at least seven hours, suggesting that electricity could be generated during parts of the night. At the moment the technology is approximately twenty years behind wind power, but plants

Figure 5.3. The world's largest solar farm located in California: First Solar Desert Sunlight Solar Farm. Credit: US Department of the Interior and www.flickr.com.

already exist in the Mojave Desert in California, in Spain, and in India. A consortium of European and Algerian companies, including Deutsche Bank, Siemens, and E.ON, has joined in a €400 billion (US$600 billion) plan known as the Desertec Project to build concentrated solar-power facilities in the Sahara Desert covering over seventeen thousand square kilometres. Combined with high-powered transmission cables, it is claimed that the project will be capable of supplying 15 percent of Europe's energy needs.[424] However, the project has stalled because of political unrest in North Africa, and as a result some investors have withdrawn. Availability of water is an issue as the technology requires water to generate steam—a scarce resource in desert areas.

Photovoltaic (PV) solar power is generated by cells consisting of a semi-conducting material and a metal that can transform light into electricity at an efficiency rate of approximately 10 to 15 percent, which may further improve. The current cost is around fifteen cents per kWh and is expected to fall sufficiently to be competitive with coal in another five to ten years. Government-backed financial incentives such as the generous German-guaranteed feed-in tariff have led to an explosion in solar-power use and have made Germany the leader in grid-connected PV solar power (Table 5.4).[425]

Solar power also brings environmental costs. If a solar voltaic energy electricity plant were to supply electricity for a large urban area, it would require a large amount of land, and the cost to the environment of covering the land with panels would depend on its alternative use. If the land is already degraded, the total impact on the environment is less than if the land is forested or used for agriculture. Furthermore, the manufacturing of panels is energy-intensive and generates highly toxic by-products. However, most studies show that the net carbon emissions of solar energy are far less than fossil fuel emissions.[426]

Geothermal heat

Geothermal heat has been used for electricity and home heating for well over seventy years. Conventional power production can occur only in areas close to volcanic hot springs where hot water and steam are concentrated. It is clean, very cheap, and can produce electricity at a cost of 3.5 cents per kWh. Iceland gets most of its space heating from geothermal heat, and developing countries, including the Philippines, Kenya, and Costa Rica, have found it a reliable source of power. This type of heat can be generated in many places provided one drills deeply enough, but the process is not usually commercially feasible. In most countries, geothermal heat can be used as a low-temperature resource in combination with ground-source heat pumps. The principle relies on the fact that the top three metres of earth have a constant temperature of between ten and sixteen degrees. In the winter, this heat can be led through a heat exchanger to warm up the house. The heat pumps can be reversed in the summer as air-conditioning units, pumping the cooler air into the house. However, heat pumps require electricity and cannot be a stand-alone source of power. The technology is widely available, and even though the capital cost is high for an individual household, it has payback period of only two to seven years.

Biomass

Biomass provides approximately 10 percent of the world's energy supplies, and 79 percent of renewable energy, with a larger proportion in developing countries where wood is commonly used for cooking and heating. Biomass refers to anything plant based, ranging from algae to trees and crops. It can include organic wastes from landfills, agricultural and forestry residues, or crops from energy plantations. Biomass can be used for energy in many forms, depending on the technology used in processing. For example, it can be fermented into alcohol (ethanol) and used as an additive to gasoline to fuel cars. The first cars ran on ethanol both in the United States and in Europe; Henry Ford, in a 1925 interview with the *New York Times*, claimed that ethanol was the fuel of the future because it could be made from anything grown in nature and would therefore create a new market for farm products, which was sorely needed at the time.[427] Even German locomotives were designed to run on alcohol. Since then the role of alcohol as a fuel has been governed by legislation and oil prices. For example, alcohol was given a boost in 1906 when its tax was removed—a tax introduced during the nineteenth century to pay for the American Civil War. However, Ford and other manufacturers switched to oil when oil became cheaper than alcohol, and the introduction of Prohibition in 1919 made no distinction between alcohol used as a fuel and alcohol as a drink, which destroyed the market for ethanol-based fuel. It was not until the end of Prohibition, after Roosevelt became president, that ethanol was back in business. But it could not compete with oil, which was always cheaper. Following the oil crisis in the early 1970s, ethanol production took off when it was subsidized in the interest of energy security. Following the slump in oil prices in the 1980s, ethanol receded into the background again, only to resurface following the high oil prices in the first decade of the twenty-first century.[428]

Using sugar cane as a feedstock, Brazil has been at the forefront of ethanol production. The industry dates back to the 1920s, but it was not until the 1973 oil crisis that the country embarked on heavy investments in ethanol, including subsidies for plants, fuel stations, and cars specially designed to run on ethanol. By the mid-1980s, most cars ran on ethanol, but during the period of cheap oil in the 1990s and the phasing out of ethanol subsidies, ethanol use declined as Brazilian people wanted cars using gasoline. This resulted in a demand for cars that could run on either gas or ethanol ("total flex vehicles"). About 85 percent of vehicles in Brazil can now run on both. Because of the high productivity of sugar cane, the industry is economically viable. Sugar cane has an approximate energy balance of eight, meaning that it produces eight times more energy than it uses (Table 5.5). Sugar cane yields two to three thousand litres of ethanol per acre, twice as much as maize, and can produce up to seven harvests per year. Processing gets its energy from the burning of cane wastes, not from fossil fuels.

Ethanol is also produced from maize, grains, sugar beets, cellulose, and potatoes. The US government introduced large subsidies to try to increase the use of maize-based ethanol in cars to 20 percent by the year 2020, while EU policies mandate 10 percent biofuels by 2020, and India 20 percent by 2017. The growing of maize requires considerable use of fertilizers and results in more soil erosion than other crops. The harvested maize is ground and mixed with water and heated. Enzymes are added to turn the cornstarch into sugar, and to transform sugar to alcohol requires the addition of yeast for fermentation and then distillation. The energy required for distillation either comes from the burning of natural gas or coal. Greenhouse gases are generated in the production of the nitrogen used in fertilizing the corn, in the fermentation, and finally in the burning of fossil fuels.

Despite its drawbacks, the use of biomass for energy is often seen as a possible way of decreasing carbon emissions as the actual production of maize or sugar cane sequesters carbon while the plants are growing. Most early studies found that using ethanol rather than gasoline reduces greenhouse gases. If the ethanol is produced from maize, the reduction is modest, but if it comes from sugar cane or cellulose, emissions decrease substantially. But these early studies did not take into consideration what the land was used for before it was turned into energy production. If the maize is grown on new agricultural land obtained by clearing forests or plowing up grasslands, it will release carbon that was previously stored in the trees and grasslands into the atmosphere. If farmers divert cropland from food crops into energy crops, the same will occur because of the impact on food prices. Less food produced will result in higher food prices, which will provide an incentive for farmers to add more cropland somewhere, through clearing and plowing up grassland, and therefore cause additional carbon emissions. One study concluded that the use and production of maize-based ethanol should double rather than reduce emissions over thirty years and continue to increase greenhouse gases for another 167 years.[429]

Esters produced from oil seeds such as canola (in Europe called rape) or from palm oil can be converted to biodiesel—an almost perfect substitute for conventional diesel for diesel engines. However, biodiesel requires the growing of crops to produce the oil and therefore suffers from similar problems to maize-based or sugar-based ethanol. During recent decades, vegetable oil production has been the fastest-growing sector in world agriculture. The major

Table 5.5. Energy balances for biomass (output/input)

Biomass source	Energy per unit of output/input
Corn	2.3
Sugar cane	8.3
Biodiesel (made from soybeans)	5.54
Cellulose from switchgrass	3.96

Sources: http://www.usda.gov/oce/reports/energy/2008Ethanol_June_final.pdf, http://www.usda.gov/oce/reports/energy/EnergyLifeCycleSoybeanBiodiesel6-11.pdf. Biodiesel made from palm oil has approximately the same energy balance as soybean derived biodiesel. http://www.researchgate.net/publication/237897773_Greenhouse_gas_emissions_and_energy_balance_of_palm_oil_biofuel, http://cenbio.iee.usp.br/download/publicacoes/JEPO2750.pdf. http://www.ag.auburn.edu/biopolicy/documents/Energy%20Balance%20Cellulosic%20Biofuels.pdf.

products are palm oil, soybeans, canola, and sunflower seed. Between 1979 and 1999, the oil crops sector grew at an average of 4.1 percent per year compared with an average of 2.1 percent per year for the entire agricultural sector.[430] The reasons were increased demand for palm oil for cooking in developing countries, increased use of soybeans for livestock feed, and increased industrial use of vegetable oil in the chemical industry to aid in the manufacture of paints, detergents, lubricants, ethanol, and biodiesel.

Palm oil production has more than doubled since 2000. The oil palm is grown on large plantations in South East Asia. The reason for its popularity is the inherent productivity of palm oil production combined with low labour costs. While one hectare of soybeans yields 0.44 tonnes of oil and one hectare of rapeseed 0.65 tons, one hectare of oil palm can produce up to 4.17 tonnes of oil.[431] Currently 84 percent of biodiesel comes from rapeseed oil, but the use of palm oil is increasing The demand for palm oil in rich countries has also increased in response to the health risks associated with the use of hydrogenated vegetable oils (trans fats) in food processing.

Increased vegetable oil production is responsible for a large part of the expansion of agricultural land in both poor and rich countries and has also led to the shifting of land out of cereal production and into oil seed production.[432] The expansion of agricultural land has led to the destruction of tropical rainforests, particularly in Malaysia, Indonesia, and Brazil.[433] Rich rainforest ecosystems are being replaced by biological deserts. One direct effect is the destruction of the habitat for many endangered species such as orangutans, tigers, and rhinos in Southeast Asia and the destruction of biodiversity in general.

Because of pressure from environmental groups, a certification scheme for palm oil was initiated in 2004 by the Roundtable for Sustainable Palm Oil, with involvement of the World Wildlife Fund. The Roundtable promotes palm oil production practices that help reduce deforestation, preserve biodiversity, and respect the livelihoods of rural communities in oil-producing countries. It aims to ensure that no additional primary forest or other high-conservation-value areas are sacrificed for palm oil plantations, that plantations apply accepted best practices in terms of fertilizer and pesticide use, and that the basic rights and living conditions of millions of plantation workers, smallholders, and indigenous peoples are fully respected.[434] Producers of half the world's crop have subscribed to the practices, and the first certified oil reached the market in 2008. Many of the world's major consumers of edible palm oil, such as the multinational consumer goods company Unilever, have committed to buy only certified palm oil by the year 2015. Some environmental groups claim that certification does not go far enough as new plantations are planned on sensitive peatlands in Indonesia and Malaysia. The clearing of peatlands is particularly problematic because it releases a large amount of CO_2 into the atmosphere.

Most studies show that a large-scale switch to growing crops for fuels would require a vast amount of land. The scale of energy use and the land requirements are so large that such a plan is not feasible. For example, one study shows that if the United States were to supply 55 percent of fuel through home-grown fuel crops, the country would have divert so much land from growing food that it would have to resort to food imports.[435] Similarly, replacing 10 percent of fossil fuels by biofuels in the European Union would use up 38 percent of the total agricultural acreage.[436]

In 2013, 3.5 percent of the world's transport fuel was from biomass—approximately 80 percent of that from ethanol and 20 percent from biodiesel.[437] The concerns about the impact of the growth of crops for biofuels on food prices during the food crisis of 2008 to 2009, as well as studies showing that impacts on carbon emissions were marginal at best, led to a push for so-called second-generation biofuels. These are produced from non-edible biomass, in particular from cellulose and lignum obtained as by-products from either forestry or agriculture, or produced on abandoned lands. The technology is still in its infancy, with some research going on in Europe and North America. One method employs a biochemical process in which enzymes are used to break down the material into sugars that are then converted to ethanol, often referred to as cellulosic ethanol. An alternative process can be described as thermochemical; it uses heat to gasify the raw material. The gas can then be liquefied and converted to biodiesels—known as BTL diesels (biomass-to-liquids technology). A study sponsored by the International Energy Agency and OECD estimates that using 10 percent of the world's agricultural and forestry residues could provide between 4.2 and 6.2 percent of current transport demand.[438] The capital costs are high, and it is difficult to estimate the feed cost as there is no market for residue; as well, it may not be possible for a factory to locate enough feedstock to operate. A vast amount of agricultural waste is produced every year worldwide, but as it is so thinly spread it would be very costly to collect. Currently, residue is most often left behind in the fields or forests, providing nutrients for the soil. If the residue is removed, the loss in soil fertility would require the addition of fertilizer requiring fossil fuels in its manufacture.

Another source of second-generation biofuels is algae grown in large open ponds or in photobioreactors. During photosynthesis, algae absorb carbon dioxide from the atmosphere and convert it into oxygen and biomass, which can be used for biofuels. With applications of carbon dioxide, algae growth can double its volume overnight and is capable of producing fifteen times more oil per acre than palm oil.[439] Currently, it is not commercially viable and does not appear to decrease emissions, as algae cultivation requires a liberal application of fertilizer and thus is not carbon neutral unless it can be used to neutralize nutrient-rich waste water. It is possible that genetic engineering may be able to design algae that secrete oil more efficiently and therefore make the production cheaper.[440]

In conclusion, fuel made from biomass can reduce greenhouse gas emissions but will not eliminate them. Biomass cultivation is associated with significant problems in terms of water and land use, food production, and food prices.[441]

Alternative energy for transportation

One of the major challenges in reducing the demand for fossil fuel is to accommodate the needs of the transport sector, which accounts for 20 percent of all energy consumed and 60 percent of oil consumption. In the world as a whole, 73 percent of transportation energy use is in road transport (light passenger vehicles use 53 percent, trucks 17 percent, and buses 4 percent), while air uses 10 percent, water 10 percent, pipelines 3.4 percent, and rail 3 percent.[442] A Japanese study shows that while a car uses on the average sixty-eight kWh per one hundred passenger kilometres, the equivalent figure for buses was nineteen kWh, rail six, air fifty-one, and sea fifty-seven.[443] For this reason, the use of public transport decreases the energy use in transportation and should be encouraged. However, public transportation is not necessarily the solution for reaching a carbon-free economy, as that requires the total elimination of fossil fuels in transportation. Electric vehicles that run on batteries can provide the solution since they do not emit any pollutants, but whether they are actually carbon neutral obviously depends on how the electricity is generated. If it is generated by a coal-fired station, electric vehicles cannot be carbon neutral, but because of their superior efficiency (they use six to twenty kWh of energy per one hundred kilometres compared with seventy kWh of a conventional car), they are still equal to or better than the best fossil-fuel cars.

Electric vehicles are not unusual; trains run on electricity in many parts of the world, as do trams and trolley buses. But people are less familiar with the fact that electric cars were developed in the middle of the nineteenth century, and by the twentieth century both electric cars and electric trains were commonplace. Before the lighter combustion engine was perfected, electric cars held both distance and speed records. With the refinement of more efficient combustion engines, electric cars were phased out. Following the introduction of zero-emissions regulations of new vehicles in California in 1990, General Motors introduced the electric car EV1 to the California market on a very limited scale. Approximately a thousand vehicles were produced and leased to the general public between 1996 and 1998, and Chrysler, Ford, Nissan, Honda, and Toyota also produced a limited number of electric vehicles for the California market. In 2003, GM recalled its electric vehicles and destroyed them, supposedly because the company felt there was no market for them. The makers of the documentary film *Who Killed the Electric Car?* claim that the real reason was massive lobbying from the oil industry to reduce public acceptance, since the oil industry stood to lose a lot of money. Be that as it may, there is now a surge of interest in electric cars, with all the major car companies actively involved in developing and marketing their own versions.

Electric cars can be classified as hybrids, plug-in hybrids, extended-range electrical vehicles, and pure electric cars.[445] Hybrid electric vehicles combine a fossil-fuel power and electric propulsion. A prime example is the Toyota Prius, which has been on the market since 1997. Electricity is generated while the car is running and is stored in the battery. A regenerative brake system also stores additional energy in the battery, which is sufficient to allow the car to run on electricity at low speeds, but at high speeds the gasoline engine takes over. Hybrid cars are not emissions free because they use a combination of electricity and fossil fuels, but many of them save a considerable amount of fossil fuels. For example, gas consumption of the Prius is 30 percent lower than that of conventional vehicles. The electric motor can be used separately or at the same time as the gasoline engine, but the main propulsion is still the combustion engine. Plug-in hybrids, on the other hand, have larger batteries, allowing them to travel longer distances on electricity alone; later versions of the Prius are plug-in models. Extended-range vehicles such as the Volt, produced by Chevrolet, use the combustion engine only if the electric battery runs out. In conventional hybrids, the power for the wheels comes from an electric motor, a gasoline engine, or both, but wheels in the new extended-range vehicles are powered only by a large electric motor. They are not fitted with a gas engine. Instead, for short trips the car runs on a battery and for longer trips, a gas-powered generator creates electricity and the motor runs on battery power alone.

Pure electric vehicles are emissions free if the electricity used to charge the batteries is generated from emissions-free sources such as nuclear or solar power. As these cars have no backup power, they need an infrastructure to support the recharging of the batteries, which some cities are now starting to provide. Typically, electric vehicles using standard lead-acid batteries need recharging every sixty kilometres—not a very long range. Using lithium-ion batteries, the advanced Tesla sports car has a range of nearly four hundred kilometres. Because of the high costs of electric cars, many countries have introduced substantial subsidies ranging from £5,000 (~US$7,500) per car in the British Isles to €5,000 (~US$6,650) in Ireland, and over US$9,000 in China.[446] Norway has the largest proportionate ownership of electric cars as a result of policies such as sales tax exemptions—the tax is 25 percent on other cars—free charging, free downtown parking, no road tolls or ferry fees, and automatic access to bus-only lanes.[447] After a long period of disappointing sales, there is now some indication that growth in demand is accelerating.[448]

While electricity is a viable option for land transport, it is not for shipping. Water transport contributes 4 to 5 percent of CO_2 emissions, and the options for reducing emissions are few. Nuclear-powered transportation is already used in ocean shipping, with 150 nuclear-powered ships including submarines

Figure 5.4. The nuclear-powered NS Savannah. Source: US Government Archives.

in existence in 2014. These are employed mainly in the world's major navies and as icebreakers in Russia.[449] Russia also has a nuclear-powered cargo ship in operation, and the United States launched the nuclear-powered NS *Savannah* in 1959. Designed as a combined cargo/passenger ship, its main purpose was to showcase US technological advances (Figure 5.4). While its fuel costs were negligible, its operating costs were very high, and it was decommissioned in 1972. The Chinese shipping giant Cosco is considering building nuclear-powered cargo ships.[450]

Shipping fleets have been able to achieve considerable reductions in fuel costs by steaming at lower speeds. Another way of decreasing the use of fossil fuels in shipping is to use wind power, which of course was the only method of propulsion until early nineteenth century, when sailing ships were replaced by steamships. It is highly unlikely that a full-scale return to sailing ships is possible in cargo and passenger transportation as the wind is intermittent and does not always blow from the right direction. It is more likely that some investments will be made in hybrid ships using a combination of engines and sail. The German firm SkySails makes aerial kites that can be attached to tankers and freighters to help drag them across the seas, which could have a considerable impact on fuel costs (Figure 5.5).[451] During its first transatlantic voyage, the MS *Beluga SkySails* claims to have cut fuel costs by 20 percent. The Dutch company Dykstra is designing small hybrid container ships using automatic sails and sophisticated technology capable of tracking the optimal routes for sailing.[452] Another potential technology is the use of hybrid hydrogen fuel-cell-battery systems for ships.[453] These are already in use for small boats in Germany and are being developed for larger ships. As with hybrid cars, they need an infrastructure of hydrogen fuel stations.

The options for reducing fossil-fuel use in air transport, the fastest-growing transportation mode, are even more restrictive.[454] Engineers are also working on a new generation of airships using helium rather than the explosive hydrogen to carry the craft and solar energy to propel them at low speeds. But none of the designs have yet gone further than the drawing board. Nuclear power is not an option because of the difficulties of shielding crews and passengers from radiation, and wind power is not possible for obvious reasons. It is possible to use liquefied hydrogen as jet fuel, and one study claims no technological barriers exist to the development of hydrogen-fuelled aircraft, and the aircrafts would be faster and more efficient than conventional aircraft.[455] The International Air Transport Association (IATA), an industry lobby group, aims to achieve annual efficiency improvements of 1.5 percent between 2009 and 2020 and to a

Figure 5.5. The cargo ship MV Theseus fitted with an aerial kite. Credit: "Theseus-Quelle WesselsReederei" by Reederei Wessels - Reederei Wessels/Fotoflite. Licensed under CC BY-SA 2.5 via Wikimedia Commons - http://commons.wikimedia.org/wiki/File:Theseus-Quelle_WesselsReederei.jpg#/media/File:Theseus-Quelle_WesselsReederei.jpg

50 percent reduction in emissions by 2050.[456] So far most of the improvements in fuel efficiency have come from using lighter materials in building aircraft, more efficient engines, and retrofitting aircraft with wingtip devices (winglets).

There are few technical barriers to producing jet fuels from biomass, and commercial flights have already taken off using fuel made from reprocessed vegetable oils (including used cooking oils) and animal fats.[457] Research is ongoing on reprocessing ethanol and using sugar as a feedstock. However, without subsidies, costs are a substantial barrier to widespread adoption. A recent study on the cost of alternative jet fuels estimates that under the best possible conditions, oil prices would have to reach $384 per barrel for microalgae to be competitive, $255 for fuel from *Pogamia pomata* (an oil-seeds tree), and $168 for fuel from sugar cane.[458]

Can we get to a zero-carbon economy?

In theory, the global technical potential of renewable energy is larger than current and future energy demand.[459] How we achieve a complete transfer to renewable energy is another matter.[460] David MacKay, in his book *Sustainable Energy: Without the Hot Air*, makes detailed calculations for energy use and renewable energy availability for the United Kingdom.[461] While the UK is different from many other countries because of its high population density, its long coastline, and its cool climate, it is instructive to examine his findings. The left-hand column in Figure 5.6 shows the challenges involved in living on renewable energy. On the average, a person in the United Kingdom uses forty kWh per day in driving a car, thirty kWh using commercial airlines, and thirty-seven kWh for heating and cooling. These figures, probably not that different for other industrialized countries, indicate that substantial energy savings could be found by employing energy conservation measures in homes and by discouraging car driving and airline travel. MacKay's other major item is "stuff," which is the energy required for making and disposing of goods ranging from new homes to computers and pop cans. In total, the energy demand adds up to 195 kWh per day per person (compared with the average American, who consumes 250 kWh). The right-hand column indicates how this

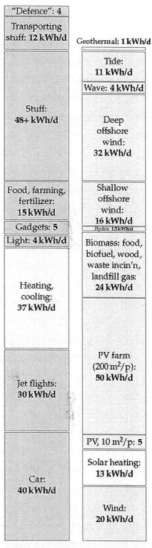

Figure 5.6. David MacKay's rough calculations showing whether the UK can live on renewable energy. Source: David MacKay, Sustainable Energy: Without the Hot Air, p. 118. Downloaded from www.withouthotair.com. The left-hand column shows energy demand per person.

energy demand could be fulfilled by renewable energy under highly favourable conditions. The United Kingdom is very windy and thus has a great potential for wind power. According to MacKay's calculations, approximately 38 percent of renewable energy could be generated by wind. Some of it would be onshore wind power, requiring 10 percent of windy areas to be covered by wind farms, doubling the current number of wind farms in the world. Off-shore wind farms would offer even more potential, but this option is problematic because of such farms' proximity to major shipping lanes and deep-sea wind turbines are not economical at present. MacKay argues that the logistics of building this number of wind farms are not realistic. Similarly, solar heating of hot water, if it were installed in every house, could contribute thirteen kWh per day, and if 5 percent of the UK land area were covered by photovoltaic farms, another fifty kWh could be provided. Tidal and wave energy would not make a major dent in energy supplies. The total amount of potential renewable energy is less than total energy demand (Figure 5.6), and MacKay concludes that the United Kingdom could become carbon free only by investing in nuclear energy and by importing solar-generated electricity from the Sahara. He sees the solution for the world as a whole to be a combination of solar power and nuclear power.

Denmark has been a model of energy conservation and the development of wind power. Primary energy consumption is the same as it was in the early 1970s. A recent study claims that Denmark can achieve 100 percent renewable energy in electricity generation by 2050, relying on biomass for 22 percent, wind for 63 percent, solar for 9 percent, and wave energy for 5 percent.[462] The biomass would be obtained from wood, straw, energy crops, and algae. Home heating would come from heat pumps, solar, and biomass, and in cities district central heating would mainly come from new technology using large-scale heat pumps, biomass, and waste incineration. The study assumes that household electricity demand will be reduced by 25 percent and industry 45 percent through best practices, product standards, energy information campaigns, building codes, high-speed trains. Changes in urban design will create more incentives for walking and cycling.

In another study, Mark Jacobson and Mark Delucchi show that it would be possible to achieve 100 percent reliance on wind, water, solar, and geothermal energy for new energy projects by 2030 and replacement of existing structures by 2050.[463] Table 5.6 shows how.

Their renewable world would rely entirely on electricity and hydrogen to power homes, industries, and transportation, from cars to aircraft. The proposed infrastructure would achieve energy efficiencies that would reduce energy

Table 5.6. Number of water, wind, and solar devices needed to power the world, 2030

Energy technology	Rated power of one plant or device (MW)	Percent of 2030 power demand met by device	Number of plants and devices needed
Wind turbine	5	50	3.8 million
Wave device	0.75	1	720,000
Geothermal plant	100	4	5,350
Hydroelectric plants	1,300	4	900
Tidal turbine	1	1	490,000
Roof PV system	0.003	6	1.7 billion
Solar PV plant	300	14	40,000
Concentrated solar-power plant	300	20	49,000
Total		100	

Source: Mark Z. Jacobson and Mark A. Delucchi, 2011, p. 1160.
Note: 70 percent of hydro capacity is already installed; 50 percent of wind turbines are assumed to be offshore.

demand by 30 percent. Hydro power would be used to even out loads caused by fluctuating wind and solar power. They estimate that the additional wind and solar plants would require only an additional 1.9 percent of the total land area (outside the Antarctic) for footprint and spacing. They also analyze the material requirements for such a large investment, arguing there should be no problem in supplying steel and concrete, but there may be a problem in sourcing the neodymium required for electric motors and generators and platinum required for fuel cells and lithium-ion batteries. Very efficient recycling of these materials would be essential.

While relying on wind and solar energy as the prime sources of energy creates problems because the daily and hourly variations in power do not match the variations in the demand for power, Jacobson and Delucchi claim that the systems are more reliable than the traditional fossil-fuel plants. For example, the average coal plant in the United States was non-operational for 6.5 percent of the time because of unscheduled maintenance and for 6 percent because of scheduled maintenance, while wind turbines on the average are down for only zero to 2 percent on land and zero to 5 percent on water. Solar power has downtimes of 1 percent.[464] In order to operate a renewable energy system, they suggest that it is essential for electricity grids to be interconnected between areas (including between countries) because if no wind is blowing in one area, wind in other areas could make up the difference. Non-variable energy resources such as hydro could be used to make up for sudden shortages. Other measures to spread demand over the day are smart meters and storage of electric power at the generating site for use at peak demand. This could be done by using the surplus energy to produce hydrogen or store the surplus in electric-vehicle batteries. Improved weather forecasting should also improve planning. They estimate the investment costs over a 20 year period would be US$100 trillion (approximately US$5 trillion per year—6 percent of current world GDP)[465].

While a dramatic growth in renewable energy has already occurred, the required new investments are huge. Between 2004 and 2008, total annual global investments in renewables increased by 400 percent. Solar photovoltaic capacity increased by 600 percent, and wind-power capacity by 250 percent, with significant increases in small hydro, geothermal, and biomass electricity generations and with similar expansions in the industries producing the hardware.[466] These increases in capacity have continued through the recent recession—between 2010 and 2011 wind capacity increased by 36 percent and solar by 19 percent.[467] Despite these increases, renewable electric power capacity made up only about 5.6 percent of the total in 2012 (not including power generated from large hydro dams). Wind power consists of 43 percent of the total renewable capacity, followed by small hydro power and biomass power. Solar photovoltaic power is a distant fourth at approximately 5 percent.

The expansion of renewable energy has been supported by a bewildering array of policies, ranging from legislated standards mandating the desired proportion of renewable energy in total energy consumption (known as renewable portfolio standards) to tradable green certificates, production subsidies, tax credits, and feed-in tariffs. An example of the first kind of policy is the so-called 20-20-20 directive of the European Union, which by 2020 aims to reduce greenhouse gases by 20 percent from their 1990 levels, reduce primary energy use by 20 percent, and increase the proportion of renewable energy in total energy consumption to 20 percent from the current 9.2 percent.[468] Each country is free to set its own targets, which range from 10 percent in Malta to 49 percent in Sweden. This directive became EU law in 2009. As of 2011, 118 countries and states had policy targets for renewable energy.[469] New targets were proposed in 2014 to a reduction in primary energy use of 40 percent and a target of renewable energy of 27 percent.[470] Tradable green certificates exist in conjunction to the legislated quotas. Non-renewable energy producers must purchase the certificates from renewable energy producers to fulfill their quota. The tradable certificates therefore subsidize renewable energy production. Most countries offer R&D subsidies and many corporate tax credits for using or producing renewable energy. Power companies in over sixty countries and states give preferential feed-in tariffs for electricity produced from renewable sources.

Is it effective to provide these types of incentives for renewable energy?[471] Given the large increases in renewable investments, it obviously is. In particular, studies have shown that buyback tariffs are effective in promoting solar power. Effective carbon taxes would also help, particularly if the tax revenue was used to finance investments in renewable energy. However, as was noted in the previous chapter, carbon taxes are not popular with the general public, which has an aversion to new taxes and is often not impressed by the need to mitigate climate change. Therefore, renewable energy is frequently promoted by government for reasons other than climate concerns such as the creation of employment, regional development, security of energy supplies, and technological development and innovation. Indeed, evidence shows that the renewable energy sector generates more jobs than the fossil-fuel-based sector per unit of energy produced.[472] Some countries have also pursued an early-mover strategy—an example is Germany, which developed wind power very early, and as a result was able to corner the market in wind-related technology.

The answer to the question of whether it is possible for the world to live without energy derived from fossil fuels is a qualified *yes*. It is possible, but only with huge investments in wind and solar power combined with a new energy infrastructure. The appropriate mix depends on the specific conditions in each country. However, whether it can be done without nuclear power is questionable. Indeed, four well-known climate scientists in an open letter have argued that renewable energy sources cannot be installed quickly enough and at a sufficiently large scale to avert climate change, and therefore nuclear power has to play a substantial role.[473] This view is shared by the IPCC in its *Fifth Assessment Report*.

The cost to the world economy of a total transformation is likely to be very high, but has to be weighed against the benefits of mitigating warming. As this chapter has demonstrated, we are already on the way toward switching—whether we can do it quickly enough to avert climatic catastrophe is open to debate. Much depends on the ingenuity of people in developing new technologies, the incentives provided by governments, and the willingness of the population at large to adopt novel solutions.

6

The Importance of Natural Environments: Biodiversity and Ecosystem Services

*Human attitudes to natural environments. The current
state of biodiversity. Aggregate measures of the state of the
natural environment: the Living Planet Index, the Ecological
Footprint, and the Millennium Ecosystem Assessment.
The economic value of biodiversity and ecosystem services.
International conventions. Where do we go from here?*

THE DISCUSSION OF RESOURCES will now shift from the all-important subject of the exploitation of energy resources and their impact on climates to the subject of nature as a resource. Without nature and what it provides, human life is not possible. The focus in this chapter is on biodiversity and ecosystem services, why they are important, and how they can be maintained. The remaining chapters will focus on particular aspects of our reliance on nature such as our need for forests, agriculture, water, and the oceans.

The word *biodiversity* is an abbreviation of biological diversity; it was first used in the mid-1980s to describe the richness and variety of life on earth. Biodiversity can describe the various life forms in an ecosystem; for example, in wetlands or rainforests (ecosystem biodiversity); in the variety of species, ranging from algae to monarch butterflies to people (biological biodiversity); or in the variety of genes in individuals, be they people, animals, or plants (genetic biodiversity).

The planet's biodiversity is contained in the biosphere—the thin membrane of organisms that surrounds the earth. There is mounting evidence that a rich biodiversity improves the productivity and stability of ecosystems.[474] Healthy ecosystems are essential in providing services critical to our survival such as water purification, the necessary soils to grow our food, and the direct provisioning of plants and animals for food. We also rely on nature for firewood, building materials, and many drugs, and all crops and household animals can be traced to species in the wild. Ecosystems are natural assets and, like capital assets, they depreciate if they are overused or misused. They differ from capital assets in that their depreciation is often irreversible and can collapse rapidly, without any warning. It is usually impossible to replace a degraded system with a new one, since ecosystems are not like machines that can be replaced or repaired when they wear out. As Chapter 1 showed, the ancient Mayas and the Babylonians are examples of civilizations that disappeared because of degraded systems. It will become clear in this chapter that biodiversity is a resource we squander to the detriment of our children and all future generations. The famous biologist E.O. Wilson writes in his book *The Future of Life*:

> The central problem of the new century . . . is how to raise the poor to a decent standard of living worldwide while preserving as much of the rest of life as possible. Both the needy poor and vanishing biological diversity are concentrated in the developing countries. The poor, some 800 million of whom live without sanitation, clean water, and adequate food, have little chance to advance in a devastated environment. Conversely, the natural environments where most biodiversity hangs on cannot survive the press of land-hungry people with nowhere else to go.[475]

This chapter first examines how our attitudes to the natural environment have changed over time and the likely reasons for the changes, topics that lay the foundations for the subsequent analysis of the current state of biodiversity and ecosystem services and their significance in today's economies. The last section offers some suggestions for how nature can be protected in a world increasingly dominated by humans, many of whom depend on it for their livelihoods.

Human attitudes to natural environments

Humans have prospered because our superior brains enabled us to control and appropriate an ever-increasing share of the earth's environmental resources.

We survived through cultural and technological adaptations that made it possible to increase the availability of resources. As hunter-gatherers we were inseparable from natural ecosystems, and we developed an extensive knowledge of the natural world which in turn generated a deep respect for animals as shown in early cave paintings. The process of human domination accelerated with the development of agriculture, which allowed us to grow food from seeds and domesticate animals for food and for work. A necessary part of the domestication process involved capturing and taming wild animals. Dogs were the earliest domesticated animals (at least fifteen thousand years ago) and are direct descendants of wolves. Sheep, cats, and goats were first domesticated in Western Asia, and today's horses trace their origin to wild horses roaming the Asian steppes. Increasingly humans came to rely on manipulating ecosystems to survive. Humans subsequently came to believe they were superior to animals and taming wilderness was beneficial.

Elephants were kept in captivity in India as long ago as 2000 BC, and antelopes are shown with collars on early Egyptian tombs. For the rich and powerful, the collection and display of exotic plants and animals emerged as a form of conspicuous consumption designed to impress friends and enemies, and animals were used as curiosities.[476] Zoological gardens have a long history. For example, in the second century BC, the Chinese Empress Tanki kept zoos; King Solomon in biblical times did as well. Most of the Greek city states had collections of wild animals that were used for study, and in the fourth century BC, Alexander the Great furnished these zoos with animals brought back from his military expeditions. The Romans had animal collections in private zoos, but some were destined for arenas where they were used in gory public spectacles involving either fights among wild animals such as lions and rhinoceros or fights between people and animals. The emperor Trajan (first century AD) is reputed to have celebrated his victory in Dacia with a staged animal hunt in the Coliseum in Rome involving eleven thousand animals and ten thousand gladiators. Zoos also existed outside Eurasia, according to the reports of the Spanish conquistador Cortez, who was much impressed when he came upon a very large zoo in Mexico in 1519.

The first modern zoos were built in Vienna in 1752, in Madrid in 1775, and in Regent's Park in London in 1828. The rationale for building zoos had by that time changed from curiosities to scientific research and education, and a huge number of wild animals were captured. Many died in transit, and many died because they could not bear confinement in small spaces. They were afflicted with various conditions, including stereotypy—a kind of madness that makes

Figure 6.1. Five kidnapped members of the Kawesqar tribe, Tierra del Fuego, Chile, displayed as part of human zoo exhibits in 1881. They all died within a year. Source: Universitat Zurich and http://www.spiegel.de/ fotostrecke/photo-gallery-europe-s-human-zoos-fotostrecke-50706.html.

the animal pace back and forth—cannibalism, self-mutilation, and eating disorders.[477] Circuses during the nineteenth and twentieth centuries also included menageries that included animals confined to very small spaces and made to perform in various circus acts. There was nothing scientific about menageries—they were for display only to the curious public. Not only did zoos and circuses display exotic animals, they also exhibited "exotic" humans, sometimes put in cages. The human zoos involved the abduction of indigenous peoples from all over the world, often complete with fake villages, which were designed to show the superiority of the white races—a practice we would now find abhorrent. Many were brought to Europe by the founder of the Hamburg zoo, Carl Hagenbeck. They included eleven Indians from Tierra del Fuego who were captured and transported across the Atlantic in 1881. One died at sea, five were sent back home, and the remaining five were exhibited at the zoo and died within a year. Their bones were finally brought home for burial in 2010 after having been found in a Zurich museum.[478] Another infamous case involved Ota Benga, a Congolese native of the Mbuti pygmy tribe who was displayed in a cage together with monkeys, first at the St. Louis World Fair and later at the Bronx Zoo. He committed suicide after he was released.

Botanical gardens, probably more benign than zoos in terms of their impact on the environment, were built not just for show but as early centres for growing fruits, herbs, and medicinal plants. They were common in ancient China and around the Mediterranean, and by the end of the eighteenth century they were common throughout Europe, spurred by interest following the development of the science of botany. Many important botanists were directors of botanical gardens. Created in 1759, the London Kew Gardens currently hold the world's largest collection of plants. These gardens were famous for its plant collecting expeditions and for assisting in their distribution across the world. Examples are such familiar plants as coffee, tea, cocoa, banana, and various timbers.

The industrial revolution saw wildlife and other natural products as any other goods sold on an open market. The natural environment was primarily seen as a resource to be exploited which led to a rapid decimation of wildlife. Nature in general was regarded as savage and brutish and, unless it was tamed to human tastes, something to avoid. This attitude changed during the latter part of the 19th century, when the focus shifted from artificial displays of flora and fauna in zoos and botanical gardens to the establishment of national parks or protected areas. Wilderness and nature were now seen as romantic and sublime and a source of solace in an increasingly industrialized world; ideally nature had to be pristine and untouched by humans. These ideas spread to the United States through the writings of Henry David Thoreau, who became known for the often-quoted line, "in wildness is the preservation of the world," and others such as John Muir who became the advocate for the national parks movement in the United States. The first national park was Yellowstone National Park, created in 1872, which became the model for national parks in other countries. The first parks in Europe were set up in Sweden in 1909, and the first parks in Africa were established in the now Democratic Republic of the Congo in 1925 and Kruger National Park in South Africa in 1926. Most of the new parks were based on the Yellowstone model with the idea that natural areas should look like they might have before humans appeared; as a result, people who had lived there for hundreds of years were often forcefully removed with little regard for their welfare.[479]

Worldwide, the total amount of land set aside did not exceed one million square kilometres until the end of World War II, but has since then grown at a rapid rate to almost seventeen million square kilometres, with 160,000 protected areas around the world covering 12.7 percent of terrestrial and inland water areas. The parties to the Convention on Biological Diversity have recommended that the protected areas be increased to 17 percent by 2020.[480] This expansion has largely occurred in response to concerns over biodiversity loss and its likely impact on human well-being. A protected area, according to the International Union for the Conservation of Nature, is "a clearly defined geographical space, recognized, dedicated and managed, through legal and other effective means, to achieve the long-term conservation of nature with associated ecosystem services and cultural values."[481] Protected areas range from wilderness reserves to cultural landscapes. Often, areas of stunning scenery are protected that are not necessarily areas needing protection from an ecological viewpoint. Only 7.2 percent of the oceans' territorial waters are protected, with an even smaller area of 1.6 percent in extraterritorial waters. Some of the areas in developing countries may be protected in name only, because if a country is poor and not well governed it may be unable to set aside sufficient resources for the management of protected areas, in which case illegal logging and poaching frequently occur.[482]

While the increase in protected areas is important, they can only be maintained if people care about them. Rapid global urbanization is expected to continue into the foreseeable future, which raises the question of whether urbanized people will maintain their connection to nature. If people do not appreciate nature in all its manifestations they are less likely to support measures encouraging conservation or to pay the taxes necessary to maintain protected areas. Survey results from twenty countries show that visits to protected areas have been increasing at a rate faster than population growth, an indication that people in many countries still appreciate a natural environment, and for poor countries, nature-based tourism may offer employment opportunities while still preserving natural areas.[483] However, visits to North American national parks are declining.[484] This is particularly striking for one of the most famous national parks in the United States: Yosemite in California where the number of visitors has dropped for nine of the past thirteen years.[485] This trend away from nature-based recreation was confirmed in a larger study that included not only national parks visits in the United States, but also data on game licenses issues and on time spent hiking and camping.[486] A similar trend was found in Spain and Japan. Is this decline caused by a total disengagement from the natural environment caused by an obsession with games and television, or do national parks or wilderness areas not offer enough rewards compared with, for example, birding, adventure tourism, or gardening, all of which have increased in popularity?

Some argue that conservationists, by being completely opposed to development of better tourist facilities in the parks, are driving people away.[487] Others point to a generation of young adults and children obsessed with video games and social media. Children in North America are often not brought on camping trips because wilderness is now thought to be hazardous. One oft-quoted study linked the decline in visits to US national parks to the increased obsession with *videophilia*, which is defined as the recent human tendency to focus on sedentary activities involving electronic media.[488] Engaging with nature electronically tends to both sensationalize nature and give an impression that it is hazardous and boring. A disconnect from nature at an early age may lead to a future generation of adults making choices that are not conducive to a sustainable future.

The current state of biodiversity

Today, the main rationale for expanding the number and extent of protected areas is to preserve biodiversity and halt species loss. Protection of biodiversity requires knowledge of the species the earth harbours, but there is little agreement among biologists how many species currently exist, and estimates vary between 0.5 million and 10 million, but many of these are no better than guesses.[489] A widely quoted number is 8.7 million, including 2.2 million marine species.[490] It is believed that 86 percent of land species and 91 percent of ocean species have not yet been discovered or described.[491] Species include microbes, of which bacteria is one type, and these are found almost everywhere in the world including in the thermal vents at the bottom of the ocean where the water is boiling. Bacteria also inhabit the hot sulphur springs in Yellowstone; one type of bacterium can survive radiation one thousand times stronger than the radiation from the atomic bombs dropped over Hiroshima and Nagasaki. The secret to its survival is the possession of a unique ability to repair broken DNAS. Surprisingly, bacteria and fungi also inhabit porous rock three thousand metres below the earth's surface, which gives some credence to the idea that there is life on other planets. On tidal flats there are gastrotichs, gnathostomulids, kinorhynchs, tardigrades, chaetognaths, placozoans and orthonectids; all tiny creatures, barely visible. There are over ten thousand types of ants, five thousand amphibians, five thousand mammals, and almost three hundred thousand lowering plants. Even more surprising, over four hundred new species of mammals have been discovered since 1993. One example is the olinguito—a distant relative of racoons—discovered in the Andes in 2013 (Figure 6.2).[492] A virtual Garden of Eden has recently been discovered in the remote Foja mountains of Indonesia, with previously unknown species of geckos, frogs, wallabies, and butterflies.[493]

Figure 6.2. *The newly discovered olinguito that looks like a cross between a cat and a teddy bear. Credit: Mark Gurney, Wikimedia Commons.*

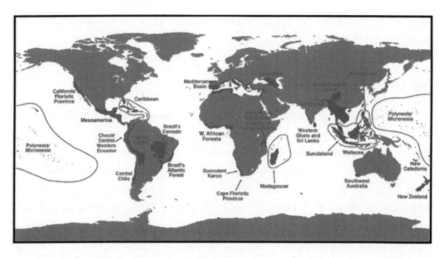

Figure 6.3. Biodiversity hot spots. Source: Norman Myers, et al. "Biodiversity Hot Spots for Conservation Priorities." Nature 403 (2002): pp. 853–58.

It is believed that over 50 percent of species are found in the tropical rainforests even though they only occupy 6 percent of the earth's land surface. One hectare in the Atlantic forest in Brazil contained 425 kinds of trees; one hectare in a national park in Peru, thirteen hundred species of butterflies. A recent scientific paper on tree species in the Amazon area estimates that it contains an astounding sixteen thousand tree species—227 of these species account for 50 percent of the trees, while the rest are rare.[494] British environmentalist Norman Myers and his associates identified twenty-five biodiversity hot spots, which take up 1.4 percent of the earth's surface and are home to 44 percent of the world's plant species and more than one-third of mammals, birds, reptiles, and amphibians. These hot spots include the tropical rainforests of the Atlantic Coast in Brazil, the forests of southern Mexico and Central America, the tropical Andes, Indonesia, and the Philippines.[495]

The world's incredibly rich biodiversity is under severe threat from human activity because of the growth in world population, but our impact on biodiversity is ancient. For example, Australia was first populated approximately sixty thousand years ago, at which time the continent had a fauna including huge animals: giant flightless birds, lizards seven metres long, rhinoceros, and lions. They all disappeared after the humans arrived, a slaughter that continued following the next wave of human migration when the European colonists arrived.[496] Madagascar has a similar history. Before the arrival of humans, it

Figure 6.4. Skeleton cast and model of the giant dodo at the Oxford University Museum of Natural History. Credit: BazzaDaRambler and Wikimedia Commons.

had a unique fauna of big animals: elephants, birds ten feet tall, giant sloths, aardvarks, and many species of lemurs. Within a short time they were hunted to extinction. New Zealand is yet another case, where a thousand Polynesians managed to destroy 160,000 moas—the large flightless birds. The European colonists brought pigs, goats, and rats that destroyed most of what was left of the original flora and fauna.[497]

It is estimated that before humans arrived, the average extinction rate was one species per million species per year, but a more recent paper claims that it was probably less: 0.1 species per million per year, or one per decade.[498] In terms of evolution, species extinction is a natural phenomenon. Either a species dies out or evolves into a totally different species. The reason it dies out may simply be bad luck; for example, environmental conditions may suddenly change for the worse. The average lifetime of a species is thought to be five million years. Evolution creates new species and destroys others, and every species today has an evolutionary ancestor. Biologists call these losses background extinctions as they are continuous, compared with mass extinctions, which have happened five times, destroying 20 to 96 percent of all species (Figure 6.5). The causes of these extinctions are varied and not all known. It is widely accepted that the last extinction (the late cretaceous) that wiped out the dinosaurs was caused

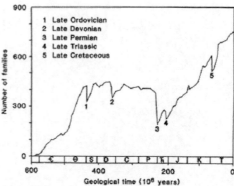

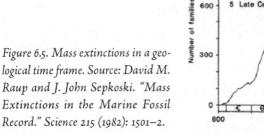

Figure 6.5. Mass extinctions in a geo-logical time frame. Source: David M. Raup and J. John Sepkoski. "Mass Extinctions in the Marine Fossil Record." Science 215 (1982): 1501–2.

by a giant meteorite that hit the Gulf of Mexico. It is believed that the first extinction was caused by glaciation, and the largest (the late permian) by a series of volcanic events.[499]

There is a debate among biologists about whether we are currently experiencing another mass extinction—a sixth extinction—as the extinction rate is now estimated to be many times higher than the background extinction rate. The likely rate is hotly contested but may be 1000 times higher than the background extinction rate which would translate into 100 species per million species per year.[500] If the existing number of species is 8.7 million, approximately 870 species per year will become extinct.

Humans are the most invasive species of all, having increased from a population of a few million at the onset of the agricultural revolution to seven billion today. It is estimated that 40 percent of the net primary production of the biosphere is currently appropriated by humans, crowding out other species.[501] The International Union for Conservation of Nature (IUCN) keeps a continual record of species under threat. It has nine categories for species: extinct, extinct in the wild, critically endangered, endangered, vulnerable, near threatened, least concern, data deficient, and not evaluated.[502] If a species is vulnerable, endangered or critically endangered, it is put on a "Red List." In 2014, 76,199 species were examined, of which 22,413 were threatened with extinction, including 41 percent of amphibians, 26 percent of mammals, and 13 percent of birds.

Why should we care about extinctions? There is the philosophical argument that extinctions deprive us of the future ability to experience the inherent miracle of each and every species.[503] A species loss breaks a previously unbroken continuum of life that has evolved over billions of years through all the ages of the earth's environment. It is also in our own self-interest to minimize extinctions because each extinction reduces the diversity and complexity of life, where all life is interconnected in ways we are often not fully aware of. If the chain of interconnected life is broken, the consequences may be dire: the balance of nature could forever be altered and ecosystems destroyed, threatening our own survival. The protection of some species—keystone species—is particularly important because their disappearance would have a disproportionate effect on the survival of other species. The concept of keystone species originated in a 1966 study by Robert Paine of the removal of the carnivorous starfish from an area, which led to local extinctions of several other marine species.[504] Since then, the list of keystone species has been extended to include, among others, sea otters, beavers, Nile crocodiles, grey wolves, brown bears, and lynx.[505]

Historically, many extinctions were caused by overhunting, a situation that continues even today and threatens the existence of many large mammals such as African elephants, Asian tigers, snow leopards, orangutans, rhinoceros, and sharks, to name a few. Table 6.1 shows that the culprits for the decline in animal populations are exploitation through hunting and fishing, destruction and degradation of habitats, followed by climate change, invasive species, pollution, and disease. The expansion and intensification of agriculture are the main causes of habitat destruction and degradation. The particular problem with agriculture is that it leads to homogenization of heterogeneous landscapes. This is of course exacerbated when it is focused on very few crops and particular crops of very limited number of strains. World trade has contributed to the process as demonstrated by a recent study that attributed 30 percent of biodiversity loss in developing nations to international trade in commodities such as coffee, rubber, cocoa, palm oil, fish, and forestry products.[506]

It is estimated that 35 percent of the earth's surface has been converted to agriculture, and the livestock sector represents by far the largest use of land. Sixty percent of temperate hardwood and mixed forests, 30 percent of conifers, 45 percent of tropical rainforests, and 70 percent of tropical dry forests have been lost to agriculture.[507] A loss of 10 percent of a forested area leads to a decline of 50 percent of the original

Table 6.1. Primary Threats to Animal Populations

Threat	Percentage of population declines
Exploitation	37.0
Habitat degradation	31.4
Habitat loss	13.4
Climate change	7.1
Invasive species/genes	5.1
Pollution	4.0
Disease	2.0

Source: *Living Planet Report, 2014: Species and Spaces, People and Places*, p. 20.

number of species. This is part of so-called island ecology: large islands have more diversity than small islands and large biological reserves have a larger variety than smaller ones. When forests are reduced to an area of less than twenty-seven square kilometres, 10 to 15 percent of species will become extinct within one hundred years.

Modern agriculture relies on pesticides for minimizing the damage to crops from insects. Not surprisingly applications of pesticides have adverse effects on biodiversity, not only because of their effects on insects but also on animals that feed on the insects. One study[508] discovered that contaminated streams in Europe had 42 percent fewer invertebrate species such as mayflies and dragonflies, and another found that applications of the most common seven pesticides had a disastrous effect on the mortality of the common European frog.[509] Neonicotinoid insecticides—the most widely used insecticides in the world—have been identified as one of the causes of the global collapse of honey bee populations. They have also been shown to have an adverse effect on soil invertebrates.[510]

Other sources of habitat destruction are urbanization and pollution from mining, energy production, and industrial development. Currently, more than half of the human population lives in cities, a figure expected to increase to 80 percent by 2050, and because so many cities are on the coasts, urban development creates particular challenges for the biodiversity of coastal areas. Of particular concern is the increased nutrient load in waterways caused by effluents from humans and agriculture. However, new evidence shows that human-dominated habitats can maintain native biodiversity.[511] It is well known that many tropical forest animals can prosper outside their native habitats. The areca nut palm farms in the Western Ghats of India contain 95 percent of the bird species in the adjacent native forests despite having been in continuous production for two millennia.[512] It is estimated that human-dominated habitats make up 75 percent of global land surfaces and contain large amounts of biodiversity that has been largely ignored in scientific studies. Conservation efforts should not only focus on protected areas but also on maintaining and increasing biodiversity in inhabited areas and in agriculture.

Apart from habitat destruction, much damage is caused by the introduction of invasive species—a process that started with the European discovery of North America (known as the Columbian Exchange)—and this is true in both rich and poor countries. According to one study for the United States, 59 percent of all species introduced there since 1906 have caused harmful ecological and economic damage to agriculture, forestry, and fisheries. The direct costs include reduced harvests, the cost of eradication, and pest control. The economic damage to the United States was estimated to be close to $100 billion—a very high figure.[513] Plants including tansy, ragwort, leafy spurge and tamarisk, and aquatic species such as zebra mussels and lampreys have caused major problems. However, the proportionate damage by invasive species to countries such as South Africa, India, and Brazil was estimated to be even higher. Poor countries have been affected by witchweed, grey leaf spot, the large grain borer, and the water hyacinth in aquatic systems. Rats have caused an incredible amount of damage both to crops and to ecosystems and still do, while wild goats and wild pigs have wreaked havoc on many tropical islands including the Galapagos Islands. The introduction of invasive species is linked to trade and human settlements, and not surprisingly, islands are particularly vulnerable.[514] Cargo and passenger ships accidentally brought rats and seeds of foreign species, and immigrants brought familiar animals and plants that reminded them of home. For example, European settlers to New Zealand introduced many European bird species that outcompeted the native birds, many of which disappeared.

However, in some cases, invasive species can be beneficial in saving biodiversity.[515] On Rodrigues Island in the Indian Ocean, after the forests on the island were cut down in the 1950s and '60s, two bird species and a fruit bat that only occurred on the island almost disappeared because they depended on the native forest. The island was reforested in the 1970s with fast-growing non-native species, and the birds and bats not only survived but flourished. There are other examples. Invasive grasses can substitute for native grasses in providing nesting places for prairie birds, and non-native birds in Hawaii have taken over the role of now-extinct birds in dispersing seeds and therefore maintaining the long-term survival of native trees and plants. Indeed, the argument has been made that even on the oceanic islands, invasions outnumbered extinctions and as a result, biodiversity actually increased. For example, while the number of native species on Easter Island declined from fifty to forty-three after humans arrived, the total number of species has increased from fifty before humans to 111.[516] The point is that while the introduction of some exotic species is highly destructive to ecosystems, others are not.

Climate change is another form of habitat destruction as most species have temperature thresholds beyond which they cannot survive, and small changes in moisture availability could be devastating to some species. In response to warmer temperatures, species try to move either toward the poles or to higher elevations. Migrating birds arrive earlier, frogs sing earlier, and plants flower earlier with the result that over the last thirty years spring signs have appeared

15.5 days earlier than before—an average of five days per decade as a result of an average decennial temperature change of 0.4 degrees.[517] With an expected increase in temperatures of two to five degrees over the twenty-first century, this process will accelerate. Some animal species adapt or move quite well, but in other cases, the habitat they rely on does not move as quickly. For example, butterflies may be able to move quickly, but not the plants they depend on. An example of migration of insects is the northward movements of the spittlebug nymph on the California coast, and an example of climate-induced expansion of insect populations is the disastrous population explosion of the pine beetle in the western Canadian forests. The beetle is native to western Canada, but its population was kept in check through winter die-offs and occasional forest fires. A combination of warmer winters and fire suppressions resulted in an increase in the volume of trees killed by the beetle from five million cubic metres in 1996 to four billion in 2005 with devastating effects on the forest industries.[518] In the Southern Hemisphere, the grey-headed flying fox moved its range 750 kilometres southward in Australia. Polar bears are thought to be particularly vulnerable to climate change as they typically hunt their main prey of seals from sea ice. The increased retreat of the Arctic sea ice during the summer months makes the hunting more difficult and makes them vulnerable to starvation. Ocean acidification, the result of the buildup of carbon emissions in the atmosphere (Chapter 4), may have catastrophic effects on the ocean ecosystem because of its likely impact of increased acidity on the calcium-rich shells of crustaceans such as shellfish and corals.

The final cause of biodiversity loss is disease. Today, air travel and tourism can be blamed for the spread of potentially deadly viruses and fungi that in many cases are killing native species at unprecedented rates. For example, frog populations are declining in many parts of the world because of the spread of a type of chytrid fungus called *Batrachochytrium dendrobatidis*, and the current die-off of bats from white nose syndrome is caused by the fungus *Geomyces destructans*.[519]

Aggregate measures of the state of the natural environment: the Living Planet Index, the Ecological Footprint, and the Millennium Ecosystem Assessment

The emphasis on the current and expected future rate of extinctions has come under criticism as it does not measure the state of biodiversity, and not all extinctions are of equal importance. Various attempts to devise overall measurements of biodiversity have been made; these are important in formulating policies. The best known is the Living Planet Index, the result of the collaboration between the World Wildlife Fund for Nature and the World Conservation Monitoring Centre of the United Nations Environmental Programme (UNEP).[520] Published in the biannual *Living Planet Report*, the Living Planet Index's 2014 version is based on population estimates of 10,380 populations of 3,038 species of vertebrate animals—mammals, birds, fish, and reptiles, subdivided into temperate and tropical species from various ecosystems. Table 6.2 shows that it is further subdivided into terrestrial, marine, and freshwater indices. The base year is 1970, and separate counts are made for each year to form subindices.[521] For the overall index, a geometric average is taken of the subcomponents. No insects and plants are included on the lists because baseline populations are too difficult to establish, and it is assumed that had they been included, the overall picture would not change as these populations would likely follow the overall population trends.

Not surprisingly, the overall index declined between 1970 and 2010. The terrestrial index declined by 39 percent, with the largest decline (56 percent) in tropical species. The sharp decline in the tropics, particularly serious in South America and the Caribbean, occurred because of the loss of natural habitats to pasture or cropland (Table 6.3). The marine

Table 6.2. Living Planet Indices of biodiversity in 2010 relative to 1970

	2010 species population index compared with 1970 (% change)
Temperate index	−36
Tropical index	−56
Terrestrial index	−39
Marine index	−39
Freshwater index	−76
Global Living Planet Index	**−52**

Source: *Living Planet Report, 2014: Species and Spaces, People and Places.*

Table 6.3. Living Planet Indices of biodiversity in 2010 relative to 1970 by region

Region	2010 population index compared with 1970 (% change)
Nearctic (North America)	−20
Palearctic (Europe, Northern Asia, North Africa)	−30
Neotropical (Caribbean, South America)	−83
Afrotropical (sub-Saharan Africa)	−19
Indo-Pacific (Southeast Asia, India, Pacific Islands, Australia, New Zealand)	−67

Source: *Living Planet Report, 2014: Species and Spaces, People and Places.*

index showed a decline of 39 percent with the largest effects in the Indian, Southeast, and Southern Oceans, caused by overfishing. The freshwater index declined by 76 percent, again with a sharp decline in the tropics. The main causes here were overfishing, invasive species, pollution, and habitat destruction through dam building. The loss of mangrove forests in coastal areas is of particular concern as they provide nursery habitats for 85 percent of commercial fish species. The emphasis in the media has been on the destruction of rainforests, but mangrove forests have been destroyed at twice the rate of tropical forests, and it is estimated that one-third of the area of mangrove forests has been lost to rice paddies and shrimp ponds. This was raised as a serious issue following the devastating impact of the 2008 cyclone Nargis in Burma, where the native mangrove forests would have softened the impacts of the high waves whipped up by the cyclone. While shrimp ponds are lucrative for some segments of the local population, they incur considerable costs to the local communities as the cutting of mangrove forests has decreased flood protection. Table 6.3 also confirms that biodiversity loss is also very high in the Indo-Pacific region.

Questions arise about the reliability of these overall measures. So much depends on the choice of the baseline year, in this case 1970, which may have been an abnormal year. Had another year been chosen, the results may have been different. Furthermore, indices are based on a limited list of species exclusively made up of vertebrates, which may have created a bias in the whole index, as plant populations and other animal populations may have behaved differently. The question of the base year also arises with the Red List.[522]

The *Living Planet Report* includes information on the Ecological Footprint. The Ecological Footprint analysis was pioneered by Canadian William Rees of the University of British Columbia and further developed by his PhD student Mathis Wackernagel in the book *Our Ecological Footprint*.[523] The footprint tries to measure the extent to which the earth's productive or regenerative capacity can keep up with the increasing demand on resources. The Ecological Footprint measures the area (in global hectares and excluding oceans) of productive land and water necessary to provide enough resources for the world population to survive and to absorb the waste generated, including CO_2 through carbon sequestration. Figures for 2010 show that the total ecological footprint for the earth was 18.1 billion hectares of land needed to produce resources and absorb the wastes.[524] Given the world population in 2010, the Ecological Footprint's findings translate into a demand on the earth's resources of 2.6 hectares per person. The total ecological footprint is compared with the available resources—the biocapacity—which is the total productive area capable of supplying resources and absorbing wastes. In 2010 it was estimated at 12 billion hectares: 1.7 hectares per person, implying that we are exceeding the earth's capacity by approximately 50 percent—the demand is 1.5 times greater than the capacity, which means we are using up our natural assets by depleting fisheries and forests and by emitting CO_2 at a faster rate than is removed naturally. Not surprisingly, the largest footprints are created by the richest countries. Qatar tops the list with a footprint of 11.68 followed by the United Arab Emirates at 8.44 (see Table 6.3). Qatar and the United Arab Emirates are tiny desert countries with hardly any arable land but are major oil producers that create large footprints because of CO_2 emissions. Canada has a large footprint but also the largest biocapacity because of the large land area. Most countries, including poor countries, use more resources than they have, which is obviously unsustainable resulting in a case of real resource scarcity that we will have to deal with soon.

Table 6.4. Ecological footprint and biocapacity, selected countries, 2008

Country/Region	Ecological footprint/person	Biocapacity/person
World	2.70	1.78
High-income countries	5.6	3.05
Middle-income countries	1.92	1.72
Low-income countries	1.14	1.14
Qatar	11.68	2.05
United Arab Emirates	8.44	0.64
United States	7.19	3.86
Finland	6.29	12.19
Canada	6.43	14.92
Brazil	2.93	9.63
Cuba	1.90	0.71
Australia	6.68	14.57
China	2.13	0.87
India	0.87	0.48
South Africa	2.59	1.29
Mozambique	0.78	2.21
Malawi	0.78	0.67
Eritrea	0.66	1.47

Source: Adapted from Table 2, *Living Planet Report, 2012: Biodiversity, Biocapacity and Better Choices.*

The ecological footprint concept has become popular as a handy guide to understanding the stresses we put on the planet. A website is even available to assist individuals in calculating their own ecological footprint. It is doubtful, however, that this and other aggregate indices or measures add to our overall knowledge of environmental degradation; thus, they are not of great value in guiding environmental policies. For example, Canada and Australia live within their ecological limits only because they have large land areas relative to the population—a difficult situation for other countries to emulate and thus of little use in providing environmental guidance. It could be argued that the ecological footprint analysis is more of an analysis of national endowments of natural resources than a guide to sustainable living. It also neglects measures of land quality. For example, a country with a high rate of land degradation—which is not sustainable—could have a low ecological footprint.[525] Nevertheless, although the methodology is open to criticism, ecological footprint analysis still gives an indication of the extent to which the rate of resource utilization is out of balance with regenerative capacity.

Another major attempt to assess the health of the planet was initiated by the United Nations in 2001 under the rubric the *Millennium Ecosystem Assessment*. Its purpose was to assess the impacts of ecosystem changes on human well-being and to establish scientific backing for proposals to ensure the sustainable uses of ecosystems. Its 2005 report provides a comprehensive assessment of the health of the world's ecosystems and the services they provide.[526] Ecosystem services are divided into four categories: supporting, provisioning, regulating, and cultural. Supporting services are necessary for all ecosystems to function; examples of such services are nutrient cycling and the formation of soils. Provisioning services include the ability to grow food; the provisioning of grazing for animals; the production of fibre (wood used for pulp and paper, wool, and cotton), wild fruits, animals, and fish; genetic resources and plants for pharmaceutical products; and the supply of fresh water for consumption. The regulating services are those we get for free such as the clean air from the interactions of plants with the environment; water purification services; natural hazard regulation such as flood control; the control of local and regional climates; erosion control; pollination; and the natural buffers to some diseases and pests. Cultural services include spiritual, religious, and aesthetic values derived from the environment as well as recreation and ecotourism.

In the *Millennium Ecosystem Assessment*, out of the twenty-four ecosystem services examined, fifteen were degraded or used unsustainably, including the provision of fresh water, fisheries, the purification of air and water, the regulation of regional and local climates, and the regulation of natural hazards and wastes. One of the few services that has improved over the last forty years is food production, but at the expense of some other services such as fresh water, genetic resources, and soil quality. The decline of these services is the inevitable result of the doubling of world population in the last forty years and a sixfold increase in world GDP, which led to a 250 percent increase in food production, a doubling of water use, a tripling of wood fibre production (pulp and paper), a doubling of electricity generation from hydro and a 50 percent increase in timber production. While human well-being improved and the number of people in poverty fell, it came at a considerable cost to the environment. The deterioration of ecosystem services disproportionately affects people living in poor countries, creating a significant barrier to the achievement of the eight Millennium Development Goals agreed on in 2000.[527] The assessment report warns that climate change and nutrient overload in waterways are creating an environment prone to the danger of sudden and potentially irreversible changes in water quality, which will result in an increased number of dead areas in coastal regions. Deteriorating water quality in conjunction with overfishing may lead to an imminent collapse of fisheries.

In conclusion, regardless of the measure used, biodiversity and ecosystem services are deteriorating, but not uniformly; indeed, in some areas the situation is improving. The worst problems are found in the tropics, in lakes and rivers, and in the oceans. The extent to which climate change will accelerate the damage depends on its severity and the policies implemented for mitigation and adaptation.

The economic value of biodiversity and ecosystem services

How can we ensure that biodiversity and ecosystem services are protected? Economists claim that the reason for the decline in these facets of nature is that they do not have a price, and consequently the solution is to attach a price or a value. Should nature be valued like any other commodity in terms of its impact on human well-being? E.O. Wilson, arguing that nature is special, coined the term *biophilia*, meaning that there is an instinctive bond between humans and nature, and regular contact with nature and other species is critical for human mental health and overall well-being.[528] This is because we are part of the animal kingdom, complex mammals in need of variety and stimuli in our place in the biological world. We were hunters and gathers for approximately 99 percent of our existence, which must have influenced the development of our brains both cognitively and emotionally. Biodiversity can therefore be considered one of the essential human needs that include food, shelter, sex, and companionship. The hypothesis that our behaviour has been shaped by a distant past has been further developed by evolutionary psychologists, who point out that evolution likely favoured individuals who learned to adapt to the environment. The support for this hypothesis is based on evidence of biophobia (fear of nature) as well as biophilia.[529] Many psychological studies show that humans in general fear snakes and spiders, a remnant of the times when they were a threat to survival. Evidence also suggests some genetic preference for certain landscapes with savannah or park-like scenery with proximity to water—the type of savannah scenery where humans first evolved because it provided certain advantages for survival in terms of protection from predators. In general, people do not like landscapes with closely spaced trees or trees with lots of dense underfoliage and rough terrain. An additional argument in support of biophilia is that natural settings appear to have a restorative and calming effect on people. For example, an often-quoted study shows that post-operative patients in a room with a window where they could see trees recovered more quickly and required fewer painkillers than patients in room where they could see only a brick wall.[530] The idea of biophilia has been embraced in developmental psychology, preventative medicine, and architecture, but the hypothesis can be criticized on several grounds. One is that social selection is a more powerful factor in the evolution of the human species than the environment. Another criticism is that because it takes a mere ten thousand years for evolutionary changes to occur, by now humans have likely adapted to culturally shaped environments formed by agriculture and urban settlements; thus our preference for parklike scenery is of a more recent origin.[531] A third criticism is that biophilia does not necessarily support the maintenance of biodiversity as the landscapes humans prefer may be devoid of any dangerous animals such as snakes, wolves, tigers, spiders, or sharks.

Nevertheless, plenty of evidence suggests that interaction with nature is good for both our health and our general well-being. For example, evidence shows that the presence of animals (pets) has beneficial health effects on their owners by lowering blood pressure and cholesterol, that proximity to plants and garden settings make people feel better, and that landscapes and wilderness experiences have therapeutic effects.[532] More recently, a major statistical study in the United Kingdom using smartphones and twenty thousand volunteers showed that people were significantly happier being outdoors in a natural environment than being indoors.[533]

However, the fact that nature makes humans feel good and is good for their health supports an argument for conservation but is not very helpful in policy-making. Humans also benefit from having meaningful work, having friends, and being in good health. How can a government prioritize the cost of maintaining biodiversity compared with the costs of maintaining health and education services, infrastructure, and so on? In making public choices, we need to put a value on biodiversity even though it could be argued that the value of biodiversity is infinite because without it we would not survive. Markets do not put a price or a value on biodiversity because it cannot be traded, but public policy requires some measure of its value, otherwise it becomes impossible to make informed decisions about the importance of biodiversity and ecosystems among the range of options in the allocation of scarce public money. Valuation is difficult but necessary—after all, we accept the fact that insurance companies put a price on a human life.

Biologists claim that the world's ecosystems are being destroyed at a rate that has not been seen since the periods of mass extinctions. Why should this be of concern to humans, particularly if economic growth can continue for perhaps decades after ecosystems have been severely compromised? There are many reasons. Natural assets matter precisely because they are valuable. Biodiversity preserves the capability of ecosystems to adapt to temporary climatic change such as drought. It also preserves evolutionary potential. Climate change will impose largely unknown stresses on ecosystems, and a rich biodiversity has more potential for adaptation as some species may grow and flourish and take over the role of less adaptable species. Genetic plant diversity is also important in the continual search for new varieties that are more resistant to plant diseases and insect infestations. On a grander scale, the most important value of biodiversity is the ability to stabilize an ecosystem which has evolved over three and a half billion years.

A vast number of studies have confirmed that some aspects biodiversity and ecosystem services have considerable economic value.[534] The economic value is derived from *use*, both directly and indirectly, as well as from *non-use*, which means that even though we do not derive immediate monetary benefit, we value biodiversity because it exists. For example, many of us derive pleasure from the knowledge that there are still tigers in some parts of the world. The direct use value is the value of agricultural products, forest products, and recreational products, while the indirect value is in the value of ecosystem services such as soil retention, water quality, and the maintenance of habitats.

Different methodologies have been developed to assess use values with existing market data. For example, the total economic value of insect pollination for agriculture is estimated to €153 billion (US$214 billion, assuming an exchange rate of €1 = US$1.4), equivalent to 9.5 percent of world agricultural output.[535] Studies estimating the values of non-timber forest products show that the values vary but are usually less than $100 per hectare per year in developing countries.[536] Other studies evaluating boreal forests in Nordic countries indicate that largest value came from timber ($45 to $85 per hectare per year) with other benefits such as berry picking, recreation, and CO_2 sequestration amounting to less ($35 to $50 per hectare per year, all in 2000 values). A study of forests in eight Mediterranean countries concluded that one-third of their value came from timber—the remainder was attributed to carbon sequestration, watershed protection, recreation, non-timber forest products, and grazing.[537] Another study estimates that the benefits of halving deforestation rates by 2030 would avoid 3.7 trillion in damages caused by climate change.[538]

Unfortunately, for prime agricultural land areas and high-density urban areas, the value of conversions of ecosystems to agriculture or suburbs is usually higher than their preservation, unless all benefits of preservation are accounted for. For tropical forests, the immediate commercial gains from conversion to oil palm plantation or agriculture in Cameroon were shown to be high, as were conversion to tea plantations in Ceylon and unsustainable logging in Malaysia, but if the full global benefits including ecosystem services (including carbon storage) were accounted for, tropical forest conservation would yield the largest benefits. However, because ecosystem services are not included in the value of the forests, and because alternative uses of the forest land are so valuable, it is unlikely that forest conservation will occur unless there is a transfer of money from the world community to countries with tropical forests. After all, the main benefit of their preservation accrues to the world community as a whole while the cost of foregoing the revenues from palm plantations or cattle ranching has to be borne by the countries themselves.

Another use value involves the use of plants for drugs. Considerable interest has been shown in the possibility of developing drugs from rainforest plants through bioprospecting, which involves searching for plants that have had a role in traditional medicine or screening plants for unknown compounds that may be useful in the pharmaceutical industry. An early example is the rosy periwinkle found in Madagascar and known to have medicinal properties. Research confirmed the presence of alkaloids, which when extracted could be used to cure Hodgkin's disease and leukemia. The National Cancer Institute in the United States has identified three thousand plants active against cancer cells, 70 percent of which are found in the rainforest, and it is believed that many more can be found. It is estimated that up to half of the synthetic drugs in use today have their origins in a natural plants and 42 percent of cancer drugs are plant based. Three-quarters of the world's population still depend on natural remedies.[539] Many of these plants are now threatened. Early estimates of the potential value of a hectare of land in the world's hot spots in terms of the value of the drugs that could be developed ranged from $21/hectare to $9,177/hectare, and if the latter figure is anywhere near correct, it would mean that private incentives to conservation would be greater than the revenue from development. Unfortunately a more rigorous study has indicated that the value of bioprospecting is nowhere near a value of $9,177. Instead, it is more likely to range from $14/hectare to $65/hectare, which would not be enough to save the areas from development.[540] In 1991, the pharmaceutical firm Merck signed a collaboration agreement with the Costa Rican Instituto Nacional de Biodiversidad (INBio), a private non-profit institution set up to combat the loss of biodiversity in Costa Rica. Under the agreement, Merck paid $1 million for the right to screen soil samples, plants, and other species for new molecules. Part of the money went toward the cost of maintaining forest lands. However, the great promises of wonder drugs have not materialized, and according to some estimates, the likely value of yet-to-be-discovered drugs may be between $3 billion to $4 billion to private companies and $147 billion to society as a whole, which today is not a huge amount of money.[541]

Ecotourism also provides use value, which countries such as Costa Rica have exploited to their own benefit. Revenues from tourists visiting game parks are significant sources of incomes in East Africa and in other parts of the developing world, with estimates ranging from $10 to $50 per visit from foreign tourists, less from domestic tourists. Even in the United States, economic activity generated by national parks was estimated at $13.3 billion in 2006.[542]

However, in many cases the value of biodiversity and ecosystem services cannot be estimated with market data, so other methods are employed, using the concept of non-use value.[543] Non-use value consists of existence value and bequest value. The existence value is the price an individual is willing to pay for preserving something for its own value; and the bequest value the price an individual is willing to pay to leave something to future generations. These values can be estimated by asking people what they are willing to pay for protecting an animal, or a forest, or an ecosystem.[544] Adding up the prices that all individuals concerned would be willing to pay gives an estimate of the implied value of the animal, the forest, or the ecosystem. Willingness-to-pay studies have estimated that people would be willing to pay $20 per year to preserve wetlands, creating a fund that would increase by $14 billion per year if every adult in rich countries contributed. Another willingness-to-pay study estimates that the citizens in the United Kingdom would be willing to pay the equivalent of $48 person per hectare to conserve an additional 5 percent of the world's tropical forests, amounting to a yearly total of $912 million. If all industrialized countries were willing to do the same, the money would increase to $26.8 billion.[545] An oft-cited but much criticized study published in 1997 in the prestigious journal *Nature* attempted to put a value on the world's ecosystems by aggregating results from 1994 willingness-to-pay studies, arriving at a figure of $33 trillion per year with a confidence interval of $16 to $54 trillion.[546] Apart from serious methodological problems, the study's results are patently absurd because in 1994 global GDP was only about $5 trillion. To put this into perspective, it would mean that individuals on average would be willing to pay approximately six times their annual earnings to save the world's ecosystems.

There are many valid criticisms of the usefulness of these types of estimates of non-use value. Willingness to pay does not necessarily mean that people would actually pay the amount they claim. Talk is cheap. Furthermore, if people are willing to pay $48 per hectare to protect forests in the Amazon they may not be willing to pay an additional $20 per year for wetland preservations. In reality, the world spends far less than the willingness-to-pay studies indicate they would.[547] For example, the costs of reducing extinction risks of globally threatened birds—species that people are willing to pay for to conserve— is estimated to be $0.875 to $1.23 billion per year, but currently only 12 percent of this cost is funded.[548] The total costs of meeting the 2020 target for protected areas are estimated to be $76.1 billion per year. This is equivalent to 20 percent of the value of global consumption of soft drinks, or, to use another example, it is a minute proportion of the trillions of dollars spent in the United States and Europe on bank bailouts following the financial crisis of 2008.

Estimation of non-use value also assumes any aspect of nature is important only if it is of perceived value to humans. This is problematic, as humans have negative feelings about quite a few living things—for example, insects, algae, and fungi—most of which are critical for the existence of other life forms and therefore for our own survival.[549] Indeed, several studies have shown that the value individuals put on individual species to some extent depends on how attractive or how useful the species is to humans. The "cute" factor appears to be important, especially with regard to eye size (note the successful campaign to stop the Canadian killing of baby harp seals, which are not endangered).[550] People may not be willing to pay for the conservation of snakes and fish even though they may be of critical importance in some ecosystems.

Finally, one can ask what the economic valuations of nature really mean. George Monbiot, the *Guardian* columnist and blogger, has pointedly questioned their use. In discussing a report by the Natural Capital Committee set up by the UK government he writes:

> It claimed, for example, that if fresh water ecosystems in this country were better protected, the additional aesthetic value arising from that protection would be £700 million. That's the aesthetic value: in other words, what it looks like. We will value the increment in what it looks like at £700 million. It said that if grassland and sites of special scientific interest were better protected, their wildlife value would increase by £40 million. The value of their wildlife—like the chalk hill blues and the dog violets that live on protected grasslands— would be enhanced by £40 million. These figures, ladies and gentlemen, are marmalade. They are finely shredded, boiled to a pulp, heavily sweetened.... In other words and still indigestible they are total gibberish.[551]

Payment for ecosystem services is a newer approach to conservation involving direct payments to providers of ecosystem services. The payments can be made either by the user of the services (an example might be a hydroelectric-power producer paying upstream users to preserve the watershed) or by governments or international organizations paying the owners for services to third parties (e.g., carbon sequestration, where everyone benefits). Payments for services have been used in Costa Rica and Mexico, and in the United States and Europe.[552] The payments idea has been embraced by both environmentalists and development specialists as an innovative approach that simultaneously protects the environment and helps poor people, as the likely recipients would be poor farmers. It is a major feature of the REDD program for forest protection, discussed in Chapter 7. Payment for ecosystem services has been seen as a solution to the age-old dilemma of people versus parks, of nature protectionists versus social conservationists. These can be payments for pollution control in the form of waste elimination projects; for conservation of natural resources such as wetlands and forests; and for tree planting for carbon sequestration and the control of soil erosion.[553] For these schemes to be effective, the farmers must want to participate and there must be no legal or financial barriers to participation, such as lack of land tenure. As well, these

types of programs may not necessarily benefit poor people because by restricting the use of agricultural land, the programs may increase food prices, only
benefiting those farmers who own land considered to have high potential for
providing environmental services. Thus payments for ecosystem services may
not be the most efficient means of simultaneously achieving the two objectives
of conservation and helping poor people.[554]

International conventions

Biodiversity loss affects people both locally and globally and, in common with
other global problems such as climate change, solutions require international
cooperation, typically expressed in treaties or conventions. So far over 150
environmental treaties have been signed, but clearly they are not very effective
or the environment and biodiversity would not be in such a deplorable state in
a large part of the world. Some treaties are ineffective because they do not get
enough signatories to come into operation. A treaty can only come into force
when all participants (or an agreed-upon minimum number) have signed and
ratified. Obviously, a free-rider problem exists here. If every country except one
signs and ratifies, the miscreant country will likely benefit even though it does
not have to bear any of the costs. Other treaties are ineffective because they
lack mechanisms for updates, compliance, and enforcement.

The first convention relating to nature was the Convention for the Protection of Birds Useful to Agriculture, signed in 1902 and superseded in 1950 by
the International Convention for the Protection of Birds. Better known and
perhaps more effective is the 1979 Convention on the Conservation of Migratory
Species of Wild Animals (the Bonn Convention) with 108 signatories. Migratory animals are particularly vulnerable as they are subject to potential dangers
in several countries. Even if one country protects them, the measures may not
be effective unless other countries do so as well. The convention, requiring
signatories to prevent the killing or taking of endangered migratory animals,
asks parties to conclude agreements regarding other migratory species such as
ducks and swans. The Convention on Wetlands of International Importance
(the Ramsar Convention 1971) was designed to deal with wetlands because of
their critical importance in maintaining biodiversity. International cooperation was needed, since two or more countries are often involved. For example,
river basins can involve several states. Pollution affecting wetlands may also
originate far from the affected areas. The participating countries commit to
include wetland conservation in land-use planning in order to promote "the wise

use of wetlands in their territory" (Article 3.1 of the treaty). There are detailed guidelines on wetland policies and management for wetland sites.

The Convention on Biological Diversity, better known as the Biodiversity Convention, was adopted in 1992 at the Rio Summit. It has three aims: conservation of biological diversity, the sustainable use of its components, and the fair and equitable sharing of benefits from genetic resources. It is legally binding on the parties; in signing, they commit to implement the Biodiversity Convention. The convention has been ratified by most countries with the exception of the United States, which signed the treaty but did not ratify. At the time of the Senate hearings, opponents were convinced that the convention would herald in the controversial Wildlands Project, which aims to set up wildlife corridors across the United States for the preservation of biodiversity. This was seen as a red flag by many conservatives, who felt it would lead to severe incursions into individual property rights.

In 2002, the parties to the convention agreed to achieve a significant reduction in the rate of biodiversity loss by 2010 and to establish a variety of indicators or measures of the loss including the trends of various components of diversity, trends in sustainable use of the environment, and threats to biodiversity such as the introduction of alien species and excessive nitrogen deposition. In the report preparing for the 2010 meetings, it was noted that the target of the significant reduction in the rate of biodiversity loss had not been achieved.[555] On the other hand, 170 countries had adopted biodiversity strategies and action plans as well as monitoring mechanisms, and while many countries had achieved progress in halting the rate of deforestation, insufficient actions had been taken to integrate biodiversity into broader policies.

In 2011, at the tenth meeting of the Conference of the Parties to the Convention in Nagoya, Aichi Prefecture, Japan, a revised and updated strategy plan for biodiversity was adopted that includes new targets to be reached by 2020, and later the same year the United Nations declared 2011 to 2020 the decade of biodiversity and desertification. The strategic plan consists of general goals to be achieved during the decade, including addressing the underlying causes of biodiversity loss; reducing the pressure on biodiversity and improving sustainability; improving the status of biodiversity in safeguarding ecosystems, species, and genetic diversity; enhancing benefits to people from ecosystem services and biodiversity; and enhancing the planning and implementation process.[556] The plan also includes specific targets—the Aichi biodiversity targets. These are the elimination of harmful subsidies; halving of the rate of loss of natural habitats by 2020 and if possible reducing the rate of loss to zero;

sustainable management of all fish, invertebrate stocks, and aquatic plants; protection of at least 17 percent of terrestrial and inland waters and 10 percent of coastal and marine areas; prevention of extinction of threatened species; and integration of traditional knowledge in national plans. The targets call for restoration of at least 15 percent of degraded areas. There is also a specific mention of the urgent need to protect coral reefs—a target to be achieved by 2015 rather than 2020.

However, without adequate financial backing, particularly in developing countries, the necessary increase in biodiversity protection will not occur. Biodiversity conservation does not rate high on the list of financial priorities in rich countries, and poor countries do not have adequate resources to enforce targets and policies. In 2012 at a meeting in Hyderabad, it was agreed that the financial support to developing countries for biodiversity conservation be doubled by 2015 from a total of $5 billion to $10 billion, but so far firm commitments from individual countries are lacking. In a somewhat desperate measure, the parties and NGOs were invited to become "biodiversity champions" by committing funding or expertise to the achievement of specific Aichi targets.[557] In an interim 2014 progress report, it was noted that while progress has been made on a few of the targets, including the number of protected areas, other targets require additional efforts such as those for habitat loss, species extinction, and ecosystem restoration.[558]

Apart from lack of funding, another problem is that the high-profile conventions tend to become politicized; examples are the International Convention for the Regulation of Whaling and the Convention on International Trade in Endangered Species of Wild Fauna and Flora (CITES). The politics are unfortunate because the original purposes and goals become distorted. The Convention for the Regulation of Whaling had fifteen signatories in 1946 and came into force in 1948. The objectives of the convention include regulation of whale fisheries to ensure conservation and development of whale stocks, which includes protection from overhunting. It is authorized to set limits to the size of catches and declare open and closed seasons as well as areas for whaling. It is interesting to note that the stated purpose was not to stop whaling but to ensure that it was done in a sustainable fashion; its original fifteen signatories were the countries actively involved in whaling with the exception of Japan, which joined the convention later. The International Whaling Commission (IWC) was established to administer the convention. However, its authority is limited as membership is voluntary and not backed by treaty. Initially, the IWC was dominated by the main whaling states and set quotas at levels that were clearly *not* sustainable. In the 1970s, concern grew that whales were being overfished, and the path-breaking 1972 United Nations Conference on the Human Environment in Stockholm recommended a ten-year moratorium on commercial whaling. CITES also identified several whale species as being in danger of extinction. Meanwhile, the membership of the commission grew to eighty-four, including many landlocked countries with no interest in commercial whaling, thus causing the political balance to gradually shift against whaling. In 1982, the IWC voted with the necessary 75 percent majority for a moratorium on commercial whaling to come into effect in 1986. The moratorium (which excludes whaling for scientific purposes and for aboriginal subsistence purposes), which was intended to be temporary, is still in effect, and is highly controversial but has been very effective as the number of whales hunted has declined from sixty-six thousand in 1961 to two thousand in 2008.[559] As early as 1991, the Scientific Committee of the IWC recommended that on the basis of population estimates, two thousand minke whales could be culled without adverse effects on the population, but the commission voted to maintain the moratorium. The members of the commission could not and cannot agree on a formula for estimating a total allowable catch if the moratorium were lifted—called the Revised Management Scheme (RMS)—and now whaling for "scientific" purposes is increasing.

The commission is split into pro-whaling and anti-whaling factions. Since the 1970s, conservation groups, including the World Wildlife Fund, encouraged non-whaling countries to join to shift the balance of votes in favour of a moratorium. It is alleged that conservation groups paid the membership dues and travel support for new anti-whaling members. However, the tables have now turned, and Japan is accused of using similar tactics in buying votes in favour of lifting the moratorium, a charge that Japan does not dispute. As a result, the balance has shifted from a 75 percent majority in favour of a moratorium in 1986 to a fifty-fifty split; any change requires a 75 percent majority. The IWC cannot agree, and it is powerless because governments that object to amendments to the convention can exempt themselves by lodging a complaint. Currently, Japan, Norway, Iceland, Denmark (representing Greenland and the Faroes), Russia, and the United States are engaged in "scientific" or aboriginal whaling, with the largest fleets run by Norway and Japan.[560] Whaling was even done in the Southern Ocean Whale Sanctuary established by the commission. However, in a major victory for anti-whalers, the International Court of Justice ruled in 2014 that Japanese whaling in the Southern Ocean could not be considered scientific research.

CITES is another organization subject to political infighting. Enacted in 1973, CITES aims to control international trade in endangered animals or plants, or parts thereof. The parties to the convention were and are expected to enact their own laws to control the trade within the framework of the convention. The convention offers three levels of protection, according to what appendix the species is listed on. Species listed in Appendix I are under the threat of extinction and cannot be traded commercially; Appendix II lists species in which trade may threaten future survival and therefore trade is closely controlled through export permits if necessary; and Appendix III lists species protected by countries wanting assistance from other countries in controlling trade which can only occur if appropriate permits or certificates have been obtained. Trade is prohibited in approximately six hundred species and three hundred plants, including all primates, whales, and dolphins, cats (leopards and tigers), bears, elephants, rhinoceros, crocodile-type animals, sea turtles, and boa-type snakes, basking and great white sharks, many cacti and orchids, and some lumber products (Appendix I). Trade in an additional thirty-three thousand species is strictly limited through Appendix II. Member countries are expected to impose trade sanctions against violators.

Trade in animals is very large. Legal trade in animals alone was estimated to have been between $3 and $4 billion in the 1980s and grew to an estimated $10 billion at the turn of the century.[561] A recent study commissioned by the World Wildlife Fund puts the value of illegal timber trade at $7 billion per year and illegal trade in wildlife at $7.8 to $10 billion per year.[562] Animals are sold for pets and for zoos, and some are killed for food (e.g., gorillas for bush meat), clothing and accessories (e.g., fur coats, shoes, and handbags), and traditional medicines. Illegal trade poses the greatest threat to the survival of some mammals such as the Asian tiger, the rhinoceros, and the Asian bear. Tiger bones are supposed to have anti-inflammatory properties and are used for arthritis, rheumatism, headaches, and to cure general weakness; a tiger skeleton can fetch $20,000 on the international market.[563] Tiger claws are thought to cure insomnia and tiger eyeballs to cure malaria and epilepsy.

Rhino horns are used in Asia as an aphrodisiac and for medicines that are believed to cure anything from rheumatic fever to cancer. The street value of one kilo of rhino horn is now estimated to be near $100,000, and because of illegal killing to support this trade, the number of rhinos has decreased catastrophically. For example, in 1970 there were in excess of seventy thousand black rhinos; now there are probably three thousand. While the CITES ban was working well initially—in 2007 only thirteen rhinos were killed in South Africa—it is no longer effective as the number of rhinos killed in 2013 increased to over one thousand. The main reason appears to be a surge in demand, which has pushed up prices to such an extent that poaching has become highly profitable in the absence of adequate surveillance. The buyers are the increasingly wealthy businessmen and officials in Vietnam, where rhino horns are believed to cure cancers and hangovers. Because of the high price, rhino horns have become a status symbol and therefore a prized gift.[564] South Africa is currently lobbying CITES to allow a onetime sale of a stockpile of rhino horns, which they argue would drive prices down to such a low level that poaching would no longer be profitable. However, as long as the demand for rhino horns is increasing, a onetime sale is unlikely to decrease prices in the long run and will thus not address the root of the problem. Another possibly more effective approach is the injection of poison into rhino horns. This solution has been tried by the Tembe Elephant Park in South Africa, and the park has enlisted the efforts of conservation organizations to spread the word in Vietnam that the horns are poisonous.[565] No more rhinos have been poached in the park, and the demand for rhino horns has dropped by 33 percent in one year in Vietnam.[566] However, the main reason is probably a very successful information campaign in Vietnam dispelling the myth that rhino horns are beneficial to health.

Bile from bear gall bladders is used in many traditional medicines for the treatment of various illnesses. Bears are the only mammals producing urso-deoxycholic acid (UDCA), which is used in Chinese medicine for treating liver and cardiac ailments as well as anything from headaches to skin rashes. It has also been shown to be effective in Western medicine in treating cirrhosis of the liver and gallstones. Because of overharvesting, the population of Asian bears is

Figure 6.6. Mother and baby rhinoceros killed for their horns. It is (falsely) believed in Southeast Asia that ground rhino horns provide health benefits. Credit: Hein Wasche-for and Wikimedia Commons.

declining. To increase the supply of bears, China has set up bear farms, which are reputed to hold up to twenty thousand bears. The bears, kept in small cages, are fitted with tubes that extract the bile on a continuous basis.[567] The consumption of bear bile in China rose from fifty kilograms per year to approximately four thousand kilograms per year by the mid-1990s. Reputedly, there is little poaching in North America, where bear gall bladders can be sold legally in many American states and Canadian provinces. North American bears are listed in Appendix II of the CITES convention, meaning that trade can occur under controlled circumstances. Asian bears are in Appendix I, under which rules no trade can occur. Harvesting of UDCA from bears is quite unnecessary as it can be artificially produced from cow bile.

In 1989, the CITES parties agreed to move elephants from Appendix II to Appendix I in order to protect their decline, resulting in a ban of the trade in ivory. The ban was initially successful, with a sharp decline in the price of ivory from $3,800 per tusk to $35 per tusk after the ban, and a reduction in poaching.[568] Before the ban, ten thousand elephants were killed per year in Tanzania, and after the ban, one hundred. In 1997, CITES succumbed to political pressure from some African countries, sanctioning the sale of government stocks of ivory obtained from elephants that died from natural causes or were culled for other reasons in Botswana, Namibia, and Zimbabwe. In 2008, another onetime sale was allowed; it included ivory from South Africa in addition to the other three countries. Occasional sales of stockpiled ivory are highly controversial, with some claiming legal sales bring down ivory prices, which discourages poaching, while others claim legal sales promote the ivory trade and therefore do not ensure the long-term survival of elephants.

The ivory ban was considered to be one of the success stories of CITES, and elephant populations have been rising by 4 percent per year in South and East Africa, where they have been well protected.[569] Indeed, in Botswana elephants have become a pest in some areas as the populations have ballooned. However, in other parts of Africa, elephants are not faring well. In 2002, a huge horde was confiscated in Zambia, with tusks from three thousand to sixty-five hundred elephants, yet Zambia had reported only 135 animals killed in the previous ten years. A survey of African forestry elephants indicated that the population declined by 62 percent between 2001 and 2012, caused by habitat loss but also by poaching.[570] Because of increased wealth in Asia and the resulting renewed increased demand for ivory, prices have increased from $200 per kg in 2004 to $2100 per kg in 2014, and poaching is increasing at an alarming rate.[571] Evidence shows that profits from ivory sales are financing attacks by the terrorist organization Al-Shabaab.[572] Again, the solution must be in controlling demand. The initial ban was successful because at the time the main customer was Japan, where publicity efforts by the government and newspapers in campaigns against the use of ivory were successful, reducing Japanese imports from five hundred tonnes per year in the mid-1980s to five to ten tonnes per year. The main customer for ivory is now China, where a similar publicity campaign headed by celebrities tries to persuade the Chinese to forego products made from ivory. In 2015, the Chinese government pledged to end the processing and sale of ivory, and urged other countries to follow.

While trade bans alone cannot solve the problem of protecting endangered animals, they are critically important. For example, in 1992 the United States banned the import of parrots for pets, which appears to have been instrumental in reducing poaching rates for parrots. Trade in big cats has also decreased, following bans, and the ban on trade in vicuna (a type of llama) and its wool was successful in stabilizing the population. However, in most cases bans might control the supply in the short run, but unless demand is reduced, prices will increase and provide an incentive to poachers. Consumers have to be persuaded that the products are not desirable, which is difficult in the case of traditional Chinese medicines. Substitutes can be found, but unless buyers believe they are as effective as the original product, they will not be bought.

Wildlife farming can help in saving species in the wild. Most skins from alligators, crocodiles, and caimans now come from captive breeding. The Chinese have been successful in bear farming and want to do the same with Asian tigers. Conservationists argue that this will not save the tiger because people believe wild tigers render more potent medicine. Furthermore, poached tigers would be cheaper for dealers to acquire, as a poor peasant probably would charge a price below the cost of a farmed tiger, which might run to thousands of dollars. Another danger for tigers is the destruction in habitat, which CITES can do nothing about.

CITES has had particular problems in obtaining agreement on commercial marine species because of the vested interests of fishing nations. While CITES lists commercially valuable species such as sturgeon, basking sharks, and whale sharks, attempts to put the highly valuable bluefin tuna to Appendix I were unsuccessful despite the fact that the populations in the Atlantic and Mediterranean have been reduced by 80 percent because of overfishing and the tuna is listed as critically endangered. Most of the catch goes to Japan for making sushi, a much-loved delicacy. The management of the stock was left to the International Commission for the Conservation of Atlantic Tunas (ICCAT), which failed miserably. One year, the scientists recommended a catch of fifteen thousand tonnes, the commission recommended a limit of thirty thousand tons and the catch was sixty thousand tons.[573] Monaco proposed a ban at the CITES meeting in Doha in March 2010. The arguments against the ban claimed that tuna was too commercially valuable to ban and that ICCAT was already controlling the catch—not persuasive arguments by any standards. The fact that in the absence of a ban no commercial catches would happen within three years does not seem to have been an issue. Conditional upon the results of additional research into fish stocks, the ban had full support of the United States and Norway, with further conditional support of the European Union. Not only did Japan, through its traditional policy of buying votes through investment in poor countries' fisheries, swing many votes cast by poor countries, but for purely internal political reasons Canada also voted against a ban to protect a mere three hundred fishermen on the Canadian east coast.

Where do we go from here?

The obvious conclusion of this chapter is that biodiversity and ecosystem services are critically important for all of humankind, and their degradation will negatively affect our future welfare. This is particularly the case in many poor countries that are still directly dependent on local products to provide a subsistence standard of living from an increasingly degraded environment. A hundred years ago, nature and biodiversity were not scarce resources but instead were abundant in relation to the demands of the population. Today's problem is that populations have increased to such an extent that biodiversity and ecosystem services have become scarce resources, but unlike other scarce resources they do not command a price because they cannot be traded on markets. But if biodiversity is to be maintained, these resources must be valued for what they are—essential assets that must be conserved or preserved, locally and globally. However, in our human-dominated world, any conservation strategy must recognize the fact that the improvement of human well-being must go hand in hand with the preservation of biodiversity, and thus conservation efforts have to be based on local conditions and local support.[574]

International conventions for the protection of biodiversity and endangered species are clearly insufficient. While they raise awareness, they often lack adequate enforcement mechanisms to be effective, and their purposes often become thwarted by various interest groups, be they environmentalists, political parties, big corporations, or local interest groups lobbying their own government to take a stance in their favour. Nor do they recognize the fact that protection requires cooperation of local populations. What can we do?

Protection of biodiversity requires the setting up of more protected areas of sufficient size to ensure survival of the species they contain. The areas should contain all examples of local ecosystem types in their natural range and abundance, and nothing should interfere with natural processes such as fires or predators. This is particularly important for the world's hot spots referred to above. The selection of hot spots has been criticized because it is based primarily on the number of species present, with all species being of equal importance. This is not necessarily true from an ecological viewpoint since some species play more critical roles than others in preserving biodiversity. Nevertheless, the hot spots are good places to start. The protected areas must be supported by a well-developed infrastructure to ensure that poaching and logging do not occur. While clear-cutting and hunting are usually beneficial at least in the short run to local communities in terms of both timber revenues and opening up new land for agriculture, many of the benefits of conservation such as preservation of biodiversity and mitigation of global warming accrue to the world community as a whole. Unless local communities benefit, protected areas are unlikely to achieve their objectives. The benefits could include direct transfers from the world community for education and infrastructure. They could also include revenue from ecotourism or from sustainable harvesting of products from the protected areas.

However, biodiversity exists outside pristine areas and hot spots, and more emphasis should be placed on saving green spaces wherever they may be.[575] Humans have interfered with the environment for millennia, and there is no such thing as a Garden of Eden–style stable environment that can be maintained in a pristine state in perpetuity. For example, evidence shows how the Australian aborigines managed much of the Australian continent for their own benefit through the selective use of fire and planting, doing so much more successfully and sustainably than the new arrivals from Europe. Indeed, an argument could be made that at the time the Europeans arrived, little wilderness existed.[576] This is also the case on the east coast of North America, where Indians had managed the landscape over centuries for their own benefit. Indeed, we now have evidence that even the Amazon area had been subject to human interference on a large scale before the arrival of Europeans.[577] We should continue to manage the environment for our own benefit using science to support concurrent multiple functions, such as the growing of food, the preservation of biodiversity, the maintenance of ecosystem services, and carbon sequestration.[578]

Many countries have perverse subsidy policies under which environmentally harmful activities are subsidized. They should not be subsidized; rather, they should be taxed. The destruction of wetlands—critically important for bio-diversity and other ecosystem services—was subsidized in many countries to increase agricultural yields. An example is the Common Market Agricultural Policy, which made the draining of wetlands highly profitable with returns as high as 20 percent. These subsidies have now stopped and subsidies are given to return the wetlands to their previous conditions. Biodiversity protection, including wetland protection, should be an integral part of land-use planning. For example, if a developer destroys one wetland, there should be an obligation to finance the protection of another.[579] Similarly, if a developer has to cut down trees, there should be a similar obligation to plant new trees, not necessarily in the same place.

Heroic efforts to indiscriminately save species from extinction may be unre-alistic, and it should be recognized that not all species are worth saving as the cost would be prohibitive. Captive breeding programs have been successful in saving several species, but unless the species can be successfully reintroduced into the wild, the value of breeding programs is questionable, and the zoos housing the animals would revert to their historical function of exhibiting "curiosities." For example, giant pandas—listed as an endangered species—have been used by the Chinese both as goodwill ambassadors and money earners. In return for a ten-year lease of a panda, receiving zoos have to pay $1 million per year to China and an additional $600,000 per year for each offspring born in captiv-ity.[580] The benefit to the receiving zoos is an increase in visitations, resulting in revenue increases of up to 70 percent because pandas are seen by the public as cute and adorable. The Chinese have been successful in breeding pandas in captivity but less successful in reintegrating them into the wild, partly because not much wilderness is left for them to integrate into.

Instead, scarce resources should be allocated to the protection of keystone species that are most important for maintaining an ecosystem—perhaps a system of triage should be developed, with top priority given to certain spe-cies. It should also be recognized that even endangered animals can be locally abundant and populations can become too large. For example, the elephant population in parts of Botswana and Kenya has become so large that it has impacted large areas of the countryside, and Kruger National Park has had to resort to culling. Elephants uproot trees in areas where trees are scarce and are also destructive when they rampage over farmers' fields, a problem that must be dealt with.

Biodiversity conservation is also assisted by the maintenance of seed banks. Kew's Millennium Seed Bank currently stores seeds from over twenty-four thousand plant species, many of which are endangered, with a final aim of having seeds from seventy-five thousand species, representing 25 percent of all bankable species, by 2020.[581] A seed bank ensures that the plants included do not go extinct and can be reintroduced if necessary. The Norwegian govern-

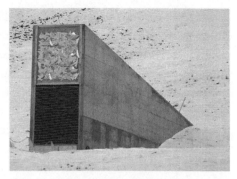

Figure 6.7. Svalbard seed depositary. Credit: Erlend Bjørtvedt (CC-BY-SA) and Wikimedia Commons

ment has established a seed bank in an underground vault on the Arctic Island of Svalbard that houses duplicates of seeds stored in other seed banks across the world. It is intended as a "doomsday" vault from which seeds for agriculture can be retrieved in case of a global or regional catastrophes.

Most studies show that the main alternative value of forests lies in carbon sequestration. If this is not taken into account, the dominant value of the forest land is in clearing the land and turning it into agriculture. A carbon tax is essential to wean us away from fossil fuels and to prevent further climatic deterioration with the ensuing negative impacts on biodiversity. A portion of the revenue of such a tax could be transferred to countries that commit to stop further land conversions. The problem here is to design an accounting and audit system to ensure the money is used for the purpose it was intended. The receiving countries would have to use the funds in such a way that the local population benefits, otherwise the incentives for illegal logging and poaching will be strong. Not all areas are suitable for ecotourism, and few people can be employed in policing protected areas. Money could flow into local enterprises involved in using sustainably harvested forest products and into improvements for existing agriculture that also preserve biodiversity. Product certification (discussed in Chapter 8) and consumer boycotts may be effective in steering consumer demand toward those products that have been sustainably harvested. Consumer boycotts were quite effective in halting the clear-cutting of old-growth forests in British Columbia, Canada, during the 1990s.

The preservation of biodiversity and the rebuilding of healthy ecosystems should work hand in hand with urbanization. While urbanization disconnects people from nature, creates pollution, and often uses prime agricultural land, it also has advantages from an environmental viewpoint. Depopulation of the countryside encourages the maintenance of biodiversity and the rehabilitation of many natural areas. Urbanization also creates opportunities for human creativity and innovation.[582] Urbanization has two implications. One is that agriculture must become more productive to be able to feed the urban populations, and the other that the design of cities should change. The end of cheap energy, assisted by the removal of perverse subsidies, should help in designing compact cities where people walk or cycle to work, live and work in energy-efficient buildings that collect rainwater for uses such as the flushing of toilets, and use energy generated from biogas obtained from waste food and sewage. High-density buildings should be separated by the planting of trees and bushes, interspersed with allotments for growing food. Rooftop gardens should also be encouraged; some North American cities already have many. Measures like these should help to alleviate some of the pressures on the world's ecosystems.

Not only must agriculture become more productive but also more protective of biodiversity in order to feed the world's population with minimum impact on the environment—an important topic discussed in Chapter 8. Water resources are also of critical importance as fresh, clean water is no longer an abundant resource available for free. Water pollution has ruined the ecological integrity of many rivers and streams to such an extent that they cannot be used, and fresh water has become a scarce resource that must be priced accordingly, topics discussed in Chapter 9. Another major problem is overfishing, which has radically decreased the biodiversity of coastal areas with species after species becoming locally extinct. This is dealt with in Chapter 10. The next chapter, Chapter 7, will return to the topic of forestry.

7

Forests—the Lungs of the Earth

*Perspectives on trees and forests: historical development of forest
use. Forest resources and commercial forest products. The causes
of deforestation and forest degradation. Toward sustainable
forestry. Forest certification. The growth of plantation forests.
Public or private forests: the issue of ownership. Forests and climate
mitigation: the REDD+ program. Concluding observations.*

NOT BEING ABLE to see the forest for the trees is a familiar expression that
describes a situation in which someone becomes too obsessed with details
to see the whole picture. In general, people are familiar with the role of forests
as a source of wood, but few have a full appreciation of their critical role in the
natural environment. Not only do forests support a commercial industry that
provides products ranging from building materials to fine papers, valued in
billions of dollars, but forests also provide non-wood items such as medicinal
and food products accounting for 15 percent of the total value of forest product removals. Indigenous peoples developed an intimate knowledge of forests
and trees and how their fruits, roots, leaves, and bark can be used for food and
medicines, a rapidly disappearing store of knowledge held by the indigenous
tribes of the Amazon, the Bushmen of the Kalahari, the Australian aborigines,
and the First Nations peoples in North America. Add to this the considerable
non-cash benefits of forests to local people, helping them to survive in many

Figure 7.1. The giant ash Yggdrasil holding the earth in its crown according to Nordic mythology. Original image by Friedrich Wilhelm Heine. Source: Wikimedia Commons.

parts of the world by providing firewood, fodder for cattle, and fruit and berries to supplement meagre diets. Forests provide habitat for most of the world's species and are essential in providing ecosystem services such as flood control and climate control. Forests are critically important in regulating the earth's atmosphere in absorbing carbon and producing oxygen through photosynthesis.

Trees and forests are also a source of spiritual nourishment for many people. Trees have been worshipped as temples of the gods in many traditional societies, partly because of their long lives, and they are often treated with the same respect as the elders of tribes. There are sacred groves, cosmic trees, sky trees, trees of wisdom, and trees of knowledge. In the Northern Hemisphere, the oak was sacred to the ancient Druids, and even today its significance is recognized by both the United States and the United Kingdom; each has chosen it as their national tree because of its grandeur, beauty, and traditional importance of providing for people. According to Nordic mythology, the world is contained in Yggdrasil, a giant ash tree, with its branches reaching into heaven and its roots extending into three holy wells. Another ash, the wafer ash, is sacred to the First Nations of North America. In rural Ireland, the ancient yews of

Clonfert Abbey are still recognized as sacred trees and are decorated with ribbons, tokens, and prayer notes. The baobab tree, which can have a circumference of over forty metres, is regarded as special in parts of Africa because of its long tradition of providing water and nourishment. The leaves, fruit, seeds, and pulp can all be eaten. At the death of a tree, people in Burkina Faso have been known to give the baobab a proper funeral with rites usually given only to chiefs.[583] The fig is a sacred tree in India, and it was under the Bodhi tree—a fig tree (*Ficus religiosa*)—that Buddha achieved enlightenment.

While forests have always been regarded as important, over the centuries their larger role in human societies became subservient to the expansion of agriculture and the need for timber. However, the last fifty years have seen a complete transformation of the view of forest management from an emphasis on when to cut, plant, and harvest in order to give an optimum yield of timber to a holistic view of sustainable forest management, taking into account the protection of biodiversity, climate mitigation, and community needs. The difficulty lies in creating an appropriate balance among the often-competing uses of forests, which include the maintenance of the ecological integrity of forests, their role as carbon sinks, the need for commercial timber, the demand for more agricultural land to feed the expanding world population, and the traditional provisioning for most of the world's indigenous peoples. This chapter begins with a brief history of the role of forests and forestry, followed by an account of the present state of the world's forests and the commercial markets for forest products. Deforestation, logging practices, forest certification, and plantations are discussed as well as the whole issue of forest ownership and sustainability of current forestry practices.

Perspectives on trees and forests: historical development of forest use

For thousands of years, forests have been regarded as an obstacle to human progress as well as a necessary resource for survival. When people became agriculturalists, forests were an obstacle that had to be cleared for fields, but at the same time they provided food, shelter, and heat, and later materials for building boats. Without wood, transportation could not have developed. While stone axes were surprisingly effective in felling trees, the advent of metal axes thirty-five hundred years ago, saws in the Middle Ages, and chain saws during the twentieth century made clearing much easier. Even today, people's attitudes toward forests range from regarding forests only as a source of timber to be exploited, to a desire to return forests to some sort of primeval paradise untouched by humans. However, in most parts of the world, this earthly paradise has not existed for millennia. There is mounting evidence that since the end of the last ice age—approximately ten thousand years ago—humans have had a major impact on forests, initially through the use of fires.[584] It is likely that even before humans learned to start fires, much effort went into maintaining naturally occurring fires induced by lightning. These sources of fires were used to burn the forests to flush out large mammals for easy hunting as well as edible insects, lizards, and rodents. The fires would also clear the areas of poisonous snakes and spiders. It is likely that the wide-ranging extinction of large mammals such as mammoths, giant deer, and woolly rhinoceros during the paleolithic/mesolithic times was caused by a combination of hunting, climate change, and induced fires. In more recent times, human-induced fires created similar extinctions in Madagascar with the arrival of Polynesians fifteen hundred to two thousand years ago. The Maoris arrived in New Zealand 900–950 AD and encountered a large population of giant flightless birds (the moa). By the middle of the thirteenth century, they had managed to destroy millions of hectares of forests by burning, and they had hunted the moa to extinction.

In Europe, early inhabitants lived at the edges of forests and used fires for hunting. The neolithic peoples who lived between 4500 and 2000 BC were agriculturalists. They typically lived in timbered longhouses on cleared flood plains that were able to support garden-type cultivation and grazing. It is believed that in order to survive, each settlement of approximately six families needed over six square kilometres of cleared woodland to survive, which is equivalent to twenty hectares per person.[585] The impact on the forest cover must have been substantial. Early agriculture in the Americas had a similar effect. For example, according to some estimates, the Hurons of Ontario would have needed 0.9 hectares of cropland per person. By the time of the European conquest of North America, over 3.2 million hectares of forest (approximately 3 percent of today's cropland in eastern North America) had been affected.[586] Early eyewitness accounts from New England report parklike forests with little undergrowth. The arrival of the Europeans and the diseases they brought decimated the native populations, and forest covers started to increase.[587] The forests of 1750 likely showed fewer signs of human interference than the forests at the time of Columbus. Recent research has shown that tropical forests were also affected. They are not the virgin forests we imagine them to be. In the Amazon basin, most soils show the presence of charcoal, and it is probable that as much as 40 percent of tropical forests in Central and South America is

Figure 7.2. The world's oldest tree is believed to be a spruce Old Tjikko found in northern Sweden. It is estimated to be 9,500 years old. It has adapted to climate change by sometimes surviving as a tree, sometimes as a low bush. Credit: Karl Brodovsky, Wikimedia Commons.

secondary forest grown back over clearings, with most of the remainder having been subject to some degree of modification.[588]

Even parts of the Middle East were covered by forests until 3000 BC. The *Epic of Gilgamesh*, written approximately 2100 BC, describes how the hero Gilgamesh sets off to gain fame by killing Huwawa, the protector of the cedars of Lebanon—the first literary account of deforestation.[589] The seafaring Phoenicians used the cedars to build their ships, and when they suffered a shortfall of wood, they had to import cedars from Crete. But Crete soon also ran out of trees, as the Minoan inhabitants needed a large amount of wood to fire the furnaces used to make bronze. The large cedar forests on Crete had disappeared by the time of the birth of Christ. On the other hand, the Greek city states blossomed because they were able to build up important trading connections, having been blessed with long coastlines with ample wood supplies that were used for shipbuilding.

Agriculture changed Europe and shifted influence from southern Europe to the fertile flood plains of the rivers of northern and western Europe. The Middle Ages brought many technological and cultural changes. Technologically, the wheeled plow was introduced, which made it easier to cultivate the heavy forest soils. Water power was harnessed, aided by the construction of wooden mills. Iron was widely used, manufactured in furnaces that required a vast amount of wood. The prevailing view changed from humans being seen as part of nature to nature being at the service of humans. Peasants relied on forests for firewood, building materials, grazing, and as a source of new land.

Trees were often coppiced—pruned back annually to the trunks—and the branches used for such purposes as charcoal making, wattle-and-daub building, and making poles to support hop vines. Rulers, on the other hand, saw the forests as their own domain for hunting, which led to conflicts with the local population—note the legend of Robin Hood and his outlaws. The New Forest in England, for example, was established as a royal reserve by William the Conqueror in 1079, uprooting many peasants, and according to legend they took their revenge by killing two of his sons.

The religious orders, in particular the Benedictines and the Cistercians, encouraged the clearing of forests. A wave of deforestation occurred in the later Middle Ages between 1000 and 1300, mainly caused by population growth. In 600 AD, Europe had around eighteen million people. By the thirteenth century, its population had expanded to almost seventy-six million.[590] A similar round of deforestation happened in China and Japan, but far less is known about it. Deforestation in Europe came to a halt with the Bubonic Plague (1347–1353), which reduced the population by one-third, and the Hundred Years War between England and France (1337–1453). By the early modern period (1500–1700), forests were seen as dangerous and repulsive places full of wild animals and outlaws as described in fairy tales such as *Hansel and Gretel*, *Little Red Riding Hood*, and others. In Nordic folklore they were populated by trolls, elves, and other little creatures that if crossed, would do terrible damage. Swedish author Kerstin Ekman, in her book *Herrarna i skogen*,* recounts an incident from the 1970s when she and her husband were building a house in northern Sweden. They were beset by endless problems and delays. A neighbour told them that their problems would continue until they gave an offering of silver to placate "the little people" whose throughways they had crossed. To this day, many Swedish families put out a bowl of rice porridge on Christmas Eve for *tomten* (a mythological little elf) who will play nasty tricks if they don't. The tricks may involve a chimney that will not draw or a cow refusing to yield any milk.

Shipbuilding during the seventeenth and eighteenth centuries required a vast amount of wood. The building of a large warship of one hundred tons used fourteen hundred to two thousand oak trees, each one hundred years old.[591] Oak was indigenous to most of Europe, but the masts had to be made from fir, which only grew in northern Europe. By then, countries like the Netherlands had no oak forests left and had to import the necessary timbers from the Baltic.

---

*Translated: *Masters of the Forest*.

Restrictions on Baltic trade became a major incentive for forest exploitation in North America, especially for the British during the Napoleonic Wars. Later, the building of railways also created an almost insatiable demand for wood, particularly in the tropics where the wooden sleepers lasted less than ten years.

The waves of immigration to North America led to the clearing of millions of hectares, supported by homesteading policies both in the United States and Canada, which gave the settlers 160 acres (64.8 ha) of land in return for clearing the land for agriculture. Some of the trees were burned in place, some were used for house construction and fences—for example, cedar snake fences required a large amount of wood—and some were burned for fertilizer (potash). There was also an enormous demand for fuel wood. By 1840, 60 percent of all wood in the United States was used for fuel.[592] Forests disappeared on both sides of the Atlantic, and only gradually came the realization that planting had to be done, even in North America where clearing by newly arrived settlers was almost sacrosanct. The upper classes also wanted trees to adorn their considerable country estates. A forest conservation movement began to emerge, first in Europe, where some universities, particularly in Germany, started to teach forest science, partly with the aim of using forests as a cash crop.[593] The German ideas, relying on planting and harvesting a few coniferous species, took hold on both sides of the Atlantic. In the United States, a system of forest reserves was established in 1891, which became known as national forests. Initially the primary focus of the national forests was on sustainable timber production. The subsidiary goals of recreation and the maintenance of wildlife came only later, mainly because of John Muir, the enormously influential Scottish born naturalist who became the co-founder of the Sierra Club.

Deforestation was also happening in the tropics during the eighteenth and nineteenth century, partly because of expansion of the indigenous populations, but also because of exploitation for profit by the colonial powers, involving plantations of tobacco, sugar, coffee, cocoa, and tea and exports of tropical hardwood such as teak. In particular, the forests of Brazil and Southeast Asia saw massive transformations. By the 1920s and 1930s, global forestry clearing was around eleven million hectares per year, 70 percent of which took place in the tropics. By mid-century, three types of forested areas were categorized in the world: those managed on a sustainable yield basis for timber production and leisure, those cut down for agriculture or timber with no concern for regeneration (mainly in the tropics), and those left to themselves—inaccessible areas of boreal and rainforests. With an aim to conserve their own forests, Japan and many countries in Europe imported what they needed from the tropics, where an additional 318 million hectares were cut between 1950 and 1980.[594] To put this in perspective, it is estimated that in the same period eleven million hectares were harvested in China, seven million in Europe and North America, eleven million in the USSR and twelve million in the rich Pacific countries. Most of the clearing was for agricultural land. The introduction of chainsaws and bulldozers greatly assisted in the carnage.

Forest resources and commercial forest products

There are many different types of forests. They can be broadleaf (deciduous), needleleaf (coniferous), or mixed, and they can be classified according to climatic zones—rainforests within ten degrees of latitude of the equator, taiga or boreal forests between fifty-three and sixty-seven degrees of latitude north of the equator, and temperate hardwood forests and tropical dry forests covering the remainder.[595] Forests cover approximately four trillion hectares, 30 percent of the world's land area (see Table 7.1). Between 1990 and 2000, forested areas decreased by 2 percent, equivalent to a yearly loss of 0.2 percent.[596] In the following decade the average yearly loss declined to 0.1 percent, with the most severe losses experienced in parts of Africa, Southeast Asia, and Central America. The average yearly loss measured in hectares was the highest in Latin America (3,997,000 ha); the second-highest was in Africa (3,414,000 ha). Large plantations in China have reversed the trend in Asia, where forests actually increased despite severe deforestation in Southeast Asia, particularly in Indonesia. Forest covers in Europe increased while North America saw a decline mainly through deforestation in Mexico. It is clear that deforestation is a now predominantly tropical occurrence and is associated with poverty and bad governance. It is also interesting to note that the largest forestry resources in terms of growing stock are found in the Russian Federation.

Some researchers claim that climate change is unlikely to lead to large changes in forest cover, but others disagree. The largest temperature changes are predicted to occur in high latitudes, but there is little agreement how quickly forests will migrate into the more northerly regions. Increased carbon dioxide in the atmosphere is likely to benefit forest growth as carbon dioxide acts as a fertilizer, particularly in areas rich in moisture.[597] However, warmer climates may adversely affect forests because of possible increases in infestations, diseases, and forest fires. Examples are the pine-beetle infestation of western Canadian forests and drought-induced forest fires in Russia during the summer of 2010,

Table 7.1. World forest resources, 2010, selected statistics

| Country* | Total forest area, 2010 | | | |
	(Area measured in 1,000 ha)	Percentage of total land area	Annual rate of change 1990–2000	Annual rate of change, 2000–2010
Democratic Republic of the Congo	154,135	68	−0.2	−0.2
Central African Republic	22,605	36	−0.1	−0.1
Total Central Africa	**254,854**	**48**	**−0.3**	**−0.3**
United Republic of Tanzania	33,428	38	−1.0	−1.1
Madagascar	12,553	22	−0.4	−0.4
Total East Africa	**73,197**	**18**	**−0.9**	**−1.0**
Sudan	69,949	29	−0.8	−0.1
Morocco	5,131	11	−0.1	0.2
Total North Africa	**78,814**	**8**	**−0.7**	**−0.1**
Angola	58,480	47	−0.2	−0.2
Zambia	49,468	67	−0.3	−0.3
Total Southern Africa	**194,320**	**33**	**−0.5**	**−0.5**
Mali	12,490	10	−0.6	−0.6
Côte d'Ivoire	10,406	33	0.1	0.1
Total West Africa	**73,234**	**15**	**−1.1**	**−1.1**
Total Africa	**674,419**	**23**	**−0.6**	**−0.5**
Turkmenistan	4,127	9	0	0
Kazakhstan	3,309	1	−0.2	−0.2
Total Central Asia	**16,016**	**4**	**0**	**0**
China	206,861	22	1.2	1.6
Japan	24,979	69	0	0
Total East Asia	**254,626**	**22**	**0.8**	**1.2**
India	68,434	23	0.2	0.5
Nepal	3,636	25	−2.1	−0.7
Total South Asia	**80,309**	**19**	**0**	**0.2**

* The two countries with the largest forest areas are selected from each region.

(Continues on next page)

Table 7.1, continued

Country	Total forest area, 2010			
	(Area measured in 1,000 ha)	Percentage of total land area	Annual rate of change 1990–2000	Annual rate of change, 2000–2010
Total Southeast Asia	214,064	49	−1.0	−1.4
Iran	11,075	7	0	0
Turkey	11,334	15	0.5	1.1
Total Western Asia	27,498	4	0.2	0.5
Total Asia	592,512	19	−0.1	0.4
Russian Federation	839,090	49	0	0
Sweden	28,203	69	0	0.3
Total Europe	1,005,001	45	0.1	0.1
Cuba	2,870	26	1.7	1.7
Dominican Republic	1,972	41	0	0
Total Caribbean	6,933	30	0.9	0.7
Guatemala	3,657	34	−1.2	−1.4
Honduras	5,192	46	−2.4	−2.1
Total Central America	10,499	38	-1.6	-1.2
Brazil	519,522	62	−0.5	−0.5
Peru	67,992	53	−0.1	−0.2
Total South America	864 351	49	−0.5	−0.5
Canada	310,130	34	0	0
United States	304,022	33	0.1	0.1
Total North America	678,961	33	0	0
Australia	149,300	19	0	−0.4
Papua New Guinea	28,726	63	−0.4	−0.5
Total Oceania	191,384	23	0	−0.4
Total world	4,033,060	31	−0.2	−0.1

Source: Adapted from the Food and Agriculture Organization, *State of the World's Forests, 2011,* Table 2.

covering over seven hundred and fifty thousand hectares at an estimated cost to the Russian economy of US $15 billion.[598]

The main commercial use of forests is in the form of lumber used for a variety of products. The Food and Agriculture Organization (FAO) of the United Nations classifies wood products as woodfuel, industrial roundwood, sawnwood, wood-based panels, pulp for paper, and paper and paperboard.[599] World production of woodfuel is larger than world production of industrial roundwood because many developing countries still use wood for heating and cooking. Use

Table 7.2. Production of woodfuel and industrial roundwood, selected countries, 2012

Country/region	Woodfuel (000 m³)	Woodfuel as % of word total	% change in production, 2008–2012	Industrial roundwood (000 m³)	Industrial roundwood as % of world total	% change in production, 2008–2012
Ethiopia	103,966	5.6	5.6	2,935	negligible	0.0
Democratic Republic of the Congo	78,854	4.2	6.1	4,596	negligible	0.0
Total Africa	**644,309**	**34.5**	**4.7**	**69,399**	**4.2**	**−7.4**
India	308,244	16.5	0.0	23,192	1.4	0.0
China	182,100	9.7	−7.1	144,035	8.7	3.0
Indonesia	57,288	3.1	−11.9	62,026	3.8	15.3
Total Asia	**754,627**	**40.4**	**0.0**	**328,499**	**19.8**	**4.5**
Russian Federation	44,700	2.4	0.0	136,375	8.2	−0.2
Total Europe	**149,702**	**8.0**	**−11.2**	**502,069**	**30.3**	**−0.8**
USA	40,437	2.0	−7.3	320,729	19.4	−4.8
Canada	1,443	0.0	−54.0	151,151	9.1	11.1
Total North America	**85,005**	**4.5**	**−10.4**	**471,880**	**28.5**	**0.0**
Mexico	38,840	2.1	0.0	15,938	negligible	−23.2
Brazil	140,916	7.5	2.9	146,804	8.9	27.2
Total Latin America	**288,681**	**15.4**	**2.8**	**228,023**	**13.8**	**16.1**
Total Oceania	**15,881**	**0.1**	**0.0**	**56,873**	**3.4**	**6.0**
Total world	**1,869,539**	**100**	**0.0**	**1,656,708**	**100**	**2.3**

Source: Adapted from the Food and Agriculture Organization, *FAO, Forest Products, 2008–2012.*

of woodfuel is still expanding in Africa and in parts of Latin America, but is declining elsewhere (Table 7.2). Woodenergy makes up twenty- seven percent of primary energy supply in Africa, thirteen percent in Latin America, and five percent in Asia and Oceania.[600] Very little is traded across borders as it is mostly consumed and produced locally. However, in the quest for green energy, Europe and North America now produce, consume, and trade woodfuel in the form of woodchips or wood pellets. Because of the EU mandated goal of achieving 20 percent renewable energy by 2020, the demand for wood energy increased in Europe to such an extent that demand exceeds supply in Sweden, the Netherlands, Belgium, Italy, Denmark, and the United Kingdom, resulting in imports of wood pellets from other parts of Europe and North America.[601] Pellet exports from the United States almost doubled between 2012 and 2013, and is expected to exceed 5 million tonnes in 2015.[602] In Sweden, for example, where some towns are heated centrally, the heating was initially generated by burning wood residue from local sawmills. When this supply dried up, it was replaced by residue from logging operations (branches, treetops, etc.). The Swedes now have to import wood pellets all the way from British Columbia in Canada to feed the furnaces. Environmentally, the practice of using every part of the tree, including branches, is not benign as no nutrients are returned to the soil.

The use of wood for fuel is believed to be carbon neutral because a growing tree sequesters carbon from the atmosphere, and the same amount of carbon is released when the wood is burned. Therefore, over the period of time in question, the tree neither adds to nor reduces the amount of carbon in the atmosphere. However, as is the case with biofuels such as ethanol or biodiesel, the use of wood as fuel is not necessarily an improvement over burning fossil fuels, because much depends on the efficiency at which the energy conversion takes place, the productivity of the land where the forest was grown, how the fuel is harvested, and the time span.[603]

Industrial roundwood includes all wood not used for fuel. Most industrial roundwood is used in construction, and the remainder is equally divided between pulp production and the production of veneers and composites. The raw-material sources consist of old-growth (virgin) forests that have never been logged before, secondary-growth forests that have been cut before then regrown, and planta- tion forests. Industrial roundwood production is still dominated by Europe and North America. The world's largest producer is the United States with 19 percent of the total, followed by Canada with 9.1 percent, Brazil with 8.9 percent, China with 8.7 percent, and Russia with 8.2 percent (Table 7.2). However, the largest roundwood exporter is Russia, which has 16 percent of world exports and 23 percent of the global forest stock. Since 2007, Russia has been trying to limit exports of roundwood to promote its own processing industry through the use of export taxes.[604] These taxes raise the price of a country's exports and divert the product to the domestic market. The increased supply leads to lower domestic prices, making it easier for domestic producers of secondary products to compete. Canada also has a hundred-year-old policy of prohibiting exports of logs from provincial and federal lands in order to encourage further processing. Among tropical countries, Indonesia and Malaysia are relatively large producers but still account for only 3.8 and 1.1 percent of world production. China is the largest importer of roundwood, with 34 percent of total world imports. These imports are used for furniture and construction—China has now overtaken Italy as the world's most important producer of furniture.

The largest pulp producer is the United States, with 24 percent of world production, followed by Canada Brazil, Sweden, and Finland. The largest pulp exporter is Canada (18 percent of world exports), followed by Brazil and the United States. The largest paper producer is the United States, followed by China, while the largest paper exporter is Canada, followed by approximately equal shares for Sweden, Finland, and Germany. Brazil is currently the cheapest place to make paper; clearly northern countries like Canada and Russia will have increasing difficulties competing with countries with climates more conducive to growing trees. Trees planted in subtropical areas can add a volume of ten to fifteen cubic metres per year per hectare, depending on local conditions, compared with growth in the temperate areas of two to five cubic metres per year.[605] The original competitive advantage for these northern countries was based on excellent wood quality, but that now matters less because of developments in wood engineering.

The FAO statistics do not include the value of non-wood tree products such as breadfruit, bananas, coconut, mangoes, and medicinal plants, estimated at US$ 90.4 billion in 2011[606]. Many of these products are also sources of non-cash income for many people and are critically important for their survival.

The causes of deforestation and forest degradation

The main causes of deforestation through history, as was noted above, were clearing for agriculture, for the building of houses and ships, and for fuel. Table 7.1 shows that today's deforestation mainly occurs in developing countries. While there are regional variations, a recent study attributes 40 percent of deforestation in developing countries to commercial agriculture, 33 percent to subsistence agriculture, 10 percent to the building of infrastructure, 10 percent to urbanization, and 7 percent to mining.[607]

Examples of commercial agriculture are large-scale cattle-ranching and soybean farming in South America, and palm oil plantations in Asia. The second largest contributor, subsistence agriculture, is either practiced intensively on small plots, or through shifting cultivation, and provides a living for millions of people around the world. Shifting cultivation ("slash-and-burn"), which has been practiced over millennia, is not sustainable when population pressures necessitate shorter rotation periods, meaning that the forest cover does not have enough time to recover between clearings. Clearing for small-scale ranching has been the major factor in deforestation in the Amazon, helped by the network of highways built during the 1970s.[608] The Amazon rainforest has shrunk significantly on both its eastern and western edges. In the east, most is controlled by Brazil, and in the west, Peru, Bolivia, and Ecuador have large tracts of the Amazonian lowlands, with Colombia and Venezuela controlling smaller areas. Most of the population of the western countries has traditionally lived in the Andean highlands, but poverty and population pressures have led to a migration toward the lowlands, aided by the building of highways (to a large extent financed by aid agencies) and government policies that encourage migration. Social upheaval also followed the discovery of oil, resulting in forest settlements suffering from poor planning, lack of markets, and inadequate infrastructures. Many Andean peasants were not comfortable in the forests, instead have an innate desire to create open country. Cattle ranching is the preferred form of agriculture as it requires little labour, no infrastructure, and the cattle can walk to market. This has resulted in large-scale deforestation and environmental degradation.

In Brazil, migration has been westward along the Amazon, aided and abetted by successive governments trying to promote economic development in the Amazon basin. In the past, this was partly to counter the influx of Peruvian and Bolivian peasants in the upper part of the basin at a time when the borders still were not clear. Roads were built and settlements followed, encouraged by substantial financial incentives for clearing of the forest and cattle ranching. Since the 1960s, approximately 20 percent of the forest has been cut down.[609] Often the destruction begins with illegal logging, followed by migrants erasing the remaining trees to turn the land into pasture. They are then followed by planters of soya, which is more profitable than cattle, driving the ranchers farther into the forest. In world history, the movement into forest lands has usually been one important way for poor peasants to secure a better life. This was not the case in the Amazon. Insecure land tenure and corruption have usually meant that the land has been taken over by bigger corporate units.

However, there are encouraging signs. In Brazil, a moratorium is now in place on buying soya grown on deforested lands.[610] The rate of deforestation has slowed following the creation of the world's largest protected area network (Amazon Region Protected Areas Program) in 2002, covering 51 million hectares—15 percent of the rainforest. It is financed by government donors, NGOs, and private foundations. The Brazilian government launched the ambitious Amazon Fund in 2008, open to investments by governments, NGOs, or individuals. It is administered by the National Development Bank in Brazil and supports projects beneficial to the forest including reforestation and recovery, the development of sustainable industries, and the establishment of new protected areas. The major donor so far is Norway, which has committed $1 billion up to 2015, and the fund has started to make disbursements.[611] Other contributors are Germany, contributing $3.9 million, and the Brazilian oil company Petrogras, giving $4.3 million.[612] So far other countries have been reluctant to invest, partly because of the slow pace of the fund in disbursing money. Other countries also appear to favour the United Nations–led REDD initiative, which aims to create a more market-based approach, involving buying and selling of carbon credits earned through forest conservation measures.

While agricultural expansion has been one of the causes of deforestation in Indonesia and Malaysia, more recently, large palm oil plantations are to blame, often financed by international aid organizations. Indiscriminate commercial logging has also been a major factor. The ecological damage is enormous because of the area's rich biodiversity. For example, the island of Borneo, which is divided among Malaysia, Indonesia, and Brunei, has a greater diversity of trees than anywhere else on earth. Deforestation is a threat to the tree-dwelling orangutans, one of the world's rarest primates. The governments have tried control the situation with little success. Over the past fifteen years, Indonesia has lost 25 percent of its forest cover, but the rate of deforestation is declining (see Table 7.1). However, a recent study claims that official data underestimates the degree of deforestation which is more severe than in the Amazon.[613] The Ministry of Forestry in Indonesia sets a maximum harvest each year with a long-standing ban on exports of raw timber. However, the processing capacity of sawmills and plywood factories is thought to be three times greater than the annual allowable cut, with predictable consequences of illegal efforts to keep the mills running. Moreover, the government does not want to clamp down on illegal logging for fear of job losses in the forest products industries. In 2011, the government announced a two-year moratorium on new forest concessions, but it does not appear to be effective as it does not apply to existing concessions or to secondary forests.[614]

The costs of illegal logging are substantial and include environmental costs of the damage to areas extremely rich in biodiversity. It is estimated that 3.6 million cubic metres of wood are smuggled from Papua New Guinea to China every year. Illegal logging also deprives people of their long-term livelihoods, as it destroys the resource base of the forests. Illegal logging puts downward pressure on timber prices because the producers do not have to pay royalties. As a result, legal logging also faces low prices, often resulting in low wages and poor working conditions. According to the American Forest & Paper Association, illegal logging has depressed world timber prices by 7 to 16 percent, undermining legitimate forestry and regulated forestry management.[615] It has also reduced government revenue from royalties; for Indonesia the annual losses may be in the region of $3 billion, which is almost half of what the country earns from forest product exports.

The onus is on both producing and consuming countries to control the sale of illegally logged timber. A recent study shows that the situation is improving in Brazil, Indonesia, and Cameroon, where illegal logging has been more than halved because of improved enforcement policies.[616] The same study singled out Japan as having inadequate controls on the import of timber and saw no improvement in China and Vietnam, which are the major processing countries for tropical timbers. China is also known to import large quantities of illegally logged timber from the boreal forests of Russia. Until recently, the United States was the only consuming country with an outright ban on the import of illegally logged timber, but it did not cover wood products. However, in 2008 the Lacey Act of 1900, which covered illegal trade in wildlife, was amended to cover illegal trade in plants and plant materials, including materials made of wood. The European Union Timber Regulation also came into effect in 2013, putting the onus on wood importers to exercise due diligence in verifying its legality.[617]

Another cause for concern is the disappearance of the world's mangrove forests. It is estimated that half the mangrove forests have been cut down. In Southeast Asia, shrimp farms are often the culprits when forests are cut down to establish artificial ponds, and in other areas tourism, urbanization, marinas, and road building have had devastating effects. Mangrove forests are salt-tolerant coastal forests growing all over the tropics on saline wetlands (intertidal areas and estuaries). They are a critical part of the ecosystem, providing nurseries

Figure 7.3. Mangrove forest in India. Credit: Gautham Ramakrishna and www.flickr.com.

for most tropical fish. They filter sediments and pollutants in coastal areas, are essential for the survival of coral reefs, and serve as a buffer against tropical storms. They also provide habitats for many endangered species such as manatees, sea turtles, and Royal Bengal tigers. One in six mangrove species are in danger of extinction, according to a 2010 report by IUCN.[618]

Finally, significant deforestation is caused by mining activity. For example, gold-mining activity in the environmentally sensitive Madre Dias region in the Peruvian Amazon increased the area deforested by mining from ten thousand hectares in 1992 to fifty thousand hectares in 2012—and over 50 percent of the new mines were illegal.[619] Mining activity also affects forests in developed countries, particularly Canada, where a significant part of the boreal forest in Alberta has been cleared for oil sands mining.

However, deforestation is not the only problem facing the world's forests, but also forest degradation. Degradation is a reduction in the density and structure of the forest, its biodiversity, and the capacity to store carbon. The causes are timber extraction and logging (52 percent), fuelwood collection and charcoal production (31 percent), uncontrolled fires (9 percent), and livestock grazing (7 percent).[620] This is not exclusively an issue in developing countries. Indeed, 47 percent of forest degradation since 2000 has been in Canada, Russia, and

Figure 7.4. Deforestation caused by informal gold mining in the Peruvian Amazon. The tailing ponds are contaminated with mercury. Credit: Gregory Asner.

Alaska.[621] Canada alone is the home of the most intact forest on earth, containing 25 percent of the world's wetlands and peatlands, storing 147 billion tonnes of carbon, with the Mackenzie Delta alone storing forty-one billion tons.[622] The amount of carbon stored per area unit in a boreal forest is twice that of a tropical forest. Unfortunately, the boreal forest is under threat from logging, hydro development, mining, oil and gas exploration, and forest fires.

The critical ecological importance of the Canadian boreal forest was finally recognized in 2010 through a ground-breaking deal struck between environmental groups and forestry companies operating on public lands. Under the Canadian Boreal Forest Agreement, participating forestry companies undertake to suspend new logging and road building on nearly thirty million hectares of boreal forests and to implement sustainable harvesting on an additional 40 million hectares.[623] In return, participating environmental groups agree to suspend any negative campaign against the forest companies. A particular focus of the agreement is the protection of migrating caribou herds. No such protection is offered to the large areas of boreal forests in Russia, which lost 14 percent of its forest cover to legal and illegal logging between 2000 and 2005, a figure which is not included in Table 7.1 as the FAO data only refer to changes in land-use patterns.

It is possible that logging is not the greatest danger to the boreal forest. The costs of logging increasingly remote areas may become prohibitive because of rising energy costs and the need for costly road infrastructure; therefore, wood from boreal forests in Canada and Russia may be unable to compete with wood from fast-growing plantations in warmer climates. However, declining demand for wood in itself is unlikely to save the forests from being cut down; increasing stresses will come from large-scale mining, hydro development, and oil and gas extraction. Stricter controls are necessary.

The collection of firewood is a major cause of forest degradation in developing countries. According to Table 7.2, more trees are used for firewood than for industrial roundwood. In Africa, 90 percent of the wood removed is used for fuel and for the world as a whole, 55 percent.[624] Forty percent of the world's population relies on wood or charcoal for energy, mostly for cooking.[625] The situation becomes worse when the price of oil increases, which pushes up the prices of firewood as well as more people substitute wood for the more expensive oil. The problem is that firewood is often extracted at a faster rate than it is replenished, and for many families the cost of firewood is as high as the cost of food. Given that most cooking stoves are inefficient, the cooking of one kilogram of rice can require one kilogram of firewood.[626] One person may get enough firewood from half a hectare of forest, which is sustainable. However, in reality up to fifteen people may try to get their firewood from the same area, which is not sustainable; thus, firewood gatherers have moved deeper and deeper into the forest, which further increases the time, effort, and cost involved in collecting the wood. Obvious solutions to the firewood crisis in developing countries include better stoves and plantations, and in particular the development of community woodlots with fast-growing trees. The average cooking stove in developing countries gives only 20 percent of the heat energy of North American gas stoves, which can reach an efficiency of over 70 percent. In addition, 4.3 million deaths each year are attributed to indoor air pollution caused by inefficient wood stoves. Black carbon (soot) is now recognized as the second-most important contributor to climate change after CO_2.[627]

During the 1970s and 1980s, several prototypes of solar ovens and solar cookers were developed, but the acceptance rate was low as they were slow, expensive, and not necessarily suitable for traditional cooking. The people using them did not like them. A major effort is now underway to develop more efficient traditional cookers through a joint effort of the Shell Foundation and the United Nations Foundation set up by American media mogul Ted Turner. It involves a commitment to raise $100 million through a new foundation, the

Global Alliance for Clean Cookstoves.[628] The focus is on developing efficient woodstoves acceptable to poor women, which means that the stoves may come in many forms and shapes, designed with local culture and local foods in mind. More efficient wood-burning stoves will use less wood and should be considered as an interim measure until rural electrification makes it possible to switch to electrically generated cookers.

Toward sustainable forestry

Traditional sustained-yield forest management as it was first developed in Germany involved making decisions about when to harvest the resource, when to plant, and how much to harvest. In common with other resources, a tree is a commodity at the same time as it is a capital asset. If a tree is not cut, depending on its age, it will contain more wood if it is left for another year. Traditionally foresters have recommended that trees be cut when the mean annual increment in growth is at its maximum, which varies from species to species and is climatically determined. For example, according to this rule, a stand of Douglas firs should be cut after one hundred years. But this simple rule does not take into account economic considerations such as the cost of harvesting, the cost of replanting, the alternative uses of land, and the cost of money (the rate of interest)—factors that have to be included for efficient management. Nor are all commercial forestry owners willing or able to implement efficient management techniques as the knowledge required would take too much time and effort to acquire. They may also operate on too small a scale for the implementation of these techniques to be economically feasible.

The view of forestry as a commercial crop gradually gave way to recognition that the importance of forests goes far beyond their timber value. Instead, the sustainable use of forestry requires a balance between the need for traditional forest products and the preservation of forests as an integral part of ecosystems and as a source of livelihood for many indigenous peoples. The first attempt to lay down principles for sustainable forestry was at the 1992 United Nations Conference on Environment and Development in Rio de Janeiro:

> Forest resources and forest lands should be sustainably managed to meet the social, economic, ecological, cultural and spiritual needs of present and future generations. These needs are for forest products and services, such as wood and wood products, water, food, fodder, medicine, fuel, shelter, employment, recreation, habitats for wildlife, landscape diversity, carbon sinks and reservoirs,

and for other forest products. Appropriate measures should be taken to protect forests against harmful effects of pollution, including air-borne pollution, fires, pests and diseases, in order to maintain their full multiple value.[629]

It was hoped that the outcome of the conference would be a legally binding forest convention, but political differences among the participating countries made such a convention impossible to achieve. Instead, these principles were further developed into a set of criteria for sustainable forest management by different groups and organizations, including the Ministerial Conference on the Protection of Forests in Europe (the Helsinki Process), the Working Group on Criteria and Indicators for the Conservation and Sustainable Management of Temperate and Boreal Forests (the Montreal Process), and the International Tropical Timber Organization (ITTO). The International Tropical Timber Agreement of 1983 established the framework for the ITTO, an organization promoting the expansion and diversification of trade in tropical timber from sustainably managed and legally harvested forests. Membership consists of both producing and consuming countries.[630] Like most commodity trade organizations, it appears to have been less than effective in achieving its goals. The ITTO defines sustainable forest management as "the process of managing forest to achieve one or more clearly specified objectives of management with regard to the production of a continuous flow of desired forest products and services without undue reduction of its inherent values and future productivity and without undue undesirable effects on the physical and social environment."[631] It emphasizes the need to establish permanent forest estates that are protected by law to be kept permanently forested for the purposes of timber and other forest products, or for the protection of soil, water, and biological diversity, or a combination of these functions. Permanent forest estates therefore include both production forests and protection forests. The production forests can be either natural or planted. According to the latest study of the ITTO, permanent forest estates in member countries (which include 85 percent of total forests) is 761 million hectares, of which 403 million are production forests (53 percent) and 358 million are protected forests (47 percent). However, even though the proportion of forests managed sustainably has increased from a negligible proportion in 2005, it is still only 7 percent.[632] The report notes that some countries have made real progress, such as Brazil, Malaysia, and Gabon, while others have lagged behind because of wars and political unrest; for example, the Democratic Republic of the Congo, Liberia, and Nigeria.

Parallel to the growing international emphasis on forestry and its impact on world environments, environmental groups were working on exposing the practices of industrial forestry with a particular focus on the effects of clear-cutting. In 1993, the British Columbia government in Canada announced it would open up a vast tract of virgin forests in Clayoquot Sound to clear-cutting. These were some of the largest temperate rainforests still left globally. The announcement led to massive protests in Europe and Canada involving blockades against logging operations of MacMillan Bloedel, boycotts of the products of the companies involved, and increased criticisms of commercial logging operations. The result was more stringent regulation of commercial logging and eventual recognition by the major forestry companies that something needed to change to avoid costly consumer boycotts.

Historically, logging was done on a selective basis, taking the best trees. This practice is called high-grading and is not environmentally good practice as it withdraws the best trees from the gene pool. Following the development of modern machinery, clear-cutting became an option as it became possible and profitable to utilize everything in an area in the forest. Sometimes some trees were left for regeneration purposes, sometimes replanting was done, and sometimes no planting was done and nothing was left. The environmental effects of all types of logging are overwhelmingly negative, including the removal of carbon sinks, which are a buffer against global warming; the loss of habitat for canopy insects and bacteria; the loss of habitat for many mammals and bird species; and, particularly if logging takes place on slopes, soil erosion and habitat losses downstream. The severity of these effects depends on the size and topography of the clear-cuts, as well as their proximity to each other. Clear-cutting also deprives many indigenous peoples of their livelihood and destroys the potential for tourism, since clear-cuts are ugly. Because of criticisms over the impact of clear-cutting, forms of selective cutting have been promoted. In this case, loggers cut only some trees, not all.

Environmentally, selective cutting as an alternative to clear-cutting may not be superior. In tropical forests, it is estimated that for every tree that is cut, thirty others are affected. Selective cutting means that in order to get the same amount of timber, larger areas of the forests have to be reached, more roads have to be built, and skidding machines have to cover greater areas. The machines drag the logs out to the roadside and damage the vegetation as well as the soil through compaction, which makes regeneration more difficult. One study using satellite imagery of the Amazon basin found that 16 percent of the area selectively logged was clear-cut within a year, and 32 percent was totally deforested within four years.[633] The reason? Selective logging makes it easier for land-hungry peasants and illegal loggers to finish the job of cutting down the forest because roads make access easier.

Reduced-impact logging (RIL) is being promoted as a way of reducing the adverse environmental effects of selective logging. Under this regime, each managed area is divided into, say, thirty blocks where only one block is exploited each year, meaning a thirty-year cycle for the entire area.[634] In each block, the oldest specimens are left for regeneration. Forestry workers are trained in selecting the trees and in planning roads, which minimizes the impact on the forest. Managed schemes are connected by wildlife corridors. The earliest RIL guidelines were developed in Australia and later by the Food and Agriculture Organization of the United Nations.[635] The general guidelines typically specify the assignment of cutting areas, the laying out of roads and log landings, methods for the construction of bridges, the marking of trees, and skid trail planning. However, more specific guidelines must vary with the local conditions of the forests (e.g., the topography and the type of timber used). Minimizing soil damage is a major part of the guidelines in areas with steep slopes.

A major issue with RIL management is its profitability. Some studies have indicated that reduced-impact logging is more profitable than conventional logging mainly because it does not waste as much timber as conventional logging; others have shown it to be less profitable, particularly on steep slopes.[636] Evidence also shows that RIL is not sustainable in terms of timber yield. One study found that following a harvest of 21 cubic metres per hectare in Brazil, the second harvest thirty years later would only yield 50 percent of the original—a considerable decline in yields. Sustainable yields would require even smaller harvests and longer cutting cycles, which would also strain profitability. However, other evidence suggests that RIL sequesters more carbon than conventional logging and has a less harmful impact on biodiversity, factors that would not enter into the calculations of a commercial logging operation.

Forest certification

Faced with the threat of consumer boycotts, the idea of certification started to gain ground among forestry companies. Certification would make it possible for consumers to buy wood certified as having been produced sustainably. The first certification scheme appeared in 1990 with the SmartWood program sponsored by the Rainforest Alliance. Following the failure of the Rio Summit in 1992 to establish an intergovernmental global process for forest management, several conferences were designed to develop principles of sustainable forest management. In 1993, the Forest Stewardship Council (FSC) was formed by environmental organizations as a third-party certification scheme, where onsite accredited certifying bodies attest that the products come from well-managed forests. The council includes social and environmental criteria as a basis of certification, including the rights of indigenous peoples to use the forest. There are criteria to maintain biodiversity and limits on pesticide use. The FSC also subscribes to the idea of a chain of custody by which products can be traced back to certified forests. The products are labelled with the FSC logo, and major companies such as the Home Depot will give preference to wood certified by FSC. By 2009, 5 percent of the world's productive forests had been certified by the council.[637] The rate of certification appears to be slowing even though the number of certified forests is increasing. Unfortunately, almost 90 percent of certified forests are in the Northern Hemisphere, with less than 2 percent of tropical forests certified.

As an alternative to the stringent certification by the FSC, alternative schemes were developed by forestry owners, emphasizing economic factors rather than social and environmental factors. It was argued that the chain-of-custody rules were particularly onerous for small forest owners. In Canada, the Canadian Standards Association in cooperation with industry developed a certification program ensuring that forestry companies have management systems consistent with sustainable forest management, but inspections were not required.[638] In the United States, the Sustainable Forestry Initiative (SFI) requires companies to file reports with SFI about their sustainable management plans, and in Europe forest owners came together to form the Pan-European Forest Certification (PEFC) program. These schemes have all joined together in an umbrella organization also called PEFC, but the acronym in this case stands for Programme for the Endorsement of Forest Certification. PEFC is the largest certification body, with approximately double the area of certified forests compared with FSC. However, FSC operates in eighty countries while PEFC exists in only thirty-one countries. In response to consumer pressures and pressures from environmental NGOs, the PEFC requirements have become more stringent.[639] As of May 2013, the proportion of certified forests (FSC and PEFC) exceeded ten percent of the world's forests.[640]

FSC certification is the most common certification scheme in the tropics but includes a very small area compared with the large tracts of forests in developed countries—as mentioned, only 2 percent of tropical timber is certified. One of the reasons is that certification is expensive for the producers, costing up to

$50,000 for certification; thus, certified products must fetch a higher price in the marketplace. Unfortunately, the majority of consumers are not willing to pay more. Marketing studies by the Home Depot in North America indicate that less than one-third of their customers would be willing to pay an additional 2 percent for certified products.[641] Some other studies indicate that only high-income consumers are willing to pay between 5 to 13 percent more for certified wood products.[642] However, one of the major motivations for forestry companies in seeking certification is to avoid international consumer boycotts, so if a large share of their timber is going for export, the companies are more likely to adopt certification.[643] There is little incentive to seek certification for timber produced for local markets in the tropics.

The private sector and NGOs have played a major role in changing forestry for the better, and it might be expected that governments would have followed suit. But this is not necessarily the case. So far only twelve countries have government procurement policies: Belgium, Germany, France, Denmark, the Netherlands, the UK, and, outside the EU, China, Japan, Mexico, Norway, New Zealand, and Switzerland.[644] These policies involve either buying only sustainably harvested timber or legally logged timber, or both. China insists on its own ecolabelling and has no policy controlling illegally logged timber. The United States has no government procurement policies for timber but expressly forbids the importation of illegal timber. The difficulty here is that each country has its own requirements, which makes it difficult for timber-exporting countries and companies to comply. It is also expensive for exporting countries to establish credible systems of verification. As mentioned, certification requirements are particularly onerous for the owners of community forests and small to medium-sized companies. On the other hand, exporters of legally verified Asian timber can get a price premium of 3 to 15 percent, and high-end tropical-timber-certified products from Africa and Brazil can command a price premium of 20 to 50 percent.[645] The demand for certified and legally verified timber will mainly affect the relatively small export sectors in developing countries with little impact on the majority of forests.

The growth of plantation forests

Modern forest plantations are an extension of traditional forestry and mimic industrial agriculture in the sense that trees are treated like any other crop. Plantations of fast-growing trees such as southern US pine, Caribbean pine, Monterey pine, and eucalyptus have been the driving force of timber production in South America and parts of Africa, Asia, and Oceania.[646] It is expected that output from these plantations will increase from the current two hundred million cubic metres per year, representing 13 percent of total wood supply, to approximately seven hundred million cubic metres by the year 2050, or 41 percent of the total. China has by far the largest area covered by planted forests (forty-two million ha), followed by India (thirty-two million ha), Russia (seventeen million ha), the United States (sixteen million ha), and Japan (ten million ha).[647] It is estimated that three-quarters of plantations are used for the production of forest products and the remainder for the rehabilitation of degraded lands and for protection of soils and water as well as protection from encroaching deserts.[648]

Plantations increasingly cater to the demand for woodfuel and roundwood. They can also play a major role in shielding natural forests from encroachment by providing protective collars around them. In common with natural forests, they act as carbon sinks, and they have beneficial effects on climate mitigation as they can provide materials for biofuels and replace carbon-intensive materials for construction such as aluminum and steel. In comparison with the growing of food crops for ethanol, planting forests can be done on marginal and degraded lands and is therefore unlikely to have an impact on food prices. However, some argue that plantations may not radically slow the rate of deforestation as long as people are still hungry for new agricultural land.[649] Another negative factor is that wood from plantation forests may keep timber prices low and thus decrease the financial return from sustainable management of natural forests.

Additional problems are created in the large-scale shift toward plantation forests. Plantations on peatlands may be problematic as planting disturbs the peat, which could release more locked-up carbon than the planted trees will sequester. Concerns have also arisen that some plantations have adverse effects on the hydrological cycle and on groundwater supplies. In common with other monocultures, they may be prone to pests, and assuming that stands may be of the same age, they may be more vulnerable to storm damage, drought, and forest fires than traditional forests. But many of the adverse effects of plantations can be countered by adequate site preparation, using measures to decrease soil disturbance and increase retention of organic contents and nutrients while still leaving some trees from previous stands. Landscape diversity can also be maintained by either encouraging polyculture (more than one species) or introducing a mosaic of different monocultures.[650]

Public or private forests: the issue of ownership

Eighty-six percent of the world's forests are publicly owned, and the traditional view has been that unless governments make sustainable management a condition of tenure, not very much is likely to happen in terms of forest conservation.[651] Europe has a long tradition of government ownership dating from the Middle Ages, when many forests were reserved for the Crown. The idea that only governments were capable of managing forests was transplanted to the colonies, where governments took away the rights of indigenous peoples to manage the land. It has not been until recently that the rights of indigenous peoples have been recognized.[652]

If ownership is not clearly defined, users are likely to overharvest the resource, acting in their own interest with no regard for future sustainability. This is known as "the tragedy of the commons," a term first coined by Garrett Hardin in an article in *Science* in 1968.[653] A private owner usually has an interest in maintaining a sustainable yield, making the tragedy of the commons an often-cited argument for privatization. However, in reality good forest management is far more subtle, and plenty of evidence now exists that ownership is not the deciding factor. Ground-breaking research in this area was undertaken by the Nobel laureate Elinor Ostrom and her associates on the management of common-pool resources, which include water basins, forestry, and fisheries.[654] Common-pool resources can be government property, private property, community property, or owned by no one. In an extensive worldwide survey of the state of these resources, these researchers found that the tragedy of the commons did not always occur, and the role of government in many cases was minimal. Property rights associated with common-pool resources included the right to access, the right to harvest, the right to decide on management practices, the right to exclude others from using the property, and the right to lease or sell any of these rights. It is not ownership as such that is of crucial importance; rather, it is important that we have institutions that clearly delineate the rights of users and non-users and that are in tune with local social and environmental conditions. Anyone affected by the resource must be allowed to participate in making the rules about its use and entitled to a share of its costs and benefits, and the same individuals must be involved in monitoring the state of the resource and the design and enforcement of sanctions for breaking agreed-on rules.

These findings certainly apply to forestry. As explained in the previous chapter, protected areas do not necessarily guarantee that forests and biodiversity are protected. One study comparing community managed forests and forest protected areas across the tropics concluded that community managed forests had lower deforestation rates than protected forests. [655] A particular example from the United States compares the health of the Lulu National Forest in Colorado with the adjacent Flathead Indian Reservation Forest.[656] Both timber revenue and environmental performance of the reservation forest were superior. The management of the national forest appeared to be plagued by inefficiencies caused by litigation and excessive concentration on fighting rather than prevention of forest fires. Other studies have confirmed the importance of local monitoring and enforcement on the sustainability of forest commons. Forest commons make up 18 percent of the world's forested areas, providing benefits for nearly a billion people.[657] Therefore, in general, ownership has little effect on the health of forests in terms of biodiversity protection and carbon storage and in terms of providing livelihoods for local populations. In many cases, centralized decision making by governments that do not involve local officials is counterproductive. Instead, governance arrangements that take into account local ecology and local conditions and that involve users who consider the arrangements to be legitimate and fair are more likely to promote sustainable forestry.

Forests and climate mitigation: the REDD+ program

The critical role of forests in contributing to the carbon cycle has become a major focus in climate negotiations with particular emphasis on setting up new international financial mechanisms in which substantial rewards could come to countries or units within countries that agree to reduce greenhouse gas emissions by reducing deforestation and degradation.[658] The IPCC *Fourth Assessment Report* in 2007 highlighted the fact that the amount of carbon sequestered in forest ecosystems exceeded the amount of carbon in the atmosphere, and 17.4 percent of the world's yearly emissions come from deforestation.[659] The 1997 Kyoto Protocol committed the participating countries to reducing their greenhouse gas emissions by 2012 to an average of 5 percent below 1990 levels. The role of forests in achieving the agreed-on targets was recognized in Article 3, third paragraph, which states that "the net changes in greenhouse gas emissions by sources and removals by sinks resulting from direct human-induced land-use change and forestry activities, limited to afforestation, reforestation and deforestation since 1990, measured as verifiable changes in carbon stocks in each commitment period, shall be used to meet the commitments . . . The greenhouse gas emissions by sources and removals by sinks associated with

those activities shall be reported in a transparent and verifiable manner . . . ."[660]
While developed countries were committed to binding reductions in greenhouse
gases, developing countries were not included in such reductions. Under the
agreement, developed countries could purchase emissions credits and support
emissions reductions in developing countries through the Clean Development
Mechanism and through Joint Initiatives. By participating in the Clean Development Mechanism, developed countries could obtain emissions offsets by
supporting sustainable development of projects including those that sequester
carbon through reforestation or afforestation.

The details for including the impact of forests on emissions accounting
were outlined in the 2001 Marrakesh Accords (COP 7).[661] The accords specifically addressed land use, land-use change, and forestry (known by the acronym
LULUCF) in defining each activity and setting caps on each for the purpose of
the meeting of emissions targets. Three activities are included—afforestation/
reforestation, deforestation, and forest management—and each party must
report on each activity. Afforestation is the planting or seeding (natural or
artificial) of trees on land that has not been forested for at least fifty years,
while reforestation is the same activity on former forest lands, and both activities lead to credits while deforestation leads to an increase in emissions. If the
biomass increases in a country's managed forests, it means that carbon is being
sequestered, part of which can be used as a credit toward the emissions targets.
The total contribution of forests to emissions is thus the sum of credits from
afforestation/reforestation and forest management (any increase in the carbon
stocks of existing forest) minus emissions caused by deforestation.

In 2005, at the COP 11 meeting in Montreal, a group of countries requested a
discussion of reducing emissions from deforestation (RED). At follow-up meetings of some of the parties, forest degradation emerged as being as serious an
issue as deforestation in many countries, and the catchphrase became "reducing emissions from deforestation and degradation in developing countries"
(REDD). At the meeting of the parties in Bali in 2007 (COP 13), REDD became
REDD+ in addressing not only deforestation and degradation but also "the role
of conservation, sustainable management of forests, and enhancement of forest
carbon stocks in developing countries." In 2010, the Cancún conference (COP
16) made further progress in outlining REDD+ activities to include reducing
emissions from deforestation and forest degradation, sustainable management
of forests, and conservation and enhancement of forest carbon stocks, while
safeguarding factors such as existing forest programs and agreements, forest

governance, and the rights of indigenous peoples and biological diversity. To be eligible for funds, the developing countries would need to establish a national forest monitoring system, an action plan, and a forest reference emission level. Financing has not yet been sorted out, but so far developing countries have committed $7.2 billion. However, only a small proportion has been disbursed for capacity building and pilot projects.[662]

While REDD+ is potentially a major advance in climate mitigation and promotion of sustainable forestry, many problems need to be addressed, including sustainable financing and ensuring the benefits are equitably shared in the receiving countries. As always, tensions simmer between the advocates of market-based approaches based on carbon trades and those who favour fund financing. It does not help that the carbon market is uncertain following the failure to negotiate a successor to Kyoto.[663] Another difficult issue is the ownership of forest carbon rights. Carbon rights include the property rights to the already-sequestered carbon contained in trees and soil and the rights to the benefits that arise when these are transferred.[664] REDD credits are already playing a role in voluntary carbon markets, which raises important questions. Does the right to take credit for sequestered carbon or ecosystem services belong to the property owner or the national governments? Can carbon rights be separated from the land or do they come with the land? These are important issues given the large amounts of money potentially involved. If national governments take ownership, how can it be ensured that the owners of the forests are compensated?

There are three ways to deal with the issues. One suggestion is for national governments to receive compensation for REDD+ activities, subject to performance assessment and national accounting of greenhouse gas emissions. In another scenario, national governments would receive the compensation or credits and pass them on to non-government organizations, and in a third scenario, local projects would be given marketable carbon credits, bypassing national governments. Only in the last two cases would it be critical for property rights to be established. How this is achieved will depend on how national REDD+ legislation fits in with existing national laws. Even in the first case, equitable sharing of benefits allocated to national governments would have to be developed.[665] What happens when property rights are not clearly defined, as is the case in many developing countries where forest areas are often managed under customary forms of tenure, but where land ownership has not been clarified because of outstanding land claims by indigenous people?

Concluding observations

While the world's temperate forests are increasing and tropical deforestation is slowing, the challenge is to save the remaining tropical forests and to prevent forest degradation. Much of today's tropical deforestation is a result of population growth and grinding poverty. This was the case historically and it is still the case, and unless attempts are made to give local populations alternative sources of living, it is going to continue. In its latest report, the ITTO is pessimistic about the future of natural tropical forests because continuing low tropical timber prices do not provide adequate financial incentives for sustainable forestry practices. It claims that in the long run, the fate of tropical forests depends on the extent of payments for ecosystem services by developed countries.[666]

Governments have an essential role in setting up protected areas and enforcing bans on illegal logging, but they have to do more. Deforestation policies can only be successful if they are combined with policies that ensure that the local population can earn a living from the forest that does not involve cutting it. For example, it is critically important that the rights over non-wood forest products be recognized, since these often make a significant contribution to living standards for local people. As well, clear property rights are essential. For example, cattle ranching—the main culprit of deforestation in the Amazon—is apparently very unproductive, with only one head of cattle per hectare.[667] The already-cleared land could be converted to agricultural land with modest investments in fertilizer, which would provide a higher income for the occupants. However, unclear property rights are a barrier because much of the land was illegally logged, which makes financing for land improvement very difficult.

The REDD+ initiative provides a promising solution to halting deforestation and improving forest management, but its success also depends on defined property rights and equitable sharing of benefits. A handful of countries have pledged a total of $7.2 billion, but what will happen after the money has been used is not clear, as the prospects for a world carbon market are poor without a successor to Kyoto. Carbon taxes would be an effective way of raising money to fund REDD+, but there is no sign that they will be adopted. There is also a danger that the current singular focus on REDD+ will lead to centralization of decision making and will reduce the multiple functions of forests to one—climate mitigation—to the detriment of many of the world's poor who rely on forest products for their livelihoods.

While forest certification has been reasonably successful in promoting the sale of forest products that have been grown and harvested sustainably, it covers only a minute area of tropical forests. Unless a radical change occurs in adoption rates, certification will not have a large impact on forestry practices in most developing countries. The spectacular growth of plantation forests could alleviate some of the pressures on traditional forests, and, as discussed, properly designed and managed plantation forests could provide similar ecosystem services as do natural forests. On the other hand, if increased timber production from plantation forests leads to lower timber prices, the value of the natural forests may decline to such an extent that their alternative use for agriculture is economically superior, requiring increasingly large transfers of money from developed to developing countries to prevent further conversions to agricultural land.

Last, but not least, environmental campaigns focusing on consumer boycotts have had an impressive impact on forest conservation. Consumer pressure led to the development of forest certification and to the Canadian Boreal Forest Agreement. Consumer boycotts or the threat of such boycotts have also resulted in a recent commitment of forty major buyers and sellers of soy, palm oil, woodpulp and cattle to establish policies to exclude deforestation from their supply chains—a notable example is Cargill, the largest private company in the United States with annual sales of $135 billion.[668] It is of fundamental importance for conservation groups to continue their work with consumers to promote sustainable forestry.

8

Agricultural Resources and the Challenge to Feed a Future World

A brief history of agriculture. The main food crops. Current land degradation problems. Environmental impacts of modern intensive agriculture. The controversy over genetically modified organisms. Should we stop eating meat? The problem of price instability of agricultural products. Is there a food crisis? Food security and the sustainability of agriculture.

THE EARTH'S ABILITY to support agriculture is completely dependent on the conditions of the thin layer of topsoil—the top fifteen centimetres of soil that can be likened to the skin of the earth. Soil as a resource is the mainstay of civilizations because without soil we cannot grow the food required to sustain humans, nor will trees grow, nor will we have biodiversity. Soil is continuously being formed and destroyed. If the rate of formation is greater than the rate of erosion, the soil cover will thicken. If the erosion is greater than the formation, the soil cover will ultimately disappear, and with it, the vegetation it supports. Soil provides plants with essential nutrients of nitrogen, potassium, phosphorus, and trace elements such as iron, manganese, zinc, copper, and cobalt. Apart from supporting the growth of plants and animals by recycling nutrients and providing the medium for plant growth, soil provides essential ecosystem services including water filtration, drainage regulation, and carbon storage.

Soil is either formed directly from rocks through physical and chemical weathering, or indirectly from secondary materials such as glacial or windblown deposits.[669] Physical weathering occurs when pressure under the earth's surface forces rocks to expand and fall apart, a process that is accelerated by weather-induced freezing and thawing cycles and heat. Chemical weathering, which needs heat and moisture, occurs when rainwater dissolves some minerals (potassium, magnesium, and calcium) and transforms them into clays, which are critical in promoting the growth of living organisms. Once plants become established, their roots bind the soil and promote the formation of more soil. The plant cover begins to enrich the soil with organic materials and encourages animals to graze. Animals return nutrients to soil through manure and through their own decaying bodies when they die. Earthworms serve an important function in mixing organic materials from the surface with the underlying soil. Indeed, Charles Darwin, who later in his life became a gentleman farmer, became so intrigued by worms that he wrote a scientific treatise about their role in soil formation.[670] They digest organic materials and return them to the soil in the form of worm castings, which are high in nitrogen and potassium, beneficial for plant growth. They are joined by a whole army of soil-dwelling microorganisms that facilitate the weathering of the buried rocks and the breakdown of organic materials.

Soil formation depends on local conditions such as geology, climate, topography, available microorganisms, and the time horizon. Granite usually results in relatively infertile sandy soils, basalt in very fertile clay soils, and limestone in hardly any soil at all as the stone tends to dissolve—note the weathering that occurs on buildings and statues made from limestone. In colder regions physical weathering is more prevalent than chemical weathering, creating mineral-rich soils. Steep slopes typically result in thin soils, while a combination of high temperatures and high rainfall promotes intense chemical weathering, which tends to produce clay-rich soils. Most tropical soils receive all their nutrients from plants as the nutrients in the underlying clay soils have been leached out by the heavy rainfall. The type of clay is critically important. Silicate clays produced in temperate and relatively dry climates have a high capacity for absorbing nutrients, while iron and aluminum clays produced in hot and wet tropical countries have an extremely low capacity for taking up or retaining nutrients. Dense and lush rainforests live on recycled nutrients, and when the forest cover is removed, the soils become barren and even the addition of artificial fertilizers will not improve fertility. Temperate soils are subject to less rainfall and therefore less leaching of nutrients, and in many cases they are very fertile because of the continuous adding of organic matter from the vegetation cover.

Arid regions can only support very sparse vegetation that adds little organic material to the soil and therefore makes it less fertile.

Soil erosion also depends on local conditions. The structure of the soil—the mix of organic material, silt, sand, and clay—determines its erodibility. Soil structure is vitally important, determining not only the erodibility but also the soil's hydrologic properties—the ability to absorb, retain, and transmit water. Soil structure is often extremely fragile and easily destroyed by loss of organic material (humus) and poor tillage practices. The more organic materials and the more clay materials are present, the less erodible is the soil—the more sand, the more erodible. In general, the steeper the slope the higher the erosion rate, and wind erosion can be a problem in arid and semi-arid areas. High rainfall is a mixed blessing: it promotes plant growth, which improves the vegetation cover and therefore reduces erosion, but it also increases runoff and therefore erosion.

At the present time, the rate of soil loss outstrips the rate of soil formation. Estimates for world soil loss range from ten to one hundred tonnes of soils per hectare, which is a rate of removal ten to one hundred times the rate of creation, and that means that we are mining the soil which is not sustainable.[671] Approximately one-third of agricultural land has been lost in the last forty years—a huge problem that few people are aware of. Soil erosion and decreased soil fertility are not new occurrences and have, in some cases, shaped human history. The focus of this chapter is on how the trend of deteriorating soils can be reversed to enable the world to grow sufficient food to feed the current and expected future world population. Following a brief account of the history of agriculture and food crops, the chapter will examine the environmental, economic, and social effects of today's agriculture, with an emphasis on land degradation issues and on the impact of industrial agriculture on the environment. How can these environmental problems be solved while at the same time we try to increase food production to ensure the world's poor can afford to buy more and higher-quality food? This leads to the important question of the optimal design of national and international agricultural policies to enhance food security and cushion the impact on the poor of high and fluctuating food prices.

A brief history of agriculture

It is generally agreed that agriculture started in the Middle East ten thousand years ago with parallel evolution somewhat later in northern China and Central America. Following the latest glacial period, hunters and gatherers populated the upper reaches of Euphrates and Tigris (also known as Mesopotamia), living on large antelope herds.[672] Population increases meant that the carrying capacity of the land came under severe stress and people had to find new ways of feeding themselves. Wild wheat and barley could be adapted for cultivation relatively easily, as could legumes. Sheep and goats were domesticated about eight thousand years ago and cattle six thousand years ago, and a symbiosis developed between animal husbandry and plant production. Cattle were used to pull the newly developed plows and provided milk and meat to supplement diets. They also returned fertility to the fields through manure, which contains potassium, nitrogen, and phosphorus, all necessary for plant growth.[673] The invention of the plow and the use of oxen made it possible for individual farmers to produce more than their own immediate needs, which revolutionized agriculture and the structure of primitive societies by creating the need for specialized labour and laying the foundations for towns. Agriculture spread westward into Europe over the next couple of thousand years (6300–4800 BC).

Meanwhile, population pressures in Mesopotamia forced the farmers from the mountainous areas onto the drier areas around the rivers. Elaborate irrigation channels were built and cities developed, where society was stratified with an elite at the top overseeing the distribution of food. Agricultural yields were high and the population kept expanding, resulting in more pressures to increase agricultural production through more intensive irrigation. Problems started to appear in the form of silted-up irrigation channels and gradual salt buildup in the soils (salinization) caused by excessive irrigation. Groundwater in semi-arid regions contains salt, and with rapid evaporation the salt rises to the surface, where it is deposited. Most plants are not salt tolerant, and the land becomes useless for growing crops. By 1800 BC, the land could no longer support a large population and the area fell into a long-term decline.

Egypt was a different story. The people in the Nile delta used the yearly fluctuations of the river to great advantage. During the rainy season, floodwaters brought fertile silt from the upper reaches of the river and deposited it on the flood plains. When the river receded during the dry season, the level of the groundwater dropped, preventing salt from building up in the soil. However, problems of salinization began to appear when year-round irrigation was introduced to support cotton growing during the nineteenth century. The completion of the huge Aswan Dam in 1976 added to the problems, and the Nile water no longer delivers fertile silt—the silt is deposited on the bottom of Lake Nasser—and salinization has become a big problem in some of the areas of the delta. Agricultural production is no longer possible without massive doses of chemical fertilizer produced by cheap power generated from the dam. After seven thousand years of continuous use, the legendary fertility of the Nile delta is gone, and Egypt is now one of the world's largest grain importers.

Intensive agriculture developed in China as early as seven thousand years ago, which over time created adverse consequences, but in this case the problems were caused by soil erosion rather than salinization. The fertile loess soils of the river valleys were and are exceptionally erodible. Agriculture was first practiced on the slopes beside the major rivers, requiring the removal of the tree cover and resulting in large-scale soil erosion that increased the sediment load of the rivers. The Great River became the Yellow River in the first century BC, reflecting the change in colour caused by the increased presence of silt. Population pressures forced people to move on to the flood plains, and levees were built for flood control. Sediment settled in the river channels in front of the levees, raising the surface level of the river. In response, the levees were raised, setting the stage for later catastrophes when they were breached because of increased floodwaters. In 1852, the Yellow River broke its levees, killing millions of peasants.[674] By the 1920s, the surface of the river was ten metres above the floodplains.

Agricultural land has also been ruined by soil erosion in other parts of China. Northwestern China is a barren region where much of the topsoil has disappeared. In 1920–21 half a million people died and millions were starving after drought hit the area. Occasional famines appear to have been a recurrent feature of Chinese history. Soil-erosion specialists in China are now warning that nearly one hundred million people in southwest China will lose their land to infertility within thirty-five years if present trends continue, and harvests in northeastern China are expected to decline by 40 percent.[675] Obviously this will have a severe impact on poor people who live in the affected areas and on China's ability to feed its large population.

The Mediterranean basin was severely eroded during antiquity, largely due to deforestation.[676] Both the Greeks and the Romans recognized the importance of tending the soil in ensuring farming could produce enough food to sustain a growing population. They knew about the fertilizing properties of manure and compost, and the importance of terracing in stabilizing the soil. They also knew that different plants required different soils to prosper. However, if terracing was not used, plowing on slopes rapidly increased the erosion rates, and while farmers may not have noticed a very large change in their lifetime, the cumulative effect of annual losses of a few centimetres of topsoil resulted in an almost total loss of topsoil over a few centuries. The soil was washed down the rivers and, as a result, many of the ancient seaports are now kilometres

Figure 8.1. Terracing built by the Incas (Peru). Credit: Nathan Nelson. https://www.flickr.com.

from the sea—an example is Ostia, the port of Rome. By the time of the birth of Christ, the countryside around Rome could no longer feed the population, food was imported from North Africa (areas now controlled by Tunisia and Algeria), and history repeated itself. Rome's African breadbasket is now ruined, and the former great Roman cities in Africa are buried under topsoil washed down from the rocky slopes. Agriculture cannot feed the current population.

Terracing was employed in many other parts of the world as a measure of erosion control. It was extensively used by the Incas and was also introduced in rice cultivation in Southeast Asia. Until 2,500 years ago, rice was grown on dryland fields, but at that time paddies were introduced where terraces were flooded, encouraging the growth of nitrogen-fixing algae that greatly improved fertility and made it possible to recycle human and animal wastes. Crop rotation and the recycling of human and animal waste were introduced in most parts of the world as a means of maintaining soil fertility.

The presence of loess soils creates particular problems for agriculture. One-fifth of the earth's land surface is covered in loess, which is soil formed from windblown particles. Loess soils have a high mineral content and are thus very fertile, but they erode rapidly if the vegetation cover is stripped off. Loess soils are particularly prevalent in North America, Europe, and China. The Great

Plains in Canada and the United States were once covered with thick grass, grazed for millennia by buffaloes, and the grass cover protected the highly erodible loess soils. Traditional plows could not cut through the thick root network that had developed over the centuries. The disk plow, which cut through the thick turf with little difficulty, was invented in 1838. The disk plow, combined with tractors, meant that the average farmer could work fifteen times as much land in the early twentieth century as the average nineteenth-century farmer, and by the end of the nineteenth century, 50 percent of the potential farmland in North America was under cultivation.[677]

The Great Plains are semi-arid and subject to high winds. When the top layer of vegetation was removed, the easily erodible loess soil started to disappear, and by 1909 it was reported that almost four and a half million hectares of land were abandoned because of soil erosion. Relatively high rainfall from 1910 to 1930 created a false sense of security among farmers that soil erosion was not a problem; thus little was done to prepare for the coming disaster—aptly named the Dust Bowl—that followed a few years of little rainfall. The first sign appeared in 1933 in South Dakota, when a sudden windstorm removed a great deal of the topsoil. The day after, the sky remained dark from dust particles. In May of the following year, Montana and Wyoming were hit. Soon the dust had reached Buffalo in upstate New York, and a few days later the Eastern Seaboard. The air was so thick with dust that there were hours of total darkness in the middle of the day. The disappearance of the topsoil forced many farm families to pack up and leave, and in the following years, approximately 2.5 million people moved to California and the Eastern Seaboard. The Dust Bowl coincided with the Great Depression, exacerbating the situation not only in the United States, but also in Canada.

Similar scenarios played out in the Soviet Union following the Virgin Lands program—a major attempt to increase food production by plowing up the central Russian steppe. State farms were ordered to convert sixteen million hectares into agricultural land between 1954 and 1965.[678] Severe erosion quickly rendered much of the newly plowed land useless, and the Aral Sea disaster compounded the tragedy (see Chapter 9). Aiming to become self-sufficient, in the 1950s the Soviet government expanded cotton growing in the area around the Aral Sea by turning the whole area over to cotton, applying massive amounts of fertilizers and pesticides and using the lake water for irrigation through a large network of irrigation channels. The lake level began to drop, and by 1993 it was almost seventeen metres below its normal level and the surrounding lands started to dry out. Dust storms removed the topsoil, again resulting in a large outmigration of people.

No account of the history of agriculture is complete without an examination of the role of fertilizers. We now know that in order to grow, plants need potassium, nitrogen, phosphorus, and other elements such as calcium and sodium. Potassium is readily available in most rocks but phosphorus is not; it has to be added for plants to grow on a continuous basis. Nitrogen, which is needed is the largest quantities, is available in the atmosphere, but plants cannot use it directly because it has to first be combined with carbon, oxygen, or hydrogen. Bacteria associated with legumes (for example clover, peas, beans, and alfalfa) can "fix" nitrogen directly from the atmosphere and can therefore increase soil nitrogen content. It has been known for a long time that crop rotation involving legumes makes the soil much more productive. Advances in soil chemistry occurred in the late eighteenth and early nineteenth centuries, laying the foundations for the development of chemical fertilizers. As already described in Chapter 1, the beneficial effects of guano had been known in Peru since the time of the Incas, and it was now discovered that not only was guano rich in nitrogen like other manure, but it was also rich in phosphorus and thus highly desirable as a fertilizer, creating a guano boom in the 1850s. The discovery of large phosphate deposits in South America led to the development of artificial fertilizers combining phosphoric acid, potash, and ammonia. These new fertilizers were high in potassium, phosphorus, and nitrogen, enabling small farmers to grow crops without needing livestock to provide the necessary manure. During World War I, German scientists managed to produce liquid ammonia artificially (hydrogen nitride) by extracting nitrogen from the air and combining it with hydrogen from coal, which allowed for massive increases in the production of ammonia, using natural gas as the principal feedstock. Cheap nitrogen made it possible to increase food production to previously unimaginable levels.

Adding nitrogen to wheat crops had its own problems as it promoted plant growth, and the wheat straw became too tall and fell over before it could be harvested. Research went into breeding short-strawed wheat, work that was continued by Norman Borlaug in his efforts to breed high-yielding wheat in Mexico in the 1950s. Borlaug introduced his new wheat to India, where famines were prevalent. By 1974, India had become self-sufficient in food largely because of a tripling in wheat production. This became known as the Green Revolution.[679] Unfortunately, the higher-yielding grains also required more fertilizer, more pesticides, and more irrigation that small-scale farmers in the developing countries could ill afford. Nevertheless, half of the farmers in developing countries use Green Revolution seeds, but the impact of the Green Revolution has been extremely uneven.[680] Large-scale farmers could lobby for subsidies to enable them to buy the new seeds and fertilizer and to invest in irrigation and tractors. Small-scale farmers were left out of the process. Regionally, Asia benefited, but the Green Revolution had little impact on sub-Saharan Africa, where three-quarters of the world's poorest people live.

Since then, even higher crop yields have been achieved through genetic modification. Genetically modified (GM) grains, requiring fewer pesticides, are promoted as less harmful to biodiversity and to people, as many pesticides are toxic. The development of GM wheat has been much slower than the development of GM maize and rice, largely because of consumer resistance—an issue discussed in more detail below.

The main food crops

The history of agriculture is also closely linked to the development of the main food crops. Cereals are the most important source of calories for the world as a whole and will continue to be so into the foreseeable future.[681] The world population is predicted to increase from the current seven billion to 9.15 billion by the year 2050 and ten billion by 2100 and is expected to stabilize at that level. The calories needed to feed the expanding population are likely to come from three sources: wheat, maize, and rice. However, the share of cereals in per-capita consumption is declining because of rapid increases in consumption of vegetable oils and meat products. When people become richer, they demand more variety. The share of wheat in cereal consumption has increased while the share of coarse grains including maize, barley, sorghum, rye, oats, and millet has declined.

The current pattern of grain consumption and production dates back to the period of the major transatlantic migration during the nineteenth century that contributed to the spread of known varieties of grain across continents. Early European colonists tried to recreate the familiar in foreign lands, sometimes successfully and sometimes less so. Colonial administrators in Africa and Asia also introduced new crops in local communities (examples are the South American tuber cassava, maize, and cotton in Africa, and sweet potatoes in New Guinea).[682]

Maize was first grown in Mexico about six thousand years ago. How it was developed is a puzzle, since no wild relative has ever been found.[683] Because maize seeds are found in husks, maize cannot reseed itself—it needs help from humans. The most accepted theory is that it is an example of early plant breeding using a mountain grass (teosinte), which is its closest relative. Maize is called corn in North America, short for Indian corn. Its use spread to other continents through the influence of the early settlers to North America, and it is now the largest grain crop in the world (see Table 8.1) with the United States the biggest consumer and producer. In the US, it is mainly used to feed livestock but also for ethanol. China is the second-largest producer, followed by Brazil, Mexico, India, Argentina, Canada, and France. Maize is also a major food product for many people in developing countries, where it is often ground into cornmeal and then stewed. Table 8.1 shows that only 16 percent of coarse grains (of which maize makes up over 80 percent) is used for food, 57 percent is used for cattle feed, and the remaining 26 percent for ethanol; in the case of the United States, 38 percent is used for ethanol.[684]

Wheat is the second-largest cereal crop after maize and is the major food grain, used for making bread, pasta, noodles, couscous, beer, and alcohol. The provinces of Saskatchewan and Alberta in Canada have opened ethanol plants using wheat as the primary input. The top producers of wheat are the EU, China, India, Russia, the United States, and Canada. Wheat is the most important grain in terms of acreage sown but not in terms of the tonnage harvested, having been surpassed by maize. The price of wheat is highly dependent on weather conditions in the major growing areas, but in the last decade the prices of wheat and other cereals have also been affected by the price of oil. The higher the price of oil, the larger is the demand for cereals for ethanol production. Even though this primarily affects maize, it means there are incentives to reduce wheat acreages in favour of maize and other crops such as rapeseed and soybeans used in biodiesel production, which creates upward pressure on all grain prices. Other factors contributing to increased prices include expanding demand for meat in emerging economies as animals are frequently grain fed; and fertilizer prices, which are tied to oil prices.

The story of wheat is very much the story of agriculture. The early economist Thomas Malthus based his predictions about starvation on the observation that improvements in wheat yields cannot keep up with population growth. This was based on what he saw in Britain in the latter part of the eighteenth century. During the nineteenth century, wheat production increased because of the opening up of new lands in North America, Argentina, and Australia. However, Old World wheat was not suitable for these new lands as the growing season was shorter—in North America because of frost, and in Australia and Argentina because of heat and drought. For example, wheat lands in the Canadian Prairies could not be effectively exploited until the introduction of red fife (believed to have originated in Ukraine) that normally ripens in ninety-one

Table 8.1. Estimated world food utilization[1], 2013–2014

Commodity	Food utilization (million tonnes) and percentages of total utilization	Exports (million tonnes) and exports as percentage of utilization
Wheat	689.1	157.3 (23%)
Food	481.7 (70%)	
Feed	128.6 (19%)	
Other	78.8 (11%)	
Coarse grains[2]	1236.5	157.9 (13%)
(Maize)	(1010.9)	
Food	202.8 (16%)	
Feed	708.3 (57%)	
Other	325.4 (26%)	
Rice	492.1	39.7 (8%)
Food	410.3 (83%)	
Total cereals	2417.8	354.8 (15%)
Food	1094.8 (45%)	
Feed	851.0 (35%)	
Other	472.0 (20%)	
Oil seeds	511.2	
Meat and meat products (2013)	308.3	30.9 (10%)
Sugar	177.7	55.0 (31%)
Milk and milk products	773.4	68.8 (9%)
Fish and fishery products	162.9	58.8 (36%)

Source: FAO, *Food Outlook: Biannual Report on Global Food Markets*, October 2014.

Notes: 1. Utilization is different from production. Each year the amount of food used equals the amount that has been stored from previous years, plus the current production minus any surplus at the end of the period that will be added to food stocks. 2. "Coarse grains" includes maize, barley, sorghum, millet, rye, and oats, but maize makes up 81 percent of coarse grains.

days. This still made wheat growing marginal, considering the average frost-free period in the province of Alberta was ninety-four days. Much effort went into plant research even during the nineteenth century, resulting in several new strains that could be successfully grown in the new lands.[685]

Like wheat and maize, rice is of ancient origins, with some evidence of use going back ten thousand years. It is believed to have been domesticated in the Yangtze River basin four thousand years ago. Today it is the main food source for 40 percent of the world's population, particularly in Southeast Asia and parts of Africa, and is the third-largest cereal crop. But because large producing

Figure 8.2. Rice paddies in Laos. Credit: https://www.flickr.com/photos/75243296@N08/

countries also tend to be major consumers, relatively small quantities of rice are traded across borders—only 8 percent compared with 23 percent for wheat (Table 8.1).[686] Many people in Southeast Asia eat boiled rice three times a day. In some areas, glutinous rice is preferred; in other areas, the more distinctively flavoured basmati rice. There are also specific regional preferences for short- and long-grained rice. Compared with maize and wheat, rice produces more energy and protein per hectare; hence, an association exists between population density and rice cultivation.[687] Rice can be cultivated in almost any climate with high rainfall and is often grown by small farmers in paddy fields. The cultivation of paddy rice is both labour intensive and water dependent. The rice is first grown as seedlings and then transplanted into the fields, which have been prepared by being plowed and levelled, using water for the final levelling. After the seedlings have been transplanted, the fields are flooded, often to a depth of one hundred millimetres—a level of water that is maintained during the growing season.

Many Asian cultures revere rice and rice growing. For example, in Japanese culture the whiteness of the rice is likened to the purity of the soul, and rice is the only dish shared at the table from a common bowl, symbolizing the harmony and commonality so central to the culture.[688] Rice cultivation is often considered to be a way of life and is part of a nation's cultural fabric, which explains the emotional attachment to a landscape with paddy fields and the protection of domestic rice producers in Japan and other countries.

In recent decades, vegetable oil production has been the fastest-growing sector in world agriculture. The major products are palm oil, soybeans, rapeseed (canola), and sunflower seed. Other locally important products are oils made from groundnuts (peanuts) and sesame seed, coconuts, and olives. The reasons were increased demand for palm oil for cooking; increased use of soybean for livestock feed; and increased industrial use of vegetable oil in the chemical industry to aid in the manufacture of paints, detergents, lubricants, ethanol, and biodiesel.

The world's most widely produced vegetable oil is soybean oil, followed by palm oil—a tropical oil grown from the oil palm native to Africa and now the world's most traded vegetable oil product. The United States, Brazil, Argentina, China, and India are the major producers of soybean oil, while Malaysia is responsible for almost half of global palm oil production, followed by Indonesia and several African countries.[689] The rising popularity of palm oil, which is largely grown on big plantations in Southeast Asia, is caused by several factors: higher demand for food in developing countries and the use of palm oil for biodiesel. Palm oil is popular with growers because of its inherent productivity. Adoption of palm oil can result in up to tenfold increases in yield per hectare (see page 172). Higher vegetable oil production is responsible for a large part of the expansion of agricultural land in poor countries, also causing a shift of land out of cereal production and into oil seeds production.[690] The expansion of agricultural land has in turn led to the destruction of tropical rainforests, particularly in Malaysia, Indonesia, and Brazil, where rich rainforest ecosystems are being replaced by biological deserts.[691] One direct effect is the destruction of the habitat for many endangered species such as orangutans, tigers, and rhinos in Southeast Asia and of biodiversity in general.

The emergence of biofuels constitutes a real threat to food production.[692] The development of bioethanol in the United States was centred on maize because of successful lobbying by maize growers and Arthur Daniel Midland, one of the largest food processors in the world in the early 1980s. As a result of this successful lobbying, the industry was subsidized to the tune of $8.9 billion despite the fact that bioethanol is competitive with ordinary gas if the price of petroleum is $60 per barrel or higher. The subsidy as well as the punitive tariff on imports of ethanol aimed at Brazil was stopped in December 2011.[693] However, the industry still receives legislative support mandating the use of ethanol in gas. In 2005, legislation called for the use of 7.5 billion gallons of biofuels per year to increase to thirty-six billion by 2022, sixteen billion of which must be second generation. Brazil has also heavily subsidized its ethanol production, which is built on sugar cane, not maize. The European Union subsidizes the production of biodiesel made from rapeseed and sunflower seeds. The impact of these subsidies on food production is serious—increased demand for crops for fuel has resulted in an increase in food prices affecting poor people in both rich and poor countries. It has also diverted land from food production to the more profitable biofuel production.[694] It is even possible that continued support for maize-based ethanol production in the United States could turn the US into a food importer with ripple effects throughout the globe.[695] It is estimated that replacing 10 percent of fossil fuels by biofuels in the EU would use up 38 percent of the total agricultural acreage.[696] As a result of these concerns, the EU is moving to capping the proportion of food based biofuels (maize, palm oil, rapeseed, and soybeans) to 6 percent within the 2020 target of 10 percent for renewable transport fuels.

As discussed in Chapter 5, the switch from petroleum to biofuels can have some environmental benefits. Most studies show that burning ethanol creates less greenhouse gases than burning petroleum-based gasoline, but to a large extent the net impact depends on the source of the fuel—for example, if the ethanol is maize based or sugar-cane based—and the land use before the planting of biofuel crops. Are the crops grown on previously forested land or on land used for growing food?

Current land degradation problems

Land degradation results from factors often working together—damage to soil structure, soil erosion, lack of drainage leading to waterlogged soils, salinization, acidification, and industrial contamination. Waterlogging happens when poorly drained soil is overirrigated, which makes it impossible for crops to grow. Acidification occurs naturally depending on the underlying rock, but intensive agricultural practices—in particular, excessive use of nitrogen fertilizer—can make the soils too acidic and unsuitable for crops. Contamination of soils from industrial and agricultural waste is a problem in many parts of the world, particularly if the waste contains heavy metals such as lead and cadmium. If these metals enter the food chain, they are known to have adverse effects on human health. Salinization can cause yield decreases of 10 to 25 percent and can render the land totally unusable—witness ancient Mesopotamia. The FAO estimates that approximately 3 percent of agricultural land is affected by salinization.[697]

Many lessons from history have been forgotten, and land degradation resulting in low biological and economic productivity is still a major problem.

When land degradation happens in drylands—arid, semi-arid, and dry sub-humid areas—it is usually referred to as desertification, and is estimated to affect 10 to 20 percent of drylands.[698] Drylands cover approximately 41 percent of the earth's total land area and are home to more than two billion people. Forty-four percent of all cultivated areas are located in these dry areas, which are found on every continent except Antarctica. Drylands have high population growth, and populations lag far behind other areas in terms of human well-being. Per-capita incomes are lower, infant mortality rates are higher, and health outcomes worse, partly because of the lack of clean water. These poor outcomes occur primarily because people in drylands rely on degraded ecosystem services for their livelihoods to a larger extent than anywhere else. They typically eke out a living from agriculture, animal husbandry, or from the collection of fuel wood and construction materials. Desertification occurs when previously productive savannah forests and grasslands turn into unproductive deserts, with losses of livelihood to millions of rural dwellers. A recent study has found that large areas are threatened by desertification, including the Mediterranean area, the savannahs, the temperate steppes, and the Prairies, with the greatest threats in North Africa, the Middle East, Australia, and southwest China.[699] The United Nations estimates that up to one billion people are currently affected.

Not only does desertification directly impact people, it also has serious environmental effects. These include detrimental effects on biodiversity, because plants and animals can no longer survive, and climatic impacts. Desertification increases albedo as the land becomes a lighter colour because of drier and sparser vegetation. In this process more sunlight is reflected, decreasing the surface temperature, which in turn reduces air movements that promote rainfall, and as a consequence the region becomes even drier. Desertification also affects carbon sequestration, another concern. It is estimated that one-quarter of all organic carbon is stored in dryland soils, and desertification means that the carbon in the soils is released in the atmosphere. Finally, the frequency of dust storms increases, but it is not clear if more dust in the atmosphere leads to a warmer or cooler temperature. The presence of dust may reflect more sun light and therefore have a cooling effect, or it could act as a blanket and keep more heat in. Dust storms are a frequent occurrence in China, and if they reach urban areas they can have serious health repercussions.

Desertification is often exacerbated by periodic draught, or in some cases by climatic change, but a major cause is overcultivation and overgrazing.

Figure 8.3. Dust storm over China. Credit: NASA.

Traditionally, people in dryland areas survived by hunting and gathering and by cattle-herding (pastoral nomadism), all of which were sustainable because people moved over large areas, giving the landscape an opportunity to recover. However, population pressures led to increased conflicts between herders and farmers wanting access to the same lands, which led to overgrazing and too-short crop rotations, both contributing to desertification. The introduction of irrigation, which was often not conducted in an appropriate manner, led to salinization and waterlogging as well as damage to water courses. Burning was an integral part of land use; while it can improve the quality of the forage, if done too frequently it is another important contributor to desertification.

In 1992, desertification was raised as a major issue at the UN Conference on Environment and Development (the Rio Conference). The result was the legally binding UN Convention to Combat Desertification (UNCCD) which was ratified and came into force in 1996.[700] The main purpose of the convention is to improve livelihoods and ecosystems in dryland areas. Desertification can be halted and in some cases reversed. A critical factor is improved water management integrating both traditional and new technologies—an important topic

Figure 8.4. A shepherd guiding his sheep in search of grazing, Morocco. Credit: John Tarantino and Wikimedia Commons.

that will be discussed in Chapter 9. In many cases, substantial benefits can be gained from integration of pastoral land use and agricultural cropping. Agroforestry, which tries to combine native nitrogen-fixing trees such as *Faidherbia albida* (a type of acacia) with cropping, has been remarkably successful in the Sahel region of Africa.[701] The trees shade crops and provide some protection from winds. They also assist with moisture retention and provide fodder to cattle, and perhaps most importantly, they fertilize the soil by absorbing nitrogen from the atmosphere, leading to yield improvements of 30 to 100 percent. Other measures to combat desertification include planting more drought-tolerant crops and crops that require less water. It is also important to take pressure off the land by providing the local population with alternative opportunities not involving traditional agriculture or husbandry.

Environmental impacts of modern intensive agriculture

Environmental problems caused by agriculture are not restricted to dry areas. The environmental impacts of modern agriculture, whether the introduction of new seeds, poorly conceived tillage methods, or excessive fertilizer use, have not been benign. The introduction of chemical fertilizers and conventional genetic manipulation made it possible for us to avoid the Malthusian trap by radically transforming agriculture, making wheat, maize, rice, and barley the dominant crops. The question is whether this expansion can be sustained to feed an additional two billion people by the year 2050.

The new seeds increased the dependence on fertilizer and irrigation, and agricultural output per unit of fertilizer has started to decline—the application of fertilizer follows the law of diminishing returns. Some of the chemical fertilizers are taken up by plants as intended, but there is a limit to how much nitrogen soils can hold, and any surplus is leaked away in drainage water or dissipates into the atmosphere. In rich countries, excessive use of fertilizer has resulted in increased eutrophication of water courses with a subsequent negative impact on fishing and biodiversity in general. Studies from the United Kingdom and Germany show that the environmental cost of pollution from agriculture has reached one-third of the value of agricultural output.[702] Chesapeake Bay, Lake Erie, and the Baltic are examples of water bodies that are almost dead because of overfertilization by excessive use of nitrogen and phosphate.

Agriculture is also a major contributor to greenhouse gases through the emission of nitrous oxides from fertilizers and manure, and methane from ruminating cattle. Both nitrous oxides and methane are more powerful greenhouse gases than CO_2. The IPCC estimates that if the clearing of forests for agriculture is included in calculations, up to 32 percent of anthropogenic greenhouse gases originate in agriculture.[703]

The only solution for feeding the growing world population is either to open up more land, which usually means cutting down more forests, or improving crop yields (or investing in fisheries and aquaculture, a topic discussed in Chapter 10). Currently, 10 percent of the earth's land surface is under cultivation, 20 percent is grassland, and another 20 percent is forested.[704] The remainder is desert, ice, and mountain chains. Estimates vary wildly on how much new land can be cultivated. Some studies claim we can double the amount of land used for agriculture from 1,505 million hectares to 3,325 million hectares by putting marginal land back in production, while others are far more cautious, pointing out that much marginal land has been severely degraded and is not suitable for agriculture.[705] Turning forested land and grasslands into agriculture is not desirable for reasons of biodiversity and its likely impacts on carbon emissions. Sprawling cities, most of which were originally founded in areas with the most fertile soils, also continue to destroy prime agricultural land.

However, Brazil is an example of a country that has managed to become a major food producer in only thirty years by turning its grasslands (the Cerrado) into a breadbasket, contrary to the prediction by the father of the Green Revolution, Norman Borlaug, that the soils were too acidic and lacking in nutrients to ever become productive. The Cerrado covers 21 percent of the country and, like most savannahs, is a mixture of grasslands, forests, and stream valleys. Borlaug was wrong, and the success can be attributed to several factors.[706] In 1973, an agricultural research station was established—Empresa Brasileira de Pesquisa Agropecuaria—that over the years developed into the world's leading tropical research station. As a result of the research, massive amounts of lime were poured on the land to reduce soil acidity—up to five tonnes per hectare. Researchers bred special bacteria known to fix nitrogen in legumes and added the bacteria to the soil, thereby decreasing the need for fertilizer. They managed to adapt soybean cultivation to tropical lands by cross breeding, making it possible to generate two crops per year. A fast-growing African grass adapted to local conditions was introduced, greatly improving pasture areas. Researchers are currently experimenting with agroforestry by alternating crops and pasture and providing additional pasture for livestock by surrounding areas with trees.

Food production in Brazil is concentrated in big industrial operations. Out of five million farms, 1.6 million account for 76 percent of output. The environmental consequences of this massive transformation are uncertain, particularly if climate change leads to less precipitation as predicted by most of the climate models. After all, North American and Soviet history demonstrated that fluctuations in rainfall can lead to large-scale environmental disasters on semi-arid lands. Some of the Cerrado area is classified as an environmental hot spot with

Figure 8.5. Soybean cultivation in Brazil. Credit: Tiago Fiereze and Wikimedia Commons.

more than seven thousand species of plants—more than any other savannah area in the world.[707] Only 2.2 percent of the area is protected, and many animal and plant species are threatened with extinction.

A growing number of soil-science specialists agree that large-scale industrial farming has been an ecological disaster and is not sustainable. In order to continue to feed the growing world population, we need a new green (ecological) revolution that reintroduces traditional farming techniques as well as some new ones. Food production doubled in the last fifty years because of a 700 percent increase in the application of nitrogen and a 350 percent increase in the application of phosphorus. This cannot be repeated as the plants cannot absorb any more fertilizer. According to estimates by the FAO, the rate of growth in agricultural productivity is declining. The average growth has been 2.3 percent per year since 1960. Within the next twenty years, it is expected to decline to 1.5 percent and by 2050 to 0.9 percent.[708] The yield potential of various crops is the yield that can be obtained under ideal conditions; the difference between the yield achieved in a certain area and the yield potential is the "exploitable yield gap."[709] The key to closing the yield gap in many areas of the world seems to be in improving nitrogen efficiency. Field experiments on rice fields in Asia have shown that careful applications of nitrogen in the right amount and at the right time have great potential. A study published in *Nature* claims that the yield gap can be closed by changes in agricultural practices through better management of nutrients and water, which could lead to production increases in the range of 45 to 670 percent for most crops.[710] Apparently, timing of application of fertilizers is critical. However, much more research is needed combining science with extensive knowledge of local conditions—in some areas lack of nitrogen is the limiting factor, while in others, phosphorus, water, and the quality of seed are more problematic.

Organic farming may offer some solutions. Organic farming uses natural fertilizers such as manure, and organic materials are returned to the soil through mulching. Crops are rotated and no pesticides are used. Field experiments conducted between 1981 and 2002 as part of the Rodale Institute Farming Systems Trials in Pennsylvania compared growing grains in conventional and organic farming systems.[711] The experiments confirmed that, not surprisingly, the soil on the organic plots contained more organic matter, which made it easier to conserve water and soil resources. The input of fossil fuels was 30 percent lower while labour input was higher but more evenly distributed through the year. There were fewer pest problems and an increase in biodiversity, but nitrogen leaching from the organic plots was no less than the leaching from conventional farming. Organic farming also required more land because of the need for crop rotation. But according to a recent study, organic farming on average has 25 percent lower yields than traditional farming, with a yield differential ranging from 5 percent to 34 percent lower.[712] The main reason for this differential, which is more pronounced for grains than for fruit and oil seeds, is that organic systems do not provide enough nitrogen and there are problems in managing phosphorus. The lower yields of organic farming are problematic because growing is less profitable—the Rodale Institute estimates that organic food must command at least a 10 percent price premium to be profitable. As the organic market appears to be growing, it must be a premium consumers are willing to pay.

Integrated Soil Fertility Management, pioneered in Africa, is based on combining synthetic fertilizers with organic methods.[713] These measures rebuild the soil, and studies have shown that crop yields can be maintained. Other measures that are effective in conserving the soil are zero-tillage and minimum-tillage techniques, where the soil is disturbed as little as possible to maintain soil structure and prevent erosion. These techniques were first developed in North America. Instead of using plows to turn over the soil to open up the ground, disks are first used to mix organic debris into the top layer of the soil followed by chisel plows, which push seeds into the ground. The organic material is used as mulch, mimicking the natural processes of soil formation. By 2001, zero tillage was used on 60 percent of Canadian crops and 23 percent of US crops (2004).[714] Not only does zero tillage reduce soil erosion (in some cases by an astonishing amount of almost 100 percent), but it is also economically advantageous; energy costs are reduced by up to 50 percent because plowing is not required. However, zero tillage does not work well on poorly drained clay soils that must be plowed to avoid compaction. It also requires liberal applications of herbicides.

So far, on a worldwide basis, only 5 percent of agriculture is practiced with zero-tillage techniques, but they have been used successfully in developing countries because they are easily adapted for small landholders. Again, the land is not plowed; instead, hoes are used to create small, permanent basins where seeds or crops are planted directly into the soil. Another method is to use a "ripper" pulled by a tractor or an ox, which creates a small trench for the seeds. This means that fertilizers—organic or inorganic—can be applied exactly where they are needed. Zero tillage is one of the cornerstones of a growing movement toward *conservation agriculture*. Compared with traditional agriculture, conservation agriculture follows three principles: avoiding continuous mechanical disturbance of the soil (zero-tillage techniques), maintaining permanent organic soils cover, and proper crop rotation.[715] The FAO claims that conservation agriculture is economically viable despite being more labour-intensive than other forms of agriculture. It creates healthier soils, is less intensive in water use, and helps to sequester carbon as the organic material is returned to the soil. *Evergreen agriculture*, developed in Africa, is another variation of conservation agriculture. It involves the integration of nitrogen-fixing trees, particularly *Faidherbia albida*, into the crop system. It is the logical solution when artificial fertilizers are beyond the reach of farmers. The trees maintain continuous coverage of the growing area throughout the year, and as well as improving fertility, they improve soil structure, carbon sequestration, and biodiversity, and they are also an important source of fibre and fuel for the farmers.[716] Evergreen agriculture has achieved impressive successes in Zambia, Malawi, Niger, and Burkina Faso.[717]

The new thinking embodied in conservation agriculture combines "bottom-up" and "top-down" approaches. Ideally, it requires sophisticated agricultural research carried out in laboratories followed by work with farmers at a local level to determine the most appropriate measures for local conditions. Monkombu Sambasivan Swaminathan, who is widely credited with introducing the Green Revolution to India, is a proponent of conservation agriculture and argues that what is now needed is an "evergreen revolution" to counter the extensive ecological damage done to the environment by modern farming.[718] He is an advocate of "precision farming," which recognizes that each farmer is faced with different circumstances in terms of soils, climate, weather, and other specific conditions. Because of this, all farmers would benefit from tailored information on suitable seed varieties, seed density, optimal fertilizer use, the best time to plant and harvest, local weather conditions, and presence of pests. This information could be made available on a local basis using the global-positioning system (GPS), geographic information systems (GIS) technology, and various databases, allowing farmers to fine-tune their uses of fertilizer and pesticides. Swaminathan has been instrumental in persuading the Indian government to finance hundreds of community-based agricultural knowledge centres in India, where such information is available for free to farmers. He also believes the information could be made accessible to farmers using cell phones, the Internet and FM radio—communications technologies that are increasingly available in developing countries.

The controversy over genetically modified organisms

Genetic engineering has been promoted as a potentially new, greener Green Revolution designed to achieve increased crop yields using fewer herbicides and thus ensuring long-run food security. Genetic engineering improves crop yields by protecting plants against herbicides, insects, and viruses through the introduction of toxin-producing genes that kill certain pests or a gene from a bacterium that is resistant to commonly used herbicides.[719] This means that herbicide applications used for weed control can be reduced, which saves costs—and in some cases lives—and limits the impact on the environment. For thousands of years, plants have been bred for local conditions (note the development of maize), but genetic engineering is different because it permanently alters the plant DNA. The biotech company Monsanto pioneered the application of genetic engineering to agricultural crops. An early example was the insertion of *Bacillus thuringiensis* (Bt), a natural insecticide, into the DNA of cotton plants, eliminating the need for additional application of insecticides. GM cotton seeds were introduced on the market in 1996 and have since taken over in many parts of the world. By 2014, the percentage of acres planted with Bt seeds in the United States had reached 91 percent of the seeded acreage of cotton.[720] The same technology has been used to alter the DNA of maize and other crops. Genetic engineering has also been widely used to make plants resistant to the common herbicide glyphosate (commercially known as Roundup). This means that fields can be sprayed with the herbicide without killing the crop itself, promoting the use of Roundup rather than the more toxic herbicides such as 2,4-Dichlorophenoxyacetic acid (2,4-D), metolachlor, and diuron that are known to have adverse effects on human health.

The introduction of genetically modified organisms in food crops (GM crops)—the first was genetically engineered soybeans in the mid-1990s—has been very controversial. In general, people appear very suspicious of the application of new technology to food production, particularly if the technology is controlled by big multinational corporations such as Monsanto. This has led to an extensive regulatory framework and initially to a moratorium in EU, declared illegal under a 2006 ruling by the WTO, but most European countries have implemented their own policies limiting the use of GM seeds and products because of strong consumer resistance. This in turn led to several developing countries refusing food aid if it included GM grains. There was little resistance in North America, where GM products include maize, soybeans, canola, squash, and potato. GM crops are now grown in twenty-five countries, accounting for 8 percent of the world's total crop area in 2008, with herbicide-tolerant soybeans accounting for 53 percent of total area, followed by herbicide-tolerant maize.[721] Farmers who adopted GM seeds have lower costs of production and higher crop yields because of cheaper weed control and smaller losses from insect infestations. These benefits have been particularly impressive for Bt crops in China and

India, where insect infestation is a serious problem. For example, a study on the impact on smallholder Indian farmers found that Bt cotton led to a 24 percent increase in cotton yield per acre and a 50 percent gain in profits.[722] The positive impact on profitability has been smaller in North America than in other parts of the world because the strong patent protection in North America requires farmers to pay high technology fees for using the seeds.[723]

There are additional benefits. A US study published in 2010 concluded that GM crops had fewer adverse effects on the environment than did non-GM crops.[724] In particular, improvements were found in water quality because GM crops require less herbicide use (and typically use the less toxic herbicide Roundup). The crops also made reduced tillage possible, creating less soil erosion due to runoff. The decreased insecticide use of Bt-modified crops has also been shown to have proven benefits for human health. Users in China and South Africa were shown to have a lower incidence of pesticide poisoning than non-users, and there was less pesticide residue in food products.[725]

Given that the net benefits of GM grains are substantial, why is public resistance so large? The opponents of GM food grains have been particularly concerned with their long-term environmental and health effects. One of the claimed benefits of GM grains is that there is a reduced need for herbicides and insecticides; apparently, this is true for insecticides but not for herbicides. While insecticide applications have decreased through the use of Bt crops, herbicide use in the United States has increased because of the emergence of Roundup-resistant weeds, which has made it necessary to apply larger and more frequent doses of herbicides, and because of the wider utilization of zero tillage, which requires more weed control.[726] Between 1996 and 2011 in the US, herbicide use increased by 239,000 tons and insecticide use decreased by 56,000 tons, resulting in a net increase of pesticide use of 183,000 tons—a total increase of 7 percent. This is of potential concern for several reasons. One is that traces of Roundup were found in 67 to 100 percent of air samples and rainfall in Mississippi and Iowa, with unknown effects on the environment and on humans. Evidence shows that Roundup affects the survival rates of amphibians and has a negative impact on soil microorganisms.[727] Second, applications toward the end of the growing season can lead to larger residues in silage and forage, with the potential of Roundup chemicals entering the human food chain. Third, a documented increase in Roundup-resistant weeds will cause pressure to return to more toxic herbicides such as 2,4-D. Seeds that are 2,4-D resistant have already been developed, but so far they have not been given approval.[728]

Concern has also been raised over possible effects on genetic diversity and therefore on biodiversity and wildlife. However, it has been pointed out that biotechnology can be, and often is, applied to many strains of the same type of grain compared with Green Revolution grains, and therefore, in itself, should not adversely impact genetic diversity. An additional worry is that GM seeds may have detrimental effects on beneficial insects as well as lead to a faster introduction of resistant insects that would encourage generation of new pathogens.

The debate about health impacts includes possible allergic effects and the risk of gene transfers. An example of an adverse gene transfer would be if antibiotic resistant genes from GM foods were transferred to bacteria in the human gut in which case antibiotics would not work in controlling some illnesses. So far no adverse health effects on humans have been discovered.

Even though no studies show adverse health effects on humans, the American Academy of Environmental Medicine, in a 2007 position paper on GM foods, concluded that "because of the mounting data, it is biologically plausible for genetically modified foods to cause adverse health effects in humans."[729] The conclusion was based on a few studies on animals showing that GM foods can result in changes to the immune system, potentially causing allergies and inflammations as well as changes in the kidney, pancreas, liver, and spleen, and accelerated aging and infertility.[730] Arguing that GM foods "pose a serious health risk in the areas of toxicology, allergy and immune function, reproductive health, and metabolic, physiologic, and genetic health," the Academy recommended a moratorium on GM foods, more research, labelling of GM products, and for physicians to consider the possible role of these foods in diseases.

However, this report is contrary to other scientific reports. The first comprehensive evaluation of GM crops was done in the United Kingdom in 2002.[731] It had three parts: a wide-ranging public debate, an evaluation of the costs and benefits of GM crops, and a review of the science. The public debate indicated that people were profoundly uneasy with GM crops, having considerable concern about the potential risks to health and the environment and hostility toward the companies involved, particularly Monsanto. As a result, the evaluation of the costs and benefits downplayed the benefits because of consumer attitudes. The scientific evaluation found no evidence of adverse impacts on human health. Field experiments also showed that the seeds were unlikely to invade the surrounding area and have deleterious effect on wildlife.[732] The European Union, in a 2010 report reviewing evidence from the last decade, concluded that the use of biotechnology and of genetically engineered plants did not lead to higher risk than conventional breeding or production technologies.[733] A 2011 literary review, surveying both long-term and multigenerational effects of GM foods, found no scientifically credible evidence that GM foods have an adverse effect on health in animals.[734] Another review in 2013 concluded that no adverse effects on humans have been documented.[735]

Because of continued resistance to GM foods, consumers in many countries have requested that labelling be introduced. But labelling of GM foods is a controversial issue, and the American Medical Association has come out against it as it creates an impression that GM products are hazardous to human health, and according to the AMA, there is no such evidence. GM products have entered into international trade and are among the most heavily traded commodities of cotton, maize, soybean, and canola. The last three are mainly used for animal food, but they enter the human food chain in many processed foods. Aspects of this trade fall under the Cartagena Protocol on Biosafety, which was adopted in 2000 and ratified in 2003.[736] It is a supplement to the Convention on Biological Diversity (discussed in Chapter 6) and covers living modified organisms (LMO) created through biotechnology and traded across borders. The purpose is to provide importing countries with sufficient information to make informed decisions. A Biosafety Clearing House was set up as part of the Protocol, which requires that when a country approves a commercial variety of a GM product, it should be reported to the clearing house within fifteen days. Exporters of any products containing GM varieties have to include a declaration with each shipment stating that the shipment *may* include GM products. As exporters of GM products, Canada, the United States, Australia, Argentina, Chile, and Uruguay are not part of the Protocol, the main reason being the difficulty of separating GM grains from other grains since they are frequently intermixed. However, this reporting requirement is not onerous, and furthermore, it does not provide any useful information for the importing country.[737] In 2006, it was proposed that all clearly identified GM products be accompanied by a declaration, while other shipments were required to be accompanied by a declaration that they *may* contain such products, and the declaration must include a list of what varieties they may contain. This provision has not been implemented. The vagueness of the current rules have put the onus on importing countries to implement stringent food safety laws and expensive testing procedures on imported food grains, options that are not realistic for developing countries, many of which have resorted to the cheaper option of product bans—Malawi, Nigeria, Sudan, and Zimbabwe among others.

The evidence so far is that genetic engineering is a positive development in plant technology and may provide even more benefits in the future. For example, researchers have successfully introduced beta-carotene in rice ("golden rice"), a modification that could radically reduce malnutrition in children in many countries where the main diet is rice.[738] Likewise cassava—a staple diet for many in developing countries—has also been engineered to contain beta-carotene and iron. Recent research has indicated that it is also possible to introduce genes that make plants salt resistant and genes that improve the ability of plants to better utilize nitrogen and phosphorus fertilizer or to fix their own nitrogen from the air. These breakthroughs would greatly improve the quality of water in many rivers and lakes. Researchers at Roehampton are working on developing grains that do not need any herbicides. It is possible that future developments may see new seeds that will lead to large increases in yields, greatly improving our ability to feed the world in the future.

Should we stop eating meat?

Another controversial issue relates to the environmental impacts of livestock production. When people become wealthier they can afford a more varied diet, which usually includes more meat and milk products. Worldwide, meat consumption in developing countries grew at a yearly rate of 5–6 percent per annum in the last few decades, consumption of milk and milk products by 3.4–3.8 percent per annum, compared to cereal consumption that increased by 1–2 percent.[739] The demand for meat and milk products is projected to increase by 73 and 58 percent by the year 2050. This is of concern as it will make it far more difficult to limit greenhouse gas emissions. The 2006 FAO report *Livestock's Long Shadow: Environmental Issues and Options*, claimed that livestock was responsible for 18 percent of greenhouse gas emissions worldwide—an even larger share than the transport sector.[740] This finding generated a huge debate whether humans should decrease their consumption of meat. A subsequent study, also by FAO, revised the figure for livestock's contribution to greenhouse gas emissions downward to 14.5 percent—still a larger share than the transport sector.[741] Beef production generates 41 percent of the emissions, milk 20 percent, pigmeat and poultry 9 percent, and eggs 8 percent. Forty-four percent of the emissions are in the form of methane, 29 percent nitrous oxides, and the remainder CO_2. Methane is produced in the digestive system of ruminants, nitrous oxides in manure storage and processing, and carbon dioxide in meat processing and transportation.

There are other problems with livestock production. Many would describe industrial feedlots as ecological disasters, where grain and forage grown on irrigated fields are often fed to cattle concentrated in large animal pens with poor facilities for disposing of the manure and urine, resulting in the contamination of water courses with nitrates and phosphorus pollution. The animals are routinely fed antibiotics because of the risk of disease in crowded conditions, which has led to a growth in antibiotic-resistant pathogens. The resulting beef is fatty and high in omega-6 fatty acids, proven to be a major contributor to heart disease, cancer, and stroke. A recent UK study claims that if people in the United Kingdom reduced their meat consumption to 210 grams per day, forty-five thousand people could be saved each year from an early death from heart disease, cancer, and stroke.[742]

Apart from adverse climatic, ecological, and health effects, meat production is often seen as an inefficient use of agricultural resources.[743] It is more efficient for us to eat grain products directly instead of first feeding the grain to livestock and then eating the meat. Cattle do not convert grain efficiently into meat compared with pigs and chickens. On average, it takes five to ten kilograms of grain to produce one kilogram of beef depending on the breed (see Table 8.2). In total, livestock consume one-third of cereal output, a figure which is expected to increase to 45 to 50 percent by the year 2050.[744] According to projections by the FAO, 1.45 million tonnes of cereal will be used for animal feed in 2050. Assuming that a kilo of cereal gives approximately 3,000 calories compared with a kilo of livestock, which gives 1,500 calories (much of the animal cannot be used for food), and assuming that on average one person requires 3,000 calories per day, simple calculations show that diverting cereal production from animals to people could feed an additional 3.5 billion people in 2050.[745] However, this figure is probably a substantial overstatement, since people cannot live on grain alone.

Table 8.2. Feed conversion efficiency for farm animals

	Feed conversion of kg cereals to kg of animal weight
Broiler chicken	1.7
Laying hens	2
Pigs	2.43
Cattle	5–10

Source: Garnett (2009), p. 494. The data are from North America and UK.

Nevertheless, there are arguments to be made in favour of meat consumption. Measures can be taken to reduce cattle emissions by using better-quality feed and improved breeding and animal health to enhance the efficiency of livestock production.[746] Cattle also provide milk, leather products, and traction in many parts of the world; they also provide manure that improves the soil where it is applied, and the handling of manure could be improved to recycle nutrients and reduce nitrous-oxides emissions. Furthermore, not all cattle are grain fed; in many cases they graze on marginal land that cannot be used for growing crops.

Meat from goats, pigs, and chicken often provides a necessary addition of protein, fat, calcium, iron, zinc, and vitamin B_{12} to meagre diets. Pigs and chickens are not ruminants and therefore do not produce methane in their digestive systems. Pigs are very efficient converters of food scraps with no alternative use. The reprocessing of food waste into animal feed stops the waste from going into landfills, which are sources of methane and other pollutants. Unfortunately, animals are no longer fed food scraps in many Western countries because of fear of bovine spongiform encephalopathy—better known as mad cow disease—which killed over 150 people in the United Kingdom. The epidemic was not related to food scraps, but to feeding animal protein from diseased animals. For religious reasons, many cultures shun pigs and pig meat. Following the outbreak of swine flu, Egypt killed three hundred thousand pigs reared by the Christian community and entirely fed on food scraps, a policy that had the unintended consequence of leading to a garbage crisis.[747]

The conclusion is that there is no easy answer to the question of whether we should stop eating meat. People in industrialized countries eat too much meat and should reduce their consumption for health reasons, and people in poor countries eat too little. How can we decrease meat consumption in rich countries? The simple answer is to make meat more expensive. Environmentally damaging feedlots should be discouraged either through stricter regulation of effluents or through greenhouse gas taxes, which in this case would focus on methane. New Zealand proposed a tax on methane emissions in 2003. It became known as a "fart tax" (rather than the more aptly named "belch tax"), but it was vigorously opposed by the farming lobby and had to be dropped, and it has not been tried in any other jurisdiction. Proper water pricing should also be implemented, where the operators would pay the full cost of their water use. These measures would increase the price of feedlot-produced meat and therefore discourage consumption. It would also give an incentive for producers to become more efficient.

Is there a food crisis?

In 2007, food prices started to escalate (see Figure 8.6), leading to concern over the earth's ability to feed a growing population. This happened at the same time as high metals prices led to a discussion about whether the world's supply of fossil fuels and minerals was in the danger of running out. As was noted

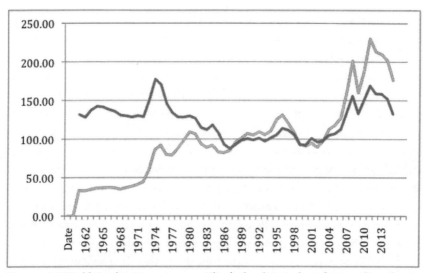

Figure 8.6. World Food prices 1961–2015. The darker line is the inflation-adjusted price (2002–2004=100). Source: http://www.fao.org/worldfoodsituation/foodpricesindex/en/.

in Chapter 2, the high metals prices could mainly be attributed to increased raw-material consumption by China and India. The reasons behind escalating food prices were more complex. Not only was the increased wealth of China and India to blame, but other factors were at play on the supply side. First, big food importers such as China found buffer stocks unnecessary and expensive, given the perceived bountiful supply of food. By the year 2000, global food stocks started to decline from 110 days' supply to only sixty days' supply in 2004, putting pressure on prices.[748] Second, agricultural yields had stagnated following years of underinvestment in the agricultural sector because of low grain prices. Third, escalating oil prices led to higher fertilizer prices and transportation cost, increasing the cost of production. Fourth, the high price of oil led to grain and oil seeds being diverted from food to biofuels, encouraged by government subsidies. Fifth, the depreciation of the US dollar contributed to the escalating prices because many agricultural products are denominated in US dollars. Finally, droughts in major producing countries in 2005 and 2006 led to further reductions in grain supplies, and prices escalated by 50 percent between July 2007 and July 2008. In total, food prices increased 140 percent between January 2002 and February 2008. The result was a major food crisis with protests and riots in Mexico, Egypt, Indonesia, Bangladesh, and Mozambique. Approximately thirty countries introduced food export restrictions that further reduced supplies and pushed up prices. In response, many poor importing countries introduced price controls and food subsidies that they could ill afford.

Higher food prices can have serious consequences for our ability to improve living conditions for the world's poor. The 1996 World Food Summit agreed on the objective of reducing the number of people who are not getting enough to eat from 823 million in 1990 to 400 million in 2015. The United Nations Millennium Goals included a goal to cut the number of undernourished people in the world from 16 percent to 8 percent by 2015. High food prices can likely to push many people in the world back into a life of malnutrition and poverty. Calorie intake is not as adversely affected as dietary diversity. Poor people are unable to buy protein-rich food and green vegetables, to the detriment of young children's development. Poor diet can have long-term effects on brain development and general health in adult life.[749]

As a consequence of higher food prices, the FAO pessimistically estimated that the number of undernourished people had risen to 1 billion in 2009, approximately 15 percent of the world's population, which is a reversal of a steady improvement since the late 1960s. Asia was not as adversely affected as Africa, where the proportion of undernourished increased by 8 percent compared with Asia's 0.1 percent.[750] However, newer estimates by the FAO, using better data and slightly different methodology, were far more optimistic.[751] In the 2012–2014 period, the number of undernourished was estimated to be 805 million, 11.3 percent of the global population and 13.5 percent of the population in developing countries. This is an astonishing decline in the proportion of undernourished in developing countries from 23.2 percent in 1990 to the current 13.5 percent—a mere twenty-five years. The FAO argued that food price spikes had a smaller-than-expected effect on world hunger, and developing countries were not as adversely affected by the global recession as were developed countries.

However, there are still 805 million undernourished people, and according to the FAO, the progress toward eliminating hunger is slowing and the situation in sub-Saharan Africa is worsening, not improving. The problem is not a lack of food on a global basis but its distribution. For example, the average daily calorie consumption in the world was 2,772 in 2005–2007, which is plenty to live on.[752] However, the average hides the fact that many people are too poor to buy food, or they do not produce enough of it. Seventy-five percent of people in developing countries live in rural areas, many on farms of less than two hectares. Over two billion survive on less than $2 per day and 880 million on less than $1 per day, not enough for an adequate diet.[753]

What about in the future? The world population was seven billion in 2014 and is expected to reach approximately 9.15 billion in 2050—an increase of nearly 30 percent. The estimate for the necessary increase in food production ranges from 100 percent to 60 percent.[754] The lower estimate is presented in a 2012 study prepared for the FAO showing that in order to feed the population in 2050, agricultural production must increase by 60 percent and grain production by 50 percent.[755] It is based on the assumption that present trends will continue toward more meat- and dairy-based diets in developing countries, and that average daily calorie consumption will increase to 3,070 compared with the current 2,772. Today, average calorie consumption in western Europe and North America is close to 3,660 compared with an average of 2,619 in low-income countries.[756] Assuming this scenario is realistic, the world needs to produce an additional 940 million tonnes of cereal and two hundred millions tons of meat, implying that a considerable proportion of the cereals will be used for cattle feed. If the estimated conversion rate of three kilos of grain for each kilo of meat is true, the production of an additional two hundred million tons of meat would require an additional six hundred million tons of cereal. Another factor is that the growing population in poor countries will continue to flock to urban areas, which are expected to grow by 3.2 billion people. This means larger populations will have to be fed from rural areas with fewer people working the land.

The FAO study argues that 80 percent of the growth in crop production will have to come from higher yields and the remainder from opening up more agricultural land in developing countries, which is possible according to FAO calculations. More land can be opened up for agriculture in sub-Saharan Africa and Latin America. They estimate that to feed the world would require a 9 percent increase in arable land, which the authors claim is possible without deforestation or incursions in protected areas.

Is it possible to increase food production by achieving higher yields in some parts of the world? Cereal yield increased by 1.9 percent per year from 1961 to 2007, but the average yield increase is expected to decline to 0.9 percent in the period to 2050.[757] According to the FAO estimates, the exploitable yield gap—the difference between what is currently achieved and what is possible—is such that yield improvements are possible with appropriate agricultural policies in place.

However, projections based on assumptions that present trends will continue are fraught with difficulties, as we learned in Chapter 1 from the failed projections of the Club of Rome. Population- and income-growth projections were based on United Nations and World Bank data and are obviously highly speculative. The assumption of continued expansion of meat- and dairy-based diets may also be questionable in view of increasing awareness of their adverse health effects. Add to this scenario global warming. If temperatures increase by more than two degrees, crop yields could decline by 20 to 40 percent in lower latitude countries in Africa, Asia, and Latin America. It is expected that the climate will be more susceptible to large variations in rainfall as well as lower levels of precipitation in parts of the world. If fossil-fuel prices resume their upward climb, food production may be diverted to biofuel production, with severe implications for feeding the poor. This scenario is perhaps less likely if second-generation biofuels come on stream. A continued sluggishness in the world economy will make investments in agriculture exceedingly difficult and will also make it difficult for poor countries to raise enough funds for necessary food imports.

Another major constraint on food production is the availability of water. Agriculture is water intensive, accounting for 69 percent of world water use, and the demand is increasing because of irrigation. For example, between 1961 and 1999 the area of irrigated land in Asia increased by 256 percent.[758] In many cases, irrigation is highly inefficient with much water wasted through evaporation; as a consequence, a high percentage of water diverted never reaches the crops. In other areas, too much water is applied, resulting in salinization and contamination of drinking water. However, some countries use irrigation efficiently. In particular, Israel, Taiwan, and Japan have been able to achieve efficiencies in excess of 50 percent, meaning that 50 percent of the water diverted actually reaches the plants, while countries such as India, Mexico, and Thailand reach efficiencies of only 25 to 40 percent. In many cases, too much surface water is taken, which means rivers run dry during part of the year. When groundwater is used for irrigation, the water table often drops, endangering the supply of drinking water. Global warming is likely to exacerbate these problems because many rivers get their water from melting glaciers—a source of water that is likely to diminish. The problem of water will be further discussed in Chapter 9.

The last decades saw neglect in investments in agriculture. Most developing countries invested only a small proportion (5 percent on average) of government revenue in farming, and Western aid to agriculture fell by 75 percent during this period.[759] Agricultural yields during the Green Revolution years improved by 3 to 6 percent per year, but recently there has been no increase in poor countries' yields.

Since 2009, governments and international organizations have committed to increased support for agriculture. For example, the World Bank announced an increase in spending on agriculture by 50 percent to a total of six billion in

2009. The G8 summit in 2009 in Aquila resulted in a $20 billion commitment by the participating countries to investments in smallholder agriculture. Small farmers are among the poorest people in the world, lacking funds to buy fertilizers, better seeds, and irrigation equipment. Increased funding for agriculture would allow countries to help small farmers acquire seeds and fertilizers at highly subsidized prices. Even a small subsidy such as providing free delivery of fertilizer to the farmers at the time of harvest could significantly enhance crop yields.[760] A recent study by the World Bank has demonstrated that giving poor farmers access to the Internet allows them to learn the maximum and minimum prices paid for their crops, which can increase the prices received for their products and therefore increase farm incomes.[761] Higher farm incomes would allow investments in education and other assets, which could trigger other benefits such as the development of farm credit organizations or microfinance.[762] Jeffrey Sachs, the well-known American development economist, argues that there is a need for a new international agency to coordinate all the efforts by the World Bank, the FAO, the World Food Program, and others in order to avoid costly duplication and rivalry among competing organizations.

The problem of price instability of agricultural products

The increase in food prices 2007–2011 drew attention to the fact that large fluctuations in prices are a constant feature of commodities markets and price instability is a serious problem, particularly for producing countries.[763] During the 1970s, the United Nations Conference on Trade and Development (UNCTAD) targeted the instability problems of commodity markets with the aid of international commodity agreements that tried to stabilize prices through the use of buffer stocks and production quotas. This meant establishing a target range for prices by attempting to control quantities on the world markets. In the case of bumper harvests, buffer stocks were increased in order to prevent excess supplies from reaching the market and depressing prices, while poor harvests led to the selling of buffer stocks to prevent prices from increasing above the target range. Examples included the International Coffee Agreement, International Cocoa Agreement, International Rubber Agreement, International Tin Agreement, International Sugar Agreement, and the United Nations–sponsored Common Fund for Commodities. These agreements were always designed with the producers in mind and usually failed; the price support programs were impossible to maintain in the long run because of difficulties in setting the price at the right level and difficulties in ensuring that everyone followed the agreed-on production quotas (note the example of cocoa in Chapter 1). Consumers of cash crops such as coffee and cocoa are mainly in rich countries, meaning high prices benefit developing countries. Grains are different, since grain prices affect both producers and consumers in poor countries. High grain prices that lead to high food prices can lead to starvation and death of millions of people in poor countries and can also have a negative impact on low-income families in rich countries. High grain prices are beneficial to countries that are net grain exporters and detrimental to net grain importers, but even within a country there are gainers and losers. Farmers who produce a marketable surplus will gain but the large urban populations will lose. Subsistence farmers who often do not produce enough food for their families and have to buy food products on the market will lose. For countries in which the average person lives on less than a dollar per day, food accounts for 50 to 77 percent of expenses, which means changes in food prices will have a significant effect on living standards.[764]

The increases in food prices heralded the end of twenty-five years of low prices. Events of 2007 and 2008 made the world wake up and take note. Food riots occurred in 2008 in Haiti, Madagascar, Indonesia, Egypt, and Morocco, among other countries. Poor countries responded in a variety of ways to shield their populations from high prices, in many cases turning away from the markets with a new emphasis on food self-sufficiency rather than food security.[765] Several countries used their previously built-up grain reserves to deal with the situation; others decreased import barriers by cutting tariffs. For example, Morocco cut tariffs on wheat from 130 to 2.5 percent and Nigeria on rice from 100 to 2.7 percent. Others resorted to price controls and high penalties for hoarding grain. The ability to import food was often compromised by the lack of foreign exchange. The world's largest rice exporters, Thailand and Vietnam, banned rice exports in 2008, causing many countries to rethink their trade policies. Russia, China, Egypt, India, and others also limited food exports. Recent studies have shown that these types of policies were successful in limiting price increases in China, India, and Indonesia.[766] Unfortunately, this led to further increases in international grain prices, as lower import barriers increased world demand, while the introduction of export restrictions limited world supplies. Price controls and social programs with direct subsidies to the poor were introduced; in addition, programs were created that were designed to assist the farmers directly through subsidized seed and fertilizer purchases.

China, Indonesia, the Philippines, and Senegal declared food self-sufficiency to be a priority by investing in food subsidies both aimed at consumers and producers. For example, the Philippines adopted a target to grow 98 percent of its rice consumption by 2010. Even Senegal, which currently imports 80 percent of its grain, announced its goal to become self-sufficient in staples.[767] Richer countries tried to secure their own food supplies by acquiring farmland in other countries. China, Japan, Kuwait, South Korea, and Saudi Arabia are known to have bought or leased twenty million hectares of the best farmland in parts of Africa, Brazil, Russia, and the Ukraine to produce food for their own countries. The Korean company Daewoo Logistics leased 1.3 million hectares in Madagascar, three-quarters earmarked for corn and the remaining one-quarter for palm oil. A commitment was also made to invest in infrastructure such as port facilities. But following food riots and the toppling of the Madagascar government, the project was cancelled in 2009.

While such purchases of farmland could have positive effects in some countries through the introduction of better crop technologies and seeds and much-needed infrastructure, it is difficult to see how these types of investments could be politically sustainable. They push up prices of farmland, making it difficult for locals to buy land. Scenarios can be imagined in which local poor people in need of food would watch large amounts of grain leaving the country to feed foreigners, scenes that have not been seen since the Irish potato famine when grain was exported to England, while local people were starving. Indeed, these initiatives have been viewed by many as a new form of colonialism. The desire for self-sufficiency and the distrust in free markets is understandable, particularly since the free markets advocated by the developed countries were never particularly free; witness the farm subsidies in the European Union, milk marketing boards in Canada, and US subsidies for sugar production and recently for the development of biofuels. However, the drive for self-sufficiency is trading the vagaries of the market for the vagaries of the weather. If we are going to feed a world population of nine billion people in 2050 in the face of climate change, lack of water, degraded farmland, and lack of new farmland, agriculture has to become superefficient, and trade should be encouraged between regions with food surpluses and regions with shortages. Relying on local products does not necessarily lead to less price volatility. It has been shown that price volatility of traditional staples such as cassava and sorghum is higher than for internationally traded goods as these staples are subject to varying local conditions such as drought.[768] Policies of self-sufficiency will not achieve the goal of achieving food security.

High food prices and price volatility are likely to continue because of continued increases in populations, lack of suitable agricultural land, low yield increases, impact of energy prices on agricultural prices, and increased vagaries of weather due to climate change. In theory, it is possible for producers to hedge the risk of price fluctuations through put options on the commodities exchanges, since both coffee and cocoa are traded on the LIFFE and NYBOT exchanges. In practice, however, this is not a realistic option, because the average farmer lacks the sophistication to use such risk-management instruments. Furthermore, contracts are available only for large standardized amounts of the product. Most importantly, these contracts are not available in developing countries because their markets are not big enough to support local exchanges. One solution could be to establish local branches of today's major exchanges as well as local intermediaries whose purpose would be to consolidate volumes from many small farmers and purchase options. The intermediaries could be producer cooperatives, commodity traders, or local banks.[769]

Food security and the sustainability of agriculture

There is a food crisis. We are living in a paradox of plenty. In the industrialized world, there is too much food, and for millions in Asia and Africa, there is not enough food. The surplus could easily feed poor countries' deficit. Many of us in the West were told by our mothers to always finish what was on our plates at mealtimes—we should not waste because so many people in the world were starving. Most children's immediate reaction to this was to offer to package the food and send it to the starving children, a solution parents explained was not possible because the food would spoil, and it was better to send money. On one level, this was not bad advice as the poor do not have enough money for an adequate diet, but of course the problem is much more complex. Today we talk about the need for *food security*. According to the FAO: "Food security is a condition in which all people, at all times, have physical and economic access to sufficient, safe, and nutritious food to meet their dietary needs and food preferences for an active and healthy life."[770]

Much has been written about food security. Long-term food security can be ensured only by a large-scale shift to conservation agriculture. Modern agriculture is not sustainable because of its impact on soils, excessive use of fertilizers, inadequate irrigation practices, and impact on climate through emissions of greenhouse gases. All of these problems have to be addressed. Long-term food security also requires investments in developing countries aimed at helping farmers to close the yield gap and thereby raise farm incomes. Plenty of agricultural research has been conducted, but most of it has not been directed toward the actual circumstances of smallholder farms in poor countries. Governments and aid organizations should fund more research into precision applications of phosphorus and nitrogen and on soil fertility in general. Genetic engineering should be used in this effort—the technology can be seen as part of a continuum of attempts to develop plants for the benefit of humans. Genetic engineering has great potential in developing drought-resistant seeds and seeds that are more efficient in utilizing fertilizers, which could have a positive impact both on crop yields and the environment, particularly on water courses.

There must be dissemination of research findings to farmers, improved access to markets, improved infrastructure, including better access to water resources, and access to credit. Precision farming as discussed on page 276 offers some hope, and microcredit has been remarkably effective in supporting small-scale enterprises. In many countries, women carry the brunt of feeding the families through small-scale agriculture, so it is particularly important to target women in agricultural outreach projects. Women and girls are usually responsible for collecting water and firewood, and in many cases they participate in planting, weeding, harvesting, seed selection, and storage. As a result, women often hold a store of knowledge about local plants and local soil conditions that is often ignored in designing agricultural policies. Depending on cultural sensitivities, it may be critical for some agricultural extension officers to be female. Migration into cities of men searching for work has led to a large proportion of female-headed households remaining to work the land. Many countries have legislation that does not recognize women's rights to own land, a situation that obviously should be remedied, if it is politically possible.

Security of land tenure is critically important. Without security there is little incentive for farmers, male or female, to improve their land and invest in soil management. Secure land tenure is a major problem in former communist countries. For example, following the fall in communism in the Soviet Union, private ownership of land was allowed, but no adequate legal framework existed for buying and selling land. In China, land is still collectively owned but can be leased to peasants, but the leases are only thirty years and severe restrictions are placed on what they can do on the land. Land tenure and land reform are also extremely problematic in former colonial countries. Politically, land reform is always popular because land is frequently owned by former colonial elites. In many cases, small farms are more productive than big ones, so land reform may also be economically desirable. But land reform can sometimes go horribly wrong. An obvious example is Zimbabwe, where land was expropriated and in many cases was allocated to friends and allies of the ruling party who had little experience with farming. As a result, agricultural production plummeted and the former breadbasket now has to import food. In South Africa, whites owned 87 percent of farmland at the end of the apartheid regime. The new ruling party, the African National Congress, set a target that 30 percent would be transferred to blacks by 2014 following a principle of willing buyers and sellers.[771] However, very little land changed hands, not because whites were not willing to sell but because few blacks could afford to buy. There was also a government stipulation that the land could not be subdivided. Consequently, groups had to get together and buy and run the farms, which in many cases was not efficient. Shared equity schemes seem to have more promise. The original owner stays on as a shareholder and helps to run the farm, and over time more and more equity is transferred to the new owners. This provides some assurance that the farms are run in an efficient manner.

Trade liberalization efforts have not had much impact on agriculture. As discussed on page 290, many people feel that food security would be improved if every country became self-sufficient—note, for example the campaigns in rich countries to buy only local produce. Following the food price hikes in 2008, many poor countries changed their agricultural trade policies by imposing export bans, which in turn led some importing countries to try to promote self-sufficiency in food production by generous subsidies and high import duties. However, self-sufficiency in agriculture is a policy the world can ill afford. First, good agricultural land is not evenly distributed. Second, self-sufficiency would mean the world's major food exporters would have to decrease production of their export products and increase production of products they previously imported. For example, the Canadian Prairies would produce fruit and vegetables instead of grains, which would not be the best use of land, given climatic conditions. The diets of residents in northern countries would be severely restricted, and without a well-developed world trading system, it would be difficult to provide emergency supplies to countries suffering crop failures.

Some poor countries argue that liberalized agricultural trade would be more beneficial to them than aid, but unfortunately most industrialized countries do not provide tariff-free access to their products. The Uruguay Round, which was concluded in 1995, only managed to include a clause in the final agreement in which countries agreed to convert their import quotas on agricultural products to tariff equivalents, with the intention of making the quotas more transparent. Agricultural tariffs and subsidies were left alone. The Doha Round of trade negotiations started in 2001, the main purpose of which was to liberalize trade in agriculture and services. Liberalization of trade in agriculture is seen to benefit mainly poor countries and is therefore highly desirable from a development viewpoint. However, an agreement has proven to be elusive, to say the least. While the Doha Round of trade negotiations was finally completed in December 2013, the preliminary agreement does not address agricultural trade liberalization.

Would agricultural trade liberalization improve food security in the sense of improving conditions for agriculture in poor countries? Rich countries' tariffs and subsidies have different impacts on agricultural prices and thus on producers and consumers in developing countries. Subsidies encourage production, leading to lower world market prices that benefit consumers, while tariffs increase prices, which benefits producers. Therefore, the removal of subsidies would increase prices, benefit producers, and hurt consumers while the removal of tariffs would decrease prices, benefit consumers, and hurt producers. The impacts on developing countries depend on whether the countries are net food importers or net exporters, and whether trade liberalization involves cutting subsidies or tariffs, or both. There would also be differential impacts within countries, as farmers often both buy and sell food.[772] For example, in Bangladesh and Zambia, only one-fifth of farmers sell more food than they buy; hence, any decrease in food prices will assist most farmers. On balance, a reduction in rich-country tariffs would likely benefit poor countries the most.

The wastage in food production must be addressed. It is shocking that on average between 30 and 40 percent of food is wasted across the entire food chain.[773] In the developing world, most of the wastage occurs at the production end because of lack of knowledge of farm storage technologies, lack of funds to invest in facilities for storage, inadequate transportation infrastructure, and lack of cold-storage facilities in distributing products to consumers. Often the farmers have to sell all their produce in the harvest season, which leads to wastage if the infrastructure cannot handle the produce. The solution here lies in building better roads and better storage facilities and improving education. The situation in developed countries is different—most of the waste takes place at the retail level (shops and restaurants) and at home. Rich consumers do not want blemished products, which are thrown out even though they are perfectly edible. Legislated "best-before" dates also lead to waste, since in most cases the food is perfectly safe if the best-before date is exceeded by a few days. An additional factor is restaurant marketing ploys offering supersize portions as special deal, portions that are often far in excess of what people are able to eat and thus discarded. Most of the wastage ends up in landfills rather than being reprocessed into animal feed. The problem of how food waste can be minimized is difficult, as food is so cheap that people do not bother to keep any excess. One solution is to force people and businesses to bear more of the cost of disposal through garbage fees, which also could encourage reprocessing of waste, with appropriate safeguards, for animal feeds. Governments should also examine legislation regarding best-before dates to ensure a more appropriate balance between food waste and food safety.

There should be some mechanism to deal with the vagaries of the market and the weather, at least at the national level. Because high food prices put many families at the risk of starvation, some type of social safety net that can assist the vulnerable needs to be in place—a very expensive proposition in very poor countries. In case of crop failure, some help has to be given to the farmers affected. In 2008, India guaranteed one hundred days of public works employment at minimum wages for any rural household that wanted it.[774] The government of Ethiopia has been at the forefront in devising an innovative program aimed at vulnerable farmers in the "hungry" seasons.[775] The program provides either employment guarantees or cash transfers. In cooperation with the World Food Program and the World Bank, the Ethiopian government also pioneered a pilot project of pricing drought risk using international insurance markets where the government would get a payout in case of drought. On a global level, it has been suggested that the world needs an international emergency supply of grain that could be used to avert immediate crises of food supply. Another suggestion is to create an international food agency, the role of which would be to continually monitor the international food situation. The proposed agency would perform the same role as the International Energy Agency, which provides emergency management of international energy reserves.

The trend toward organic food in developed countries is largely driven by consumers who also initiated local food movements and the promotion of urban agriculture. Urban farming delivers fresh products quickly to local consumers, and further research may make it possible to design urban sewage systems in such a way that the nutrients are returned to the soil. The drive toward local food and urban agriculture may be helped by increasingly expensive energy. While urban agriculture is unlikely to have much impact on the world's food security, for some countries it may provide both food and incomes for the urban poor. Food can be grown in backyards, on rooftops, on abandoned industrial sites, on hospital and school grounds, under high-tension lines, and along roads and railway lands. The International Development Research Centre in Ottawa, Canada, has made research on urban agriculture a priority.[776] Long-term food security also involves an effective use of oceans and aquaculture in providing fish, an important part of many people's diet—a topic discussed in Chapter 10.

Finally, food security cannot be achieved without political stability. In case of warring nations and failed states, food supplies usually become severely disrupted because of destruction of infrastructure and neglect of agricultural land. Wars have disrupted agriculture in countries such as Sudan, Afghanistan, Somalia, Syria, and Iraq.

9

Water Resources

Water in culture and history. Modern uses of water. Failures in water management. How to deal with water scarcity. Market approaches to water management. Water conflicts and war. Concluding thoughts.

WATER IS THE MOST CRITICAL of constraints for life on earth and the survival of human beings. On average, an individual can live without food for up to three weeks, but cannot survive without water for more than three days. We need a minimum amount of two litres per day—more under desert conditions. Lack of water leads to dehydration that in severe cases can lead to falling blood pressure, fever, delirium, unconsciousness, and finally death. Water is also essential for basic hygiene, for transportation, for cooking, for maintaining ecosystems, for growing food, and for many industrial processes.[777] Some water is obtained for free from rainwater, rivers, and lakes; some is transported at a cost through pipelines and irrigation ditches or obtained from wells tapping into groundwater or aquifers. In some places water is exceedingly scarce and in others abundant, but physical abundance does not always translate into access to clean water because many water sources are now contaminated. Seasonal and yearly availability also must be contended with, and drought and widespread flooding are common occurrences in many parts of the world.

Until the Renaissance, scholars could not believe that rain alone could account for the flow of the great rivers and the presence of fresh water.[778] Instead, they believed that the source of rivers and lakes was seawater that had seeped into big underground reservoirs where the salt had been filtered out. Underground rivers transported the water to mountaintops from where it was discharged into surface rivers. This belief was supported by the Bible: "All the rivers run into the sea; yet the sea is not full; unto the place from which the rivers come, thither they return again" (Ecclesiastes 1:7). Modern knowledge about the movement and distribution of water dates back to 1654, when Pierre Perrault published a book that featured scientific data on rain and water flow in the Seine drainage basin—a precursor to modern hydrology.[779] The data laid the foundation for the concept of the hydrological cycle, which explains how water moves around the earth, from the oceans to the atmosphere, back to earth and then back to the oceans again. During the cycle, water is temporarily stored in rivers, lakes, soils, and groundwater, and it is this stored water that is available for use. Solar energy evaporates water from oceans and lakes, and the water vapour is carried across continents by prevailing winds. Depending on atmospheric conditions, some of the water falls as precipitation in the form of rain or snow, and at high latitudes the snow can accumulate and form glaciers or ice caps where the frozen water can be stored for thousands of years. Some rain is caught by vegetation, in which case it evaporates again into the atmosphere.

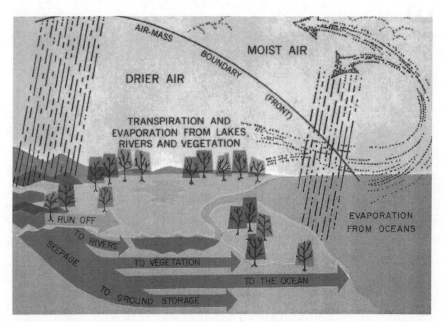

Figure 9.1. The hydrological cycle. Credit: John Havel and www.flickr.com.

Some water reaches the ground and remains on the surface, where it collects in streams and water courses, sometimes generating floods. Some soaks into the soil, where it either becomes groundwater or moves laterally as subsurface runoff. Most rivers are fed from subsurface water; only ephemeral streams in dry areas are entirely fed by rainwater. If the water permeates deeply enough, it will form aquifers that can remain intact for thousands of years. Plants take up water from the soil, most of which is returned to the atmosphere through the process of transpiration, a necessary part of photosynthesis. Transpiration also transports nutrients from roots to leaves and allows the plant to adapt to heat. If precipitation falls as snow, the same processes occur when the snow melts. The term *evapotranspiration* describes the combined effects of transpiration and evaporation.

Seventy-five percent of the earth's surface is covered by water, and the estimated volume of water is huge. However, salt water in the oceans, which makes up 97.5 percent of the total water supply, cannot be used for human consumption or agriculture unless it is desalinized. Barely 1 percent is fresh water obtained from lakes, rivers, and wells in the ground. The remainder is locked up in polar ice. Groundwater can be replenished, but it takes a long time depending on climatic conditions. The time period can vary from hundreds to thousands of years. Thus, in most cases, withdrawal of groundwater is unsustainable and is equivalent to the mining of a finite resource.

Approximately 70 percent of the total fresh water is used for irrigation with large local variations because of climatic conditions. For example, in the United Kingdom, agriculture accounts for only 3 percent of water use, while in India it accounts for 90 percent and in the United States 40 percent.[780] Higher living standards, improved hygiene, and industrial and agricultural expansion led to an increase in global water use by 600 percent during the twentieth century, or twice the rate of increase in the world population. It is expected that this trend will continue, leading to moderate to severe water shortages for two-thirds of the world's population by 2025. In response, the United Nations General Assembly declared 2005–2015 as the International Decade for Action: "Water for Life."[781] The purpose is to promote efforts to meet international commitments relating to water such as the Millennium Development Goals, which include a goal to reduce by half the proportion of people without access to safe drinking water and sanitation by 2015. Focus on water also led to attempts to have access to water declared as a basic human right. After intensive lobbying and several failed attempts, the United Nations General Assembly passed a non-binding resolution in 2010 that access to safe and clean drinking water and sanitation is a human right essential for the full enjoyment of life and other human rights.[782]

This chapter examines the role of water in past and modern times, including some well-known examples of water mismanagement such as the shrinking of the Aral Sea. Approaches to water management are discussed, with particular emphasis on the need for water conservation and water pricing as well as possible solutions to the challenge of producing enough food with reduced water availability. A common perception is held that water scarcity will lead to water wars, and the chapter concludes with a discussion of water as a source of conflict and of attempts at shaping international law to govern international disputes over water.

Water in culture and history

Water has inspired mythology, legends, and religious practices in most of the world's cultures, with water appearing in many creation myths. For example, the ancient Egyptians believed that originally the earth was covered in churning water, and during each recession of the water, a bit of land emerged over which the sun god Ra could rise. According to Iroquois beliefs, the earth was first inhabited by water creatures and the sky by sky people. When a sky woman fell to earth, she was caught by the water animals, which dived down to the bottom of the seas to collect mud for her to stand on. The mud was spread on the back of the turtle, and this became the North American continent. The primordial importance of water is also reflected in science. According to Darwin, life on earth began in the equivalent of a warm pond, and the presence of water is seen as a necessary requirement for life to exist on other planets.[783]

Water was often believed to be inhabited by magical creatures such as sirens and mermaids, who perched on rocks in the sea or in rivers, singing such beautiful songs that sailors jumped into the water and drowned while attempting to join them or forgot to steer their boats clear of cliffs and rocks so that the boats foundered and the sailors died. Indeed, Ulysses had to be tied to the mast by his crew to prevent him from succumbing to the sirens' song. In Nordic legends, a handsome violin player, *näcken*, sat beside a river or a stream and played his violin so seductively that any young girl who listened would approach him and fall into the river and drown. Water bodies also hide imaginary monsters—for example, the Loch Ness Monster. Some Muslims believe that under the Dome of the Rock in Jerusalem lies the source of all the fresh waters of the whole

Figure 9.2. A ceremonial blessing with holy water of newly purchased cars in Copacabamba, Bolivia, 2009. Note the priest with a bucket of holy water and the car adorned with flowers. Credit: Ingrid Bryan.

world, and in Arabic *shari'a* was originally a term relating to the laws of water. The literal meaning is "way" or "path to the water resource." The well of Miriam (that gave water to Moses and the tribes of Israel wandering in the Sinai Desert) was thought by some to be the centre of cosmic energy: if you immersed yourself in the well's waters you would understand the secrets of the universe. Water also figures prominently in the rituals of childbirth in many religions, including Christianity, through baptism. There are hundreds of holy wells in Ireland and Britain, where the waters are said to have healing powers, and the sprinkling of holy waters is still an important part of Roman Catholic ritual.

The ritual of baths was one of the reasons the Romans became masters at constructing aqueducts.[784] Over a period of five hundred years, they built a network of eleven aqueducts leading water into Rome, which, at its peak, had one million inhabitants. The aqueducts were capable of supplying each inhabitant with one cubic metre of water per day, which is more than the water supply of many modern cities. Most of the aqueducts were buried; it was only in places where this was not possible that they were above ground. They could not be

Figure 9.3. Roman aqueduct in France, an example of early water engineering. Credit: Wikimedia Commons.

turned off, and were the equivalent of having rivers flowing to the city as they relied entirely on gravity for the flow. Also built to impress, aqueducts were constructed for two hundred other cities in the Roman Empire.

Rivers are of particular significance in India, the most holy of which is the Ganges. In Hindu mythology, the supreme Lord Rama created the river, promising that when he returned he would reside along the river. Many Hindus still make an effort to immerse themselves in the now heavily polluted river at least once in a lifetime, and many families keep some water from the Ganges in their houses, believing the water cures various illnesses. It is also customary to spread the ashes of the deceased on the river.

As mentioned in the previous chapter, irrigation has played a major role in the development of early societies. Indeed, Karl Wittfogel, a German historian, hypothesized in the 1950s that irrigation required the development of a bureaucracy to control water rights, necessitating the development of the first authoritarian states.[785] This became known as "the hydraulic hypothesis," which has been much debated because it can also be argued that the reverse is true: the development of strong states made it possible to develop irrigation systems. Between two thousand and six thousand years ago, advanced agricultural societies relying on irrigation developed in the Middle East around the Euphrates and the Tigris. The first recorded use of irrigation was at Choga Mami in Meso-potamia, dating back to 4700–4600 BC.[786] This first Sumerian civilization was followed by the Babylonians', whose famous king Hammurabi (1792–1750 BC) laid down a comprehensive set of laws. The Code of Hammurabi contained detailed rules about the responsibility of landowners to maintain irrigation channels. For example, if a levee broke and an adjacent property was flooded, compensation had to be paid.[787] The Babylonians were followed by the Assyr-ians, who were equally adept at the techniques of irrigation. Shortly after 700 BC, the Assyrians built an eighty-kilometre canal to bring water to the capital Nineveh, which is still considered one of the engineering marvels of the world. Irrigation also developed in the Indus flood plains in what is now Pakistan, the Nile Valley, and the Yellow River basin in China. In addition, there is evidence of early irrigation in central Mexico and Peru. Many of these prosperous societ-ies ultimately declined because of a combination of climate change, salinization, and civic unrest that interfered with the maintenance of the canals.

Some early desert civilizations perfected collection of water runoff for agriculture. For example, remnants of 5,200-year-old irrigation infrastructure, designed to take maximum advantage of meagre rainfall, have been discovered in the desert highlands of Yemen.[788] The Nabateans—an ancient Arab civilization that colonized part of present Israel, Syria, and Jordan around 600 BC—devel-oped ingenious practices for using runoff rain water.[789] The Nabateans inhabited the Negev Desert, an area of strategic importance on the spice route between the Orient and the Mediterranean. It was necessary for the trading caravans to have access to water on their journeys—a challenge in a desert area with an annual rainfall of approximately one hundred millimetres and with no rivers. The Nabateans developed the ability to store and collect water for themselves and for the caravans passing through with a remarkable level of sophistication. Water was collected from runoff via connected cisterns placed strategically on hillsides for maximum catchment. In order to support a growing population, they also had to develop agriculture uniquely suited to desert conditions. The farmers devised a system for collecting runoff from the slopes and concentrat-ing the water in terraced, cultivated areas on the flatlands. In humid regions, farmers typically aim to prevent runoff by having the soil absorb the moisture, but the Nabateans aimed for the opposite by promoting runoff on slopes to divert the maximum volume of water to relatively small areas that were levelled and terraced to promote conservation of both soil and water. Remains of hun-dreds of farms have been discovered across the Negev Desert near the ruins of old towns. Some of these early structures still function today—a testament to their effectiveness. Interestingly, the Anasazis in the US Southwest developed similar agricultural techniques about 100 AD.

Modern uses of water

In contrast with water use in many early civilizations, modern usage is built on the notion that water is plentiful. Water usage is typically divided into three categories: agricultural, industrial, and municipal. Apart from some local exceptions, agricultural use is by far the most important, followed by industrial use. This categorization of water use does not include the very important need for water to maintain biodiversity and ecosystem services. Worldwide, irrigation accounts for 70 percent of water use and in some developing countries up to 95 percent. Industrial water use accounts for approximately 20 percent of the total. Water-intensive industries include the energy industry—particularly thermal power stations—pulp and paper, steel, mining, and of course the beverage industry. Even the high-tech industry requires water, which often has to be of better quality than drinking water. However, water withdrawal and water consumption are two different things. For example, water withdrawn for cooling in thermal power stations is subsequently returned to the waterways and is not consumed. Unfortunately, such water is seldom adequately treated and is therefore returned in polluted form. This is also true for irrigation.

The development of large-scale modern irrigation required a sophisticated knowledge of hydraulics and irrigation technologies. Most of the advances took place during the latter part of the nineteenth century by British engineers in India, who built a vast network of canals and who were also involved in dam building on the Nile River in Africa. The United States also developed expertise in building huge dam structures, starting with the Hoover dam in the 1930s. It is estimated that in 1800 the total irrigated area in the world amounted to eight million hectares, by 1900 it had grown to forty million hectares, by 1950, one hundred million hectares, and by 1995, 225 million hectares.[790] India, China, the United States, and Pakistan account for approximately half of the irrigated area, and the top ten irrigating countries account for two-thirds of the total area. Forty percent of the world's food comes from irrigated areas. Without irrigation, world food production could not have kept up with food demand as Green Revolution grains require additional water, and in warmer climates irrigation allows for several crops per year.

However, irrigation has many adverse effects. Agriculture is now the main contributor to global environmental change through its impact on the hydrological cycle both in terms of quantity and quality.[791] In areas of deforestation, evapotranspiration has decreased, while in areas of heavy irrigation it has increased with impacts on climates and ecosystems. Modern agriculture has also affected the quality of water by doubling nitrogen use and tripling phosphorus use, which leads to eutrophication of water courses and to hypoxic (oxygen-free) zones. The results are adverse impacts on downstream fisheries, drinking water, and recreational uses as well as reduced water for coastal ecosystems and wetlands.

The main problem with irrigation is the buildup of salt—a factor that contributed to the decline of many of the early civilizations. All water contains certain amounts of mineral salts, and when the water is used for irrigation, the salts are deposited in the soil. If a farmer adds ten thousand tonnes of water to a hectare of land, between two and five tons of salt will be added every year.[792] This becomes a particular problem if irrigation water is reused downstream. In addition, if irrigation channels are unlined and water seeps through fields, the groundwater level may rise, waterlogging and killing the plants. In very dry climates, the plants draw the water to the surface, where it evaporates and leaves the salt behind. Salinity affects a substantial proportion of irrigated soils in arid and semi-arid regions of the world, including Asia, Australia, South America, and the Mediterranean countries of the European Union.[793]

Compared with irrigation and industrial need, the volume of municipal water used for drinking, cooking, and washing is small—10 percent of the total. But municipal water is hugely important for human welfare. It is estimated that more than 700 million people (11 percent of the world population) do not have access to safe drinking water, and 2.5 billion people (36 percent of the world population) are without access to basic sanitation, with predictable impacts on human health, particularly infant mortality. Nearly 80 percent of diseases in developing countries such as diarrheal illnesses and parasitic infections are caused by contaminated water. Estimates by the World Health Organization indicate that each dollar invested in water supply and sanitation generates a potential return of $4 to $12 in terms of health benefits alone.[794] Lack of sanitation not only affects human health but can also affect educational outcomes. For example, inadequate toilet facilities are often a deterrent to girls staying in school because they are too embarrassed to relieve themselves in a nearby field. In addition, women and young girls often have to hike large distances to collect water from communal water sources, time that could be better spent in school or working in fields. The Millennium Development Goals adopted by the United Nations in 2000 included the specific goal of reducing by half the proportion of people in the world who lacks access to safe drinking water and basic sanitation by 2015.[795] In a 2014 review of progress in meeting the goals, the UNDP concluded that the drinking-water goal was met in 2010, but the sanitation goal could not be met by the required date.[796] Even though the progress toward improving the access to safe drinking water is impressive, it still leaves 11 percent of the world without safe drinking water, and 15 percent lack basic toilet facilities. Water monitoring in many areas is inadequate, and there are large regional variations in access to water—sub-Saharan Africa lags behind.

Even though most of the health concerns in developing countries relate to poor water quality caused by microbial contamination, industrial and agricultural chemicals are a threat to water quality in both poor and rich countries. The issues of mercury and arsenic contamination and leakages from tailings ponds was discussed in Chapter 2, and the adverse effects of excess fertilizers on water courses in Chapter 8. However, increasingly, chemicals used in personal-care products and pharmaceutical products have become a concern. Many of these chemicals are easily dissolved in water and are not removed in water-treatment plants and therefore enter water courses. A study by the US Geological Survey found that most of the streams sampled in the United States contained traces of steroids, detergents, fire retardants, hormones, and antibiotics.[797] Estrogen and some other synthetic hormones have been associated with feminization of fish and some other aquatic organisms, and little is known about the long-term impacts on ecosystems and on human health.

Water use has been increasing twice as fast as world population. Does the world have enough fresh water? The answer would be yes if water was easily transportable from region to region and water trading could occur, but water is heavy and expensive to transport over large distances, usually requiring expensive infrastructure such as pipelines or canals. As a result, there is no world market for water—with the exception of the very small market for bottled drinking water. Water is not evenly distributed across the globe because of regional variations in rainfall and access to rivers, lakes, or aquifers. For example, Iceland has a potential 1.6 million litres of water available per capita per day, while Kuwait has just thirty litres of fresh water available per capita.[798] In Kuwait's case, the available fresh water is not sufficient for human survival, forcing water needs to be largely satisfied by desalinization of seawater. Water scarcity can also be seasonal. For example, the parts of Asia that are subject to monsoon rains may have water scarcity for parts of the year and an abundance of water during other parts of the year. Most countries in the Near East and North Africa face water shortages, as well as parts of Mexico, Pakistan, southern Africa, and India, but nowhere is water scarcity as serious as in China, where most environmentalists agree that the scarcity of clean water is a larger problem than air pollution.[799] Per-capita water availability in China is one-quarter of the world average, while water use per unit of GDP is three times the world average.[800] Two-thirds of Chinese cities suffer water shortages, three hundred million rural residents do not have access to clean drinking water, and 80 percent of lakes suffer from eutrophication.

The question of what constitutes water scarcity is hotly contested, and the answer depends on the definition of water scarcity.[801] The most widely used indicator is the Falkenmark Water Stress Indicator. Based on statistics of average water use for households, agriculture, industry, and the needs of the environment, it is assumed that a minimum yearly per-capita consumption of water is 1,700 cubic metres. If a country's per capita supply of water (excluding water from aquifers) is less than the benchmark, the country is experiencing water stress. If it is less than one thousand cubic metres, the country suffers from water scarcity and if less than five hundred, from absolute water scarcity. The indicator is easy to calculate and to comprehend, but it suffers from several problems: it does not include the efficiency with which the available water is allocated or differences in water demand in different countries because of culture and climate. There are many other indices and measures of water scarcity but no index that is universally accepted.

Regardless of the measure utilized, most would agree that access to water is a global problem that will become more severe over time because of population growth, the shift toward more meat-based diets, the production of biofuels, water pollution, depleted groundwater supplies, and climate change.[802] Population growth means increased food demand and in turn more demand for water for irrigation and household purposes. Increasing incomes in developing countries lead to a larger demand for water for drinking, cooking, and washing and to changes in eating habits in favour of Western-type diets, rich in animal products. The increased popularity of meat- and dairy-based products means that far more water is required. To produce a kilogram of wheat requires eight hundred to four thousand litres of water while the production of a kilo of beef requires two thousand to sixteen thousand litres. The average Chinese person who ate twenty kilos of meat in 1985 consumed approximately fifty kilos in 2009, increasing water consumption by 390 cubic kilometres. In comparison, the average consumption of meat in the United States is 125 kilograms per person.[803] Another factor is the increased production of grains used for biofuels. One litre of biofuel needs between one thousand and four thousand litres of water.

Depleted groundwater supplies create particular problems as the necessary water has to come from somewhere else. Increased water pollution also means that not all the available water can be used unless it is treated. Add to this the complications of global warming. Evidence shows that climate change will speed up the hydrological cycle, which means water will evaporate more quickly and fall again as rain or snow. The majority view is that global warming will lead to increased precipitation in areas that already have plenty of water and decreased precipitation in areas that don't. Climate change will also result in more extreme events including increased frequency of floods and droughts. The melting of glaciers will decrease the water supply of some rivers, particularly on the Indian subcontinent and South America. However, a 2007 study on river basins, integrating climate models, hydrological models, and socio-economic data, predicts that by 2050 increased domestic water use in developing regions because of increased incomes will in general have a larger impact on water scarcity than climate change or population changes.[804] A secondary influence on future water scarcity will be increased water use by industry and agriculture.

Concerns about water scarcity have led to calls for labelling of products for their water content. "Virtual water" has become a popular concept, describing how much water is implicitly embedded in the products we consume. The term was first coined by John Allen of King's College London in 1993 when studying water scarcity in the Middle East.[805] Table 9.1 shows the average virtual-water content of a selection of commodities. Not surprisingly, growing rice and raising animals is very water intensive. The water content varies considerably depending where the product is made or grown. For example, paddy rice grown in Australia requires 1022 cubic metres of water per tonne, while rice grown in Brazil requires

Table 9.1. Average virtual-water content (m³/ton) of selected products

Product	Average virtual water (m³/tonne)
Paddy rice	2,300
White rice	3,000
Wheat	1,300
Maize	900
Soybeans	1,800
Sugar cane	175
Cotton	3,600
Barley	1,400
Coffee (green)	17,000
Coffee (roasted)	21,000
Beef	15,500
Pork	4,850
Goat	3,900
Mutton	6,100
Chicken	3,900
Eggs	3,300
Milk	1,000
Cheese	4,500

Source: Arjen Y. Hoekstra and Ashok K. Chapagain, *Globalization of Water: Sharing the Planet's Freshwater Resources*. Wiley-Blackwell Publishing, 2008, extracted from Table 2.3, p. 14.

3022 cubic metres because of differences in climates, the price of water, and local soil conditions.

The virtual-water concept led to development of the concept of "water footprints"—following the path of ecological footprints as discussed in Chapter 6. Proposals have been put forward to include water use or water footprints in product labelling with the implicit message that we should try to avoid consuming food such as meat and dairy because of their water content. For example, Maude Barlow, a well-known Canadian activist specializing in water issues, argued that the recently negotiated Canada–EU trade agreement threatened Canada's water because it allowed for increases in Canadian pork and beef exports.[806] This raises the question of why products or an exporting country should be penalized for using a natural resource that is or may be used sustainably? The water-footprint concept makes no distinction between the use of rainwater, which comes for free, and irrigation water, which does not, nor does it take into account how efficiently the water is used. For example, it assumes that if we limit the number of sheep in mountain areas to save water, the water saved could be diverted to a more productive use. This is probably not true in many cases because the land may have no other use; it may be too steep or the climate may be too cold for agriculture.

It is also claimed that international trade can be seen as a trade in virtual water. From this perspective, water-scarce regions should import products with high virtual-water content as a way of economizing on scarce water; conversely, water-rich countries should export products with high water content. It is argued that such trade in water should be encouraged as it increases the efficiency with which water is used globally. But virtual-water trade is an idea which is neither novel nor useful as a guide to more efficient water allocations.[807] There is a long history in the theory of international trade as seeing product trade as a substitute for trade in factor services such as labour and capital. For example, countries endowed with an abundance of labour compared with capital are relatively more efficient in manufacturing labour-intensive products (examples are China and India) and will therefore tend to export them, which means, in a sense, that they are exporting labour. Similar arguments could be made for water. Countries endowed with a relative abundance of water compared with other resources tend to export water-intensive products if there is a market price for water—but in general this is not the case. Water and farming are often subsidized so water users often do not have to pay the price of water based on scarcity value. For example, Saudi Arabia has offered its farmers large subsidies to grow wheat since the 1980s— Saudi Arabia was a wheat exporter until dwindling water supplies required the government to take steps in 2008 to phase out the policy.[808] The idea of virtual-water trade also assumes that the availability of water is the only determinant of food production and trade, ignoring factors such as the quality of land and the productivity of the agricultural sector.

The promotion of virtual-water trade is not helpful, as it does not take account of alternative uses of water and whether the water use is sustainable. There is no evidence that the promotion of virtual-water trade would improve world allocation of scarce water compared with a general promotion of agricultural trade through the elimination of trade barriers and policies to improve the management of water resources.

Failures in water management

This present world of water scarcity has been created not only by population pressures but also through water mismanagement as exemplified by the often unsustainable use of groundwater, ecologically damaging water-diversion projects, and inadequate irrigation practices. With the exception of Africa, where major unexploited aquifers remain, the possibilities of expanding the supply of water are slender because of depleted groundwater. Groundwater accounts for nearly one-third of the world's water supply, but in general it is not used sustainably in the sense that extraction is higher than long-term recharging. For example, in the United States, the Ogallala aquifer spans eight states—Texas, Oklahoma, New Mexico, South Dakota, Nebraska, Wyoming, Colorado, and Kansas—and provides one-fifth of the irrigated water in the United States. Industrial-scale withdrawals of groundwater did not start until World War II, creating very prosperous farming conditions.[809] In western Texas, the number of wells tapping into the aquifer was 1,166 in 1937, and by 1971 they had increased to sixty-six thousand. The rate of depletion is eight times the rate of refilling.[810] The water table has dropped precipitously since the 1930s, in some cases as much as fifty metres, forcing farmers to abandon wells.

Unsustainable use of groundwater, partly caused by excessive irrigation and energy subsidies, is also a serious problem in much of India, Pakistan, and China. For example, India has provided free electricity for irrigation purposes, which has led to overinvestment in tube wells, resulting in rapidly decreasing groundwater supplies.[811] Many of the world's largest cities—Beijing, Calcutta, Bangkok, Buenos Aires, Cairo, Mexico City, Jakarta, Karachi, and Manila— are located in regions with severe water stress. The world's third-largest city,

Mexico City, was built on a series of islands in Lake Texcoco. Over time, the lake was drained and the city expanded over the dry lakebed using the remnant of the lake—the Mexico City Aquifer—as a source of water. Withdrawals have exceeded the aquifer's replenishment by rainfall, and as a result the city is slowly sinking into the emptying aquifer. Parts of the city have sunk by forty-two feet, leading to severe structural damage to buildings and water lines.[812]

Many countries have resorted to water-diversion projects to provide water to drier areas. Such projects can lead to environmental disasters. An example is the destruction of the Aral Sea, which used to be the fourth-largest lake in the world and is now the eighth-largest lake in the world. Between 1960 and 2006, the surface area shrunk by 74 percent and the lake level by twenty-three metres. The salinity increased from ten grams per litre, which is slightly saline, but fresh enough to support a fish population, to one hundred grams per litre, which is far too salty to support aquatic life.[813] The water level of the Aral Sea is determined by the balance between the inflow from two rivers, the addition of groundwater, and evaporation. There is no river flowing out of the sea. If a balance is maintained between inflow and evaporation, the water level will remain constant. The story of the shrinking lake dates back to the collectivization of agriculture during the 1930s in the Soviet Union and the desire to develop an export crop: growing cotton on the dry steppes of Turkmenistan

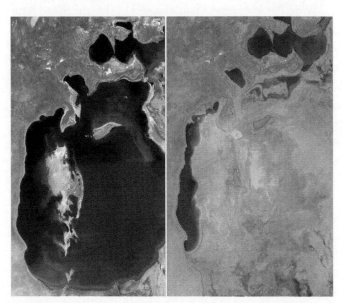

Figure 9.4. The Aral Sea in 1989 and 2014. Credit: NASA.

and Uzbekistan using massive irrigation with water from the two rivers—the Syrdar'ya and the Amudar'ya—that drain into the Aral Sea.[814] The Amudar'ya is the biggest river in central Asia, and the two rivers provide fresh water to approximately thirty million people. In 1956, the first canal was opened, tapping into the Amudar'ya River, and it was followed by several others diverting water from the rivers for irrigation purposes. A proposal to divert two northern rivers (the Ob and the Lena) to the area never got off the ground. The water level in the Aral Sea started to drop. Before the canals were built, the rivers carried fifty cubic kilometres of fresh water a year to the sea, and by 1980 no fresh water reached it. The shoreline receded rapidly, leaving ships stranded at old wharves. Former harbours were now miles from the shore. By 1987, the sea had split into two: the Large Aral Sea (the southern section) and the Small Aral Sea (the northern section). By 2005, the Large Aral Sea had split into three bodies. The previously productive fisheries collapsed because most fish could not live in the increasingly saline waters. The former lakebed now has a high concentration of salt that enters the atmosphere during dust storms, causing severe health problems among many of the residents. Attempts to flush out the salt on the irrigated land by adding even more water increased the concentration of pesticides and fertilizer in the runoff, and the sea became even more toxic.

After the breakup of the Soviet Union, the new countries of Kazakhstan and Turkmenistan shared the sea. The slightly wealthier Kazakhstan, with the help of funding from the World Bank, embarked on a project to save the Small Aral Sea by altering irrigation channels and building a dam separating the two parts of the lake. Completed in 2005, this appears to have had some success—the water levels in the sea have risen and the fisheries are expanding. The United Nations, the United States, and the European Union have also been involved in restoration efforts. However, while there is some success with the Small Aral Sea, it is too late for the Large Aral Sea, and it has more or less been left to its fate.[815]

Water-diversion schemes can turn toxic, as demonstrated by the Kesterton environmental disaster. Some of the wealth of California depends on the Central Valley Project—a huge network of dams, pipes, and open irrigation channels carrying water to farmers. The Imperial Valley project involved diverting one-fifth of the water in the Colorado River to Southern California to irrigate thirsty crops such as rice, cotton, and alfalfa. Salinization quickly became a problem in the Central Valley as the heavy clay soils, derived from old marine sediments, had natural salt content in addition to having been poorly drained.[816] Irrigation moved the salt into the groundwater. A canal was built to transport the salty drainage to the Sacramento–San Joaquin delta near San Francisco, but for various reasons, the canal was stopped at a reservoir at Kesterton. Situated on a migration fly path, the reservoir had attracted many birds. By 1983, with dead and deformed birds turning up in large quantities and deformities in local cattle also appearing, it was clear that an environmental disaster was in the making. The culprit was selenium, traces of which are necessary for human survival, but which is toxic in large quantities. The soils in the valley were rich in selenium, and the selenium had washed out through irrigation and concentrated in the runoff. The reservoir was reclassified as a toxic waste dump and was subsequently drained. Some other areas of the United States were also found to have very high selenium levels.

The presence of heavy metals, arsenic, and fluoride in drinking water can cause potentially life-threatening diseases. The case of Bangladesh is particularly tragic. The surface water was contaminated with human effluent, causing high infant mortality, and numerous tube wells were sunk to provide uncontaminated water. Unfortunately, the water obtained from the tube wells contained arsenic, poisoning millions of people.[817] Groundwater contaminated by arsenic is not uncommon in many other parts of the world.

The impact of unsustainable irrigation practices on the world's rivers has been severe. Many of the large rivers do not reach the sea. So much water is withdrawn that the riverbeds dry up for part of the year, with adverse effects on wetland and riverine habitats. These include the Colorado, the Rio Grande, the Murray-Darling River in Australia, the Indus, and the Yellow River in China. Freshwater ecosystems account for only 0.8 percent of the world's surface but support six percent of the species, and as was shown in Chapter 6, freshwater species and habitats belong to the world's most endangered. Dams are usually built with the purpose of flood control, generation of hydroelectricity, and water supply for irrigation and human consumption, but often with little consideration for downstream activities. They destroy habitats for fish and other aquatic animals and destroy crucially important wetlands and their ability to filter pollutants. They prevent rivers from bringing nutrients to the sea, causing a negative impact on ocean habitats as well. An influential study published in *Nature* in 2010 on the state of the world's water resources pointed out the inherent conflict between human water security and biodiversity.[818] While dams improve access to water, their impacts on the environment are severe. The study argued that water resource development in the form of dams and pollution from industrial, agricultural, and municipal sources were the most serious threats to human water security and biodiversity. Other significant stressors on the world's rivers were disturbances of catchment areas—for example, deforestation—and factors such as invasive species. The study found that the state of the world's rivers was a threat to the water security for 80 percent of the world's populations.[819] Areas of intensive agriculture and dense settlements that include large sections of the United States and Europe, central Asia, the Middle East, India, and eastern China are particularly affected. Rivers, which account for 65 percent of the global annual discharge of water, are moderately or highly threatened. Only a very small fraction of the world's rivers shows no human influence.

Despite mounting evidence of the adverse environmental impacts of dams and water-diversion schemes, huge projects are currently underway in China. Northern China suffers from a severe water shortage, partly because of lack of natural rainfall and partly because of intensive farming and industrial development. Twenty-seven thousand rivers are no longer flowing because of excessive water use. Four-fifths of water resources are in the South while fifty percent of the population lives in the North which also has two-thirds of the farmland needing irrigation. Lack of water threatens further development of coal-fired generating stations as well as the development of the country's shale-gas reserves. In order to solve the water shortage, the Chinese government approved a fifty-year project in 2002—the South–North Water Transfer Project—aimed at connecting the Hai, the Huai, and Yellow Rivers with the Yangtze River via three canals, each one thousand kilometres long, carrying approximately forty-eight cubic kilometres per year of water at an estimated cost of $80 billion.[820] It is the largest engineering project the world has ever seen—even larger than the Three Gorges Project on the Yangtze. The eastern phase opened in 2013 and the middle phase in 2014.[821] The western phase, initiated in 2013, will take ten years to build and goes across the Himalayan plateau. Other diversion projects are planned that include the upper reaches of the Brahmaputra and Mekong Rivers—projects that would impact water flow in India and Vietnam. India, which also suffers from water stress, has proposed to link the upper reaches of its major rivers at a cost of $120 billion, diverting water from water-surplus basins to water-deficit basins. The project would adversely affect water supplies in both Nepal and Bangladesh. This project quickly ran into opposition, and so far there are no signs it will be implemented.[822]

How to deal with water scarcity

Water-diversion projects are the least desirable solution to water scarcity because of their environmental effects and high costs. In many parts of the world it is still possible to increase water availability by more traditional methods. Apart from using rainwater, tapping into groundwater may be a solution for sub-Saharan Africa, where underutilized groundwater resources are still available.[823] Groundwater exists almost everywhere, is often of very high quality, and compared with the infrastructure needed to develop irrigation, it can be put in place relatively quickly with less capital cost using tube wells and mechanical pump technology.[824] The groundwater is available during dry seasons and can provide irrigation on demand, which is much less wasteful of water. It can be made more sustainable by artificial recharging of aquifers during the wet seasons, if climatically possible, and by mixing the groundwater with waste water for irrigation purposes.

In some areas, it is possible to tap into previously unexploited aquifers. Libya, a desert country, is rich in oil. In 1953, some exploratory oil wells in the Al Kafra region of the Libyan Desert produced water, not oil. It turned out that the water was part of the huge Nubian Sandstone Aquifer System containing twenty thousand cubic kilometres of water to a depth of two thousand metres. The aquifer was created during the last ice age fourteen thousand to thirty-eight thousand years ago.[825] Later, an additional three large aquifers were found, also containing large quantities of water, a potential source of water for the coastal areas of Libya where the major cities suffer from an acute water shortage. In 1984, construction was started on the first phase of the Great Man-Made River Project, which involved a sixteen-kilometre pipeline leading the water from the desert aquifer to the coastal areas. With its diameter of four metres, it is capable of transporting 6.5 million cubic metres per day. This part of the project is finished, and further pipelines are under construction tapping into the other aquifers. The entire project will be completed in another twenty to twenty-five years at a total cost of $33 billion. Libyan engineers estimate that the water will last for 4,860 years, given current withdrawal rates. No consideration has been given to the fact that Libya shares the aquifer with Egypt, Sudan, and Chad; obviously, Libyan water withdrawals will have an impact on the amount of water available for the other countries.

The issue of whether to tap fossil groundwater that cannot be replenished comes down to water management. We do not hesitate to exploit a mine or an oil well, so why should we hesitate in exploiting a fossil aquifer? To use water to grow wheat in the desert is perverse, but to use it for drinking may not be; ultimately, water should be allocated to uses where it creates the largest benefits.

Given the abundance of seawater, desalinization is seen by many to offer an easy solution to water shortages. There are two methods of desalinizing water: by filtration or by distillation.[826] Distillation technology is well known and requires water to be heated, creating water vapour that is then condensed into fresh water. It requires a substantial amount of energy. Filtration, on the other hand, uses membranes to remove salt and other contaminants in a process of reverse osmosis that is also energy intensive. Desalination plants exist in 130 countries, with half of the capacity in the Middle East, and their use is increasing. Because they are expensive, they are used only for providing drinking water. Other alternatives are usually cheaper if they are available. The cost of desalinization, which depends on the salinity of the water and the size of the plant, is difficult to estimate as the plants are often subsidized. Energy costs are large, ranging from 40 percent of operating costs for a filtration plant to 60 percent for a distillation plant. Reported costs for desalinized water seem to indicate a range from $1 to $3 per cubic metres, which is considerably higher than most urban dwellers in rich countries are charged for their water.

The adverse environmental impact of desalinization should be taken into account. The plants along coastlines suck in a large amount of seawater, which may contain plankton, fish eggs, larvae, and small fish, all of which have to be disposed of. Thus it is critical for the marine environment that both the location and technology of the input pipes are well designed. Another problem concerns how to dispose of the effluent of very salty water. The brine is usually twice as salty as the seawater and has higher density. It can also contain chemicals such as chlorine used in the desalination process to kill algae and other organisms. Corrosion in the plant caused by salt water also leaches heavy metals into the waste water. The waste water is sometimes discharged straight into the ocean, or into evaporation ponds. It can also be disposed of on land in deep wells or ponds. All of these disposal methods create their own environmental problems.

Possible technology solutions to water shortages range from high tech to low tech. Inventor Max Whisson has proposed the concept of a "Water Road," which would transfer seawater inland using large surface areas, allowing the salt water to be distilled by solar and wind energy.[827] He also proposes the use of wind turbines at an approximate cost of $43,000 per turbine to extract water from the air, pointing out the huge amount of water vapour contained in the lower one kilometre of the atmosphere. Whisson, like others, was inspired by the physiology of the Namib Desert beetle *Stenocara gracilipes*, which obtains water by catching moisture from early-morning fog on its wings by keeping them at a certain angle. The wings have both water-attracting and water-repellent features, which encourage the formation of tiny droplets that roll down its back into the beetle's mouth.[828] Another promising technology is the so called Warka

Watertower that collects condensed water from the air at a cost of $500, and is capable of producing 95 litres per day.[829]

A cheap and simple source of water in foggy areas is the employment of fog catchers, consisting of giant nets aimed perpendicular to prevailing winds. The coastal areas of Chile and Peru are deserts—some of the driest in the world—but for much of the year fog blows in from the Pacific Ocean. In the 1980s, a Chilean project sponsored by the Canadian development agency IDRC and UNESCO funded the use of plastic netting commonly employed in protecting fruit tree saplings to catch the water droplets found in fog. Small water droplets stick to the large net, clumping together and falling into gutters that collect the water in tanks. Even though the technology yielded an impressive amount of water, the Chilean project was not a success because the villagers did not think the water was of equal quality to the water brought in from other sources. Currently, the National Geographic Society is funding a similar project around the hills of Lima, Peru.[830] If conditions are right, one single net (four by eight metres) can yield 568 litres of water per day.

In the case of China and many other countries, a large proportion of the available water is unclean, a problem not solved by bringing in water from other areas. Proper sanitation would greatly alleviate the water crisis. The amount of water required for domestic use is modest compared with water required for agriculture. This is especially true in developing countries without flush toilets, showers, washing machines, and gardens. As a result, domestic water use varies between twenty and fifty litres per person per day, compared with Europe, where daily consumption is two hundred litres per person per day, and North America, where consumption exceeds four hundred litres per person.[831] Almost 90 percent of the water used for domestic purposes can be recycled if properly treated, while 40 to 90 percent of water used in agriculture cannot, as it is lost through evapotranspiration. The control of waterborne diseases would make a large difference to the general well-being of the population in many countries. It is estimated that at any given time, nearly half of the population in poor countries suffer from diseases caused by polluted water. These include diseases caused by bacteria such as diarrhea and diseases spread by waterborne parasites such as malaria and schistosomiasis. In many cases, there are cheap, short-term solutions. For example, Swedish inventor Anders Wilhelmsson has invented a plastic bag lined with material that can break down the harmful bacteria in human feces and urine.[832] After each use, the bag can be buried or collected at collection points, and the bag and its contents can be used as fertilizer.

Other measures can be taken to improve water efficiencies and decrease wastage. For example, China gets $8 worth of output for each cubic metre of water used, while the equivalent number for Europe is $58 worth.[833] This gap could be closed with better water-treatment facilities, improved water infrastructure, more efficient irrigation practices, and better water pricing, which will be discussed in the next section.

Since most of the world's water is used for agriculture, it makes sense to improve the efficiency of agriculture's use of water. One solution is to develop more efficient rain-fed agriculture, another to improve the efficiencies of existing irrigation systems, and a third to introduce less thirsty crops and develop crops resistant to salinity. A fourth solution is for the world to eat less meat and more grains and vegetables—an outcome that is difficult to achieve. Improvement in rain-fed agriculture is seen as offering the best potential for increased food production. In particular, sub-Saharan Africa is largely underdeveloped, and with better management of water and soil resources, much more food could be grown using a combination of soil moisture management and supplemental irrigation where water storage is feasible.[834] The ancient practice of runoff farming and small-scale rainwater harvesting has been revived in parts of Africa and may make a difference in many dry areas. According to one study, small catchment reservoirs could increase cereal production in low-yield areas of up to 35 percent.[835]

The most irrigation occurs in dry and warm climates, and much of the irrigated water is lost through evaporation. Indeed, the irrigation methods in many parts of the world have not changed for thousands of years. Essentially, they involve the construction of irrigation ditches or channels from the main water supply to the agricultural fields with a gate system that can turn on or shut off the water supply. When the gates are opened, a whole field is flooded or water is led over the fields in furrows. Some of the water reaches the roots, some moves down and reaches the groundwater, some excess runs off at the other end of the field, and some evaporates. According some estimates, almost 50 percent of the water disappears from the fields. While the excess water can often be used downstream, in many cases, the water quality has declined substantially by that time.

One way of achieving more efficiency is drip irrigation, a method of delivering water to the roots directly through a series of perforated plastic tubing either below or above the surface. Using low water pressure, the water is delivered in drops. If this is combined with technology of assessing water needs accurately, it can be very effective in saving water. Field studies showed it can cut water use by 30 to 70 percent. In addition, it has been proven to improve plant yields by 20 to 90 percent.[836] While the idea goes back a long time, the modern development of drip irrigation was pioneered in Israel. According to the International Commission on Irrigation and Drainage, the use of drip irrigation has spread but not as fast as was hoped, partly because it is more expensive than other systems. While the largest user of drip irrigation is India, it only accounts for 3 percent of the total irrigated area, compared to Israel's 74 percent and Spain's 48 percent.[837] However, new low-cost drip irrigation technologies have been developed in Kenya and in India. In India, the locally developed Pepsee kit made from disposable polytubing used in making frozen lollipops (called Pepsee), gave yields as high as the large-scale modern irrigation kits used in the West and increased crop yields by almost 100 percent.[838]

Recent thinking about water-saving technologies casts doubt on their ability to save water. One reason is that leakages from traditional irrigation benefit downstream farmers, and another that if farmers can save water by using more efficient sprinklers, or drip technology, it might give them an incentive to expand their use of irrigation even farther; hence no water is saved. One recent study on the Upper Rio Grande Basin in the United States confirmed that subsidized water-saving technologies do not in fact save water.[839]

There also appears to be a great need to modernize existing irrigation systems by repairing irrigation channels—in many cases they are unlined, which means water drains out of the system. As well, more sophisticated methods of allocating and storing irrigation water and reusing waste water need to be developed. Some crops are more salt tolerant than others and thus can probably do with lower-quality water. According to a review of the literature for the Food and Agriculture Organization, barley, wheat, rye, oats, canola, and cotton are salt tolerant. Rice, on the other hand, is sensitive, and so are sugar cane and corn, but less so. Most fruit and vegetables are also salt sensitive.[840]

In theory, it may be possible to make plants more drought resistant and therefore influence the demand for water. For example, rice is very sensitive to drought, and in many parts of the world the traditional paddy fields are in danger and may have to be abandoned for dry fields. Maize is also an important plant that is not very drought tolerant. Traditionally, plants adapt to a dry environment by improving the efficiency with which they draw water from the surrounding soils, by improving the water retention capacity within plant tissues, by minimizing transpiration, and by adapting by flowering only during wet seasons. Most desert plants employ all of these methods. Adaptations to sudden droughts usually involve the inhibition of shoot growth, allowing the plant to concentrate on survival rather than providing yield. Using these known characteristics of desert plants, more drought-tolerant varieties of rice and maize could be developed through traditional plant breeding. However, this is very time consuming, and few varieties remain that are suitable for breeding, as the current varieties have been chosen for their ability to render high yields using plenty of water. Genetic engineering may be the only solution in developing drought-resistant varieties.[841]

All the measures proposed so far are targeted to alleviate water scarcity. However, it is critically important that measures are taken to control the demand for water, including market-based approaches that rely on prices in governing allocations among competing uses.

Market approaches to water management

Water planners tend to look at water allocations among competing uses as a separate planning exercise for each particular drainage basin or catchment area. This view of water management dates back to the Tennessee Valley Authority in the United States, created in 1933 to coordinate activities on the Tennessee River. The approach clearly recognizes the interconnectivity of water use. However, it is problematic for two reasons. One is that most drainage basins stretch across several administrative boundaries, often involving several countries with different laws, cultures, and social structure, often making an integrated approach unattainable. The other problem is that the approach does not necessarily make economic sense. The 1992 International Conference on Water and the Environment in Dublin was the first international public forum that recognized the importance of economic factors in the management of water resources. The conference led to agreement on four principles governing water management. The first is the recognition that fresh water is a finite resource essential for life, development, and the environment. The second is that water development and management should be participatory; the third that women play a central role in the provision and management of water; and the fourth that water has an economic value in all its competing uses and should be recognized as an economic good.[842] The last principle was highly controversial, as economics had been absent from most previous discussions. However, the world summit in Rio made the four principles part of Agenda 21. In 1996, the Global Water Partnership was founded with the support of the World Bank, UNDP, and the Swedish International Development Agency, promoting a process called Integrated Water Resource Management, defined as "a process that promotes the coordinated development and management of water, land,

and related resources, in order to maximize the resultant economic and social welfare in an equitable manner without compromising the sustainability of vital ecosystems."[843]

While it is true that water is a free gift from nature and one can argue that access to water is a basic human right, that does not necessarily imply it should be provided for free. Worldwide, water may be abundant, but locally it may not be. Cherrapunji, reputedly the wettest place on earth, suffers from frequent water shortages.[844] Who should pay the price for getting clean water to the people through pipes, pumps, chlorination, and filtration equipment and, last but not least, for cleaning the water before it is returned to nature in the form of effluent? The most common solution is for the provision of water to be paid for by the state and be provided for free or at minimal costs to consumers, be they individuals, agriculture, or industry. Although this happens in many parts of the world, it usually is not a good idea; it has resulted in severe water shortages and often inferior water quality in many rural areas where people, particularly women, have to walk long distances every day to collect water. The problem is particularly acute in cities in developing countries. The state or municipality may be unable to raise sufficient revenue to pay for adequate facilities, leading to wastage. For example, in thirty-two out of fifty Asian cities, more than 30 percent of the water does not reach the intended consumers because of leakages.[845] Between 40 and 70 percent of the water is lost in most of Latin America; and about 50 percent is lost in Bangladesh, the Philippines, and Thailand. Apparently even pipes in North London, England, are so in need of maintenance that they lose 60 percent of the treated water.[846] Who wants to economize on water use if it is almost free? According to some studies, water in poor countries is subsidized to the extent that the price of water covers only 30 percent of expenses of providing the water.[847] Usually the subsidies are not sufficient for maintenance and infrastructure investments and do not provide incentives for extending the water supply to new customers. Water pricing is often perverse in rich countries as well—note California, where residential consumers are charged a far higher rate than agricultural consumers with the inefficient and wasteful result that water-thirsty crops are grown under desert conditions.

There are two main objections to water pricing. One is that water is so fundamental to our survival that it should be free—but of course, so is food, and no one is arguing that food should be free. The second argument is that charging for water would hurt the poor. However, in many cases the poor are already at the mercy of water vendors who charge exorbitant prices for small amounts of water. The benefits of subsidized water mostly accrue to the middle classes; they have access to the water, while water mains often do not reach the poor. But this could change if water were priced with protection for the poor by either giving out free water stamps that entitle the holder to a certain quantity of water per day, or by having sliding water charges where the first number of litres is given at very low cost, or for free if appropriate, and each subsequent litre has an increasingly higher charge. In Durban, a rapidly growing port city in South Africa, every household receives six thousand litres per month free, and any amount over that must be paid for.

Another market solution to water allocation is water trading, where the rights to water can be bought and sold. Economists argue that this model leads to a more efficient allocation of water because water ends up being used where it creates the highest economic value. While control over water rests with the government, the allocation to various users is determined by time-limited contracts specifying the quantity assigned. If a farmer does not need his or her water allocation, the excess water is sold to the highest bidder, who could be another farmer, or industry, or households. This type of water trading is allowed in the western United States and in the Murray-Darling basin in South Australia. Of course, water trading can occur only within one river basin or one dam site or from one groundwater source, since water cannot usually be shipped across distances.

Charging for water may be controversial, but water privatization is even more so, for much the same reason that people are opposed to water pricing. The argument is that water is of such importance to people and the environment that corporations should not be allowed to profit from the control of such an essential good. Most people agree that control over water should rest with governments, and if private corporations are involved in the provision and distribution of water, they should be subject to strict regulation so as to prevent competition, which would lead to costly duplication of facilities. Privatization usually involves regulated Crown corporations, franchises, leases or some kind of concession agreements. Privatization has had some success in Europe, but the four large companies—Suez, Veolia, Thames, and Saur—have had very limited success in developing countries. For privatization to be successful, certain conditions have to be met. The best known are the Pacific Institute's water-privatization principles and practices. Any agreement with private companies should include provision of water not only for people but for natural ecosystems with protection of watersheds. All residents should be guaranteed basic water quantity and quality, and the poor should have subsidized rates if necessary. Public ownership of the water sources should prevail, with robust regulation of private companies and stringent oversight. There should be clear dispute resolution mechanisms, and decision making regarding water should be open, transparent, and include all interested parties.[848]

Chile is an example of successful privatization, which was introduced in the 1980s. Since then, the proportion of Chileans with access to safe water has increased from 27 to 94 percent in rural areas and from 63 to 99 percent in urban areas.[849] On the other hand, critics of privatization use the example of Cochabamba, the fourth-largest city in Bolivia, which suffers from an appalling water problem.[850] According to a United Nations report, in the early 1990s, 99 percent of the rich residents in Cochabamba had water connections and only four percent of the poor. With water heavily subsidized, it is clear that the benefit went to the rich. A concession was given to a subsidiary of an American corporation, which immediately raised water rates for poor people by 43 percent and for people in the wealthy areas by 60 percent. Though the 43 percent increase sounds excessive, the starting point was so low that even the poorest 5 percent of the population ended up paying no more than 5 percent of their income on water. Still, riots ensued, and finally in 2000 the government was forced to cancel the contract—and as a result, the poor still do not have adequate access to drinking water.

However, there is a third alternative to government-owned and -controlled systems and privately controlled systems: community owned and managed water, which entails management from the bottom up rather from the top down. Nobel laureate Elinor Ostrom and her colleagues found that compared with government-run irrigation systems, farmer-built and -maintained irrigation systems in Nepal performed better in terms of the physical condition of irrigation systems, the quantity of water available, and agricultural productivity. Similar findings are reported from Japan, India, and Sri Lanka.[851] Water is more often than not a community issue, and people in communities should have a say in the demand for and supply of water for both agricultural and household needs.

Water conflicts and war

Because of the importance of water for our survival, disputes over water are not uncommon. The disputes can be local, regional, or international. Local disputes often occur, particularly in dry regions, and usually involve conflicts between upstream and downstream users of a local river. For example, in 1935 the National Guard in the state of Arizona had to be brought in to control the local population's protests against water diversions from the Colorado River. In

India, competition for scarce water led local farmers in the state of Rajasthan to divert water from Keoladeo National Park, a world heritage site known for its wetlands teaming with birds.[852] Long-standing disputes on India's Cauvery River have led to violent clashes between the downstream state of Tamil Nadu and the upstream state of Karnataka over water for irrigation.[853] Water disputes are also common in China. Beijing gets its water from the Hebei province, which in turn depends on water from the Shandong province, which has fuelled a considerable amount of regional discontent. Water-diversion schemes in China have also created unrest because of the forced resettlement of people from lands flooded by newly constructed dams. Yemen is another country where clashes over scarce groundwater are common.[854]

When rivers or lakes involve several countries, international conflicts can arise. For example, the Nile River and its tributaries flow through ten countries and the Congo River through thirteen countries. Nineteen countries share the Danube basin. In these cases, any water withdrawals by upstream countries clearly affect countries downriver. With 263 transboundary river basins affecting half of the world's total land area,[855] the International Law Association has been very active in attempting to draft principles affecting international water disputes. In 1966, the association made the first attempt by agreeing on the Helsinki Rules governing the legalities around the non-navigational use of water courses. The rules are still in existence today in a modified form. There are two principles: the first refers to the equality of riparian states in water allocations and the second to how equitable and reasonable use can be determined by taking into account present and past use of the rivers in question. It is also recognized that the actions of one country should not harm another country. The Helsinki Rules have no formal standing but are regarded as part of customary international law; they have been used in solving a dispute involving the use of the Danube River.

Following the adoption of the Helsinki Rules, work was still being done on an international convention. In 1997, after twenty years of preparation, the General Assembly of the United Nations passed the Convention on the Law of the Non-Navigational Uses of International Water Courses.[856] It is regarded as a milestone in laying down certain principles of the management of transboundary rivers, lakes, and groundwater sources. The convention includes the Helsinki Rules and is based on four principles: the obligation to cooperate (Article 8), the obligation not to cause significant harm (Article 7), the principle of equitable and reasonable use and participation (Article 5), and the obligation to protect and preserve ecosystems (Articles 20–26). The riparian states are also under obligation to notify one another of any measure that could affect an international water course. Specific provisions are made for dispute settlements.[857] The convention is broad enough to act as a framework within which most negotiated water agreements can fit. Unfortunately, it has not received the required thirty-five signatures to enter into law. The difficulty lies in the perceived conflict between the no-harm principle and the principle of equitable and reasonable utilization. Downriver countries believe in the importance of the no-harm principle, while upriver countries sees the equitable and reasonable allocation rule as more important, which is obvious since downriver states are more likely to be affected negatively by measures taken by upriver states.[858] The International Law Commission continued its work on the Helsinki Rules, which were amended in 2005 to the Berlin Rules on Water Resources; they are now more in line with current developments in international law.[859] The new rules place more emphasis on management of international water resources and ecological integrity as opposed to equitable and reasonable utilization and appear to have strengthened the principle of no harm.

Peter Gleick, one of the directors of the Pacific Institute for Studies in Development, Environment, and Security, has been keeping a chronology of

Figure 9.5. The Atatürk Dam on the Euphrates River in Turkey. Credit: https://www.flickr. com/photos/themua/.

water conflicts and water-related issues.[860] As of March 2015 the list includes almost 350 entries, ranging from when Cyrus used water diversion as a tool in invading Babylon in 539 to the 2003 invasion of Iraq, when water systems were repeatedly destroyed or damaged by the different fighting factions.[861] The Euphrates and Tigris have their headwaters in Turkey, running through Syria and Iraq on their way to the sea. In 1946, Turkey and Syria agreed that the control of the rivers depended on flow regulations in Turkey.[862] Later, a joint technical committee was formed, joined by Syria in 1982. Turkey unilaterally allocated Syria a 15.75-cubic-kilometre yearly flow. Following Turkey's completion of the huge Atatürk Dam on the Euphrates River in 1992, the flow of the Euphrates was shut off for one month to fill the dam, which was seen as an act of aggression by the other two countries. In response, it is believed that Syria increased support for the operation of the Kurdistan Workers' Party inside Turkey, widely regarded as a terrorist organization. However, since 2008, the three countries are cooperating in a Water Institute that studies technical aspects of transborder water issues.

The Nile basin is an interesting case study of water-related conflicts. The population of the Nile basin is expected to reach eight hundred million by 2025. Up to 85 percent of the waters of the Nile originate in the Ethiopian Highlands (the Blue Nile), while the remainder originate in Lake Victoria (the White Nile). In 1929, Egypt signed the Nile Treaty, an agreement with Sudan, which was under British control, setting down the rights of the Nile and guaranteeing Egypt a yearly allowance of forty-eight billion cubic metres and Sudan four billion out of a total flow of eighty-eight billion cubic metres. The flow during the dry season was entirely reserved for Egypt. Following the independence of Sudan, another agreement signed in 1959 left 55.5 billion cubic metres to Egypt and 18.5 billion to Sudan, with even less for others. The treaties reflect the complete dependence of Egypt on the flow of the Nile. At the time, none of the other riparian states had funds to pursue any water development; therefore, water was not an issue. However, since that time, the other countries have begun to develop irrigation and have built dams on the river. In 1999, the Nile Basin Initiative was launched with the cooperation of all the riparian countries (Ethiopia, Tanzania, Rwanda, Kenya, Uganda, Burundi, Democratic Republic of Congo, Egypt, and Sudan), and was intended as a forum for cooperative discussion of riparian issues, but made little headway in recognition of the rights of upstream countries. In frustration, Ethiopia, Tanzania, Rwanda, Kenya, and Uganda signed the 2010 Nile River Cooperative Framework Agreement over the objections of Egypt and Sudan. The Agreement is designed to replace the

1929 treaty which gave Egypt veto power over any upstream project, recognizing that each country has equal rights to the Nile waters—following the principles of the UN. Not surprisingly Egypt sees the Agreement as a national security issue and a threat to its existence. The situation is not helped by the construction of the Grand Ethiopian Renaissance Dam which will affect water availability in Egypt and Sudan. The $4.5 billion project will be the largest hydro project in Africa and is scheduled for completion in 2018.[863] As a conciliatory gesture, Ethiopian Prime Minister Hailemariam Desalegn set up a tripartite committee with members from the three countries to study the likely impact of the dam. It is not clear how events will unfold, but so far cooperation over water appears to be more common than water wars.

Concluding thoughts

This survey of water-related issues has demonstrated that, in common with other resources, water is not used sustainably in many parts of the world. Many countries suffer from depleted aquifers and groundwater sources, polluted water courses, degraded river basins and wetlands, and lack of safe drinking water. Water impacts most aspects of human life and therefore should be an integral part of economic, environmental, and social planning in both rich and poor countries.

One of the most serious long-term challenges is to produce enough food for an expected world population of over nine billion by 2050 with less available water because of pollution of water courses and depletion of aquifers. More efficient irrigation does not necessarily save water; instead, it can lead to more water take-up by plants and therefore less water returned to groundwater or downstream users. The only alternative is more rain-fed agriculture, which may be a challenge in the face of climate change and may require storage if the rain is seasonal. Runoff agriculture and effective water collection may offer hope in dry areas. Other solutions include genetic engineering of crops that grow with less water.

Water planning should be part of an integrated approach. This means giving priority to investment in universal coverage of water and sanitation with graduated tariffs, guaranteeing free access to clean water for the very poor. Restoration of watersheds—that is, relying on ecosystem services to provide filtration—may in some cases be the most cost-effective way of achieving clean water. For example, New York City decided to invest $1.5 billion in restoring the Catskill/Delaware watershed rather than the alternative of a $6 billion filtration plant with an additional annual operating cost of $300 million per year, and other American cities have followed suit.[864] Urban areas should also engage in water recycling—for example, in rich areas water used for toilets and for gardens does not need to be of drinking quality. Sydney, Australia, introduced a dual water system in 2008: one for drinking water and one for other uses. Recycled water can also be used for urban agriculture. Measures should also be taken to control water demand using appropriate pricing policies—water may indeed be a human right, but that does not mean it should be provided for free in any quantity. In many poor countries, free water benefits the rich disproportionately because they often are the only households with access to running water. To protect the poor, water could be supplied with graduated tariffs, where a minimum amount would be provided free, and after the minimum is exceeded the price would increase incrementally, similar to the graduated-tariff schemes in southern Africa. Another example is Chile, which provides water stamps to poor people. Realistic water pricing may discourage consumption of water-intensive products and discourage the production of thirsty crops such as sugar beet for biofuel production in dry areas, as is currently happening.

10

Oceans and the Tragedy of the Commons

Oceans as the last frontier in the history of exploration. The rights to the sea. The tragedy of the commons: pollution. The tragedy of the commons: fisheries. Critical aspects of fisheries regulation and management. Aquaculture. Toward better management of the oceans.

Where are your monuments, your battles, martyrs?
Where is your tribal memory? Sirs,
in that gray vault. The sea. The sea
has locked them up. The sea is History.
—from the poem "The Sea Is History" by Derek Walcott

THE TITLE OF Derek Walcott's poem "The Sea Is History" is evocative because so much of human history is associated with the oceans. As well, the oceans have changed because of human impact, and they no longer contain the abundance of life described by early travellers. The oceans are critically important for our survival because they control the world's climates to a large extent by acting as a giant carbon sink. There appears to be mounting evidence that in doing so they are becoming increasingly acidified, with potentially catastrophic effects on biodiversity. But our impact on the oceans goes beyond acidification. Not only have humans hunted many land animals to extinction, but we are also doing the same to animals in the oceans, using increasingly sophisticated methods of killing. Charles Glover, in his book *The End of the Line*, describes industrial trawling as follows:

> Imagine what people would say if a band of hunters strung a mile of net between two immense all-terrain vehicles and dragged it at speed across the plains of Africa. This fantastical assemblage, like something from a Mad Max movie, would scoop up everything in its way: predators such as lions and cheetahs, lumbering endangered herbivores such as rhinos and elephants, herds of impala and wildebeest, family groups of warthogs and wild dogs. Pregnant females would be swept up and carried along, with only the smallest juveniles able to wriggle through the mesh. Picture how the net is constructed, with a huge metal roller attached to the leading edge. This rolling beam smashes and flattens obstructions, flushing creatures into the approaching filaments. The effect of dragging a huge iron bar across the savannah is to break off every outcrop and uproot every tree, bush, flowering plant, stirring columns of birds into the air. Left behind is a strangely bedraggled landscape, resembling a harrowed field. The industrial hunter-gatherers now stop to examine the tangled mess of writhing or dead creatures behind them. There are no markets for about a third of the animals they have caught because they don't taste good, or because they are simply too small or too squashed. This pile of corpses is dumped on the plain to be consumed by scavengers.[865]

Our exploitation of the oceans is not restricted to sources of food. It includes other resources such as oil and gas, sometimes with catastrophic effects on the environment as exemplified by the 2010 Deepwater Horizon explosion and oil spill in the Gulf of Mexico that leaked 4.9 million barrels of oil into the sea.[866] Deep-sea mining of some of the mineral-rich areas of the ocean floor is now being seriously considered by several mining companies, with largely unknown effects on ocean ecology. As well, the oceans are believed to hold a wealth of bacteria, viruses, and sponges of potential use in pharmaceutical products and therefore are open to bioprospecting. All these activities are difficult to control because vast areas of the oceans are beyond national jurisdiction, and compared with land resources, not enough is known about the ocean environment, particularly at great depths.

Most scientists would agree that the current use of the oceans is unsustainable and is a near-perfect example of the tragedy of the commons, as defined in Chapter 7. If a geographic population has free access to fisheries or other resources, any attempt by one country to manage the resources sustainably is undermined by other countries if they can obtain access to the same resources. The overexploitation of world fisheries has serious economic ramifications. Comparing a fishery with an asset, a study done for the World Bank showed that in 1974, 60 percent of fisheries were underperforming assets, and by 2004, 75 percent were underperforming. Because of the declining value of the assets, the yearly losses from overfishing were estimated at $50 billion with cumulative losses of $2 trillion—not counting the losses from illegal fishing.[867] Fish is an important source of animal protein, representing almost 17 percent of the total protein intake of human consumption, but almost 20 percent of the total catch is destined for fish meal, fish oil, or food for aquaculture—an inefficient use of valuable protein.

This chapter examines the reasons for this state of affairs, focusing on the lack of property rights and the difficulties of limiting access. Following a brief overview of the role of the oceans in human history and exploration, the chapter discusses how international law addresses the problem of ownership. It assesses the likely environmental effects and the need for controls of deep-sea exploitation of metals, minerals, and energy, the dumping of hazardous materials, and how the overexploitation of the fisheries can be dealt with by making fishing sustainable. The chapter also examines the development and role of aquaculture and the contribution it can make to global food security.

Oceans as the last frontier in the history of exploration

The five oceans, the Atlantic, Pacific, Indian, Arctic, and Southern Oceans, have a critical place in human history—particularly since the development of sail, which made it easier and faster to explore different parts of the world. It appears that the Egyptians first developed sailing vessels around 4000 BC, followed by the Phoenicians, who travelled to England and even around Africa. The Greeks published maps of the Mediterranean regions based on sea travel and appear to have reached northern Europe. Ptolemy, a Roman, produced an extensive world map with fairly accurately shown outlines of Europe, North Africa, India, and the oceans (Figure 10.1). The Irish monk St. Brendan may have reached North America during the sixth century AD, and the Vikings used their seafaring abilities not only to plunder and pillage in Europe but also to explore and colonize Iceland, Greenland, and a part of Newfoundland. Many of those early discoveries were forgotten during the Middle Ages, and until recently few outside China were aware of the amazing exploits of the Chinese navy. During the reign of the Ming emperor Yongle (1360–1424), the navy embarked on

Figure 10.1. The Ptolemy world map from 1482, recreated from notes by the Greek geographer Ptolemy (100 AD–175 AD). Source: Wikimedia Commons.

seven long voyages led by Admiral Zheng He, covering large areas of the Indian Ocean using a massive flotilla of ships with up to 37,000 crew members. It is claimed that the fleet reached Africa and even North America.[868] The motive appears to have been to bring trade and neighbouring countries under Chinese influence. However, the voyages finished as abruptly as they started. Following the death of Yongle, the new Emperor Hongxi refused to finance the hugely expensive voyages and ordered them to stop.

The next period of ocean travel took place during the Age of Discovery with the European search for the sea route to India and the famous Spice Islands. At this time, new discoveries followed in a rapid succession: Christopher Columbus landed in Haiti in 1492, John Cabot reached Newfoundland in 1497, Vasco da Gama reached India in 1498, and between 1519 and 1522 Magellan's ships circumnavigated the world. The three voyages of James Cook between 1768 and 1779 explored the Pacific and the Southern Oceans and mapped large areas of Australia, Hawaii, and New Zealand. The next significant event in the history of ocean exploration was Charles Darwin's voyage on the HMS *Beagle* between 1831 and 1836 around the Galapagos and other areas in the Pacific. Ships in search of whales and seals continued to explore the Southern Ocean.

Wind power could be fickle, and sail was surpassed by steam because of its promise to make the voyages faster and more reliable. There was also pressure to decrease the length of travel by connecting the Mediterranean with the Indian Ocean, and the Pacific with the Atlantic in order to avoid the hazardous and long journeys around Cape of Good Hope and Cape Horn. Based on archeological evidence, remnants of ancient canals between the Mediterranean and the Red Sea date as far back as the reign of Ramses II in thirteenth-century BC. There were several reconstructions over the centuries, but canals were difficult to maintain because of the buildup of silt, and it was not until 1869 that the Suez Canal was completed. The building of the Panama Canal was far more challenging, as the terrain is not flat and the climate is tropical. The first attempt to build a canal was made in the 1880s by the builder of the Suez Canal, Ferdinand de Lesseps, but the work was halted after the deaths of nearly twenty-two thousand people from accidents and various tropical diseases. A successful attempt was made by the United States in the early 1900s, albeit

Figure 10.2. A containership in the Panama Canal. Credit: Katja Schulz, https://www. flickr.com/photos/treegrow/

with an additional 5000–6000 lives lost, and the canal was opened in 1914. The canal cannot accommodate to-day's super large ships, and it is currently being enlarged. Meanwhile another canal, "the Grand Inter-Oceanic Canal" is being built by a Chinese consortium across Nicaragua with an expected completion date in 2019.[869] This canal—another megaproject—will cut through four nature reserves, the largest tropical lake in the Americas, as well as the Mesoamerican biological corridor (a protection route for wildlife migration). While the government of Nicaragua expects the project to generate economic growth, it is likely to have adverse consequences for global biodiversity by severely impacting a very fragile environment.[870]

In transportation circles, anticipation is growing that ice-free conditions caused by global warming will make navigation feasible through the Northeast and Northwest Passages—the continuation of the ancient dream of finding navigable waterways from Europe to the Far East.[871] Using IPCC projections for warming in the Arctic and recent sea-ice data, one study estimates that within a hundred years, the Northeast Passage above Russia will be ice free for three to six months of the year and the Northwest Passage through the Canadian Arctic for two to four months.[872] Navigating through the Northeast Passage would decrease the distance between Rotterdam and Yokohama by 40 percent, while the Northwest Passage would cut the distance between Rotterdam and Seattle by 25 percent.[873] The savings would be even more pronounced for ships currently rounding Cape Horn or the Cape of Good Hope because they are too large to enter the existing canals. It is believed that these shortcuts could cut the cost of such journeys by 20 percent. Moreover, the ships would avoid the politically unstable Middle East and the pirate-infested areas off Somalia and the South China Sea.[874] However, regular shipping through the Arctic requires the development of better charts and could be costly to the shipping lines; the ships would have to be ice-strengthened, and given the fragile Arctic environment, insurance costs would be high to cover damages in case of accidents. As well, complex political and legal issues concerning the ownership of the area's land and marine resources would have to be settled. For example, Canada claims that the Northwest Passage lies within Canadian territory, giving Canada the right to bar transit through the waters, while the United States and the European Union maintain that the passage is an international waterway that allows the right of passage for them. The opening of these northern shipping lanes would facilitate the development of Arctic mineral resources, putting further strain on an ecologically sensitive environment that is already under threat from climate change.

The remaining underexplored area of the earth is the deep sea, which starts at two hundred metres below the surface. It contains a vast volume of water that has an average depth of thirty-eight hundred metres. The Mariana Trench in the Western Pacific Ocean is the deepest part of the ocean—almost eleven thousand metres deep—and was first discovered by the British scientific ship HMS *Challenger* in 1875, but at that time the scientists could not accurately measure its depth.[875] The scientists on the *Challenger* found what was then considered to be an amazing variety of life, and the much later *Galathea* expedition of 1950–52 found animals at all depths. Most scientists previously believed that life in the deep was not possible because of the lack of light and the high pressure. More recently, the submersible *Alvin* operated by the Woods Hole Oceanographic Institute has been at the forefront of deep-ocean exploration and photography, including the photography of deep-sea vents and an astounding variety of marine life. The accepted view of life in the deep ocean has now changed from an area of little interest because of low biodiversity to an environment harbouring millions of species.[876]

The benthic (bottom) layers of the oceans are divided into the bathyal zones, which cover the continental shelf (three hundred to two thousand metres below the surface), the abyssal zones, which are the equivalent of the Great Plains in the oceans (two to six thousand metres below), and the hadal zones, which are the deep trenches (six to eleven thousand metres below). The abyssal zones contain up to thirty thousand seamounts, canyons, and mid-ocean ridges harbouring a variety of ecosystems. Underwater volcanoes give rise to hydrothermal vents, also known as smokers. These were first discovered in 1977 and were found to contain organisms never seen before, including small shrimplike creatures obtaining their energy from hydrogen sulphate (poisonous for most animals). The fact that living creatures acquire their energy from the vents rather than the sun radically altered thinking about the necessary conditions for the existence of life. It is now estimated that 95 percent of organisms in the oceans are microbial organisms such as sponges, viruses, and bacteria, many critically important in maintaining other life both at sea and on land.[877] It is believed that better understanding of their roles could revolutionize marine biotechnology.[878] Sponges are of particular interest to the pharmaceutical industry; they emit toxins to ward off predators, and these toxins are of potential use in developing drugs. Currently more than twenty marine-based drugs are being clinically tried as cancer treatments, and two drugs are already on the market.[879] While there are rules and regulations on land for controlling exploitation of biological and other resources, none exist for the portions of the oceans beyond national jurisdictions, and the challenge of creating such rules is substantial because of the absence of assigned property rights.

The rights to the sea

The first recorded attempt to assign rights to the sea dates from the Age of Discovery with Pope Alexander's division of the Atlantic into a Spanish sphere and a Portuguese sphere in the 1494 Treaty of Tordesillas.[880] According to this division, the ocean and newly discovered lands to the west of a line of demarcation—approximately two thousand kilometres to the west of the Cape Verdes—belonged to Spain, and the corresponding areas to the east belonged to Portugal, including the rights to control passage across the sea. This treaty gave no rights to the Dutch, the French, or the English, who had to resort to privateering and piracy. In response, the young Dutch scholar Hugo Grotius published a book *Mare Liberum* (freedom of the seas) in 1609, attacking the rights of the Portuguese over the oceans. He argued that anything that cannot be seized or enclosed cannot be property; therefore, the sea does not belong to anyone, and citizens of every nation are free to travel everywhere and to trade with anyone.[881] Essentially, this was a justification for the rights of the Dutch East India Company to the lucrative trade routes controlled by the Portuguese, and the treatise led to the concept of "freedom of the seas." A few years later, an English scholar, John Seldon, argued equally forcefully that the sea could indeed be owned, and by the early eighteenth century it became generally accepted that territorial rights could extend from land but only as far out as could be defended by a cannon ball (three miles), and this became known as the three-mile limit.

It became obvious during the twentieth century that exploitable resources were available beyond the three-mile limit, and the thinking was that if the continental shelf was merely an underwater extension of a country's territorial land mass, those resources belonged to the country in question. In 1945, by proclamation, the United States unilaterally extended its territorial limit to the continental shelf and later to twelve miles, with the justification that each country has the right to control and protect its own resources. Several countries in South America followed, declaring territorial waters to two hundred miles to protect its fisheries. The 1958 United Nations–sponsored conference on the Law of the Sea agreed on a legal definition of the continental shelf, which included the clause that if it was possible to exploit resources beyond the twelve-mile limit, it was part of the continental shelf and could therefore be claimed.

Subsequently, it was realized that in order to prevent chaos, more precise definitions had to be agreed on. A second conference held in 1960 resulted in no new agreements. Meanwhile, underwater oil exploration was taking place in depths previously considered impossible to reach, and the discovery of nodules with high mineral contents on the ocean floor fostered a belief that profitable mining operations were imminent. A third Law of the Sea conference was convened in 1973 and continued meeting until 1982. The final outcome was a convention that came into force in 1994—the Convention on the Law of the Sea—which is widely regarded as one of the major achievements of the United Nations.[882] It is treated as a convention even by the few countries that have not ratified, such as the United States.

The conferences and the convention addressed several issues that are still in existence today. The territorial limit is set at twelve nautical miles.* Within this area, each country can enforce any law and regulate any use of a resource. Ships have the right to "innocent passage" through any country's territorial waters, but not through inland waters. Innocent passage means that any ship, naval or merchant, cannot threaten the security of the country or break its laws. The convention guarantees the right of innocent passage through straits such as the Strait of Gibraltar between the Atlantic and the Mediterranean, the Strait of Malacca between the Indian and Pacific Oceans, the Strait of Hormuz connecting the Indian Ocean with the Gulf States, and the Strait of Bab-el-Mandeb between the Indian Ocean and the Red Sea. Coastal states are entitled to an additional twelve miles of sea (the so-called contiguous zone), where they have the right to pursue or arrest criminals who break domestic laws in relation to pollution, taxation, customs, and immigration. Special consideration is given to states made up of groups of islands (archipelagic states) such as Indonesia and the Philippines, where the territorial limit is a twelve-mile zone stretching from lines joining the outermost islands. The right of innocent passage is maintained between islands, but the state can suspend the right to innocent passage if such a move is essential for national security.

The convention set up an additional limit: the Exclusive Economic Zone (EEZ), stretching two hundred nautical miles out from a baseline, which is the low-water mark. The purpose was to give countries a better legal framework for the protection of fisheries. If two EEZs intersect each other, the rule is to draw an equidistant line between the coasts, splitting the disputed area down the middle. Coastal states have the right to exploit and manage all resources,

*1 nautical mile=1.852 km

including fish, mineral resources, and energy resources within the zone. In some cases, the continental shelf stretches beyond the two-hundred-mile limit; in these cases, the convention has established special rules to cover the rights to the shelf whereby the continental shelf, if it exists outside the two-hundred-mile limit, can be claimed, but no farther than 350 miles from the baseline. Coastal states have the right to harvest minerals and living resources attached to the continental shelf and can prevent others from doing so, with the proviso that they must share with landlocked and poorer countries some of the revenue derived from the exploitation of minerals beyond the two hundred miles.

Determining the limits of the continental shelf is a complex undertaking; it requires scientific proof that the area is indeed part of the shelf. Countries that ratified the convention before 1999 had until May 13, 2009, to stake a claim with the specially created Commission on the Limits of the Continental Shelf; others have had ten years between the time they acceded and the deadline to file. The deadlines led to a hurried scramble for territory, reminiscent of the nineteenth-century grab for colonies. The EEZs are laying claims to 131 million square kilometres, which is approximately 40 percent of the ocean, and currently the claims to the continental shelf add an additional twenty-six million square kilometres.[883] Not only do claims overlap, but other claims do not follow the rules of the convention. For example, Bangladesh, Egypt, Myanmar, and Vietnam have drawn straight lines not in accordance with the convention, and Benin, the Philippines, Somalia, and Togo claim territorial waters larger than the permitted twelve nautical miles. Japan is claiming continental-shelf rights from uninhabited rocks, which is not allowed.[884] Any disputes of the parties to the convention can either be referred to the International Tribunal for the Law of the Sea or the International Court of Justice.

The commission is involved in delicate and politically controversial work, with many of the submissions involve competing claims. For example, Russia and Canada claim that the Lomonosov Ridge stretches all the way from Siberia into the Canadian Arctic and is thus an extension of their continental shelf, while Denmark claims that the ridge is an extension off the shelf stretching from Greenland. Another area of contention is the South China Sea, where competing claims are ongoing by China, the Philippines, Vietnam, Taiwan, Indonesia, Malaysia, and Brunei, mainly concerning the rights to the Paracel Islands and the Spratly Islands.[885] This area is believed to contain a vast amount of oil, with estimates of between twenty-eight and 230 billion barrels, as well as huge gas reserves and lucrative fishing.[886] Claims to the East China Sea, which contains the uninhabited islands of Senkaku, are even more controversial.

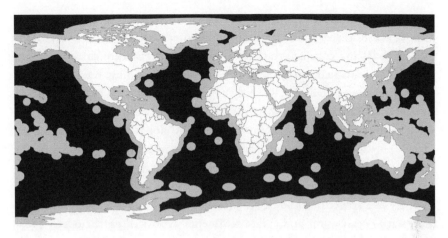

Figure 10.3. The dark ocean areas are under the jurisdiction of the International Seabed Authority and are not claimed. Source: Wikimedia Commons.

The ownership of Senkaku is hotly contested by China, Taiwan, and Japan following the Japanese government's purchase of the one of the islands from a private owner.

According to the convention, any resources beyond the continental shelf and the EEZs are deemed to be the common heritage of humanity and fall under the jurisdiction of the International Seabed Authority (ISA), which was established as part of the convention. The ISA is under obligation to adopt regulations for the protection and preservation of the marine environment, and no exploration or mineral extractions are to take place without its approval. All applications for exploration must be accompanied by an environmental impact assessment, and if commercial exploitation occurs, royalties must be paid to the ISA following a graduated royalty scheme set at 1 percent of the value of the mineral extracted to be increased by 1 percent per year until the royalties reach 7 percent. These royalties will be allocated to landlocked nations and to developing countries to ensure equitable allocations of benefits from a resource that belongs to all. However, these rules do not cover bioprospecting, which was of minor interest during the negotiations but has become important as a source of pharmaceuticals.[887] This is currently a point of contention because without rules, living matter taken from the high seas is an open-access resource.

At the time the convention was negotiated, the oceans were believed to be a large source of untapped mineral resources. Already in 1874, the British research ship HMS *Challenger* managed to scoop up nodules from the ocean floor from depths of approximately five thousand metres containing metals such as manganese, nickel, cobalt, and copper. Further sampling confirmed that an area of the Pacific known as the Clarion-Clipperton Fracture Zone is covered with nodules, inspiring great hopes for commercial mining, but these hopes have not yet come to fruition. Recently, a Japanese team claims to have found an abundance of rare earth metals on the ocean floors, asserting that even a small patch of the ocean floor could meet most of the global demand for an entire year.[888] Cobalt-crusted seamounts and sulphides, which are found along ocean vents, have also generated considerable interest. Hot hydrogen sulphides seep out of cracks in the ocean floors and react with the cold water, creating large chimney-like structures known as "black smokers." The hydrogen sulphides react with ocean water and create sediments deposited on the ocean floor. These sediments have a high mineral content; in some cases, they contain high concentrations of copper, zinc, iron, and lead as well as traces of gold and silver.

So far, most of the exploration licenses issued by the International Seabed Authority have involved explorations in the Clarion-Clipperton zone and the

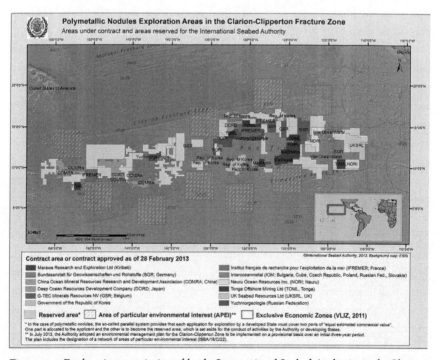

Figure 10.4. Exploration permits issued by the International Seabed Authority in the Clarion-Clipperton Fracture Zone. Source: The International Seabed Authority.

Indian Ocean. The authority has issued exploration licences to Russian, South Korean, Chinese, French, and Indian companies, among others. No commercial mining is currently taking place because of technical problems and economics. The technical problems are immense. One issue is that for ocean mining to be competitive with land mining, the operations must take place year-round under certain extreme environmental conditions, including temperatures of one to two degrees, high pressures, crosscutting currents, total darkness, and variable sea-floor characteristics.[889] While the metal concentration in individual nodules may be high, it is typically spread over a large area, which increases the cost and impact of mining operations. Companies involved have been reluctant to invest, partly because of lack of clarity within the legal regime and partly because of the proviso that a share of the profits must go to the International Seabed Authority. Commercial exploitation of deposits lying within national jurisdictions appears to be more likely, depending on the royalty regimes. Sulphides exist within the economic zone claimed by Papua New Guinea, where the Canadian company Nautilus Minerals signed an agreement with the government to start production

Figure 10.5. Hydrothermal vent (smoker). Source: US National Oceanic and Atmospheric Administration.

in 2013, fifty kilometres off the coast and at a depth of 1.6 kilometres. However, following a dispute with the government over development costs and because of growing local opposition, work was suspended on the project in November 2012.[890] The locals apparently remember the mining disaster associated with the Ok Tedi Mine (See Chapter 2). However outstanding issues between the company and the government of Papua New Guinea were resolved in 2014, removing any remaining barriers for the mine to go ahead.

The environmental impacts of mining on the ocean floor could be severe. One single mine could scoop up nodules and sediments at the rate of over three to seven hundred square kilometres per year, killing all marine life in the area. In addition, there are concerns about the impact of mining-related sediment plumes on the immediate ocean environment and on ocean circulation. The disturbed sediments could affect an area two to five times larger than the mined area; therefore, over a period of fifteen years, one mining operation alone could affect an area of fifty thousand square kilometres.[891] Mining of sulphates along stacks and vents has unknown effects due to insufficient knowledge of some of the affected ecological habitats. The hydrothermal vents support a remarkable biodiversity, which has adapted to the sulphide-laden fluids that originate from the vents.[892]

Interest is increasing in the commercial exploitation of methane gas hydrates, which are molecules of methane trapped in ice crystals.[893] They occur in great abundance under Arctic permafrost or beneath the ocean floor near the continental shelves. The amount of energy these hydrates contain is vast—some believe they contain more than the current reserves of fossil fuels. If the hydrates are heated or depressurized, they will revert to water and methane. One cubic metre of hydrates could generate 164 cubic metres of gas. But there is a potential problem in mining the hydrates: any accidental release of a large amount of methane could have catastrophic consequences for the world's climates, as methane is a much more powerful greenhouse gas than CO_2. The challenge is to find extraction techniques that can capture the gas without releasing any of it in the atmosphere. Many countries, including the United States, Germany, Russia, and Japan, are actively involved in research and development. It is believed that Japan is closest to commercial production.

The tragedy of the commons: pollution

The tragedy of the commons has affected oceans in two ways: pollution and overfishing. The oceans have always been used as a sewer and as dumping grounds for other wastes. During the period of steam, large amounts of clinker were dumped on the ocean floor, and later, nuclear waste was disposed of in many parts of the ocean. Between 1973 and 1978, pharmaceutical waste was intentionally dumped in the Puerto Rico trench, with adverse effects on the marine environment because much of the waste was toxic. This dumpsite off the east coast of the United States received approximately 36 million tonnes of sludge before its closure in 1992.[894] Little is known about any long-term effects of these examples of early dumping. Stricter controls are now in place with regard to both dumping from land and dumping at sea. Signatories to the Law of the Sea Convention are under obligation to implement legislation to prevent, reduce, and control pollution from land-based sources—a commitment that is not always enforced. The International Maritime Organization, another UN agency, is responsible for preventing marine pollution from ships; to that end, it has adopted specific regulations against dumping of oil, garbage, and sewage. The 1972 London Convention, otherwise known as the Convention on the Prevention of Marine Pollution by Dumping of Wastes and Other Matters,[895] specifically forbids the dumping of hazardous materials at sea, including mercury, cadmium, plastics, organohalogens, high-level radioactive waste, and chemicals used for biological or chemical warfare. Each state that signed the convention has jurisdiction over ships and aircraft registered in its own country and can prevent all ships from dumping in its own territorial waters. In 1992, the convention was replaced by the London Protocol, which came into force in 2006 and prohibits all dumping with some possible exceptions for sewage sludge, fish wastes, some mining wastes, organic materials, and carbon dioxide from carbon sequestration—provided it is stored in sub-seabed geological formations.

Enforcement of the anti-dumping rules is difficult regardless of the source. In 1997, Charles Moore, the captain of a sailing boat, decided to take a shortcut between Hawaii and Los Angeles, an area often avoided because of lack of wind. It is known as the North Pacific Subtropical Gyre, a vortex of slow-moving ocean currents composing the earth's largest contiguous ecosystem. Day after day, mile after mile, Moore found that he was surrounded by a sea of plastic garbage. Based on his experience, he became an environmental activist, campaigning for cleanup and for reducing the amount of plastics discarded into the environment. "The great pacific garbage patch" cannot be seen from the air because the garbage is submerged under the water's surface, but its presence has been confirmed by others sailing through. The size of the patch is not clear, with estimates varying from the size of the province of Quebec in Canada to the size of the entire United States.[896] It has now been confirmed that all five sub-tropical ocean gyres contain a large amount of plastic debris.

Figure 10.6. Beach in Connemara, Ireland. Credit: Ingrid Bryan.

The pooled findings of twenty-four scientific expeditions found that 75 per-cent (by weight) of the plastics consisted of items larger than 200 mm (the most frequently observed were foamed polystyrene items); 11 percent of items between 4.76–200 mm (the size of plastic drinking bottles); and the remain-der of micro plastics, less than 4.75 mm in size.[897] Surprisingly, 44 percent of the total was found in the southern hemisphere, far removed from the large population centres in the northern hemisphere. Plastics are harmful to fish, turtles, seabirds, and marine mammals because they become entangled, or the plastics become ingested.[898] Ingestion is known to cause hormonal disruptions and impact reproductive systems in animals.[899] Plastics break down into small, five-millimetre nodules (nicknamed "mermaid's tears" by environmentalists) and even smaller units that release toxic substances such as bisphenol A and PS oligomers when they are ingested by invertebrates. However, the full envi-ronmental impact is not entirely clear; a recent study has shown evidence that the plastics have created a unique ecosystem with algae and bacteria living off the debris and possibly decomposing it.[900] Indeed, researchers have found that most of the microplastics they expect to find in the oceans cannot be accounted for—either they are buried in sediments, or have decomposed into even smaller sizes, or are lying along the shores.[901]

Not all dumping is deliberate. Natural disasters affecting coastal areas such as the Japanese tsunami in 2011 can create large volumes of involuntary dumping. Some of the debris from the tsunami, much of it plastics, reached North American beaches, but it is likely that most will end up in the Great Pacific Garbage Patch.[902] Accidental dumping of containers appears to be quite common, with estimates of the number of containers washed overboard varying from 350 to ten thousand every year.[903] Apart from a shipping hazard, environmental effects obviously depend on the contents of the containers. Because the shipping companies are insured against the loss of containers, there appears to be little incentive for the companies to implement measures to minimize the losses.

Increasing levels of CO_2 also affect oceans and become a pollutant as approximately one-third of CO_2 emissions are absorbed by seawater and form carbonic acid, decreasing the concentration of calcium carbonate in the surface water. A group of scientists, writing in *Nature* in 2005, reported the results from an experiment in which organisms with shells were exposed to seawater lacking calcium carbonate.[904] The absence of calcium carbonate led to the dissolution of their shells. The scientists projected that low concentration of calcium carbonate in the oceans will seriously affect the Southern Ocean by 2050 and the whole of the Pacific by 2100, endangering the Great Barrier Reef off the coast of Australia, one of the best-known UNESCO world heritage sites. It is likely that organisms with calcium carbonate in their skeletons or shells, such as corals, molluscs, crustaceans, and many types of planktons, will have a particularly difficult time. One-quarter of the world's coral reefs have already been destroyed by fishing and pollution, and acidification will make the situation even worse.

Apart from acidification, climate change will have other adverse effects on oceans. Warmer water temperatures will affect the delicate balance between corals and their symbiotic algae, resulting in coral bleaching and a higher die-off affecting a whole ecosystem. Warmer temperatures will also affect the fish and crustacean populations, which may have to alter their migration routes and find more conducive conditions to spawn and feed—this is already happening.[905] In the Arctic and Antarctic, habitats of many animals, including polar bears, walruses, penguins, and many whales will be adversely affected. There is evidence that the Antarctic krill population, which is a critical source of food for many animals in the Southern Ocean, is declining. The melting of glaciers will lead to rising sea levels, which will affect coastal habitats such as mangroves and wetland areas. Species living in these areas, such as sea turtles, may not be able to migrate quickly enough to adjust to rising sea levels and higher temperatures.

Warming will also affect ocean circulation patterns, including the phenomenon known as upwelling, in which nutrient-rich colder bottom water reaches the ocean surface, creating a rich source of food for many creatures. Examples of upwelling are found off the Galapagos Islands and off the northern coast of California. The circulation of water also ensures that the bottom layers of the ocean receive oxygen—if they do not, most life will die. When ocean temperatures rise, the warmer water acts as a blanket, interfering with the natural circulation and creating hypoxic (oxygen-free) areas that already appear to be spreading, favouring animals such as jellyfish that are more tolerant of low oxygen levels.[906] A few years ago, some scientists raised alarm that climate change could lead to major changes in the Gulf Stream, which brings warm ocean water from the Caribbean basin to northern Europe, thus creating an unusually warm climate for these latitudes. (For example, the relatively temperate Stockholm is on the same latitude as the southern tip of Greenland). However, the majority of scientists now agree there is no immediate risk that the Gulf Stream will be affected. Of more immediate concern is that changes in ocean currents and temperatures could destabilize the methane hydrates and release the powerful greenhouse gas methane into the atmosphere.[907]

The tragedy of the commons: the fisheries

Not only do pollution and climate change pose a threat to the world's oceans, but so does the state of fisheries in many parts of the world, a result of unsustainable fishing practices. This is not new—records as far back as the Middle Ages give examples of human-induced declines in fish populations.[908] During that period, population growth and dictates of the church increased the demand for fish. If they had a choice, people preferred meat to fish, but the Catholic Church forbade the eating of warm-blooded animals on fast days in order to commemorate the sacrifice of Jesus Christ. Fish, on the other hand, was not considered to be warm-blooded, as it came from water, making it a "cold" food that could be eaten. Even beavers were declared to be cold-blooded as they swam in cold water—a politically expedient decision by the church during the seventeenth century, given the fondness of newly converted North American natives for barbecued beaver.[909] Fast days included every Friday, holy days, and the forty-day period of Lent, adding up to a total of 130 days. This meant that fish was in demand for approximately 35 percent of the year for those who could afford it.

Before 1100 AD, seafood tended to be local and was only lightly preserved in salt, but starting in the twelfth century, dried fish and fish preserved in salt and brine became more common, and these items could be transported over some distances. Fish populations in parts of Europe started to decline, and during the thirteenth century attempts were made in France and Sicily to regulate the fisheries in the form of seasonal closures, minimum size limits of fish and the type of fishing gear used. Such controls were uncommon, however, and both salmon and sturgeon became severely overfished, sturgeon to such an extent that the sturgeon population never recovered its former range. It is interesting to note that even at that time, evidence shows that people were aware of adverse effects on fish populations of siltation caused by dams for watermills, the clearing of forests for agriculture, eutrophication caused by towns and cities, and the effluents from mining operations.[910] The control of some rivers and the draining of swamps favoured an expansion of the eel population, which created a lucrative fishery that continued in Scandinavia until the late twentieth century, when it eventually collapsed because of overfishing.

Herring fisheries were developed commercially in the North Sea and the Baltic during the thirteenth century, and the Dutch gained control over the market during the fourteenth century. The herring fisheries in the North Sea, southern Scandinavia, and the southern Baltic all collapsed in the late Middle Ages due to climate change, overfishing, and agricultural developments that caused siltation of waterways, ruining the spawning areas.[911] Typically the herring were packed in brine-filled barrels, and preserved herring has had a long-lasting effect on Scandinavian cuisine. The traditional smorgasbord is still served with many varieties of herring dishes—never fresh, always pickled or salted. Availability of salt must have been a constraint in the preservation of Scandinavian herring as the Baltic's seawater is only brackish and not good source of salt. In response, the Swedes developed an interesting—some would say disgusting—method of preservation: the fish was left to rot in barrels with a minimum amount of salt. Bulging cans of *surströmming* (sour herrings) are still sold, and the herrings are consumed with potatoes, raw onions, crispbread, and liberal helpings of aquavit. Its smell is reputed to make it the most putrid food in the world. Airlines are not allowed to carry the cans in case they explode.

The history of the cod fisheries provides a more recent example of fishery mismanagement.[912] Cod is a lean fish, which makes it ideal to cure using simple methods. Even the Vikings learned to preserve codfish by hanging it in the cold air until it lost most of its moisture and came to resemble a thin piece of wood that could be broken off bit by bit and eaten. It became an ideal source of food on long sea voyages. During the Middle Ages, the Basques added salt before the drying process, which made it possible to keep the cod even longer.

Cod is a ground fish (a bottom feeder) common in cold waters rich in phytoplankton, typically where warm and cold currents meet. It is fished in the North Sea, the Baltic, and off Iceland, but the Basques were the first to fish the Grand Banks off the coast of Newfoundland in the early part of the sixteenth century. After John Cabot came back from Newfoundland in 1497, he and his crew claimed that the seas off Newfoundland were so full of cod that all you needed was to lower a basket into the water, and when you pulled it up it would be filled to the brim. Early reports also talked of cod the size of men. Indeed, as late as 1895, a six-foot cod weighing 211 pounds was caught off the coast of Massachusetts.[913] The reputation of the Grand Banks spread quickly. When Jacques Cartier returned from his 1534 voyage into the Gulf of St. Lawrence, he reported that he saw a thousand Portuguese ships fishing on the Grand Banks. Newfoundland became a Portuguese outpost, and many of today's place names bear witness to the fact: Port aux Basques, Cape Spear (Cabo de Espera), and Cape Race (Cabo Raso), to name a few. In 1580, Portugal came under Spanish control, and following the destruction by the English of the Spanish fishing fleet in 1585, the Portuguese dominance disappeared. However, the famous Portuguese white schooners still continued to fish on the Grand Banks until the Canadian government took control of the fishing grounds in the latter part of the twentieth century.

From the mid-nineteenth century, the most common way of catching cod off Newfoundland was to sail to the Grand Banks in relatively large ships and then lower smaller rowing boats (dories) into the sea, where the fishing would take place. When the dory was full, it would unload on the mother ship, where the fish would be gutted and salted. When the ship was full, it would head to shore to dry the fish. This practice would continue well into the twentieth century.

The most common fishing technique was the use of hand lines. In the early nineteenth century, the French introduced long hand lines, between one and eight to nine kilometres long, and every metre had a lanyard with a baited hook. The long lines were laid using dories and clearly marked with floating buoys. Long lines could be problematic as too many long lines in one area meant they could become entangled, and they were soon replaced by gill nets, in which fish gills became stuck and the fish choked. The nets had to be lifted every day and the fish collected, but sometimes they lost their anchors and began to drift, catching fish on the way. If fish went uncollected, the nets sunk to the bottom of the ocean under their own weight and after the heavy fish were eaten by other fish, the nets floated to the surface again, and the catching continued. This was known as "ghost fishing."

Following the introduction of engines in sea transport, the first steam-powered trawler appeared in 1881, dragging nets (trawls) along the ocean floor; as a result, the haul of fish increased sixfold, making the old sailing ships uncompetitive.[914] Once the technology of freezing was invented by Clarence Birdseye in 1922, factory ships were introduced and trawls could now be suspended between factory ships, making it possible for the nets to drag over rocky bottoms, catching everything. Overfishing was not a concern as better gear increased the catches and therefore created an illusion that there was close to an infinite supply of fish. According to an encyclopedia published during the nineteenth century, one codfish had been found to carry 9,384,000 eggs, "a number that will baffle all the efforts of man to exterminate."[915] Following Darwin there was a strong belief in the ability of nature to evolve in self-correcting ways.

Figure 10.7. Two girls with giant codfish in Newfoundland (ca. 1905). Source: Memorial University Maritime History Archives, the Job Photograph Collection, Image PF-315.222.

Newfoundland suffered greatly during the Great Depression, and it became clear after World War II that the cod fisheries could no longer support the Newfoundland population. As Britain neither had the resources nor the willingness to help, the only apparent solution was to join Canada. In 1948 a referendum was held, and the people of Newfoundland voted to join Canada, hoping that they would become better off. They believed that the Canadian government would be sympathetic to the problem of the fisheries. However, they were wrong, as the mindset of the Canadian government was focused on more traditional Canadian resource products (forest products, wheat, and minerals), and on developing manufacturing industries that were doomed to failure in remote Newfoundland. Following the establishment of the two-hundred-mile limit in 1977, the government saw a golden opportunity to develop a viable fishing industry, as the two-hundred-mile limit included most of the Grand Banks except for a small but very productive area called "the nose and the cone" that could still be fished by foreign vessels. As a result, the Portuguese and the Spanish now had to leave fishing grounds where they had been active for over five hundred years. In particular, it was a shock to the Spanish, who had the highest per-capita fish consumption in the West and a huge fishing fleet, but they had limited fishing grounds along their own coast. In 1986, the Canadian government continued to increase control over the Grand Banks by denying entry into Canadian ports of any foreign ships fishing off "the nose and the cone."

Since the preservation of fish stocks was not seen to be an issue, the two-hundred-mile limit was not regarded as a conservation measure. With federal government help, fish processing plants were made more efficient, with heavy investments in large factory trawlers. Cod fishing had become profitable except for small locally based inshore fisheries, which found their catches declining. In the late 1980s, all catches started to dwindle, but historically cod has occasionally disappeared from some areas only to return a few years later, and it was assumed that it would return again. This time, however, the cod did not return. In 1992, a temporary moratorium on fishing the northern cod was introduced. In 1994, it became permanent, and thirty thousand fishing industry workers were thrown out of work. So far there is little sign that cod stocks are recovering on the Grand Banks.

Another example of unsustainable fishing is the case of the bluefin tuna. Tuna is a family of fish consisting of forty-eight species; in general, they are extremely powerful and fast fish. Bluefin tuna can reach a length of 4.3 metres and weigh up to eight hundred kilograms and are capable of swimming over vast distances. Their size and flavour have made them popular with consumers and sports fishers alike. Tuna fishing is of cultural significance in many parts of the Mediterranean, particularly in Italy, where the annual season of tuna fishing evolved into a blood-soaked ritual. *La tonnara* (the tuna trap) involves the setting of a long series of nets in the coastal waters, guiding the tuna into smaller and smaller chambers—the last chamber appropriately called the "chamber of death." The killing—*la mattanza*—is set for a day when the leader of the fishers determines the conditions are right. The final net is raised to the surface, accompanied by coordinated singing and pulling of the net, and each tuna is hauled into little boats and killed with a knife.[916] But this ancient practice is disappearing because of lack of tuna. The Atlantic bluefin tuna traditionally return to spawn to the Gulf of Mexico or to the Mediterranean, where most of the fishing has occurred.

Tuna is associated in our minds with sushi, but this was not always the case; traditionally, the Japanese much preferred the whiter, more delicate species of fish.[917] It was not until the 1930s that the serving of tuna, particularly in nigiri, became accepted as a delicacy. Following the Japanese surrender to the Allies in 1945, the Japanese agreed to keep their fishing within territorial waters, but this ban was lifted in 1952, and the Japanese developed an export market for tuna to feed the tuna canneries in Europe. Following the introduction of fishing boats equipped with deep-freezing facilities, more and more tuna were destined for the sushi market as the fish could now be eaten raw. During the 1960s, sport fishing of bluefin tuna developed off Prince Edward Island and Nova Scotia in Canada, but often the fish was discarded because it was not enjoyed as a food. This coincided with the peak of Japanese exports of electronic products to North America. The products were carried by air, but the cargo planes returned empty to Japan because there was no backhaul. When Japanese businessmen realized there was a market for bluefin tuna in Japan, the empty cargo holds were filled with the fish, and soon bluefin tuna for sushi was more in demand than any other tuna. The markets in North America and Europe followed, and people who previously did not like fish embraced sushi. Prices soared from a few cents per kilo to hundreds of dollars per kilo, creating strong incentives to catch more—indeed, in 2013 a bluefin tuna fetched a record US$1.7 million at a Tokyo fish market.[918] As a result, the Eastern Atlantic bluefin is endangered and the Western Atlantic bluefin is critically endangered. The catches are controlled by the International Commission for the Conservation of Atlantic Tunas (ICCAT). In most years member nations exceeded catch limits, and in 2010 another failed attempt was made to have bluefin tuna listed as endangered under CITES, which would have banned all trade. It failed because of objections by Canada and Japan, another example of political interference trumping the available scientific evidence. In 2014 ICCAT estimated that the stocks had started to increase to the level of half the size they were in the 1970s, resulting in a controversial decision to increase the fishing quotas for both Eastern and Western Atlantic bluefins.[919]

Of course, not only cod and tuna are in decline. Historically, the big fish were most coveted, with fishing crews usually encouraged to discard the smaller ones.[920] They then turned to smaller fish or less familiar fish, and when those were gone they moved to other fishing grounds. The change in catches is referred to as "fishing down marine food webs," from a much-quoted article by Canadian scientist Daniel Pauly, who showed that between 1950 and 1994 fish landings shifted from large fish to smaller fish, particularly in the Northern Hemisphere.[921] Initially, the size of total catches usually increased, before stagnating and eventually declining. To improve marketability, dogfish was renamed rock salmon, and Patagonian toothfish became Chilean sea bass. Now, Spanish, Bulgarian, Japanese, Chinese, Mexican, and Romanian factory-style fishing boats are roaming the oceans in search of better catches, in many cases ruining the catches for local fishermen in developing countries, who have to turn to other sources of food, such as bush meat in Africa, or resort to piracy, as is the case off the coast of Somalia. A strong incentive exists to move to deeper waters, which requires different gear and is more expensive. Improved technologies and cheap fuel have allowed boats to reach far beyond territorial waters. Since 1950, electronic aids such as sonar, which was developed during World War II to detect submarines, and position fixing systems such as LORAN, Decca, and satellite GPS have been increasingly used to detect fish and to improve navigation; as noted above, the rewards in catching fish like tuna are high. The catch from the high seas increased from 9 percent of the world total in 1950 to 15 percent in 2003. Deep-sea fishing, conducted at depths of between two hundred and two thousand metres, is concentrated on slopes of the continental shelf and on seamounts or underwater ridges. Because this layer of the ocean is very dark, it cannot support photosynthesis, and fish have to go to the surface to feed or rely on dead organic matter that sinks to the ocean floor. Lack of food means fish grow slowly, and a large fish population cannot be sustained.

Deep-sea fishing of blue whiting was started on a small scale in the North Atlantic during the 1970s, with catches reaching in excess of 720,000 tons in 1987 and 2.6 million tons in 2004; the catch was mainly used for oil and fish meal. It became obvious that blue whiting stocks were set for rapid decline because of overfishing, particularly by Norway. Finally, after lengthy negotiations between the European Union, Norway, Iceland, and the Faeroes, a quota was set—still in excess of what was considered sustainable by fisheries scientists, but nevertheless hotly contested by Spain.[922] Another example of unsustainable exploitation of deep-sea fish is the orange roughy, a fish believed by many scientists to live up to 150 years. It does not reach sexual maturity until it is about thirty years old, and when it reproduces it lays only tens of thousands of eggs (compared with the codfish, which lays millions). Orange roughy was fished for a while in New Zealand, but it was quickly realized that quotas had been set far too high and had to be drastically reduced. Other examples of deep-sea fish are round-nosed grenadiers, which mature at eight to ten years and live to seventy-five years; the gulper shark, which lives to seventy and has only eight to ten offspring each year; and smoothheads, which live to thirty-eight years.[923] Many of these fish are discarded by vessels looking for more lucrative catches. Most fisheries biologists would agree that commercial fishing of deepwater species is not sustainable at current rates because of the slow growth rates and low reproduction rates.[924]

The expansion of commercial catches has included the harvesting of krill (small shrimplike creatures) in the waters off the Antarctic. Krill live in all the world's oceans but are particularly abundant in the Southern Ocean, where they are the essential foundations of ecosystems. They are used to manufacture omega fatty acids—thought to have numerous health benefits—that are in demand as a food supplement in rich countries. Krill are also used in aquaculture as fish food; they give the pink colour to the flesh of farmed salmon, replacing the small krill-like animals that are part of the natural diet of wild salmon. It is believed that the krill population has declined by 80 percent since the 1970s, probably because warmer water temperatures have melted the ice—home to plankton and algae that serve as food for the krill. A further decline in the krill population could have devastating effects on the ecology of the Southern Oceans as krill is essential food for penguins, whales, and seals in Antarctica.

In assessing the overall state of the world's fisheries, reliable statistics on catches and fish populations are crucial. In the 1950s the newly established Food and Agriculture Organization began to assemble and report on catch statistics. Even though fisheries scientists projected a decline because of severely depleted fishing areas, fish catches continued to increase throughout the 1990s. This gave an impression that plenty of fish still remained in the oceans. Canadian scientists Daniel Pauly and Reg Watson, in a highly influential 2001 article published in *Nature*, questioned the FAO statistics that were entirely based on the figures supplied by individual countries.[925] They pointed out that the catch increases were driven by reported increased catches in China, which was at odds with demonstrably depleted fishing grounds in China. If the Chinese figures are deleted from the official statistics, catches peaked in 1988 and have declined since. According to the authors, the most likely explanation for over-reporting the catches—most countries under-report their catches—was the incentives given to every Chinese state's planning unit to increase production targets. Another article in *Nature* by Ransom Myers and Boris Worm in 2003 estimated that 90 percent of the big predatory fish such as cod, tuna, and salmon had been fished out since the start of industrial fishing with severe implications for the entire ocean ecosystem.[926] In 2006, Worm et al. published a much debated article in *Science* predicting a total global collapse of fisheries by 2048—if current trends continue.[927] Based on their definitions, a fishery is regarded as collapsed if the harvest in the year of study is less than 10 percent of the maximum recorded harvest. In 2003, 27 percent of fisheries had collapsed with the proportion projected to increase to 100 percent by 2048.

Table 10.1. World fisheries and aquaculture production and utilization, 2012

	million tons	% of total
Capture		
Inland	11.6	7.4
Marine	79.7	50.4
Total capture	**91.3**	**57.8**
Aquaculture		
Inland	41.9	26.5
Marine	24.7	15.6
Total aquaculture	**66.6**	**42.2**
Total world fisheries	**158.0**	**100**

Source: Table 1, FAO, *The State of World Fisheries and Aquaculture, 2014.*

The FAO now works with better data from China. According to the 2014 study by the FAO, fish catches (inland and marine) have been relatively stable for the last five years.[928] Global marine fisheries production peaked in 1996 with a catch of 86.3 million tonnes (Table 10.1), which declined to 79.7 in 2012. Aquaculture, on the other hand has shown a steady increase and now represents approximately 42 percent of total fish production.

China remains by far the largest fish producer in the world with 17 percent of global catches, followed by Indonesia and the United States, while China, Norway, and Thailand are the largest fish exporters. Fish populations vary year from year for natural reasons that are not well understood, such as changes in currents and water temperature. Indeed, according to the FAO, 52 percent of the total catch shows large variability, some of which is natural. Areas with highly variable catches include the Eastern Central Atlantic, the Northeast Pacific, Eastern Central Pacific, Southwest Atlantic, Southeast Pacific, and Northwest Pacific. Areas that have shown a persistent decline in catches are the Northeast Atlantic, Northwest Atlantic, Western Central Atlantic, Mediterranean and Black Seas, Southwest Pacific, and Southeast Atlantic, and these areas account for 20 percent of the total. Areas with increasing catches include Northwest and Western Pacific and Eastern and Western Indian Ocean, contributing approximately 59.9 percent of the total catch. The most important fishing area by far is the Northwest Pacific, followed by the Southeast Pacific, the Western Central Pacific and the Northeast Atlantic. According to the FAO, 9.9 percent of fish stocks are currently considered underexploited and could support more fishing, 61.3 percent are fully exploited and cannot support any increase in fishing, while the remaining 28.8 percent are either overexploited, depleted, or recovering. The proportion of underexploited has decreased since 1970 and the proportion overexploited has increased.[929]

It is clear that there is now a widening discrepancy between regions. Some developed countries manage their fisheries quite well, which is not the case for most developing countries. These countries are in need of more food production and more employment, but do not yet have the capacity either for scientific assessment of fish stocks or for effective management controls. Some still have abundant stocks, which may attract illegal fishing unless strict controls are implemented. Boris Worm and Trevor Branch have highlighted areas of the oceans they call "fisheries conservation hot spots" that are particularly vulnerable because of their species richness and lack of adequate management systems.[930] The hot spots are located off the west coast of Mexico, the east coast of Africa including Madagascar, the northwest coast of Africa, and Southeast Asia.

Critical aspects of fisheries regulation and management

Fisheries regulations have traditionally concentrated on regulating technology—for example, mesh sizes and the use of methods such as explosives—and fishing seasons, but regulations have not gone far enough in controlling the use of drift nets. A drift net is a gillnet with floats and weights designed to keep the net vertical and is dragged along the surface of the ocean, catching everything in its way. The UN General Assembly banned drift netting on international waters in 1991, and the European Union brought in a total ban in 2002. Despite these measures, drift nets are still used in the Mediterranean and off the Brazilian coast in the South Atlantic.[931] Bottom trawlers (see page 330), drag heavily weighted nets along the sea floor, also catching everything along the way. The trawl crushes and levels the floor, which has severe adverse impacts on marine habitats, including nurseries for young fish.[932] There is particular concern over deep-sea bottom trawling over seamounts that are habitats to many organisms, including cold-water corals. The United States and Australia have banned bottom trawling within their own waters, but so far, the European Union has not followed. Several failed attempts have been made at the United Nations to outlaw the practice.

Bycatches—catches that are either unused, unmanaged, or thrown overboard—are another inadequately regulated aspect of the fishing industry. The waste in the fishing industry is huge, with the total discard at approximately 40 percent.[933] This does not take into account the number of living things, including whales, turtles, and birds, that are killed or injured by traps, nets, and lines. Long lines are still used for catching fish such as swordfish, tuna, halibut, and shark, but the hooks are known to catch sea turtles and birds, in particular the endangered albatross. Some of these effects can be mitigated by using weights to ensure the lines sink quickly so birds are not caught. Shrimp trawlers are especially notorious in terms of discards, as their nets' mesh sizes are very small and will catch anything in the way. The United States now requires its shrimp boats to be equipped with turtle-excluding devices—adjustments to nets to allow sea turtles to escape. In some cases, the ratio of discards to shrimp caught can be as high as ten to one, suggesting that for every kilogram of shrimp caught, ten kilos of fish is caught and either dumped because there is no market for it or because the fisher does not have a license to catch it. In many jurisdictions, shrimp licences are more advantageous than other fishing licenses because the nets' small mesh makes it possible to take a larger total bio-mass. However, there are indications that the quantity of discards is decreasing as more of the trash fish are processed as fish meal for poultry or aquaculture. But this is likely to lead to more revenue for fishers, providing an incentive to do even more fishing, with adverse effects on the whole ecosystem.[934] Discards are currently banned within the fishing jurisdictions of Alaska, the Canadian province of British Columbia, New Zealand, the Faroe Islands, Norway and Iceland, and partially in the European Union as of 2015, with a full ban taking effect by 2019. Experience from these jurisdictions has shown that discard bans are only effective if accompanied by appropriate surveillance and incentives to fishing crews to land all of their catch, and will only have a beneficial effect on fish stocks if total catches are limited to ensure sustainability.[935]

Another major problem is illegal fishing. It is estimated that one-fifth of global catches are illegal, unreported, or unregulated (commonly referred to as IUU), which is equivalent to 26 million tonnes with an estimated value of $23 billion.[936] The control of IUU activities rests with the country where the vessel is registered, but many countries are unwilling or unable to control their vessels. In recognition of the problem, some of the onus has been shifted to port states to take a stronger stance by denying access or services to IUU vessels. In 2004, the FAO recommended a voluntary agreement among port states to deny access, and in 2009 a legally binding agreement was adopted—the Agreement on Port State Measures to Prevent, Deter and Eliminate Illegal, Unreported and Unregulated Fishing—but it has not yet received the twenty-five required signatures to come into force.[937] Unfortunately, unless this agreement is universally adopted and enforced, IUU vessels will seek out lax ports to avoid detection. A related problem is the lack of unique fishing vessel identifiers, which makes it easy to rename a vessel to avoid detection. A recent study found that some IUU vessels had changed their names up to nine times and their flags of registry up to seven times.[938] However, as of 2013 fishing vessels are required to carry an identification number. The effectiveness of such requirement depends on enforcement.

Most countries are aware of the commercial value of fisheries, and most pay lip service to sustainable management of their fisheries. But it is obvious from the declining catch statistics that few countries have done it well. For example, the European Union, which has the second-largest fleet in the world, until recently lacked a credible fisheries policy.[939] Overfishing was endemic, encouraged by subsidies. The EU Fisheries Fund allocated 4.3 billion euros between 2007 and 2013 for the modernization of fleets as well as for aquaculture and sustainable fisheries practices. But as a result of the subsidies, the fleet is twice as large as is necessary for the available catches, which in any case are too large to be sustainable. A large subsidized fishing fleet leads to political pressures for quotas, large enough to keep the boats employed. Before determining Total Allowable Catches (TACs) for each species, the European Commission seeks information from fisheries scientists on sustainable catches. For political reasons, the Commission consistently set the TACs higher than those proposed by the scientists, with the result that the agreed catches could be as much as 50 percent higher than those initially recommended. The actual catches were higher still because national quotas were not properly enforced by certain member countries' reluctance to upset their own fishers, who were able to exert significant political pressure as they often lived in economically backward areas.[940]

The policy also encouraged waste, and it is believed that almost two-thirds of fish caught in some areas were discarded, usually dead, because if a fleet exceeded its quota, or caught fish species not part of the quota, the excess was thrown overboard. Cheating on quotas was rampant, making it nearly impossible to determine actual annual catches, but it was estimated that 88 percent of the EU stock was overfished. Because of declining stocks, EU fishing fleets are going farther afield to fish—for example, off the coast of Africa—with disastrous consequences for local fishing in the areas affected. Recognizing the failure to control catches, a process was launched to overhaul the EU fisheries policy. A green paper was published in 2009 identifying the main causes of the failure, including fleet overcapacity, decision-making favouring short-term rather than long-term considerations, lack of industry compliance, and lack of political will to enforce the policy.[941] This was followed by a proposal for a new fisheries policy in 2011 that called for ecosystem management of fisheries, gradual banning of discards—vessels would be obliged to bring all fish caught to port, and any extra fish caught would be deducted from their quotas—and a system of transferable fishing concessions would be implemented for vessels larger than twelve metres. The proposal also included special protection for coastal fisheries.[942] In 2013, the European Parliament passed the new policy, including the gradual banning of discards, transferrable quotas, and the phasing out of subsidies—but it was lacking a prohibition of bottom trawling.[943] The policy came into effect in January 2014 and should be an improvement provided member countries are prepared to enforce the new rules. Unfortunately, even under the new supposedly improved policy, many of the fishing quotas for 2015 exceeded the quotas recommended by scientists.[944]

The key to devising an efficient fishing policy is to combine science and economics. Fisheries biologists, using the best scientific evidence, should determine the largest possible catch size of a particular fish population that would allow the species to exist in perpetuity—the maximum sustainable yield—and then determine the TAC to be allocated among countries, fishing organizations, or fishers. Because one fish population cannot be treated in isolation from others, this is far more complex than it sounds. A sophisticated approach requires taking the whole ecosystem into account as the fishing of one species can unbalance the ecosystem with unpredictable consequences on other species. For example, the hunting of big sharks off the coast of the United States led to a large increase in their prey (skate and ray), which in turn fed on shellfish such as scallops and oysters, whose populations were thereby thrown into decline. Instead, any fish-stock decision must take into account the impact of TACs on non-target as well as target species and the impact on the ocean floor as well as on the whole ecosystem. These principles are known as ecosystem-based management.

The other leg of an efficient policy is to create property rights. It is a well-known dictum in economics that resource efficiency depends almost totally on property rights—rights that are secure, that last, that give exclusive use over the property in question, and that are tradable. Property rights in fisheries (the right to catch) can be allocated to individuals through the use of Individual Trans-ferrable Quotas (ITQS), or to fisheries cooperatives, or to certain areas through Territorial Use Rights Fisheries (TURFS).[945] Even if countries set sustainable quotas, unless these are allocated to individual fishers or cooperatives, there is an immediate incentive for licensed fishing boats to rush to catch as much as they can before the total quota is filled. This often leads to poor stewardship of the fishing resource and incentives to lobby for even larger quotas, resulting in diminished stocks and final collapse. A better policy would be to allocate rights in the form of catch shares directly to individuals or cooperatives (or communities), which would provide fishers with a secure asset and therefore an interest in maintaining it. A study of 11,135 fisheries across the world showed that the 121 fisheries with catch shares experienced 50 percent fewer collapses between 1950 and 2003.[946] Bycatches of non-target species, unwanted species, and young, less valuable fish have also been shown to decrease under catch shares because fish harvesters take a more careful approach to fishing if they do not have to rush.[947] The quality of fish is better, with less strain on processing facilities as not all produce has to be processed in a short period. For much the same reasons, catch shares make it possible to bring more fresh fish, as opposed to frozen fish, to the market.

Iceland provides a rare example of a country with a good fisheries policy.[948] Each fishing boat is allocated a transferable quota for each species of fish based on a three-year average catch, with boats allowed to carry forward 20 percent of a quota to the next year, while 5 percent of next year's quota can be claimed in advance. A fisher is also free to buy and sell quotas as he or she sees fit. Bycatches must be counted as part of a quota and cannot be discarded. Information on quotas, catches, and landings is freely available on the Internet for everyone to see, which means fishers can make rational decisions on how to maximize profits. Apart from the protection of spawning grounds, no fishing grounds within the two-hundred-mile limit are restricted. No bottom trawlers are allowed within a twelve-mile limit, and fisheries officials can order immediate closure of some areas if they judge them to be overfished. However, the system is not universally popular in Iceland. It appears to have favoured large companies that have been able to expand by buying quotas to the detriment of fish harvesters in small communities. Other jurisdictions that manage their fisheries well include New Zealand, Namibia, and the state of Alaska. In all these jurisdictions, fishing provides a significant contribution to the GDP.

Catch shares, however, do not solve the problem of fluctuating market conditions and varying conditions of fishing grounds. In some cases, less fishing effort and larger profits could be achieved if fishing were to take place in one particular area or at one specific time. A better approach would be to allocate catches to cooperatives, which would then negotiate among themselves the best way to handle the allocations.[949] One example is the Chignik salmon fishery in Alaska, which applied to the Alaska Board of Fisheries to allocate a portion of the allowable catch to a cooperative run by seventy-seven permit holders. The cooperative agreed on an equal split of the revenue from fishing, and it decided who should do the actual fishing and when and where the fishing should take place. The fishing was left to the most efficient permit holders, and the others contributed to the cooperative in different ways. This allowed them to pool the knowledge of the fish and fishing grounds and to maximize profits for the group as a whole by reducing costs and improving catches. The cooperative was very successful but had to cease operations after two years because of a court case brought by a non-member to the Supreme Court of Alaska. It ruled that in order to have a fishing permit, you must fish—you cannot leave the fishing to someone else, a tactic to which the cooperative owed part of its success. Examples of successful cooperatives can be found in New Zealand, Canada, and other parts of the United States.

Another approach is rights allocation of specific areas to groups or individuals for management through TURFS. Chile and Japan are examples of jurisdictions where these have been successfully implemented. The advantage over ITQs is that they explicitly recognize the problems of interspecies connections (fishing of one type of fish may directly impact catches of another fish), and they can provide good venues for coordinating the spatial and temporal uses of fisheries resources.

However, the principle of rights-based management is applied relatively rarely, covering only 5 percent of world fisheries and 25 percent of world catches. Many fishers are by nature conservative, disliking changes in policies that affect them unless they see an immediate benefit. As well, agreement on a fair initial allocation of quotas or rights can be difficult.

A major problem in achieving sustainable fisheries lies in the management of deep-sea fisheries that for the most part lie outside the jurisdiction of individual countries—indeed, 60 percent of oceans lie outside EEZs. The 1995 Straddling Fish Stocks and Highly Migratory Fish Stocks Agreement—part of the UN Convention on the Law of the Sea—was created to remedy the situation.[950] According to the convention, states or regional fisheries-management organizations must cooperate to ensure effective conservation and management of straddling fish stocks and highly migratory fish stocks. As a result, most of the oceans are covered by one or more regional agreements (twenty in total). Examples include the Northwest Atlantic Fisheries Organization (NAFO) in control of most fisheries resources in the Northwest Atlantic with the exception of salmon, tuna, marlins, and whales. These are under the jurisdiction of other regional organizations such as the ICCAT.[951] Are these agreements effective? We already know about the less than stellar record of ICCAT (page 351), and according to a comprehensive study of their effectiveness in controlling fish stocks, they are not.[952]

In order to prevent fish stocks from collapsing, it is obvious that catches have to be managed based on the best scientific data, but the regulation of fisheries has to be combined with a sensible tax and subsidy policy. A good argument can be made for subsidies for research and development of fisheries ecology, ocean ecology, monitoring of fish stocks, enforcement of quota regulations, and establishment of marine protection areas. These are all beneficial activities that do not usually occur without subsidies. However, most subsidies are not of this type; instead, they encourage excessive investment in fishing effort. Most analysts agree that the global fishing industry suffers from overcapacity—too many boats are chasing too few fish. In 2003, subsidies accounted for $25 to $29 billion worldwide, 60 percent of which were capacity enhancing rather than beneficial.[953] The most common subsidy is for fuel, accounting for 15 to 30 percent of the total. Fuel subsidies encourage environmentally harmful practices such as bottom trawling, which is energy intensive Examples of capacity-enhancing subsidies are those for boat and port construction and for price and marketing support. These practices increase profits by either increasing revenue or decreasing costs. In doing so, they create incentives to expand the fishing industry by increasing effort and increasing the number of people engaged in fishing. Sixty-eight percent of the total subsidies are given by governments of developed countries. One-third of the European Union's fisheries budget is spent on buying access to non-European fisheries—for example, in West Africa, mainly for the benefit of Spanish, Portuguese, and French fishing vessels. Many of the recipient countries use these subsidies neither for the development of their own fishing nor for conservation purposes. In many cases, they do not impose fishing quotas, and if they do, they are not enforced. Thus these access payments contribute to overfishing.

Many countries pay fish harvesters to stop fishing temporarily if the stocks are low. Payment may also go to the communities dependent on fishing. From a social standpoint this may be a good idea, but from a fisheries point of view it is not, as it keeps fishermen and communities tied to fishing in cases where they should get out of it. It is also common policy for governments to try to reduce capacity by buying back fishing permits or licenses. This may backfire if the buyout is anticipated and fishers try to fish as much as they can before the buyout, depleting stocks unnecessarily. Vessels may also be transferred to another part of the world, in which case the buyout may not decrease overfishing.[954]

Aquaculture

With wild fish stocks in decline, farmed fish is rapidly taking the place of wild fish. Aquaculture is the fastest-growing food sector in the world and a major source of employment in developing countries. It grew at an annual rate of 6 percent between 2000 and 2012 and now accounts for 42 percent of total fish production.[955] Sixty-three percent of fish farming is done in fresh water, mainly involving carp. The Asia Pacific region as a whole is dominant in aquaculture, producing 98 percent of carp, 95 percent of oyster, and 88 percent of shrimp and prawns. China alone produces 77 percent of all carp and 82 percent of all oysters.[956] Chinese carp rearing dates back several thousand years, but it did not spread to Europe until the Middle Ages, probably appearing in France in the eleventh to twelfth centuries.

However, most people in North America and Europe associate aquaculture with industrial salmon farming, which was first developed by the Norwegians in the 1960s. Salmon is uniquely suited for aquaculture as the eggs are quite large, and the newly hatched fish are able to live on other coarsely chopped fish from an early stage in their lives. Most other wild fish have tiny eggs with the hatchlings requiring minute bits of food, difficult to replicate in a controlled environment. The Norwegians experimented with many different types of salmon, and within a period of fourteen years of selective breeding were able to double the growth rate.[957] Salmon farming spread to other parts of Europe, North America, and Chile—a country where previously salmon did not occur in the wild. The farmed salmon market is now three times as large as its wild salmon counterpart. While wild salmon was and is an expensive delicacy, farmed salmon is not.

However, this large expansion of farmed fish has created problems. In the same way that agriculture has environmental repercussions, so does fish farming. Many of the problems are associated with salmon farming; one is the potential impact of domestic salmon on the wild salmon population. Some scientists now treat farmed salmon as a different species (*Salmo domesticus*) that can outcompete wild salmon when the former escape into the wild. But the survival of farmed salmon may not be assured as they are neither bred to hunt for their food nor to survive in a harsh environment with predators and strong currents. A second problem is that many farms are not environmentally benign. If water circulation is poor, nitrogen levels from feces and uneaten food increase, leading to algae blooming and less oxygen in the water. Crowded cages also lead to the spread of parasites (sea lice) and diseases that could contaminate the remaining wild salmon. A third concern is that salmon farming is not an efficient use of protein and has repercussions on other fisheries. Initially, the first farmed salmon required six kilograms of small fish for feed to create one kilo of salmon. The ratio is now down to three to one, but in the view of some, using wild fish as feed for aquaculture is a waste of scarce fisheries resources.

It is better to consume the small fish directly than to waste a large volume producing the bigger salmon. One-fifth of the world's total annual fish catch is now made up of small fish such as anchovies and sardines, many of which are made into fish meal.

Shrimp farming also has a well-earned reputation for being environmentally destructive. It often involves the conversion of ecologically important mangrove forests and other lands into ponds, with adverse effects on ecosystem services such as flood control, the maintenance of fish habitats, and biodiversity. Shrimp farming is known to have destroyed large tracts of mangrove forests in Thailand, Indonesia, Ecuador, and Madagascar; it also increases water pollution because of excessive feeding. When they are young, shrimp can feed on natural organisms in the water, but they need additional feed to grow large. If they are overfed, as is often the case, rotting organic material will adversely affect water quality and lead to eutrophication of coastal areas. Measures can be taken to minimize these effects by more careful siting of shrimp ponds and changes in the methods of administering feed.

While a large variety of fish is now farmed—including cod, sea bass, sturgeon, seahorses, halibut, and tilapia—not all fish can be farmed in captivity. Eels, grouper, and bluefin tuna have to be reared after having been caught in the wild, which is not helpful in conserving the species. Tuna ranching, which has been in existence for a decade, involves catching young tuna and rearing them in pens. But young tuna do not like being confined and have been known to throw themselves against the cages and break their necks.[958] In captivity, it is almost impossible to replicate their natural breeding cycle, where they swim for huge distances before spawning. An Australian company appears to have had some success in getting tuna to spawn in captivity, involving the use of harpoons to shoot hormones into the captive tuna. Even if this technique proves successful, aquaculture of tuna faces costly barriers as these fish require an enormous amount of food: twenty kilos of fish for each kilo of tuna raised.[959]

Some argue that only aquaculture will save wild fish in the oceans. But this is unlikely if aquaculture depends on wild fish for feed, as exemplified by salmon farming. Clearly, aquaculture involving carp and tilapia is preferable, since these fish feed on only vegetable matter, and the farming of shellfish such as mussels and oysters, which filter water, is better from an environmental viewpoint. Another fish that shows potential is the barramundi, native to Australia. Barramundi spawn throughout the year in salt water, live mainly on vegetable matter, and grow in freshwater ponds.[960]

Toward better management of the oceans

How can the oceans be saved? Given the increased pressures on the marine environment from risky exploitation of oil, gas, and mineral resources on the continental shelf and in the deep oceans, and given the sorry state of the world fisheries, the answer has to be that they can be saved only with great difficulty. Apart from dealing with climate change, saving the oceans is the greatest challenge we face. The challenge is to achieve an integration of fisheries, oceans, and energy policies into a cohesive whole, striking an appropriate balance between the need for resources and the need to maintain biodiversity in the oceans and on land. For areas within the jurisdiction of individual countries, this could be achieved by whole-scale zoning, where a whole area such as the North Sea would be divided into zones, and each zone would be allocated a specific function such as mining, oil and gas extraction, fishing, recreational activities, or areas where no commercial activities are allowed. This would have the advantage of separating incompatible activities.

Establishment of more marine protected areas (MPAs) is critically important for the ocean environment. The Convention on Biodiversity recommended that a target of 10 percent of all ocean areas be set aside by 2012. This target was not reached, even though the number of areas is increasing rapidly.[961] . Currently, there are 12,076 MPAs encompassing 3.4 percent of the world's oceans, with the majority on the continental shelf within the jurisdiction of one country (8.4 percent of this area is protected), with little protection for the high seas (0.25 percent protected).[962] In particular, there is little protection of the deep seabed that is part of a complex system which regulates the world's climates.[963] For example, the oceans sequester carbon by transporting organic materials (carbon and other nutrients) from the surface and from the atmosphere to the bottom of the ocean where they will be buried in sediments. Microbes on the ocean floors consume methane—another greenhouse gas, and many fish populations straddle coastal areas and the deep seas. Many protected areas are neither ecologically representative nor well managed, and many allow commercial fishing.[964] It is obviously far more difficult to come to agreements on protected areas in the deep oceans as they are mostly beyond the jurisdiction of individual countries. Currently, regional fisheries organizations can and do order fishing closures in their areas of jurisdiction, but the evidence at hand is that they are not very effective. Other organizations that can play a role are the International Maritime Organization, which can designate special areas and particularly sensitive areas for special protection from pollution; The International Whaling Commission, which can delineate whale sanctuaries and which the Japanese refuse to recognize in continuing to hunt in the Southern Whale Sanctuary; and the International Seabed Authority, which requires an environmental assessment before issuing permits for exploration.[965] Whether these organizations can prevent further deterioration of the high seas is open to debate.

While developed countries have made strides in reforming their fisheries policies, urgent measures are needed in developing countries. Seventy percent of the fish consumed in the EU and North America are caught in the EEZ zones of West and East Africa and the island nations in the Pacific.[966] Saving these fisheries requires an immediate cut in catches, the establishment of more truly protected areas, and the protection of small forage fish that are currently caught for aquaculture feed. The disappearance of forage fish would have serious repercussions for the entire ocean food chain. These measures could be achieved not only by the introduction of rights-based fishing regulations, which are proven to be more sustainable than other types of regulations, but also by elimination of subsidies and making changes to fishing equipment to make sure only targeted species are caught. One study shows that the elimination of fuel subsidies alone would likely lead to the elimination of bottom trawling.[967] More emphasis should be placed on small-scale fishing, which appears to be more benign to the environment because bycatches are smaller and the technologies used are less destructive.[968] In addition, small-scale fishing is a large source of employment in developing countries, and it can be supported by making microcredit available and by allocating catch shares to fishing cooperatives. Sustainable fishing also requires stricter controls of illegal fishing by ratifying and implementing the 2009 Agreement on Port State Measures to Prevent, Deter and Eliminate IUU Fishing as well as implementing measures to ensure that no incentives exist to reregister vessels under another flag to avoid detection.

Can anything be accomplished on the consumer side? Can consumer boycotts assist in saving the fisheries in the same way as consumers and NGOs had a positive impact on forest conservation? Changes in consumer behaviour are difficult to achieve unless consumers are informed about what they are buying and can be persuaded to change. In 2005, FAO adopted the Guidelines for the Ecolabelling of Fish and Fisheries Products from Marine Capture Fisheries. Under these guidelines, the fish must come from fisheries that are managed to ensure sustainability of target species and of ecosystems. The management must use transparent processes that include consultation with all concerned, and the fisheries must be assessed using scientific evidence by third parties.[969] Inspired by the Forest Stewardship Council, the Marine Stewardship Council was formed in 1997 by the World Wide Fund for Nature and Unilever, and it has operated independently since 1999. The standards are consistent with FAO guidelines for sustainable fisheries. Any fishery that wishes to become MSC certified and use the ecolabel is assessed against MSC standards by a third party. At the end of 2014, there were 252 certified fisheries representing 9 percent of total global capture and another 100 under assessment.[970] However, the MSC has come under criticism for being too lax, for not including bottom trawling, and for having little success in reaching out to fisheries in developing countries.[971]

The first charge that the MSC is too lax is based on a few controversial cases. For example, certification for the Alaskan pollock fishery was renewed despite the fact that recent catches had decreased by 64 percent. A fishery involving Antarctic krill was also certified, despite scientific evidence of long-term decline in the krill population due to climate change. The second charge is that the certification process pays little attention to the methods of fishing—for example, bottom trawling—despite its serious adverse environmental effects. Last, it is argued that certification favours the big, capital-intensive fisheries as only they have the funds to pursue the certification process, and little attention is paid to the plight of small fisheries in developing countries. To become certified, a fishery has to pay a private consultant $15,000 to $150,000 to perform the assessment as well as incur a continuing expense for annual audits of $75,000. Given the benefits of supporting small-scale fisheries, it is a problem that perhaps could be addressed by encouraging fisheries cooperatives to apply for certification.

11

Conclusion: The Earth in the Balance

*The human population explosion. The Anthropocene. The Gaia
hypothesis and the Medea hypothesis. Darwin and Wallace.
Cooperation and the power of ideas. The relentless pursuit of
economic growth. The challenges. The problem of designing
appropriate international institutions. What must be done.*

THIS BOOK has surveyed the state of the world's resources category by
category, beginning with non-renewable resources such as metals, minerals, and fossil fuels, and concluding with renewable resources such as soils,
biodiversity, water, forests, and fish. Even though considerable progress has
been made in forestry and biodiversity conservation, it is evident that the
most serious problems lie in the state of renewable resources, most of which
are in crisis because of overexploitation or habitat destruction, problems that
will be exacerbated by climate change. Renewable resources cannot always be
renewed: if a resource is exploited beyond its replacement level, the resource
can collapse, sometimes rapidly. Examples are the demise of the passenger
pigeon and the disappearance of the Grand Banks fisheries. In addition,
causes for great concern are the gradual erosion of the health of watersheds,
soils, and oceans and the general weakening of the earth's life-support systems
because of the buildup of greenhouse gases, acidification of the oceans, and
our nitrogen use. Each of these is of great concern, and together they may

Figure 11.1. Earthrise captured by Apollo 8 crew member Bill Anders, December 24, 1968. Credit: NASA and Wikimedia Commons.

threaten our long-term survival as a species. In the last two hundred years, we have done more damage to the earth's ecosystems than was done in the previous seventy thousand years. According to a group of scientists, we have now probably exceeded the limits, called the tipping points, of three out of nine critical indicators (planetary boundaries): carbon dioxide in the atmosphere, biodiversity loss, and our meddling with the nitrogen cycle through our excessive use of nitrogen and phosphorus.[972]

This final chapter focuses on how the current situation of unsustainable resource use arose, emphasizing the role of explosive population growth, and the implications of humans transforming earth into a totally human-dominated planet—the Anthropocene. The chapter examines whether there is a mechanism guaranteeing that earth will heal itself—and if not, what can be done to avert a catastrophe. It emphasizes the need to make resource use sustainable while at the same time allowing poor countries to increase their use of resources.

The human population explosion

The fundamental reason for the sorry state of renewable resources is the increase in our numbers. Figure 11.2 shows the remarkable explosion of the human population over a relatively short period of time, reminiscent of the explosion of some insect populations such as fruit flies in a confined environment.

Populations increase if birth rates are higher than death rates. According to Malthus, human populations increase at a geometric rate while food production can increase only at an arithmetic rate; therefore, the fate of humans is to exist on a bare minimum. If agricultural production increases because of the opening up of new lands, increased food production will improve living standards, death rates will decrease, and population will expand. In the absence of any further increases in food production, living standards will again revert to the same low subsistence level. Gregory Clark, in his book *A Farewell to Alms: A Brief Economic History of the World*, shows convincingly that Malthus was right—the average person was no better off in 1800 than in the neolithic age.[973] However, Malthus was also wrong in that he could not foresee the increases in

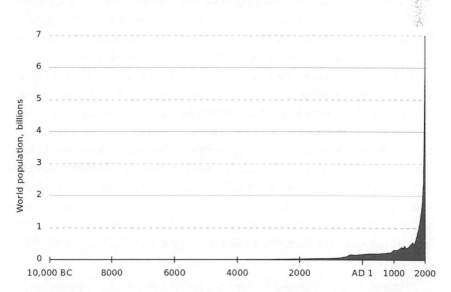

Figure 11.2. World human population (est.) 10,000 BC–2000 AD. Source: Wikimedia Commons.

food production made possible by improved agricultural technologies. Innovations in agriculture, such as the introduction of improved plows and a three-crop rotation system in Europe during the fourteenth century, led to a gradual increase in world population. The Industrial Revolution, with its reliance on science and technology, led to advances in hygiene and the treatment of diseases that in turn led to declining death rates in Europe and North America and rapidly expanding populations. Unprecedented technological progress resulted in growing incomes that could support a large population. In particular, the invention of artificial nitrogen fertilizer and the mechanization of agriculture made it possible to feed billions. At the beginning of the nineteenth century, the world population had increased to approximately one billion. By the end of 2014—two hundred years later—it exceeded seven billion. We have become the most dominant species on earth in terms of our effect on the environment.

However, world population growth is now slowing because of decreases in birth rates and fertility rates in developing countries.* The lowering of fertility rates started in industrialized countries in the late eighteenth century and continued into the early twentieth century.[974] Before this change—referred to as the *demographic transition*—the expected number of births for a married woman was eight or more over her lifetime, a figure which has now dropped to between one and two children. For example, the estimated 2013 fertility rate in Taiwan was 1.11, Germany 1.42, Japan 1.39, the United States 1.9, and Poland 1.30.[975] In developed countries, a fertility rate of less than 2.1 will lead to population declines in the absence of immigration, while in developing countries, the replacement fertility rate is higher because of higher mortality rates.

This transition to lower birth rates has started in developing countries. Table 11.1 shows that in some cases the transition has been quite remarkable. Particularly noteworthy is Iran, where the fertility rate declined from 6.5 to 1.9 in the last thirty-two years—a 71 percent reduction, and other countries in Asia (e.g., Bangladesh and Saudi Arabia) also experienced impressive decreases. In the early years of the new millennium, the United Nations optimistically projected a levelling of the world population at nine billion by 2050 because of rapidly declining fertility rates. But according to revised estimates released by the United Nations in 2012, the situation is not as hopeful. The median projection is that the world population will reach 9.6 billion by 2050 and 10.9 billion by 2100.[976] By

---

* The birth rate is the number of births per 1,000 of the population, while the fertility rate is the average number of births per woman over a lifetime. The fertility rate is thought to be a better indicator because it is not affected by the age distribution of the population.

the end of this century, populations in low- and average-fertility countries will decline while populations in today's high-fertility countries—countries where on average each woman has 4.9 children—will increase. Despite a projected decrease in the median fertility rate in high-fertility countries from 4.9 in 2005 to 2.8 in 2050 and 2.1 (replacement level) in 2100, there is no levelling of world population or subsequent decline before the end of the century. The United Nations changed its projections because the fertility rates in Africa were not falling as fast as previously projected, and most of the high-fertility countries are in Africa, as indicated in Table 11.2. Other high-fertility countries include Pakistan and Afghanistan. The fastest population growths are in sub-Saharan Africa, where the current population is slightly larger than Europe's, and by 2100 it is expected to be three times that of Europe.

Population projections are very sensitive to assumptions about future fertility rates. If the future world fertility rate is half a child more than the projected median fertility rate of 2.8, world population would reach 10.9 billion in 2050 and an astonishing 16.6 billion in 2100. On the other hand, if the future fertility rate is half a child less than the median, the figures would be 8.3 billion in 2050 and 6.8 billion in 2100.[977] It is therefore clear that the future of our planet depends on achieving lower fertility rates. The decision a woman and her partner makes about the number of children she will bear depends on a combination of factors. Research by economic historians and demographers on the reasons for the early fertility declines in Europe and North America has not been able to pinpoint one single cause, but many working together.[978] For example, if a family desires three children, but half of the children are not expected to survive childhood, the desired number of births will be six. Therefore, if infant mortality rates decline because of better medicine, hygiene, and nutrition, the number of children born should decline. Decreased infant and child mortality rates had some impact on declining fertility rates in Europe and North America, but in some countries the fertility rates started to decline long before improvements in mortality rates. Evidence shows that total childbirths declined by one-third between the fourteenth and the eighteenth centuries. One explanation for this decline is that the population decline following the Black Death favoured animal husbandry, as caring for animals did not require as much labour as traditional agriculture and could be done by women. This improvement in women's employability led to later marriages and therefore fewer children.[979]

Many studies of the modern era have also confirmed that better opportunities for women affect fertility rates because such opportunities influence a woman's

Table 11.1. Total fertility rates in high-fertility countries in 1980 and 2012

Country	TFR (1980)	TFR (2012)	Percentage decline in TFR 1980–2012
Iran	6.5	1.9	71
Maldives	7.1	2.3	68
Libya*	7.4	2.4	68
Oman	8.3	2.9	65
Bangladesh	6.4	2.2	65
Bhutan	6.6	2.3	65
Cape Verde	6.4	2.3	64
Saudi Arabia	7.2	2.7	63
Mongolia	6.2	2.4	61
Algeria*	6.9	2.8	59
Nicaragua	6.1	2.5	59
Syrian Arab Republic	7.1	3.0	58
Guatemala	6.2	3.8	58
Botswana*	6.2	2.7	56
Jordan	7.2	3.3	54
Yemen, Rep.	9.0	4.2	53
Namibia*	6.5	3.1	52
Lao PDR	6.3	3.1	51
Honduras	6.5	3.1	51
Zimbabwe*	7.1	3.6	49
Swaziland*	6.7	3.4	49
Pakistan	6.5	3.3	49
Haiti	6.3	3.2	49
Djibouti*	6.7	3.5	48
Micronesia	6.2	3.3	47
Rwanda*	8.3	4.6	45
Ghana*	6.5	3.9	40
Kenya*	7.5	4.5	40
Solomon Islands	6.7	4.1	39
Iraq	6.6	4.1	38
Côte d'Ivoire*	7.6	4.9	36
São Tomé and Príncipe*	6.4	4.1	36
Togo*	7.2	4.7	35
Afghanistan	7.7	5.1	34

*Indicates country is in Africa.

Table 11.1, continued

Country	TFR (1980)	TFR (2012)	Percentage decline in TFR 1980–2012
Central African Republic*	6.0	4.5	33
Ethiopia*	6.8	4.6	32
Senegal*	7.4	5.0	32
Comoros*	7.1	4.8	32
Madagascar*	6.5	4.5	31
Liberia*	7.0	4.9	30
Benin*	7.0	4.9	30
Guinea*	6.9	5.0	28
Mauritania*	6.4	4.7	27
Eritrea*	6.5	4.8	26
Malawi*	7.4	5.5	26
Congo, Dem. Rep.*	6.6	5.0	24
Sudan*	6.4	5.0	23
Cameroon*	6.4	4.9	23
Guinea-Bissau*	6.3	5.0	21
Tanzania*	6.7	5.3	21
Zambia*	7.2	5.7	21
Burkina Faso*	7.1	5.7	20
Mozambique*	6.5	5.3	18
Angola*	7.2	6.0	17
Uganda*	7.1	6.0	15
Nigeria*	6.8	6.0	12
Burundi*	6.7	6.1	9
Gambia*	6.3	5.8	8
Chad*	6.8	6.4	6
Congo, Dem. Rep.*	6.2	6.0	3
Mali*	7.0	6.9	1
Niger*	7.7	7.6	1
Somalia*	6.8	6.7	1

Note: The total fertility rate (TFR) is the average number of children born to women over a lifetime. The list contains countries with total fertility rates of 6.0 or higher in 1980. Source: World Development Indicators. http://data.worldbank.org/indicator/SP.DYN.TFRT.IN.

decision to have children. If a woman has to forego good wages by leaving the labour force to have a family, she is less likely to stay home and raise children. Other factors that have been shown to have an impact are housing costs—a woman is more likely to want to limit the size of her family if housing costs are high—and regulations such as stringent child labour laws and compulsory education policies, which prevent children from contributing to household income and therefore make them less desirable. Government policies to limit the size of families can also have an effect on fertility rates if the policies are enforced. One example is China's coercive one-child policy, introduced in 1979, and which was effective. However, these types of policies can have undesirable side effects. The desire for a male child led to female infanticide, leaving a socially disruptive legacy of many Chinese men unable to find women to marry.

Another factor influencing fertility is the availability and knowledge of methods of contraception. Of course, the ability to limit one's family did not originate with modern contraceptives. Traditional methods included infanticide, abortion, abstinence, withdrawal, and plants known for their contraceptive properties. These practices were often suppressed if it was deemed to be in a country's interest to have a larger population. Both the United States and many European countries forbade the spreading of contraceptive knowledge and technologies during the nineteenth century. However, three surveys of women in Europe and North America at the time show that families did indeed practice birth control, with the two main methods of limiting the number of children being withdrawal and abstinence.[980] Condoms were introduced in 1855 after the invention of vulcanized rubber but were very expensive. Recently, funding for contraceptive information and distribution in developing countries by Western aid organizations has declined as a proportion of total funding, partly because they were thought not to be very effective. Instead, it was argued that policies to promote the education of women and income growth were more likely to lead to lower population growth. Nevertheless, recent studies have shown that family planning policies, where available, have been critically important in influencing women's health and the country's fertility rate.[981] They should be an integral part of development policies.[982]

The situation in sub-Saharan Africa, particularly serious because of the challenge of feeding the rapidly growing population, will require substantial investments in the agricultural sector. For example, the Democratic Republic of the Congo, which was used as an example of the resource curse in Chapter 1, has seen only a 3 percent decline in fertility rates since 1980. The Congo is fabulously wealthy in terms of natural resources, but its ability to use these resources for

Table 11.2. Countries with total fertility rates > 3.2 in 2012 and their population in 2013

Country	TFR (2012)	Population (2013) (millions)	Country	TFR (2012)	Population (2013) (millions)
Niger*	7.6	17.8	Eritrea*	4.8	6.3
Mali*	6.9	15.3	Mauritania*	4.7	3.9
Somalia*	6.7	10.5	Togo*	4.7	6.8
Chad*	6.4	12.8	Rwanda*	4.6	11.8
Burundi*	6.1	10.2	Ethiopia*	4.6	94.1
Uganda*	6.0	37.6	Kenya*	4.5	44.4
Congo, Dem. Rep.*	6.0	67.5	Madagascar*	4.5	22.9
Nigeria*	6.0	173.6	Central African Republic*	4.5	4.6
Angola*	6.0	21.5	Sudan*	4.5	38.0
Gambia*	5.8	1.8	Yemen, Rep.	4.2	24.4
Zambia*	5.7	14.5	Samoa	4.2	0.2
Burkina Faso*	5.7	16.8	Iraq	4.1	33.4
Malawi*	5.5	16.4	Solomon Islands	4.1	0.6
Timor-Leste	5.3	1.2	São Tomé and Príncipe*	4.1	0.2
Tanzania*	5.3	49.3			
Mozambique*	5.3	25.8	Gabon*	4.1	1.7
Afghanistan	5.1	30.6	Ghana*	3.9	25.9
Guinea*	5.0	11.7	Guatemala	3.8	15.5
Guinea-Bissau*	5.0	1.7	Papua New Guinea	3.8	7.3
Senegal*	5.0	14.1			
Congo, Rep.*	5.0	4.4	Tajikstan	3.8	8.2
South Sudan*	5.0	11.3	Tonga	3.8	0.1
Benin*	4.9	10.3	Djibouti*	3.5	0.9
Equatorial Guinea*	4.9	0.8	Vanuatu	3.4	0.3
			Swaziland*	3.4	1.2
Cameroon*	4.9	22.3	Jordan	3.3	6.5
Côte d'Ivoire*	4.9	20.3	Micronesia	3.3	0.1
Liberia*	4.9	4.3	Pakistan	3.3	182.1
Sierra Leone*	4.8	6.1	Bolivia	3.3	10.7
Comoros*	4.8	0.7	Haiti	3.2	10.3

Source: World Development Indicators. http://data.worldbank.org/indicator/SP.DYN.TFRT.IN.

its own benefit has been hampered by several wars, civil unrest, and the breakdown of government.[983] Before independence in 1960, some inroads were made in establishing a social welfare system, but this has since fallen apart, leaving individuals, families, and non-government organizations trying to fill the void. The social safety net, if any, depends on extended family, church, and neighbourhood organizations. Kinship is highly valued in traditional African societies, with pressure on couples to have as many children as possible to enhance the power of the family and guarantee the survival of the lineage. A combination of high fertility rates and improved health has resulted in decreased mortality rates; for this reason, the population is expected to increase from 68 million in 2013 to 148 million in 2050. According to a 2001 survey, only 4 percent of the population used modern contraceptives and 27 percent used traditional methods of birth control, figures that have since declined.[984] The introduction of bottle feeding of infants as well as pressure to decrease the traditional period of abstinence after childbirth may also serve to keep birth rates high. With society in disarray, low levels of education, few opportunities for women, and the population desperately poor, conditions do not encourage women and families to have fewer children.

In the last fifty years, world population has doubled, our consumption of food and fresh water has tripled, and our consumption of fossil fuels has quadrupled with predictable effects on the environment. A recent study by John Dearing at the University of Southampton and his colleagues highlights the link between rapid economic growth, population increases, and the impact on ecosystem services.[985] The study used cores of lake sediments taken from the lower Yangtze basin to reconstruct records of soil erosion, sediment regulation, and water purification for the years 1800–2006 and correlated these records with measures for economic growth and population increases. The link between population size and environmental degradation was particularly strong, with a statistically significant correlation coefficient of 0.9. The sediment cores showed the impact of the various events in China such as the great Chinese famine, Mao's "great leap forward," and agricultural intensification policies starting in the 1980s. While the agricultural intensification policies reduced poverty significantly, they led to an accelerated deterioration of ecosystem services.

There is no part of the world where humans have not left a footprint. While we changed ecosystems in ancient times by hunting to extinction the large animals of the Americas, Australia, and Siberia, we have now changed the earth's atmosphere. Can the earth support a population of close to ten billion people in 2050? Do we have the resources? Can we return to a pure and pristine earth?

Clearly, the answer to the last question is no. Such a place has not existed for millennia, and any attempt to achieve a utopia devoid of human interference is futile. The next section of this chapter will discuss the idea that we have entered a new era, totally dominated by humans—the Anthropocene. Humans are at the point of no return, and we must confront a harsh reality of having to live in a completely human-dominated environment—an environment we are in the process of destroying. This discussion will be followed by an examination of whether the earth can or will heal itself, the possible reasons humans came to dominate their environment, and what can be done to avoid a catastrophic future.

The Anthropocene

Planet earth is thought to be 4.6 billion years old. Geological history is divided into eons, each distinguished by the fossil content of the rocks. Fossils appeared about 540 million years ago during the Paleozoic era; next was the Mesozoic era 245 to 65 million years ago, when plants and animals appeared. The transfers between each geological time boundary are determined by the nature of the strata—the layers of sedimentary rock. The strata must be discernibly different to belong to different geological time periods, and the difference must marked by the presence of distinctive markers or signatures. We are currently in the Holocene epoch, considered to be an unusually stable part of the Quaternary period (Table 11.3) characterized by regularly occurring ice ages. The

Table 11.3. The geological ages of earth

Million years ago	Eons	Periods	Epochs
4,600–542	Precambrian		
542–252	Paleozoic		
251–66	Mesozoic		
65–present	Cenozoic		
65–23		Paleogene	
23–2.58		Neogene	
2.58–present		Quaternary	
2.58–0.0117			Pleistocene
0.0117–present			Holocene
(70–200 years ago to the present time)			(Anthropocene)

Source: Adapted from the Geological Society of America, GSA Geologic Time Scale.

Holocene started at the end of the last ice age about eleven thousand years ago and is considered to be part of an interglacial period that is likely to be followed by another glacial period. While modern humans evolved approximately two hundred thousand years ago, during the Pleistocene epoch, the Holocene coincides roughly with the rise of human civilizations. However, there is now a move afoot to recognize formally that we have entered another geological epoch, one entirely shaped by humans—the Anthropocene, in which humans are no longer bystanders but are engineers of the workings of the earth.

Paul Crutzen, joint winner of the 1995 Nobel Prize in Chemistry for his work on atmospheric ozone, was the first to argue that we are in a new epoch set apart from the rest of the Holocene for several reasons.[986] One reason is that human activity since the Industrial Revolution has had a huge impact on the earth's atmosphere and ecosystems because of deforestation and the burning of fossil fuels. Another relates to the impact of artificial nitrogen on the natural balance of the nitrogen cycle. A third reason is climate change, which will force species to migrate if they can, and if they cannot, they will adapt or die. As discussed in Chapter 6, some biologists argue that we are in the middle of the sixth major species extinction. Finally, the ecology of oceans will change because of increased acidification. From a geological viewpoint, the critical question is whether human-induced events will be translated into recognizable changes in sedimentary rocks, marking a new geological epoch.

Already, the fallout from the explosion of the first atomic bomb in 1945 has left its mark on ocean sediments. Megacities will also likely leave their marks because of erosion and sedimentation. These markers of cities could be preserved in river deltas and remain buried for millions of years. Future geologists could readily identify them as having very distinct markers because of the unusual mixtures of materials. The markers of the Anthropocene would also include the remains of fossils of organisms that humans used and adapted for their own purposes in agriculture and forestry. For example, farm animals are distinct from their wild counterparts, and the number of farmed trees now exceeds that of trees in natural forests. But more profoundly, humans have altered the way the earth works with respect to both the carbon cycle and the nitrogen cycle. As explained in Chapter 3, the burning of oil, gas, and coal has released carbon that has been stored for hundreds of millions of years, unbalancing the natural flows of carbon in and out of the atmosphere and affecting the environment in a number of ways, leaving additional markers. The changes in ocean chemistry will have a direct effect on the sediment at the bottom of the oceans, leaving another marker. The intentional interference in the nitrogen cycle led to an explosion of crop yields but also to the eutrophication of water courses and lakes, which should also show up in sediments.[987]

The International Commission on Stratigraphy, which is the scientific adjudicator of geological time scales, is considering such recognition and is expected to make its recommendations in 2016.[988]

The issue is very controversial because some geologists do not believe changes are clear enough to merit the introduction of a new epoch. There is also the question of the date. Paul Crutzen initially proposed the beginning of the Industrial Revolution, when the human imprint became more obvious. Two biologists have argued for a starting time of between 1570 and 1620, which coincides with the European colonization of the Americas, resulting in the deaths of fifty million indigenous peoples from introduced diseases. Fewer people led to massive abandonment of cultivated lands and therefore reforestation and increased sequestration of CO_2. The ice cores taken from the Antarctic show a drop in CO_2 concentrations in the atmosphere at that time—a clear human marker. However, the stratigraphy commission appears to favour 1945, the year of the first above-ground nuclear blast. Between 1945 and 1963, there were approximately five hundred nuclear explosions that left radioactive sediment markers.[989]

The Gaia hypothesis and the Medea hypothesis

Can life in the Anthropocene continue to evolve, or have we inflicted fatal damage on the earth's life-supporting systems? The Gaia hypothesis is centred on the idea that the earth is a self-regulating system that functions like a single organism—Gaia—in seeking out a physical and chemical environment optimal for maintaining the conditions necessary for our survival. In 1965, chemist James Lovelock, while researching methods for detecting life on Mars, had the idea that the presence of life on earth was conditioned by the chemical composition of the atmosphere.[990] The atmospheres of Mars and Venus consist mainly of carbon dioxide, while the earth's atmosphere has a large presence of oxygen, which makes life possible. He argued that earth is self-regulating, implying that the physical and biological systems act together to create the atmospheric conditions necessary for life. Initially, his ideas were called "the earth feedback hypothesis," explaining the stable presence of oxygen and methane in the atmosphere and the fact that the oceans over time have maintained their salinity and acidity at levels conducive to life. He later developed the hypothesis further with the help of microbiologist Lynn Margolis, who was an expert on how microorganisms contribute to the earth's atmosphere. On the suggestion of his neighbour, novelist William Golding, Lovelock named the new hypothesis after the Greek earth goddess Gaia. In 1979, his ideas culminated in his first book, *Gaia: A New Look at Life on Earth.*[991] In it, he maintains that the earth's system strives toward physical and environmental conditions optimal for life on earth and that the earth's surface can be regarded as a living entity, almost like an organism in itself. For example, despite the fact that the sun has become hotter, the earth has been able to maintain its temperature by producing occasional ice ages, creating carbon-eating oceanic algae, and weathering rocks (weathering occurs when silicate minerals react with carbon dioxide and form calcium carbonate). Life reacts to any changes in the atmosphere and temperature by changing biological growth or metabolism. For example, during the earth's warm periods, when more greenhouse gases were present, the evolving life that needed carbon dioxide to grow absorbed the gases, which reduced concentrations to a normal level. Many of Lovelock's insights have been proven, and the idea that the earth is largely self-regulating has since been accepted by many scientists. For example, it is now known that cloud formation over oceans is partially determined by the metabolism of oceanic algae, not by purely chemical and physical processes.

Lovelock, with his colleague Andrew Watson, ran a series of computer simulations called Daisyworld, trying to provide support for the Gaia hypothesis.[992] Daisyworld is a hypothetical planet in a hypothetical solar system where the sun's temperature is gradually increasing. The planet has two plants: black daisies and white daisies. The black daisies absorb sunlight and therefore heat, while the white daisies reflect it. Initially, the planet is barren, but gradually, as the sun warms it, black daisies appear, increasing the surface temperature. This makes it possible for white daisies to appear, which will eventually cause temperatures to drop. Any decrease in the sun's temperature favours the growth of black daisies, which will cause the temperature to return to the equilibrium level. If the sun's temperature increases above the equilibrium level, the white daisies will thrive until enough sunlight is reflected back into the atmosphere for the temperature to fall. Competition among the daisies ensures that the earth maintains a constant temperature, consistent with the Gaia hypothesis. Lovelock and Watson introduced further extensions and refinements of Daisyworld. Simulations that introduced more than two species showed that the larger the number of species, the more stable was the climate. The Gaia hypothesis of a living earth became highly controversial in the scientific community, raising questions about what a living organism is. Since Gaia cannot reproduce, it surely cannot be a living organism. The fact that Gaia became adopted by New Agers and environmentalists made its scientific acceptance more difficult.

Lovelock briefly joined the doomsday prophets in his predictions that the earth is beyond repair and will become largely uninhabitable. He suggested that the powerful feedback mechanisms contained in the Gaia world have become disrupted by the large increases in CO_2 in the atmosphere.[993] Warmer oceans will disrupt the carbon-eating algae, with more CO_2 entering the atmosphere. Sea ice will melt, decreasing the albedo. The warming will also kill the tropical rainforests, further increasing the amount of CO_2 in the atmosphere. However, he no longer subscribes to this view, arguing that the warming will be too modest to be catastrophic.

In contrast to the Gaia hypothesis that earth will heal itself is the Medea hypothesis, the thrust of which is that life destroys itself. Medea was the Greek goddess who killed her own children to revenge her husband Jason, who left her for another woman. The ruthless selfishness contained in the notion of the survival of the fittest leads to species destroying themselves. The hypothesis was first proposed by paleontologist Peter Ward in his 2009 book *The Medea Hypothesis: Is Life on Earth Ultimately Self-Destructive?*[994] In the book he argues that most extinctions the earth has experienced were not caused by external factors such as volcanic eruptions or asteroid impacts, but rather by microbes—the exception was the fifth major extinction, which wiped out the dinosaurs. If CO_2 levels rise to a tipping point of more than one thousand parts per million, the ensuing warming of the oceans will slow ocean circulation, disrupting the cycle that provides oxygen to the deep parts of the oceans. This in turn will encourage sulphur bacteria to prosper since they do not need oxygen. With rapidly decreasing oxygen levels, the bacteria will reach the surface of the ocean, where they will release hydrogen sulphide into the atmosphere that will destroy the protective ozone layer and kill life on earth.

But if life is so destructive, why are we still here? One extinction was caused by an asteroid hitting the earth, and not enough is known about the causes of the other extinctions. Furthermore, if we accept Ward's hypothesis, the logical conclusion is that it is futile to try to achieve a sustainable environment as nothing is naturally sustainable in the long run. Ward himself argues that we should try to save ourselves and the planet by engaging in geoengineering on a massive scale to prevent additional buildup of CO_2 in the atmosphere, a solution fraught with problems, as discussed in Chapter 3.

Are we in the process of destroying Gaia, and why? How have humans been able to dominate earth to the point that we may even control the geological record? Part of the explanation lies in the theory of evolution.

Darwin and Wallace

Charles Darwin (1809–1882) is the father of evolutionary theory.[995] His ideas were published in 1859 in his revolutionary book *On the Origin of Species by Means of Natural Selection, or the Preservation of Favoured Races in the Struggle for Life*. His voyage as a naturalist on the survey ship *Beagle*, travelling around South America and the East Indies, convinced him that species had evolved by natural selection in response to local conditions. The unique flora and fauna on each of the Galapagos Islands particularly impressed him. He found the explanation in the specific characteristics of each individual animal or plant, some of which are more successful than others for survival, and these characteristics are passed on to future generations. Over the span of a thousand generations, the surviving animals or plants may become very different from the original species. Darwin's insight quickly became known as the survival of the fittest—an expression coined by the philosopher Herbert Spencer—and was used and misused initially to promote the notion that the existence of impoverished people is a confirmation of a natural order. These ideas became known as social Darwinism and gave rise to a belief in the superiority of some races and to eugenics, promoting sterilization of "inferior" people. Darwin himself was deeply worried about the social implications of his theories—in particular that evolution does not need any participation by God, the creator.

Alfred Russell Wallace (1823–1913), a contemporary of Darwin, was also a naturalist who worked extensively in South America, East India, and Indonesia. Independently of Darwin, he arrived at natural selection as an explanation of the diverse flora and fauna in different parts of the world. He is regarded as the father of biogeography and as the discoverer of the "Wallace line," which separates the islands of Indonesia into two groups: those with ties to the flora and fauna of Australia, and those with ties to Asia. He did not become as famous as Darwin, but he had a profound influence on evolutionary thinking through his many books. While Darwin emphasized competition among individuals as the driver of evolution, Wallace emphasized adaptation to the environment, becoming one of the first environmentalists by highlighting humans' adverse effects on the environment. While Darwin was sometimes despondent over the implications of his discoveries on society, Wallace was not; he saw the world as a beautiful, harmonious place created through evolution. Wallace also became a social activist and was influenced by spiritualism, arguing that natural selection alone could not have resulted in the higher achievements of the human mind such as musical, artistic, or mathematical ability.

While Darwin did not apply his theories to humans, evolution can explain how humans came to dominate the earth. It is widely accepted that early humans were uniquely endowed with exceptional cognition because of their unusually large brains, which gave them an advantage over other animals for survival. These large brains also allowed them to develop culture, which in turn made it possible to develop technology and pass the knowledge to future generations—an advantage that over millennia resulted in the expansion of the human race to the extent that it led to total domination of earth's ecosystems.

Cooperation and the power of ideas

The question is one of whether humans have evolved as a totally selfish species, prone to stand idly by while the world around them falls apart because of environmental degradation. How likely is it that humans will cooperate and act in their own long-term interests of survival? The animal kingdom is rich in examples where cooperation helps survival. Many pack animals—for example, wolves, hyenas, and lions—cooperate in hunting. Some animals are known to use sentinels to protect the group when they are feeding—geese, crows, prairie dogs, and the much-studied meerkats.[996] Bee and ant colonies are also examples where cooperation is essential for survival. We humans look after our young and our elderly, engage in volunteerism, donate to charity, and sign up to fight wars—all selfless behaviour. Some may believe that such behaviour will guarantee a place in heaven and thus these types of "good" acts are a sign of selfishness, but most who engage in such selfless behaviour do not expect such rewards. The question about selfishness is an important one because if, as individuals, we are all selfish, it would not be in our interest to modify our behaviour to save future generations.

Cooperative behaviour among animals was studied by the founder of sociobiology W.D. Hamilton, who proposed a genetic kinship theory built on Richard Dawkins's idea that the basis of natural selection is the gene. Dawkins, a neo-Darwinist, argued that natural selection does not act on the whole organism but rather on each of the thousands of genes in the human body.[997] Basically, genes are in competition with the bodies that house them, and in any conflict the genes will prevail. According to Hamilton, if a group of individuals carries the same gene, behaviour that benefits the whole group will make the group stronger, thus favouring that particular gene and making survival easier. He also cooperated with political scientist Robert Axelrod in applying game theory to human behaviour, trying to understand the particular circumstances where cooperation pays off. One of the earliest applications of game theory is the Prisoners' Dilemma game, which shows that selfish behaviour leads to an inferior outcome. Crook A and Crook B have committed a serious crime, but the available evidence is insufficient for a conviction. The police have enough evidence to charge them with a minor crime, which would give each of them a year in prison. They are arrested and are held in separate cells and cannot communicate with each other. Each prisoner is told that if one confesses and betrays the other, and the other remains silent, the confessor will go free while the other will spend twenty years in prison. If they both confess, they both will spend five years in prison. It is obvious from Table 11.4 that the best strategy is for each prisoner to confess. For example, if Crook A confesses, the worst that can happen to him is five years in prison if B also confesses, and the best outcome is for him to go free if B stays silent. On the other hand, if he remains silent, the worst outcome is twenty years in prison and the best one year—clearly an inferior choice. The same situation faces Crook B. Therefore, if they both confess, they will each spend five years in jail, which is worse than if they both remained silent, which gives a one-year jail sentence.

In repeated experiments, when the participants had second chances, they were more likely to cooperate. The best strategy was a tit-for-tat strategy—to cooperate unless the behaviour of other people indicated they could not be trusted. Another interesting game is about fair-mindedness. Player A is given $10, which he or she has to share with Player B. If B accepts the distribution, the amount of which is up to A, they both get to keep the money. If B does not, neither gets any money. One would expect that even if B only gets $1 and A

Table 11.4. The Prisoners' Dilemma

		Crook B	
		Confess and betray	Stay silent
Crook A	Confess and betray	Each crook serves five years in jail	Crook A goes free, Crook B serves 20 years in jail
	Stay silent	Crook A serves 20 years in jail, Crook B goes free	Each crook serves one year in jail

gets $9, B would accept, as $1 is better than nothing. But apparently this does not happen when the game is played—instead, B usually finds this distribution unfair and rejects it. The most common split is 6–4, showing that humans are not totally selfish, and cooperation is an integral part of behaviour.

This raises the question of how we can be induced to cooperate and act beyond our immediate desires and survival needs, placing more consideration on the future implications of our actions. Humans often do not make rational decisions, a fact that 2002 Nobel Prize winner Daniel Kahneman has explored in depth in his book *Thinking Fast and Slow*.[998] He argues that the human brain has two systems for decision making: System 1 is fast, intuitive, and reflexive, and usually but not always leads to good decisions. System 2 is slow, deliberate, and analytical. Using System 2 will lead to rational decisions while System 1 can end up with systematic errors. System 1 thinking is particularly susceptible to how the problem or question is framed, many examples of which are given in Kahneman's book. One example is of physicians at Harvard Medical School who were given information about the results of radiation and surgical treatments for lung cancer.[999] Half of them were told that the one-month survival rate after surgery is 90 percent, and the other half that there is a 10 percent mortality rate in the first month. The information is identical—the only difference is that in one case the information was based on mortality and in the other on survival. Eighty-four percent of the physicians in the group that were told about survival rates were in favour of surgery, while only 50 percent in the other group were—a good example of System 1 thinking.

The problem of how governments can influence people to make rational decisions without impinging on individual freedoms was taken up Richard Thaler and Cass Sunstein in the influential book *Nudge: Improving Decisions about Health, Wealth, and Happiness*.[1000] Using insights from psychology about behaviour, they showed that people can be nudged into making decisions for their own long-term benefit, or indeed for society's long-term benefit. One example relates to organ donations. High-donation countries have an opt-out form attached to drivers' licences, while low-donation countries have an opt-in form. In countries with the opt-out form, it is assumed people are willing to donate unless they have signed the form. Countries with an opt-in form require their citizens to make a conscious decision about organ donation. Many people are not comfortable confronting their own mortality, even though from society's viewpoint an organ donation would make eminent sense. The opt-out form acts as a "nudge" to donate. The idea of the nudge was used to increase savings in the United States through a program called Save More Tomorrow. By joining this plan, individuals agreed that their savings would automatically increase if their pay increased. They could opt out of the arrangement, but most never did, and the impact was an increase in savings.

For people to be nudged into "good" behaviour, good ideas have to spread and be accepted by the majority of populations. Richard Dawkins proposed that an equivalent to genes exists in culture and ideas that he called a *meme*. A gene spreads biological information while a meme spreads ideas. Like genes, memes are subject to evolution by natural selection and can self-replicate, mutate, and become extinct. The most successful memes spread rapidly through communication among individuals that can take the form of writing, talking, gestures, and rituals, while other memes do not replicate. Physical traits acquired during a lifetime—for example, some handicaps—cannot be passed on to the next generation, while memes can. For this reason, cultural evolution is far faster than genetic evolution and has been greatly accelerated in recent decades by innovations in communications technology. For example, it took sabre-toothed cats millions of years to develop their big teeth, while it took humans a couple of thousand years to develop more lethal metal daggers.[1001] In one sense, memes can defeat genes as some genes can now be eliminated through genetic engineering (which can be considered a meme). While Dawkins was not the first to suggest the idea, his ideas have caught on in parts of the scientific community.

Tim Flannery, in his book *Here on Earth: A Natural History of the Planet*, sees the rapid spread of memes, when combined with the evidence that we are not totally selfish, as a possible means of our salvation.[1002] For example, smoking is no longer socially acceptable in some cultures. Watching old movies gives an interesting reminder of how much and how quickly attitudes have changed regarding smoking, at least in the developed world. Many of us who taught on university campuses in the early 1970s frequently tolerated smoking during lectures, and many professors lit up while teaching. Rapid communications is seen by many of us to be a "good" force in promoting change—for example, in toppling repressive regimes in the Middle East—and a "bad" force in inciting riots and vandalism among young people in countries with democratically elected governments. The conclusion here is that cooperation is an innate part of human behaviour and humans can be nudged and induced to change their behaviour and cooperate for the benefit of all, provided policies are framed in such a way that they are likely to be accepted. How can we harness these forces into saving the environment?

The relentless pursuit of economic growth

Insights into the roles of nudging and memes can in theory help us to design policies to decrease resource use and make it more sustainable in rich countries. How can this be achieved? This is a very difficult question with no simple answer. Since the Second World War, the emphasis in economic policy has been on how to increase incomes—that is, the promotion of economic growth. Despite the efforts of the Club of Rome, little consideration has been given to the absurdity of limitless economic growth in the face of a finite ecological system. Higher incomes can be achieved only by either increasing resource use or by using resources more efficiently; a vast economic literature exists on how to achieve higher growth rates, but little emphasis is placed on the possibility of limits to growth within the context of a limited natural environment.

Has economic growth delivered improvement in our well-being? There is no question that it has lifted the majority of people in the industrialized world and many parts of the developing world out of poverty and misery, and growth is necessary to increase the standard of living in poor countries. Some evidence based on historical data points to the fact that if incomes reach a certain level, the environment benefits from economic growth. Statistical studies have confirmed the existence of a bell-shaped curve linking water pollution and air pollution (except carbon dioxide pollution) with GDP per capita. If a country is very poor, pollution increases when the economy starts to grow, reaches a maximum, and then begins to decrease.[1003] This has become known as the environmental Kuznets curve after the economist who first identified a similar curve linking economic inequality with economic growth. When countries become richer, they can afford better mitigation measures in response to increased concern among citizens, who have more time and disposable income on their hands to support environmental causes than those living a subsistence existence in poor countries. This is particularly the case when governments are democratically elected and are sensitive to the wishes of the population.

The issue at hand is whether further growth is desirable in rich countries. Economic growth is measured by growth in per-capita GDP, which is both a measure of the value of goods and services produced and of incomes generated from production divided by population size. Per-capita GDP is often regarded as an approximate measure of well-being because it measures the ability to acquire material goods, and the acquisition of more material goods is considered by economists to improve well-being. However, this assumed link between income and well-being or happiness is increasingly the subject of criticism.[1004] There is now a huge literature on the subject—a journal is even entirely devoted to the study of happiness, appropriately called the *Journal of Happiness Studies*. The origin of the debate was the pioneering study by Richard Easterlin in 1974.[1005] While richer people were typically happier than poorer people, rich societies were not necessarily happier than poorer societies. Based on responses to simple survey questions such as "are you very happy, pretty happy, or not too happy," one-third of respondents in the United States typically reported that they were very happy, and the figure did not change much over time despite large increases in per-capita income. This became known as the Easterlin Paradox, in which Easterlin explained that individuals became happier when they grew richer, but only when others did not become richer; therefore, what mattered most was the relative standing. Over time the proportion of happy people did not expand with incomes. Similar results were found in European studies.[1006] What makes people happy? Studies consistently find that the happiest people were the young and the old, the rich, the religious, women, highly educated people, the married, and the employed. Unemployment in particular makes people unhappy. Happy countries—among which the Scandinavian countries consistently score the highest—are countries with high incomes, low inequality, and high education levels. They are democratic, trusting, and have low unemployment. However, the Easterlin Paradox has now been challenged with better data sets that seem to prove that indeed a correlation can be found between per-capita GDP and average levels of happiness.[1007] The implication is that the pursuit of economic growth will improve human happiness, and we can never have enough goods. This idea is firmly rooted in the discipline of economics that has come to dominate public policy. Yet this was not always the case, and the belief that there is no limit to our greed is truly absurd.

The link between greed and happiness is addressed in Robert Skidelsky and his son Edward Skidelsky's 2012 book *How Much Is Enough? The Love of Money and the Case for the Good Life*.[1008] The Skidelskys emphasize the need for a shift to a service economy because it uses fewer resources per unit of output, but the emphasis in the book is on an examination of what a good life is and how can we achieve it. In 1930, John Maynard Keynes, in his essay "Economic Possibilities for Our Grandchildren," predicted that in a hundred years, technological progress would make it possible to produce the necessary goods with far less labour, and therefore humankind could look forward to a life with less work and more leisure.[1009] This is not happening—instead, productivity improvements have resulted in little change in the hours worked, and a huge expansion in the production and consumption of goods. Why? There are many plausible explanations; one is the shift in industrialized countries to the service sector with its often low wages, which makes it necessary to work longer hours to achieve the desired standard of living. Another explanation is that work has perhaps become so absorbing for some people that they prefer to work more rather than less, and increasingly they have limited capability of enjoying leisure. However, the most compelling argument, according to the authors, is that people work longer hours because they want more goods.

Why does materialism play such a strong role in most societies? There are many possible reasons. For example, psychological research has established links between loneliness and materialism. Acquiring goods can become a coping strategy for lonely people, a strategy that crowds out relationships; consequently, lonely people become even lonelier and a vicious cycle is created.[1010] Research by anthropologists and sociologists has emphasized that material goods serve many functions for individuals apart from fulfilling basic needs. We use them to signal to others what matters to us, such as social status, community, and belonging, and we purchase goods for people to notice us, to be recognized, and to be liked.[1011] More goods of a certain type make us feel we are part of society and make it possible for us to associate with people we like and make friends. Not only is this true for Western societies but for every society that has been studied. Goods not necessary for survival can be classified according to their functions into positional goods, bandwagon goods, snob goods, and Veblen goods. Positional goods are those that lose their intrinsic value if other people acquire them—examples are staying in highly fashionable resorts or dining at exclusive restaurants—thus, striving toward such status goods is ultimately self-defeating. Bandwagon goods are wanted because they are trendy and show that you are in tune with current developments. They include fashion goods such as clothing and new electronic gadgets. Snob goods are similar in that they set you apart as being ahead of the latest trend, be it new restaurants or decorating items. Veblen goods are those that advertise how wealthy and successful you are. The acquiring of such goods comes under the label of conspicuous consumption, a term coined by Thorstein Veblen in his 1899 book *The Theory of the Leisure Class: An Economic Study of Institutions.*

Capitalism has magnified these basic human desires for signalling of status goods because everything is measured in monetary terms; as well, capitalism appears to promote the love of money for its own sake. Innate in capitalism is the belief in the beneficial effects of competition among producers, but it is obvious that competition has also spread to consumers, leading to the snob and bandwagon effects. With its emphasis on growth, capitalism relies on the symbiosis of novelty, status-seeking consumers, and profit-seeking entrepreneurs. Add to these factors the insidious effects of advertising in trying to create additional wants for new goods. We want to work longer hours because goods and money appear to offer us more pleasure than leisure.

The Skidelskys argue that we will be happy only if we lead a good life. The quest for a good life has a long history, and the Skidelskys argue that it should be revived. Western and other societies that by any measure are wealthy should abandon their primary goal of maximizing per-capita GDP and consumption for its own sake in favour of the promotion of a good life. A good life would include good health, friendship, leisure, respect, the possibility of personal growth, harmony with the environment, and security, which entails job security as well as peace. What would these measures be? In their own words, an economic organization:

> . . . would have to produce enough goods and services to satisfy everyone's basic needs and reasonable standards of comfort. It would furthermore have to do so with a big reduction in the amount of necessary work, so as to free up time for leisure, understood as self-directed activity. It would have to ensure a less unequal distribution of wealth and income, not just to diminish the incentive to work, but to improve the social bases of health, personality, respect and friendship. Finally a society which aims to realize the basic goods of friendship and harmony with nature would put more emphasis on localism, less on centralization and globalization.[1012]

They go on to argue that these measures are interdependent: failure to achieve one makes it difficult to achieve any of the others. Too much inequality means that some people have to work too hard to achieve their basic needs, and their leisure will be compromised. If some people are incredible rich, others will try to achieve the same standards in terms of the material goods, encouraging excessive consumption. They claim that adopting "localism"—the banner for local government and local production and consumption—is necessary for the promotion of respect, individuality, and harmony with nature.

Balancing the rights of the individuals to have the freedom to pursue their own goals with a societal role of creating a good life is a difficult problem. The authors do not advocate coercion but propose government polices to redistribute wealth away from the rich to the poor, including an annual guaranteed income and higher taxes on the rich. They also advocate for a gradual reduction in the number of hours of work, the replacement of income taxes with consumption or expenditure taxes to discourage spending, and a tax on advertising to further discourage excessive consumption.

What would happen if these types of policies were successful in slowing or eliminating economic growth in rich countries? According to the authors, well-being in terms of what they consider to be a good life would improve. However, this begs the question of what would happen to the economies in rich countries if these policies were successful in promoting less spending. When people spend less—as they do in a recession—businesses have to decrease production and lay off employees unless the available work is spread over more people through work sharing or shorter hours. New macroeconomic models are necessary to explore how long-term stability can be achieved in a zero-growth society.[1013] Localism as opposed to globalism would also lead to lower incomes, as many of the efficiency gains from trade would be lost. Localism would have severe effects on many developing countries that need exports to rich countries to improve their living standards.

The challenges

Apart from the challenge of promoting a decreased emphasis on the consumption of material goods as an end in itself, there are other equally difficult challenges in making our resource use sustainable. Industrialized countries have been through an unprecedented period of economic growth fuelled by cheap fossil fuels, a dependence that must be severed for progress to be made. The first challenge is climate change mitigation. Mitigation by treaty has so far been a failure even though there are promising signs that, contrary to expectations, many countries appear to adopt policies addressing carbon dioxide reduction on their own. In a 2012 study of thirty-three major economies, thirty-two had adopted legislation to achieve greater resource efficiency and less carbon-intensive growth.[1014] This study included China and, according to the authors, may pave the way for a new international treaty. However, these measures are probably too late to avert some of the most serious climatic changes anticipated within the next century, and therefore they must be supplemented by adaptation measures, which will be very costly.

The second challenge is to increase food production to feed the expanding population without further endangering the environment. The third challenge is to make room for an increase in sustainable resource use in poor countries to allow these countries to grow and prosper. Poor people who feel they have no future tend not to put a high priority on environmental protection. If you think you are not going to live long or if you are living a hand-to-mouth subsistence existence, there are few incentives to care about the future—in economic terms, the future is discounted at a very high rate. Why should you care about the long-term consequences of destroying your resource base when there is no long-term future for you and your family because of grinding poverty, famine, and civil war? As was discussed above, improving living conditions in poor countries also tends to lead to a decrease in the birth rate. Of course, how to make poor countries richer is one of the most difficult problems societies face. Even though considerable inroads have been made into the reduction of world poverty, much of the development money spent over the past century does not seem to have had much effect.

We are facing problems that appear to be intractable because of our numbers, the deteriorating state of our renewable resources, and the damage we are doing to the earth's life-support systems. This book is a catalogue of what has gone wrong, with indications of how the problems can be solved, at least in theory. The critical question is whether we have the will and the political institutions to solve the world's problems. The problems we face are extremely complex. Are we up to it? Tim Flannery talks about the tendency toward "civilized imbecility."[1015] Domestic animals have less brain matter than their wild counterparts, who need bigger brains to survive in the wild, foraging and avoiding predators. Many of us feel that modern humans must be more intelligent than our ancestors in view of our technological advancement. Apparently, this is not true. Compared with people during the ice age, today's men have lost approximately 10 percent and women 14 percent of brain mass. Life as a hunter-gatherer was incredibly challenging, and examples abound of present-day hunter-gatherers who, when taken out of their culture, have excelled. In terms of evolution, this makes sense, as our day-to-day survival is easier, allowing humans to invest more energy in reproduction and fighting disease and less in building larger brains. However, this is controversial, as a smaller brain mass does not necessarily translate into lesser intelligence, and there is plenty of debate over whether we are becoming less intelligent. While the debate over what constitutes intelligence is not necessarily settled, it is widely known in psychology that average IQ scores in developed countries continued to increase during the last century. This became known as the Flynn Effect, after J.R. Flynn, who spent most of his academic career studying the phenomenon, and it is likely the same phenomenon would occur in poor countries if social conditions were to improve.[1016] Causes may be better nutrition, health care, and education. Apparently the increase is now slowing in countries such as Denmark and Australia, and it is even decreasing in Norway and the United Kingdom.[1017] Humans are clever, and it is interesting to note that we are genetically more uniform than most other mammals. Tim Flannery puts it well in saying that "There is more genetic diversity in a random sample of about fifty chimpanzees from West Africa than in all seven billion of us."[1018] This is because the human race was almost wiped out seventy million years ago, leaving only few individuals and a smaller gene pool. We are all nearly the same, and we are all capable of understanding the severity of the problems facing us and of adjusting our behaviour to ensure our own survival. Will we?

The problem of designing appropriate international institutions

Many of our problems are international in scope and require cooperation across borders. Our understanding of human action or inaction involving international cooperation in the interest of humanity can be analyzed using the theory of public goods. These are goods the market cannot supply because nobody can be prevented from enjoying them once they are produced, regardless of an individual's payment toward their upkeep. One person's enjoyment of the good has no effect on the enjoyment of another person. The classic example of a public good is defence. As long as someone is paying for it, every citizen derives the benefit of being protected, even if every citizen has not contributed to its upkeep. Some people may voluntarily contribute to national defence, but others will choose to "free ride" on the contribution of others, and voluntary contributions may not be enough to maintain an adequate defence force. For this reason, these types of goods are usually supplied by governments and financed by taxes or provided by regulation. Examples of public goods financed by taxes are defence, policing, basic education, and street lighting; an example of a good provided by regulation is the provision of clean air, in which case factories are required to install anti-pollution devices such as scrubbers. There are not only national public goods but also global public goods such as mitigation of climate change, the prevention of nuclear proliferation, and the prevention of pandemics. The problem with global public goods is that no world government exists that can levy taxes or enforce regulations.

In his book *Why Cooperate? The Incentive to Supply Global Public Goods*, Scott Barrett categorizes global public goods in five groups: those that require a single best effort, those that require every country to take part, those that require aggregate efforts, those that require mutual restraint, and those that require coordination.[1019] An example of the first is the hypothetical case of asteroid protection. If an asteroid of the same size as the one that extinguished the dinosaurs millions of years ago hit our planet today, it would lead to a total disaster that could include the elimination of humans. It is likely that such a disaster could be averted given the state of our knowledge of outer space, the quality of telescopes, and the technology of spacecraft that could be designed to change the course of the asteroid to avoid a collision. If such an asteroid were discovered, would governments spend years trying to work out agreements for what to do? This is highly unlikely—instead, each country would be motivated to try to avert catastrophe since the cost of doing nothing would be unfathomable. In economic terms, the benefits of action, particularly if the country is big and rich, would far outweigh the costs. This is also the case for geoengineering. If climate change turns catastrophic, a country may be motivated to go it alone with any of the technologies discussed in Chapter 4. It is therefore essential to come to some sort of agreement about geoengineering that will govern when it should be used and who will decide.

The second category requires every country to take part in providing this public good. An example is the eradication of a communicable disease. A massive vaccination program in one country only makes sense if other countries vaccinate as well. If this assurance is not in place, the disease will not be eradicated.

The third category involves the need for aggregate action, as in the case for mitigation policies for climate change. The actions of one country alone are not likely to have a perceptible impact on global emissions, nor does every single country have to take part, provided the emissions of the non-cooperating country are small. However, effective mitigation requires sufficient aggregate action that total emissions are cut to a level considered safe. This global good of mitigation has not yet been supplied because even though the impacts of climate change are likely to be serious, they are unlikely to be catastrophic compared with collision with an asteroid. Another reason is that climate change will not have the same effect on every country. Developing countries that have limited ability to mitigate and adapt will suffer most, while the population in some cold countries such as Canada may feel that some warming would be beneficial. Mitigation policies are costly and thus will be resisted by countries that determine the impact of climate change will be small. A third reason individual countries are reluctant to adopt mitigation measures in the absence of a binding treaty is that if they do so, there is an incentive to "race to the bottom," meaning polluting industries will move to jurisdictions with less stringent regulations where factories use older, higher-polluting technologies. As a result, unilateral policies to cut emissions could actually increase global emissions. A cut in the use of fossil fuels in rich countries could also drive down their prices on the world market, thus encouraging increased use in other countries. This means that unless all countries are part of the effort, single efforts may not be very effective because of these side effects, usually referred to as leakages. Leakages may amount to 5 to 20 percent of the total effort.[1020] In addition, corporations are not usually in favour of unilateral action because environmental policies, including carbon taxes, are costly, and could put them at a competitive disadvantage. The implication is that some sort of mechanism must be in place to punish non-compliant states. One possibility is through international trade measures as suggested by Nordhaus (see page 139). These have already been seriously considered by the European Union in a 2007 proposal to impose a carbon tariff on imports from the United States following its failure to ratify the Kyoto Accord. Whether these types of measures are allowed under the rules of the WTO is open to debate. In general, methods of production are not considered a legitimate target for trade barriers, while a country is fully within its right to control or ban the import of harmful products.[1021] Unilateral trade policy measures could lead to international trade wars. For example, the European Union moved to introduce a requirement that all airlines landing in Europe must obtain emissions permits starting in 2013. The initial allocation would have been permits allowing 97 percent emissions and decreasing to 95 percent within a year. The implementation of the policy was postponed indefinitely because of threats of retaliatory action by the United States and China.

A fourth type of a global public good is prevention of nuclear proliferation. It is costless but requires mutual restraint. Briefly discussed in Chapter 5, this appears to be increasingly difficult to maintain given the serious attempts by North Korea and Iran to acquire and use nuclear technology. These developments become self-perpetuating and threaten to undermine decades-old progress in this area. The greater the number of countries that acquire nuclear weapons, the greater is the incentive for others to follow.

The final category of public goods includes those that require coordination of rules and standards across the globe. Balancing the need for action with incentives to act, this category of public goods may indeed hold the most promise for future action on many environmental problems. Scott Barrett used the example of the introduction of double-hull tankers as an illustration. Oil tankers used to fill their empty tanks with water for ballast, which was routinely dumped at sea before the tanker went into port for another shipload full of oil. Not surprisingly, this created a substantial source of pollution, since the water dumped was contaminated with oil. Several international conferences tried to deal with the problem by mandating that no ballast water should be discharged within 150 miles off the coast. No agreement was reached until 1954, when a fifty-mile no-dumping zone was agreed to, but as there was no enforcement mechanism, the agreement had no effect. Meanwhile, in 1972, the United States proposed a new standard for the construction of oil tankers that required segregation of water ballast tanks from the oil tanks, and unless an international agreement on these standards was reached by 1976, the United States made it clear that it would unilaterally ban single-hull tankers from its ports. This measure had the desired effect. In 1978, the International Maritime Organization adopted the International Convention for the Prevention of Pollution from Ships, which has been successful. Tanker owners were eager to comply because if they were banned from entering certain countries, they would lose revenue. As well, enforcement was effective because inspections of hulls were cheap and easy to do.

Another example of technical standards having a positive effect was the phasing out of leaded gasoline with the introduction of catalytic converters in 1975 in the United States, a technology that rapidly spread to other car makers. Lead-free gas had been available in Japan since 1972, but the new catalytic converters could not run on leaded gasoline.[1022] Mexico and Canada were forced to follow in the switch to unleaded gas because without its availability, US cross-border travel and trade would be discouraged. The European Union held out until much later, partly because it did not want to damage its own car industry by introducing measures that favoured North American cars. However, given the overwhelming evidence of the damaging effects of lead, the EU followed, but legislation was not introduced until 1993.

It can be concluded from these examples that if one approach does not work in solving the problems of international action, other approaches should be tried. Technological fixes may be possible, particularly in the areas of car engines and carbon sequestration. International agreements may follow technology. Barrett, in a later article, suggests that piecemeal approaches may be the only way out.[1023] Citing the Montreal Protocol's success in achieving reduction in CFCs and the successful introduction of lead-free gas and double-hull tankers, he provides several examples of how better policies can be achieved. Aviation standards using different aviation fuels could be agreed to and phased in, and this could also be the case for new electric or hybrid engines. Barrett is also in favour of mandatory introduction of carbon-saving technology in high-energy-use industries such as those that process aluminum, iron and steel, glass, and cement.

What must be done

Stabilization of the world population at ten billion by the end of this century should make a sustainable future possible, particularly as democracy appears to be spreading. Only democracies can give security to individuals and guarantee property rights, which are necessary for individuals to care about the future. However, while the spread of democracy with its emphasis of the rights of the individual is a good thing, it does not necessarily promote sustainable environmental policies. In a democracy, it is difficult to persuade the electorate to trade short-term loss for long-term gain. As discussed above, people in general are not uniformly rational. Therefore, a truly sustainable world is possible only if environmental policies can be designed in such a manner that they can overcome the short-term bias of individuals and governments in supplying the necessary public goods. As explained above, new research in psychology has shown that we can be nudged into changing our behaviour if policies are framed in a clever way. Modern communications technologies now ensure that ideas and news (memes) spread rapidly. Social networks, mobile phones, and the Internet could be used to monitor environmental misbehaviour by individuals, corporations, or governments and promote social movements for change.[1024] Aerial drones (eco-drones) can provide low-cost surveillance of environmental infractions, such as illegal dumping, hunting, fishing and logging. In earlier eras, most transgressions could be kept secret, but this is no longer true, judging from the number of times cell-phone pictures embarrassing to governments or corporations have surfaced on the Internet and have "gone viral". Global monitoring and surveillance are now possible.

In my view, a sustainable earth requires the world to act quickly with respect to the following:

Policies to reduce greenhouse gas emissions. It is critical to implement policies to reduce emissions not only to stabilize the concentration of carbon dioxide in the atmosphere but also to prevent the further acidification of the oceans. A carbon tax should be introduced in all countries for the reasons outlined above. The money collected should be used for adaptation to climate change, for research into sustainable agricultural practices, and for necessary remediation and protection of habitats, including habitats in poor countries. While cap-and-trade policies can be equivalent to carbon taxes, they have shown to be more susceptible to political interference. As explained above, it may also be possible to devise piecemeal policies targeting specific industries to achieve the necessary emissions reductions without a new binding international agreement on climate change.

In order to facilitate the transfer from fossil fuels to renewable sources of energy, there must be continued investments in new carbon-free technologies and in advanced and updated electricity grids, making it easier to transfer electricity across borders to even out variations in the electricity supplies from renewable resources. Nuclear energy may be a necessary component of a sustainable energy mix (Chapter 5).

Policies to promote a more even income distribution both among and within countries. In terms of the global environment, it is critical that the living standards of poor countries improve. As emphasized above, people with little hope for the future are not likely to care about a sustainable environment. William Easterly, in his 2006 book *The White Man's Burden: Why the West's Efforts to Aid the Rest Have Done So Much Ill and So Little Good*, argued eloquently that top-down aid does not work because, in many cases, the planners are not held accountable, have no idea how ambitious goals can be practically implemented, and have little knowledge of what works locally.[1025] Much aid money has been squandered by corrupt governments. Aid has to be targeted and based on evidence of what works and does not work. The entire field of development studies is gradually changing, partly through the pioneering works of Esther Duflo, who introduced randomized field experiments in casting light on such important factors as what works in children's education, evaluations of dams, and the best incentives to increase fertilizer use in Africa.[1026] Targeted transfers of money and know-how to developing countries are necessary. Because many poor countries rely to a large extent on the exploitation of natural resources for their livelihoods, it is critical for them to develop appropriate resource policies to avoid the resource curse. One policy that should be considered is a sovereign wealth fund, as explained in Chapter 3. Private corporations involved in exploiting resources in poor countries should be forced to be good corporate citizens and ensure net benefits accrue to the countries that are receiving the investments (Chapter 2).

Quality of life and well-being should be encouraged through the introduction of measures such as taxing advertising to discourage excessive consumption in rich countries. Other measures should include the redistribution of income within countries through higher taxes on the rich and larger transfers to the poor.[1027] Thomas Piketty, in his influential book *Capital in the Twenty-First Century*, showed that income distribution in industrialized countries has deteriorated since the 1970s, a trend that is likely to continue, and argued forcefully for the introduction of wealth taxes.[1028] It is no accident that the Scandinavian countries, which have a more equal income distribution than most other developed countries, score highly in any measure of well-being and environmental stewardship. More equal societies tend to have higher life expectancy, higher levels of trust, and lower infant mortality rates. Murder rates and mental illness are higher in more unequal societies.[1029] A widely unequal income distribution is likely to lead to excessive materialism and resource use for reasons explained above. If society is to be successful in reducing excessive consumption, it will be necessary to combine redistribution policies with a reduction in working hours in order to minimize the effect of declining consumption rates on unemployment. An additional advantage is that reduced working hours would likely result in lower greenhouse gas emissions because on the average, leisure time does not emit as many greenhouse gases as work-related activities.[1030]

Policies to promote sustainable agriculture. In order to feed an expected population of ten billion people, agricultural investments must be increased in developing countries, particularly in Africa. The necessary investment must be in conservation agriculture as outlined in Chapter 8, using advances in genetic engineering when appropriate. Subsidies should be removed from biofuels grown on agricultural land as the net benefits of these are highly questionable in view of the impact on food prices. Agricultural protectionism should be discouraged because it does not lead to better food security; instead, it often results in less security, leaving countries even more susceptible to the vagaries of weather.

Policies to protect biodiversity. Governments must work with residents to set aside tracts of land and sea for the protection of biodiversity. Protected areas cannot be effective without the full participation of locals, who need to see tangible benefits and improvements to their well-being or the protection will exist only on paper. Also, more emphasis should be placed on protecting biodiversity in areas that are not considered wilderness, including cities (Chapter 6). A major effort is needed to save the oceans from overfishing by the introduction of rights-based fishing, the strong prosecution of illegal fishing, and the expansion of protected of areas on the high seas (Chapter 10).

Policies to make cities more sustainable. Much of the emphasis in this book has been on improving conditions facing the natural environment by improving the sustainability of agriculture, forestry, and the oceans. However, more than 50 percent of the world's population lives in cities, with the proportion expected to reach 70 percent by 2050, and it is therefore crucial to improve the sustainability of cities. From an environmental perspective, increased urbanization should be a welcome development because higher population densities in urban areas make it possible to minimize not only the per-capita input of resources such as water, land, and energy, but also the output of waste products. Cities are also known to be engines for innovation and wealth creation—conditions necessary for humans to prosper. In order to be sustainable, future cities should be characterized by more efficient building designs, improved urban designs and infrastructure, and technological improvements in waste water and garbage handling.[1031] Many cities are already at the forefront in developing policies and infrastructures to improve sustainability. For example, cities in Scandinavia use energy made from garbage. Instead of burying it in landfills, they incinerate it and use the energy generated for electricity or central heating. It has proved such a success that some cities are considering importing garbage from other countries.[1032] However, an even greater challenge is to promote sustainable cities in developing countries and transform them from stinking slums lacking in clean water and sewerage into livable and sustainable entities.

Integration of sustainability into core business practices. Corporations are the drivers of globalization, and without their participation, sustainability cannot be achieved. This means they must embrace the principle of no harm, either to people or the environment, and adhere to the United Nations Global Compact principles for responsible behaviour in the areas of environment, labour, human rights, and anti-corruption.[1033] The Global Compact already has twelve thousand corporate participants, and the challenge is to move beyond principles to action. The latest survey of sustainable business practices shows that progress appears to have stopped.[1034]

Reform of international institutions. The international institutions we are familiar with were all founded after World War II, and their designs reflect the challenges and conditions prevalent at that time. It would make sense if they were reformed to facilitate solutions to the problems facing us now. For example, trade sanctions should be recognized as legitimate retaliation for free riders, since they are the only penalties that are available short of war. It is particularly urgent to reach agreement on an international treaty on the control of geoengineering. Currently, any country can start its own geoengineering experiments without any controls or agreements from other counties.

Figure 11.3. Security fence between Morocco and the Spanish town of Mellila on the north coast of Africa. These types of barriers are being erected in many parts of the world with the sole purpose of stopping the entry of economic migrants. Source: Wikimedia Commons.

Support for scientific research. While public questioning of scientists and scientific results is necessary, it must not lead to the denigration of the importance of science in finding solutions to our current problems. For example, genetic engineering is regarded with great suspicion in many parts of the world, partly because it is based on very advanced science. Despite the fact that there is no evidence GM food is harmful to humans, many countries ban GM grains even though they may help us in providing nutritious food in many parts of the world and may be more beneficial to the environment than traditionally bred grains. Another example is the attitude among parts of the public to climate science. The fact that climate models do not give consistently accurate forecasts must not lead us reject climate science or deny the overwhelming evidence showing

Figure 11.4. Economic migrants arriving in Sicily. Today's papers are full of accounts of migrants trying to reach Europe under conditions that can only be described as desperate. Credit: Vito Manzari and Wikimedia Commons.

climate change is occurring and is anthropogenic. We have to be creative and flexible, using the latest research in arriving at solutions, not only from the pure sciences but also the social sciences; none of the necessary changes will occur unless people become informed and politically engaged and demand actions from governments. Misguided policies such as resource nationalism, the push toward food self-sufficiency, and an excessive promotion of localism will neither save the world from environmental disaster nor make the world economic system more stable.

In conclusion, overpopulation, climate change, and our squandering of renewable resources present appallingly difficult challenges for the world to over-come. If we don't do so in a timely manner, the world might resort to tribalism by putting up physical barriers to fend off neighbours hungry for resources— security fences are already in place in parts of the world—or use navies to keep out migrants. However, while aggression seems to be part of human nature, so is cooperation. Cooperation has made it easier for us to survive as a species, and therein lies our best hope for the future.[1035] Studies have shown that we are more likely to cooperate with members of our own tribe. The challenge is now for humans to see ourselves as members of one giant human tribe and to cooperate to find the solutions essential to our survival.

Bibliography

Acemoglu, Daron, and James Robinson. *Why Nations Fail: The Origins of Power, Prosperity and Poverty*. London: Profile Books, 2012.

———, et al. "A Dynamic Theory of Resource Wars." *The Quarterly Journal of Economics* 127 (2012): pp. 283–331.

Alberta Energy. Facts and Statistics. http://www.energy.alberta.ca/oilsands/791.asp.

Albright, David, and Mark Hibbs. "India's Silent Bomb." *Bulletin of Atomic Scientists* (Sept. 1992): pp. 27–31.

Albright, David. *Peddling Peril: How the Secret Nuclear Trade Arms America's Enemies*. New York: Free Press, 2010.

Alcamo, Joseph, Martina Flörke, and Michael Märker. "Future Long-Term Changes in Global Water Resources Driven by Socio-Economic and Climatic Changes." *Hydrological Sciences Journal* 52, no. 2 (2007): pp. 247–275.

Alexander, John. "The Prehistoric Salt Trade in Europe." *Nature* 300, no. 5893 (1982): pp. 577–578.

Alexandratos, Nikos, and Jelle Bruinsma. "World Agriculture towards 2030/2050: The 2012 Revision." ESA Working Paper No. 12-03, Agriculture Development Economics Division, FAO, Rome, June 2012.

Allen, Grant, et al. "Levelised Costs of Wave and Tidal Energy in the UK: Cost Competitiveness and the Importance of 'Banded' Renewables Obligation Certificates." *Energy Policy* 39 (2011): pp. 23–39.

Allsopp, Michelle, et al. *Plastic Debris in the World's Oceans*. Amsterdam: Greenpeace International, 2006. http://www.greenpeace.org/international/Global/international/planet-2/report/2007/8/plastic_ocean_report.pdf.

American Academy of Environmental Medicine. "Genetically Modified Foods." Last modified May 8, 2009. http://www.aaemonline.org/gmopost.html.

American Physical Society. *Direct Air Capture of CO_2 with Chemicals: A Technology Assessment for the APS Panel on Public Affairs*. June 1, 2011. http://www.aps.org/policy/reports/assessments/upload/dac2011.pdf.

Amoore, Miles, and George Arbuthnott. "Diamonds Ensure Mugabe Is Forever." *The Sunday Times*, August 4, 2013.

Amundsen, Bård. "Global Warming Less Extreme than Feared?" Translated by Darren McKellep and Carol Eckmann. Research Council of Norway. Last modified January 29, 2013. http://www.forskningsradet.no/en/Newsarticle/Global_warming_less_extreme_than_feared/1253983344535.

Anderegg, William R.L., et al. "Expert Credibility in Climate Change." *PNAS* 107 (2010): pp. 12107–9.

Antonioli, Silvia. "High Costs, Low Prices Hit Ferrochrome Producers." Reuters, November 15, 2011. http://www.reuters.com/article/2011/11/15/ozabs-hernic-ferrochrome-idAFJOE7AE0AX20111115.

Arctic Council. Arctic Monitoring and Assessment Program. *Arctic Ocean Acidification: Key Findings*, 2013. www.cicero.uio.no/images/AOAKeyFindings.pdf.

Armstrong, Claire W., et al. "Services from the Deep: Steps Towards Valuation of Deep Sea Goods and Services." *Ecosystem Services* 2 (2012): pp. 2–13.

Arnason, Ragnar. "Property Rights in Fisheries: How Much Can Individual Transferable Quotas Accomplish?" *Review of Environmental Economics and Policy* 6 (2012): pp. 217–236.

Arnason, Ragnar, Kieran Kelleher, and Rolf Willmann. *The Sunken Billions: The Economic Justification for Fisheries Reform.* Washington, DC: The World Bank, 2009.

Arrow, Kenneth J. "Global Climate Change: A Challenge to Policy." *The Economists' Voice*, June 2007. http://www.econ.ku.dk/okocg/VV/VV-Economic%20Growth/articles/articles-2010%20or%20later/GlobalArrow-2007_Climate_Change_A_Challenge_to_Policy[1].pdf.

Asilomar Scientific Organizing Committee. *The Asilomar Conference Recommendations on Principles for Research into Climate Engineering Techniques: Conference Report.* Washington, DC, 2010. http://climateresponsefund.org/images/Conference/finalfinalreport.pdf.

Asner, Gregory P., et al. "Condition and Fate of Logged Forests in the Brazilian Amazon." *PNAS* 103, no. 34 (2006): pp. 12947–50.

Asner, Gregory P., et al. "Elevated Rates of Gold Mining in the Amazon Revealed through High Resolution Monitoring." *PNAS* 110, no. 46 (2013): pp. 18454–9.

Auld, Douglas. "The Economics of Ethanol, Agriculture and Food." *Journal of Sustainable Development* 5 (2012): pp. 136–142.

Auty, Richard M. "High Rent Point Resources: Saudi Arabia." In *Resource Abundance and Economic Development*, edited by R.M. Auty, pp. 193–207. New York: Oxford University Press, 2001.

Baker, Mark, and Markus Hyvonen. "The Emergence of the Chinese Automobile Sector." *Reserve Bank of Australia Bulletin* (March quarter 2011): pp. 23–29.

Balmford, Andrew, et al. "A Global Perspective on Trends in Nature-Based Tourism," *PLOS Biology* 7, no. 6 (2009).

Banerjee, Abhijit V., and Esther Duflo. "The Economic Lives of the Poor." *Journal of Economic Perspectives* 21 (Winter 2007): pp. 141–167.

Barbier, Edward B. *Scarcity and Frontiers: How Economies Have Developed through Natural Resource Exploitation.* Cambridge: Cambridge University Press, 2011.

Barnhart, Charles, et al. "The Energetic Implications of Curtailing versus Storing Solar- and Wind-Generated Electricity." *Energy and Environmental Science* 6 (2013): 2804–10. http://pubs.rsc.org/en/content/articlepdf/2013/ee/c3ee41973h.

Barouski, David. "'Blood Minerals' in the Kivu Province of the Democratic Republic of the Congo." *Race and History*, June 1, 2007. http://www.raceandhistory.com/historicalviews/2007/2106.html.

Barrett, Raymond, and Matt Whittaker. "US Rare Earths Miners Would Benefit from Proposed Stockpile." *Financial Times*, November 4, 2010.

Barrett, Scott. "The Incredible Economics of Geoengineering." *Environmental and Resource Economics* 39 (2008): pp. 45–54.

——. *Why Cooperate? The Incentive to Supply Global Public Goods.* Oxford: Oxford University Press, 2010.

——. "Rethinking Climate Change Governance and Its Relationship to the World Trading System." Ferdi Working Paper No. P20, Fondation pour les Études et Recherches sur le Développement International, Paris, July 2011. http://www.ferdi.fr/sites/www.ferdi.fr/files/publication/fichiers/P20_Barrett_WEB.pdf

—— et al. "Climate Engineering Reconsidered". *Nature Climate Change* 4(2014): pp. 527–529.

Basel Convention: Controlling Transboundary Movements of Hazardous Wastes and Their Disposal. www.basel.int/.

Basel Convention Ban Amendment. http://www.basel.int/Implementation/LegalMatters/BanAmendment/tabid/1484/Default.aspx.

BBC Asia News. "Japan Bluefin Tuna Fetches $1.7m." January 5, 2013. http://www.bbc.co.uk/news/world-asia-2091930 .

BBC News. "China Asserts Sea Border Claims." May 13, 2009. http://news.bbc.co.uk/2/hi/asia-pacific/8047206.stm.

———. "Sahara Sun 'to Help Power Europe.'" November 2, 2009. http://news.bbc.co.uk/2/hi/africa/8337735.stm.

———. "Q&A: South China Sea Dispute." June 27, 2011. http://www.bbc.co.uk/news/world-asia-pacific-13748349.

———. "Western Sahara Profile." January 7, 2014. http://www.bbc.com/news/world-africa-14115273.

Beaumont, Peter and Joanna Walters. "Greenspan Admits Iraq War Was about Oil, as Deaths Put at 1.2 Million". The Guardian, September 16, 2007.

Beattie, Alan. False Economy: A Surprising Economic History of the World. Toronto: Viking Canada, 2009.

Behringer, Wolfgang. A Cultural History of Climate. Malden, MA: Polity Press, 2010 (first German ed. 2007).

Behrmann, Elisabeth. "Green Batteries' Graphite Adds to China Pollution." Bloomberg News, April 30, 2014. http://www.bloomberg.com/news/articles/2014-03-14/teslas-in-california-help-bring-dirty-rain-to-china.

Beketov, Mikhael A. et al. "Pesticides Reduce Regional Biodiversity of Stream Invertebrates". PNAS 110 (2013): pp. 11039–11043.

Bell, Michelle L., Devra L. Davis, and Tony Fletcher. "A Retrospective Assessment of Mortality from the London Smog Episode of 1952: The Role of Influenza and Pollution." Environmental Health Perspectives 112 (2004): pp. 6–8.

Benbrook, Charles. "Impacts of Genetically Engineered Crops on Pesticide Use in the US: The First Sixteen Years." Environmental Sciences Europe 24 (2012). http://link.springer.com/article/10.1186/2190-4715-24-24#.

Bernstein, Peter L. The Power of Gold: The History of an Obsession. New York: John Wiley and Sons, 2000.

Berry, Alison. Two Forests under the Big Sky. Tribal v. Federal Management. Boseman, MO: PERC Policy Series No. 45, 2009. http://perc.org/articles/two-forests-under-big-sky-no-45.

Berton, Pierre. Klondike: The Last Great Gold Rush. Revised ed. Toronto: McClelland and Stewart, 1972.

Bialik, Carl. "How Big Is That Widening Gyre of Floating Plastic?" Wall Street Journal, March 25, 2009.

Binkley, Alex. "The Arctic Is a'Changing," Canadian Sailings, October 22, 2013. http://www.canadiansailings.ca/?p=7586.

Bird, Kenneth J. et al. Circum-Arctic Resource Appraisal: Estimates of Undiscovered Oil and Gas North of the Arctic Circle. US Geological Survey Fact Sheet 2008-3049.

Biswas, Asit K., and Ahmet C. Bozer. "What Water's Worth." Project Syndicate, September 18, 2014. http://www.project-syndicate.org/commentary/asit-k--biswas-and-ahmet-c--bozer-warn-that-current-efforts-to-improve-the-management-of-water-scarcity-are-woefully-inadequate.

Black, Richard. "Action Needed on Deadly Lakes". BBC News, September 27, 2005. http://news.bbc.co.uk/2/hi/science/nature/4285878.stm

Blackwell, Richard. "Bulb Ban Unlikely to Dim Tungsten Boom." *The Globe and Mail Report on Business*, April 26, 2007.

Blanchflower, David G., and Andrew J. Oswald. "International Happiness." NBER Working Paper No. 16668, National Bureau of Economic Research. Cambridge, Mass. 2011.

Blaser, Juergen, et al. *Status of Tropical Forest Management 2011*. Technical Series No. 38. Yokohama, Japan: International Tropical Timber Organization, 2011.

Blattman, Christopher, and Edward Miguel. "Civil War." *Journal of Economic Literature* 48, no. 1 (2010): pp. 3–57.

Bleischwitz, Raimund, Monika Dittrich, and Chiara Pierdicca. "Coltan from Central Africa, International Trade and Implications for Certification." *Resources Policy* 37 (2012): pp. 19–29.

Board of Agriculture and Natural Resources. *The Impact of Genetically Engineered Crops on Farm Sustainability in the United States*. Washington, DC: The National Academies Press, 2010.

Bogoslaw, David. "Central Bank Buying Spurs a Gold Rush." *Business Week*, November 25, 2009.

Boix, Charles. "Economic Roots of Civil Wars and Revolutions in the Contemporary World." *World Politics* 60 (2008): pp. 390–438.

Bonel, Kevin Anthony, and Gregory R. Chapman. *World Metals & Minerals Review 2005*. London: Metal Bulletin PLC, 2005.

Borgeson, Scott G. "Arctic Meltdown: The Economic and Security Implications of Global Warming." *Foreign Affairs* 87 (March–April, 2008): pp.63–77.

Bowles, Graham, Richard Bowker, and Nathan Samsonoff. "Viking Expansion and the Search for Bog Iron." *Platforum* 12 (2011): pp. 25–38.

Boyd, Robert, and P.J. Richerson. "Review: Culture and Human Cooperation." *Philosophical Transactions of the Royal Society* 368, no. 1533 (2009): pp. 3281–8.

Braesicke, Peter, Olaf Morgenstern, and John Pyle. "Might Dimming the Sun Change Atmospheric ENSO Teleconnections as We Know Them?" *Atmospheric Sciences Letters* 12 (2011): p. 184.

Brandt, Adam R. "Upstream Greenhouse Gas Emissions from Canadian Oil Sands as a Feedstock for European Refineries," 2011. https://circabc.europa.eu/d/d/workspace/SpacesStore/db806977-6418-44db-a464-20267139b34d/Brandt_Oil_Sands_GHGs_Final.pdf.

Branigan, Tania. "Soil Erosion to Cut Harvests in China's Breadbasket by 40%." *The Guardian*, November 22, 2008. http://www.theguardian.com/environment/2008/nov/22/chinese-soil-erosion-farming-overpopulation.

Brichieri-Colombi, Stephen. *The World Water Crisis: The Failures of Resource Management*. London: I.B. Tauris, 2009.

Bridge, Gavin. "Contested Terrain: Mining and the Environment." *Annual Review of Environment and Resources* 29 (2004): pp. 205–259.

British Airways Media Centre. "GreenSky Project Prepares to Land in Thurrock," April 16, 2014. http://www.britishairways.com/en-gb/bamediacentre/newsarticles?articleID=20140416080250#.VDbado1oypo.

British Petroleum. *BP Energy Outlook, 2030*. http://www.bp.com/liveassets/bp_internet/globalbp/globalbp_uk_english/reports_and_publications/statistical_energy_review_2011/STAGING/local_assets/pdf/BP_World_Energy_Outlook_booklet_2013.pdf.

Brown, Ellie, and Michael F. Jacobson. *Cruel Oil: How Palm Oil Harms Health, Rainforest and Wildlife*. Washington, DC: Center for Science in the Public Interest, 2005. http://www.cspinet.org/palm/PalmOilReport.pdf.

Brown, Stephen R. *How a Family Feud in Medieval Spain Divided the World in Half.* New York: St. Martin's Press, 2011.

Bruinsma, Jelle, ed. *World Agriculture towards 2015/2030: An FAO Perspective.* London: Earthscan Publications, 2003.

Bruinsma, Jelle. "The Resource Outlook to 2050: By How Much Do Land, Water and Crop Yields Need to Increase by 2050?" Paper presented at the FAO Expert Meeting: How to Feed the World in 2050, Rome, June 24–26, 2009. ftp://ftp.fao.org/docrep/fao/012/ak971e/ak971e00.pdf.

Brühl, Carsten A. et al."Terrestrial Pesticide Exposure on Amphibians: An Underestimated Cause of Global Decline". *Scientific Reports* 3 (2013).

Bullis, Kevin. "Electric Cars Primer." *MIT Technology Review*, 2008. http://www.technologyreview.com/featuredstory/409997/electric-cars-primer/.

Bulte, Erwin, et al. "Payments for Ecosystem Services and Poverty Reduction." *Environment and Development* 8 (2008): pp. 245–254.

Butler, Rhett. "Environmental Impacts of Mining in the Rainforest." *Mongabay*, July 27, 2012. http://rainforests.mongabay.com/0808.htm.

Buxton, Herbert T., and Dana W. Kolpin. "Pharmaceuticals, Horomones and Other Organic Waste Water Contaminants in US Streams." *USGS Fact Sheet FS-027-02*, 2002. http://toxics.usgs.gov/pubs/FS-027-02/pdf/FS-027-02.pdf.

Caley, M. Julian, Rebecca Fisher, and Kerry Mengersen. "Global Species Richness Estimates Have Not Converged". *Trends in Ecology and Evolution* 29 (2014) pp. 187–188.

Campbell, Dennis. "Eating Less Meat Could Save 45,000 Lives a Year, Experts Claim." *The Guardian*, October 19, 2010. http://www.theguardian.com/society/2010/oct/19/eat-less-meat-research.

Canadian Boreal Forest Agreement. www.canadianborealforestagreement.com.

Cardis, Elizabeth, et al. "Cancer Consequences of the Chernobyl Accident: 20 Years On." *Journal of Radiology Protection* 26 (2006): pp. 127–140.

Carrington, Damian. "Bank of England Investigating Risk of a Carbon Bubble ", *The Guardian*, December 1, 2014.

Cartagena Protocol on Biosafety. http://bch.cbd.int/protocol/.

Carter, Colin, and Henry Miller. "Corn for Fuel." *The New York Times*, July 30, 2012.

Cassman, Kenneth G., et al. "Meeting Cereal Demand while Protecting Natural Resources and Improving Environmental Quality." *Annual Review of Environment and Resources* 28 (2003). pp. 315–358.

CBC News. "Parks Canada Targets Large Cities as Visits Decline." January 15, 2012. http://www.cbc.ca/news/canada/parks-canada-targets-large-cities-as-visits-decline-1.1150716.

———. "B.C. Village's Ocean Fertilization Experiment Probed." *The Fifth Estate*, March 28, 2013. http://www.cbc.ca/news/canada/british-columbia/story/2013/03/27/bc-iron-restoration-fifth-estate.html.

Central Intelligence Agency. *The World Factbook*, 2014. https://www.cia.gov/library/publications/the-world-factbook/rankorder/2127rank.html.

Chamon, Marcos, Paolo Mauro, and Yohei Okawa. "The Implications of Mass Car Ownership in the Emerging Market Giants." Social Science Research Network. *Economic Policy* 23, no. 54 (April 2008): pp. 243–96. http://papers.ssrn.com/sol3/papers.cfm?abstract_id=1108502##.

Chancellor, Edward. *Devil Take the Hindmost: A History of Financial Speculation.* New York: Farrar, Straus and Giroux, 1999.

Chang, Yen-Chiang, Nannan Wang, and Onur Sabri Durak. "Ship Recycling and Marine Pollution." *Marine Pollution Bulletin* 60 (2010): pp. 1390–1396.

Chatre, Ashwini, and Arun Agrawal. "Forest Commons and Local Enforcement." *PNAS* 105, no. 36 (2008): pp. 13286–91.

Chazelas, Jean. "La Suppression de la Gabelle du Sel en 1945." In *Le rôle du sel dans l'histoire: travaux prepares*, edited by Michel Mollat, pp. 263–65. Paris: Presses universitaires de France, 1968.

Chen, Xianyao, and Ka-Kit Tung. "Varying Planetary Heat Sink Led to Global Warming Slowdown and Acceleration." *Science* 345 (2014): pp. 897–903.

Cheung, William, et al. "Signature of Ocean Warming in Global Fisheries Catches." *Nature* 497 (2013): pp. 365–368.

Chidi Nnorom, Innocent, et al. "Evaluation of Heavy Metal Release from the Disposal of Waste Computer Monitors at an Open Dump." *International Journal of Environmental Science and Development* 1, no. 3 (2010): pp. 227–233.

Chisti, Yusuf, and Jinyue Yan. "Energy from Algae: Current Status and Future Trends; Algal Biofuels: A Status Report." *Applied Energy* 88 (2011): pp. 3277–9.

Chowdhury, Sadia, Naoko Ohno, and Pia Axemo. *Experiences with Fertility Reduction in Five High-Fertility Countries: 1980–2006: Synthesis of Case Studies*. Washington, DC: The World Bank, 2010.

Christian, Jeffrey M. *Commodities Rising: The Reality Behind the Hype and How to Really Profit in the Commodities Market*. Hoboken, New Jersey: John Wiley and Sons, 2006.

Churchill, Robin. "The Persistent Problem of Non-Compliance with the Law of the Sea Convention: Disorder in the Oceans." *International Journal of Marine and Coastal Law* 27, no. 4 (2012): pp. 813–20.

Clark, Gregory. *A Farewell to Alms:A Brief Economic History of the World*. Princeton and Oxford: Princeton University Press, 2007.

Clay, Karen, and Werner Troesken. "Did Frederick Brodie Discover the World's First Environmental Kuznets Curve? Coal Smoke and the Rise and Fall of the London Fog." NBER Working Paper No. 15669, National Bureau of Economic Research, Cambridge, MA, 2010. http://www.nber.org/papers/w15669.

Climate Response Fund. Asilomar International Conference on Climate Intervention Technologies. March 22–26, 2009. http://climateresponsefund.org/index.php?option=com_content&view=article&id=137&Itemid=81.

Clover, Charles. *The End of the Line: How Overfishing Is Changing the World and What We Eat*. Berkeley: The University of California Press, 2008.

Clutton-Brock, Tim H., et al. "Selfish Sentinels in Cooperative Mammals." *Science* 284 (1999): pp. 1640–44.

CNN. "Top Climate Change Scientists' Letter to Policy Influencers". November 3, 2013. http://www.cnn.com/2013/11/03/world/nuclear-energy-climate-change-scientists-letter/ .

Coady, David. et al. "How Large are Global Energy Subsidies?". *IMF Working Paper* 15/105 (2015). http://www.imf.org/external/pubs/ft/wp/2015/wp15105.pdf .

Coenen, R.M. "A proposal to Convert Air Transport to Clean Hydrogen (CATCH)." *International Journal of Hydrogen Energy* 34 (2009): pp. 8451–53.

Condie, H.M., A. Grant, and T.L. Catchpole. "Incentivising Selected Fishing Under a Policy to Ban Discards; Lessons from European and Global Fisheries." *Marine Policy* 45 (2014): pp. 287–292.

Colby, W. David, et al. *Wind Turbine Sound and Health Effects: An Expert Panel Review*. Prepared for the American Wind Energy Association and Canadian Wind Energy Association, 2009. www.canwea.ca/pdf/talkwind//Wind_Turbine_Sound_and_Health_Effects.pdf.

Collier, Paul, et al. *Breaking the Conflict Trap: Civil War and Development Policy*. Washington, DC: The World Bank, 2003.

Collier, Paul. *Wars, Guns, and Votes: Democracy in Dangerous Places*. New York: HarperCollins, 2009.

Comprehensive Assessment of Water Management in Agriculture. *Water for Food, Water for Life: A Comprehensive Assessment of Water Management in Agriculture*. London: Earthscan, 2007.

Connelly, Matthew. *Fatal Misconception: The Struggle to Control World Population*. Cambridge, MA: The Belknap Press of Harvard University Press, 2008.

Conservation International. "Mangrove Forests in Worldwide Decline." April 9, 2010. http://www.conservation.org/newsroom/pressreleases/Pages/Report-Mangroves-Worldwide-Decline-IUCN.aspx.

Constanza, Robert, et al. "The Value of the World's Ecosystem Services and Natural Capital." *Nature* 387 (1997): pp. 253–260.

Constanza, Robert, et al. "Beyond GDP: The Need for New Measures of Progress." *The Pardee Papers*, no. 4 (2009). http://www.bu.edu/pardee/files/documents/PP-004-GDP.pdf.

Convention on Biological Diversity. Strategic Plan for Biodiversity 2011–2020, including Aichi Biodiversity Targets, 2010. http://www.cbd.int/sp/.

———. "The Hyderabad Call for Biodiversity Champions," 2012. http://www.cbd.int/champions/.

———. Global Diversity Outlook 4, 2014. http://www.cbd.int/gbo4/.

———. "Climate-Related Geoengineering and Biodiversity." COP 10, September 2010. http://www.cbd.int/climate/geoengineering/.

Convention on International Trade in Endangered Species of Wild Fauna and Flora. http://www.cites.org/

Convention on the Law of Non-Navigational Uses of International Water Courses. http://www.internationalwaterlaw.org/documents/intldocs/watercourse_conv.html.

Cook, Christina, and K. Bakker. "Water Security: Debating an Emerging Paradigm." *Global Environmental Change* 22 (2012): pp. 94–102.

Corrigan, Colleen, and F. Kershaw. *Working Toward High Seas Marine Protected Areas: An Assessment of Progress Made and Recommendations for Collaboration*. Cambridge, UK: UNEP / WCMC, 2008.

Costello, Christopher, and Michael Ward. "Search, Bioprospecting and Biodiversity Conservation." *Journal of Environmental Economics and Management* 52 (2006): pp. 615–626.

Costello, Christopher, et al. "Can Catch Shares Prevent Fisheries Collapse?" *Science* 321 (2008): pp. 1678–81.

Costello, Mark, et al. "Can We Name Earth's Species before They Go Extinct?" *Science* 339 (2013): pp. 413–416.

Cottee-Jones, H. Eden W., and Robert J. Whittaker. "The Keystone Species Concept: A Critical Appraisal." *Frontiers of Biogeography* 4 (2012): pp. 117–127.

Coumans, Catherine. "Case Study on Marcopper Mining and the Marinduque Disaster," 2002 www.minesandcommunities.org/article.php?a=1445.

———. "Submarine Tailings Disposal," 2002. http://www.miningwatch.ca/files/01.STD-toolkit.intr_.pdf.

Council of Canadians. "Canada–EU Deal Threatens Canada's Water," October 18, 2013. http://canadians.org/blog/canada-eu-deal-threatens-canadas-water.

Cowtan, Kevin, and Robert G. Way. "Coverage Bias in the HadCRUT4 Temperature Series and Its Impact on Recent Temperature Trends." *Quarterly Journal of the Royal Meteorological Society* 140, no. 683 (2014): pp. 1935–44.

Craig, James R., David J. Vaughan, and Brian J. Skinner. *Resources of the Earth*. Englewood, NJ: Prentice Hall, 1988.

Creed, Anna, and Smita Nakhooda. "Redd+ Finance Delivery: Lessons from Early Experience." Heinrich Böll Stiftung Foundation, North America, 2011. www.odi.org.uk/resources/docs/7481.pdf.

Cressey, Daniel. "A New Breed: The Next Wave of Genetically Modified Crops Is Making Its Way to Market—and Might Just Ease Concerns over 'Frankenfoods.'" *Nature* 475 (2013): pp. 27–29.

Crutzen, Paul J. "Albedo Enhancement by Stratospheric Sulfur Injections: A Contribution to Resolve a Policy Dilemma?" *Climatic Change* 77 (2006): pp. 211–219.

———. "The Geology of Mankind." *Nature* 415, no. 23 (2002): p. 23.

Cuddington, John T., and Daniel Jarrett. "Super Cycles in Real Metals Prices." *IMF Staff Papers* 55 (2008): pp. 521–565.

Cullis-Suzuki, Sarika, and Daniel Paul. "Failing the High Seas: A Global Evaluation of Regional Fisheries Management Organizations." *Marine Policy* 34 (2010): pp. 1036–42.

Daly, Herman E. "Toward Some Operational Principles of Sustainable Development." *Ecological Economics* 2, no. 1 (1990): pp.1–6.

Darwin, Charles. *The Formation of Vegetable Mould through the Action of Worms, with Observations on Their Habits*. London: John Murray, 1881.

Davis, Lance E., et al. *In Pursuit of Leviathan, Technology, Institutions, Productivity and Profits in American Whaling, 1816–1906*. Chicago: University of Chicago Press, 1997.

Davis, R.W.D., et al. "Defining and Estimating Global Marine Fisheries Bycatch." *Marine Policy* 33 (2009): pp. 661–676.

Davison, William. "IMF Urges Ethiopia to Slow Nile Dam Project to Protect Economy." *Bloomberg News*, September 14, 2012. http://www.bloomberg.com/news/2012-09-14/imf-urges-ethiopia-to-slow-nile-dam-project-to-protect-economy.html.

Dawe, David, ed. *The Rice Crisis: Markets, Policies and Food Security*. London: Earthscan / FAO, 2010.

Dawkins, Richard. *The Selfish Gene*. Oxford: Oxford University Press, 1976.

Deacon, Robert T. *Creating Marine Assets: Property Rights in Ocean Fisheries*. Bozeman, MO: PERC Policy Series No. 1943, 2009. http://perc.org/sites/default/files/ps43.pdf.

———. "Fishery Management by Harvest Cooperatives." *Review of Environmental Economics and Policy* 6 (2012): pp. 258–277.

———. "The Political Economy of the Natural Resource Curse: A Survey of the Evidence." *Foundations and Trends in Microeconomics* 7, no. 2 (2011): pp. 111–208.

Dearing, John, et al. "Extending the Timescale and Range of Ecosystem Services through Paleoenvironmental Analyses, Exemplified in the Lower Yangtze Basin." *PNAS* 109 (2012): pp. E1111–20.

Deffeyes, Kenneth S. *Beyond Oil: The View from Hubbert's Peak*. New York: Hill and Wang, 2005.

DeFries, Ruth S., et al. "Planetary Opportunities: A Social Contract for Global Change Science to Contribute to a Sustainable Future." *Bioscience* 62, no. 6 (2012): pp. 603–609.

de Groot, Rudolf S., Matthew A. Wilson, and Roelof M.J. Boumans. "A Typology for the Classification, Description and Valuation of Ecosystem Functions, Goods and Services." *Ecological Economics* 41 (2002): pp. 393–400.

de Joinville, Jean. *Chronicles of the Crusades*. Translated by F.T. Marzials. London: Penguin Books, 1963.

de Vos, Jurriaan M., et al. "Estimating the Normal Background Rate of Species Extinction". *Conservation Biology* 29 (2015): pp. 452–462.

Delli Priscoli, Jerome, and Aaron T. Wolf. *Managing and Transforming Water Conflicts.* New York: Cambridge University Press, 2009.

Delucchi, Mark A., and Mark Z. Jacobson. "Providing All Global Energy with Wind, Water, and Solar Power, Part II: Reliability, System and Transmission Costs, and Policies." *Energy Policy* 39 (2011): pp. 1170–90.

Demarty, Maud, and J. Bastien. "GHG Emissions from Hydroelectric Reservoirs in Tropical and Equatorial Regions: Review of 20 Years of CH4 Emissions Measurements." *Energy Policy* 39 (2011): pp. 4197–200.

Demeke, Mulat, Guendalina Pangrazio, and Materne Maetz. *Country Responses to the Food Security Crisis: Nature and Preliminary Implications of the Policies Pursued.* Initiative on Soaring Food Prices. Rome: FAO, 2009. http://www.fao.org/fileadmin/user_upload/ISFP/pdf_for_site_Country_Response_to_the_Food_Security.pdf.

de Villiers, Marq. *Water: The Fate of Our Most Precious Resource.* New York: Houghton Mifflin Company, 2000.

de Vivero, Juan Luis Suárez . "The extended continental shelf: a geographical perspective of the implementation of Article 76 of UNCLOS". *Ocean & Coastal Management* 73 (2013): pp. 113–126.

Diamond, Jared. *Collapse: How Societies Choose to Fail or Succeed.* New York: Viking, 2005.

Dixon, Darius, and Climatewire. "Can Climate Change Clean Up Indoor Air?" *Scientific American,* July 12, 2010. http://www.scientificamerican.com/article/can-climate-change-clean-up-indoor-air/.

Dowie, Mark. *Conservation Refugees: The Hundred-Year Conflict between Global Conservation and Native Peoples.* Cambridge and London: MIT Press, 2009.

Drouin, Roger Real. "Wood Pellets Green Energy or New Source of CO_2 Emissions." *Environment 360.* January 22, 2015. http://e360.yale.edu/feature/wood_pellets_green_energy_or_new_source_of_co2_emissions/2840/ .

Dudka, Stanislav, and Domy C. Adriano. "Environmental Impacts of Metal Ore Mining and Processing: A Review." *Journal of Environmental Quality* 26, no. 3 (1997): pp. 590–602.

Dudley, Nigel, ed. *Guidelines for Applying Protected Area Management Categories.* International Union for Conservation of Nature and Natural Resources. Gland, Switzerland, 2008.

Duflo, Esther, Michael Kremer, and Jonathan Robinson. "Nudging Farmers to Use Fertilizer: Theory and Experimental Evidence from Kenya." NBER Working Paper No. 15131, National Bureau of Economic Research, Cambridge, Mass. 2009. http://www.nber.org/papers/w15131.

Duflo, Esther and Rohini Pande. "Dams". *Quarterly Journal of Economics* 122 (2007): pp. 601–642.

Dwyer, Devin. "Pat Robinson Blames Earthquake on Pact Haitians Made with Satan." *ABC News,* January 13, 2010. http://abcnews.go.com/blogs/politics/2010/01/pat-robertson-blames-earthquake-on-pact-haitians-made-with-satan/.

Dyer, Gwynne. *Climate Wars.* Toronto: Random House Canada, 2008.

Easterlin, Richard A. "Does Economic Growth Improve the Human Lot? Some Empirical Evidence." In *Nations and Households in Economic Growth,* edited by P.A. David and M.W. Reder, pp. 88–125. New York: Academic Press, 1974.

Easterly, William. *The White Man's Burden: Why the West's Efforts to Aid the Rest Have Done So Much Ill and So Little Good.* Oxford: Oxford University Press, 2006.

Economist. "Managing the Rainforests." May 10, 2001.

———. "The Devil's Excrement: Is Oil Wealth a Blessing or a Curse?" May 22, 2003.

———. "Damming Evidence." July 17, 2003.

————. "Irrigate and Die." July 17, 2003.

————. "The Logging Trade: Down in the Woods." March 23, 2006.

————. "For Brazilians, Land Still Has a Mythical Quality." April 12, 2007.

————. "Tapping the Power of the Sea." April 26, 2007.

————. "South Africa: Why Land Reform Is So Tricky." May 3, 2007.

————. "Dirty King Coal." May 31, 2007.

————. "Speaking across the Ages." October 22, 2007.

————. "A Fishy Tale." December 13, 2007.

————. "Some Like It Cool." December 19, 2007.

————. "Ending the Dammed Nuisance." February 19, 2008.

————. "Trade Bans and Conservation: Call of the Wild." March 6, 2008.

————. "Gulf Economies: How to Spend It." April 24, 2008.

————. "The Doha Dilemma: Does Freer Farm Trade Help Poor People?" May 29, 2008.

————. "Out of the Wilderness." July 12, 2008.

————. "Come, Friends, and Plough the Sea." December 30, 2008.

————. "All Change, No Change: Mountain Above, Volcano Below." July 23, 2009.

————. "The Economics of Natural Gas: Drowning in It." August 13, 2009.

————. "You Are What You Eat: Rice in Japan." December 19, 2009.

————. "How to Feed the World." November 21, 2009.

————. "If Words Were Food, Nobody Would Go Hungry." November 21, 2009.

————. "Fin Times: Ban the Trade in Bluefin Tuna—but Set a Clear Path to Sustainable Exploitation." March 18, 2010.

————. "Old Worry, New Ideas: After Some Moral Victories over Nuclear Matters, America's Hardest Test Looms." April 15, 2010.

————. "To the Last Drop." May 20, 2010.

————. "Water, a Survey: For Want of a Drink." May 20, 2010.

————. "Why Baobab?" July 23, 2010.

————. "Brazilian Agriculture: The Miracle of the Cerrado." August 26, 2010.

————. "A Special Report on Forests." September 25, 2010.

————. "Oil Leak: Could One of the World's Top Petroleum Producers Really Go Bankrupt?" February 24, 2011.

————. "The Fallout." April 26, 2011.

————. "A Man-Made World: Science Is Recognizing Humans as a Geological Force to Be Reckoned With." May 28, 2011.

————. "Fracking Here, Fracking There: Europe Will Have Trouble Replicating America's Shale-Gas Bonanza." November 26, 2011.

————. "Mopping Up the Legal Spill." March 3, 2012.

————. "The Dream That Failed. Special Report on Nuclear Energy." March 10–16, 2012.

————. "Combating Climate Change: Net Benefits." March 17, 2012.

————. "Europe's Dirty Secret: The Unwelcome Renaissance." January 5, 2013.

————. "Manufacturing Metals: A Tantalising Prospect." February 16, 2013.

————. "Climate Science: A Sensitive Matter." March 30, 2013.

————. "Carbon Trading: Below Junk Status." April 16, 2013.

————. "The World's Thirst for Oil Could Be Nearing a Peak." August 3, 2013.

————. "How Economic Growth Will Help Prevent Extinctions: A Special Report on Biodiversity." September 14, 2013.

————. "Oil in Ecuador: It's Hard to Be Green." September 28, 2013.

————. "All Dried Up: Northern China Is Running out of Water, but the Government's Remedies Are Potentially Disastrous." October 12, 2013.

———. "Fully Charged Tesla Gains New Admirers as It Heads towards Mass Market." March 1, 2014.

———. "Combating Illegal Fishing." January 24, 2015.

———. "Bolivia's Access to the Sea. Beaches of the Future." May 9, 2015,

Ehrlich, Paul. *The Population Bomb*. New York: Ballantine Books, 1968.

Eisentraut, Anselm. *Sustainable Production of Second-Generation Biofuels: Information Paper*. Paris: OECD / IEA, 2010. http://www.iea.org/publications/freepublications/publication/biofuels_exec_summary.pdf.

Eliasch, Johan. *Eliasch Review: Climate Change: Financing Global Forests*. London: UK Government, 2008. https://www.gov.uk/government/uploads/system/uploads/attachment_data/file/228833/9780108507632.pdf.

Emery, Katherine B. "*Tonnare* in Italy: Science, History, and Culture of Sardinian Tuna Fishing." *California Italian Studies Journal* 1 (2010). http://escholarship.org/uc/item/2nm2b772.

Encyclopedia Britannica, 15th ed., s.v. "zoological gardens."

Engel, Stefanie, Stefano Pagiola, and Sven Wunder. "Designing Payments for Environmental Services in Theory and Practice: An Overview of the Issues." *Ecological Economics* 65 (2008): pp. 663–674.

Erickson, Wallace P. et al. "A Comprehensive Analysis of Small-Passerine Fatalities from Collision with Turbines at Wind Energy Facilities." *PLOS ONE* 9(9) (2014). http://journals.plos.org/plosone/article?id=10.1371/journal.pone.0107491 .

Erikson, Marcus et al. "Plastic Pollution in the World's Oceans: More than 5 Trillion Plastic Pieces Weighing over 250,000 Tons Afloat at Sea." *PLOS ONE* 9(2) (2014). http://www.plosone.org/article/fetchObject.action?uri=info:doi/10.1371/journal.pone.0111913&representation=PDF.

Ernst & Young. "Conflict Minerals. What You Need to Know about the New Disclosure and How Ernst & Young Can Help." Ernst &Young, 2012. http://www.ey.com/Publication/vwLUAssets/ConflictMinerals_FQ0043/$FILE/ConflictMinerals_FQ0043.pdf.

Essington, Timothy E., Anne H. Beaudreau, and John Wiedenman. "Fishing through Marine Food Webs." *PNAS* 103 (2005): pp. 3171–5.

European Commission. *Critical Raw Materials for the EU: Report of the Ad-hoc Working Group on Defining Critical Raw Materials*, July 2010. http://ec.europa.eu/enterprise/policies/raw-materials/files/docs/report-b_en.pdf.

———. "Defining 'Critical' Raw Materials." Last modified November 6, 2014. http://ec.europa.eu/enterprise/policies/raw-materials/critical/index_en.htm.

———. "The EU 2020 Climate and Energy Package." Last modified December 11, 2014. http://ec.europa.eu/clima/policies/package/index_en.htm.

———. "2030 Framework for Climate and Energy Policies". January 2015. http://ec.europa.eu/clima/policies/2030/index_en.htm.

———. "An EU Strategy for Better Ship Dismantling." Communication from the Commission to the European Parliament, the Council, the European Economic and Social Committee and the Committee of the Regions, Brussels, November 19, 2008. http://ec.europa.eu/environment/waste/ships/pdf/com_2008_767.pdf.

———. *EUR 24473—A Decade of EU-Funded GMO Research (2001–2010)*. Luxembourg: Publications Office of the EU, 2010. http://ec.europa.eu/research/biosociety/pdf/a_decade_of_eu-funded_gmo_research.pdf.

———. "Reform of the Common Fisheries Policy." Last modified November 26, 2014. http://ec.europa.eu/fisheries/reform/index_en.htm.

———. "Transport and Environment: Fuel Quality Monitoring." Last modified October 30, 2014. http://ec.europa.eu/environment/air/transport/fuel.htm.

———. "Waste Electrical and Electronic Equipment (WEEE)." Last modified October 30, 2014. http://ec.europa.eu/environment/waste/weee/index_en.htm.

Evans, Alex. *The Feeding of the Nine Billion: Global Food Security for the 21st Century*. Chatham House Report. London: The Royal Institute of International Affairs, 2009. http://www.wfp.org/sites/default/files/alex_evans.pdf.

Evans, Julian, ed. *Planted Forests: Uses, Impacts and Sustainability*. Rome: FAO and CAB International, 2009.

Extractive Industries Transparency Initiative. www.eiti.org.

Farvar, T., and J. Milton. *The Careless Technology*. London: Tom Stacey, 1973.

Federico, Giovanni. *Feeding the World: An Economic History of Agriculture, 1800–2000*. Princeton: Princeton University Press, 2005

Fenical, William, et al. "The Deep Oceans as a Source of New Treatments for Cancer." In, *Chemobiomolecular Science*, edited by Masakatsy Shibasaki, Masamitsu Lino, and Hiroyki Osaka, pp. 83–91. Springer Japan, 2013.

Fiala, Nathan. "Measuring Sustainability: Why the Ecological Footprint is Bad Economics and Bad Environmental Science." *Ecological Economics* 67, no. 4 (2008): pp. 519–525.

Fiedler, Fernando N., et al. "Driftnet Fishery Threats Sea Turtles in the Atlantic Ocean." *Biodiversity and Conservation* 21 (2012): pp. 915–931.

Fields, Helen. "Fog Catchers Bring Water to Parched Villages." *National Geographic*, July 9, 2009.

Finamore, Alberto, et al. "Intestinal and Peripheral Immune Response to MON 810 Maize Ingestion in Weaning and Old Mice." *Journal of Agriculture and Food Chemistry* 56 (2008): pp. 11533–9.

Finkenrath, Matthias. *Cost and Performance of Carbon Dioxide Capture from Power Generation*. IEA working paper, International Energy Agency, Paris, 2011.

Finn, Kathy. "BP Lied about Size of US Gulf Oil Spill, Lawyers Tell Trial." Reuters. September 30, 2013. http://www.reuters.com/article/2013/09/30/us-bp-trial-idUSBRE98T13U20130930.

Fischer, Carolyn, and Louis Preonas. "Combining Policies for Renewable Energy: Is the Whole Less than the Sum of Its Parts?" Discussion Paper No. 10-10, Resources for the Future, Washington, DC, March 2010. http://www.rff.org/documents/RFF-DP-10-19.pdf.

Flannery, Tim. *Here on Earth: A Natural History of the Planet*. Toronto: HarperCollins, 2010.

Fleming, James Rodger. *Fixing the Sky: The Checkered History of Weather and Climate Control*. New York: Columbia University Press, 2010.

Flothman, Stefan, et al. "Closing Loopholes: Getting Illegal Fishing under Control." *Science* 328 (2010): pp. 1235–6.

Flynn, J.R. "Massive IQ Gains in 14 Nations: What IQ Tests Really Measure." *Psychological Bulletin* 101 (1987): pp. 171–191.

Flynn, Dennis O., and Arturo Giráldez. "Born with a 'Silver Spoon': The Origin of World Trade in 1571." *Journal of World History* 6, no 2 (1995): pp. 201–221.

Food and Agriculture Organization. "Agreement on Port State Measures to Prevent, Deter and Eliminate Illegal, Unreported and Unregulated Fishing." FAO Conference, Rome, November 22, 2009. http://www.fao.org/fileadmin/user_upload/legal/docs/2_037t-e.pdf.

———. *Aquastat, Country Profile,Turkey*. http://www.fao.org/NR/Water/aquastat/countries_regions/TUR/index.stm .

————. "Farming Must Change to Feed the World," February 4, 2009. Accessed December 13, 2014. www.fao.org/news/story/en/item/9962/icode.

————. *Guidelines for the Ecolabelling of Fish and Fishery Products from Marine Capture Fisheries.* Revision 1. Rome: FAO, 2009. www.fao.org/docrep/012/i1119t/i1119t.pdf.

————. "Planted Forests." Last modified March 26, 2012. www.fao.org/forestry/plantedforests.

————. "Rome Declaration on World Food Security and World Food Summit Plan of Action." World Food Summit, Rome, November 13–17, 1996. http://www.fao.org/docrep/003/w3613e/w3613e00.HTM.

————. *The State of Food Insecurity in the World: How Does International Price Volatility Affect Domestic Economies and Food Insecurity?* Rome: FAO, 2011. http://www.fao.org/docrep/014/i2330e/i2330e.pdf.

————. *The State of World Fisheries and Aquaculture: Opportunities and Challenges.* Rome: FAO, 2014. http://www.fao.org/3/a-i3720e.pdf.

————. *State of the World's Forests 2011.* Rome: FAO, 2011. http://www.fao.org/docrep/013/i2000e/i2000e.pdf.

————. *State of the World's Forests 2012.* Rome: FAO, 2012. http://www.fao.org/docrep/016/i3010e/i3010e.pdf.

————. *State of the World's Forests 2014.* Rome: FAO, 2014.

————.*Tackling Climate Change through Livestock. A Global Assessment of Emissions and Mitigation Opportunities.Rome:* FAO, 2012.

————. *World Agriculture: Towards 2015 / 2030: Summary Report.* Rome: FAO, 2002. http://www.fao.org/3/a-y3557e.pdf.

————. *World Review of Fisheries and Aquaculture.* Rome: FAO, 2010. http://www.fao.org/docrep/013/i1820e/i1820e01.pdf.

————, WFP, and IFAD. *The State of Food Insecurity in the World 2014: Strengthening the Enabling Environment for Food Security and Nutrition.* Rome: FAO, 2014. http://www.fao.org/docrep/016/i3027e/i3027e.pdf.

Forest Stewardship Council. www.fsc.org.

Frank, Robert H. *Luxury Fever: Money and Happiness in an Era of Excess.* Princeton: Princeton University Press, 2000.

Frankel, Jeffrey A. "Global Environment and Trade Policy." Discussion Paper #09-01, Belfer Center for Science and International Affairs, Harvard Kennedy School, April 2009. http://belfercenter.ksg.harvard.edu/publication/18968/global_environment_and_trade_policy.html .

————. "The Natural Resource Curse: A Survey." NBER Working Paper No. 15836, National Bureau of Economic Research, Cambridge, Mass. 2010. http://www.nber.org/papers/w15836.

Frumkin, Howard. "Beyond Toxicity: Human Health and the Natural Environment." *American Journal of Preventative Medicine* 20 (2001): pp. 234–240.

Gallai, Nicola, et al. "Economic Valuation of the Vulnerability of World Agriculture Confronted with Pollinator Decline." *Ecological Economics* 68 (2009): pp. 810–825.

Gammage, Bill. *The Biggest Estate on Earth: How Aborigines Made Australia.* Sydney: Allen & Unwin, 2011.

Garnett, Tara. "Livestock-Related Greenhouse Gas Emissions Impacts and Options for Policy Makers." *Environmental Science and Policy* 12 (2009): pp. 491–503.

Garrity, Dennis Philip, et al. "Evergreen Agriculture: A Robust Approach to Sustainable Food Security in Africa." *Food Security* 2 (2010): pp. 197–214.

Gassman, Kenneth G., et al. "Meeting Cereal Demand while Protecting Natural Resources and Improving Environmental Quality." *Annual Review of Environment and Resources* 28 (2003): pp. 315–358.

Gat, Azar. "The Human Motivational Complex: Evolutionary Theory and the Causes of Hunter-Gatherer Fighting." *Anthropological Quarterly* 73 (2000): pp. 20–34.

Gault, Sebastian. "An In-Depth Look at How In Situ Oil Sands Development Has Evolved." *Alberta Oil*, February 12, 2014. http://www.albertaoilmagazine.com/2014/02/in-situ-bitumen-recovery/.

Geoghegan, John. "A Legendary Offshore Danger." *Ocean Navigator* (website), February 28, 2013. Accessed December 13, 2014. http://www.oceannavigator.com/March-April-2013/A-legendary-offshore-danger/.

Gerber, P.J., et al. *Tackling Climate Change through Livestock: A Global Assessment of Emissions and Mitigation Opportunities.* Rome: FAO, 2013. http://www.fao.org/docrep/018/i3437e/i3437e.pdf.

Gholz, Eugene. Rare Earth Elements and National Security. Council on Foreign Relations, October 2014. http://www.cfr.org/energy-and-environment/rare-earth-elements-national-security/p33632.

Gilbert, Natasha. "GM Crops Escape into the American Wild: Transgenic Canola Found Growing Freely in North Dakota." *Nature News*, August 6, 2010. www.nature.news/2010/100806/full/news.2010.393.html.

Glavin, Terry. *The Sixth Extinction: Journeys among the Lost and Left Behind.* New York: Thomas Dunn Books, 2007.

Gleick, Peter H., ed. *The World's Water 2004–2005: The Biennial Report on Freshwater Resources.* Washington, DC: Island Press, 2004.

Gleick, Peter, Heather Cooley, and Gary Wolff. "With a Grain of Salt: An Update on Seawater Desalination." *The World's Water 2006–2007.* Pacific Institute for Studies in Development, Environment, and Security. Washington, DC: Island Press, 2006.

Global Water Partnership. www.gwp.org.

Globe International. The Globe Climate Legislation Initiative: First GLOBE Climate Legislation Summit in London, January 14, 2013. http://www.globeinternational.org/policy-initiatives/climate-change-initiative.

Glover, Charles. *The End of the Line: How Overfishing Is Changing the World and What We Eat.* Berkeley: University of California Press, 2006.

GMR (Great Man-Made River) Water Supply Project, Libya. www.water-technology.net/projects/gmr.

Godfray, H. Charles J., et al. "Food Security: The Challenge of Feeding 9 Billion People." *Science* 327, no. 812 (2010): pp. 812–818.

Goldman, Jason G. "Once upon a Time, the Catholic Church Decided That Beavers Were Fish." *Scientific American*, May 23, 2013. http://blogs.scientificamerican.com/thoughtful-animal/2013/05/23/once-upon-a-time-the-catholic-church-decided-that-beavers-were-fish/.

Goodell, Jeff. *Big Coal: The Dirty Secret behind America's Energy Future.* New York: Houghton Mifflin Company, 2006.

Gordon, Line J., C. Max Finlayson, and Malin Falkenmark. "Managing Water in Agriculture for Food Production and Other Ecosystem Services." *Agricultural Water Management* 97 (2010): pp. 532–539.

Goulson, Dave. "An Overview of the Environmental Risks Posed by Neonicotinoid Insecticides". *Journal of Applied Ecology* 50 (2013): pp. 977–987.

Government of Alberta. Alberta's Oil Sands. http://oilsands.alberta.ca/.

Gowdy, John M. "The Value of Biodiversity: Markets, Society and Ecosystems." *Land Economics* 73 (1997): pp. 25–41.

Goyal, Aparajita. "Information, Direct Access to Farmers, and Rural Market Performance in Central India." *American Economic Journal: Applied Economics* 2 (2010): pp. 22–45.

Graham-Rowe, Duncan. "Hydroelectric Power's Dirty Secret Revealed." *New Scientist*, February 24, 2005.

Green, Rhys, et al. "Farming and the Fate of Wild Nature." *Science* 307 (2005): pp. 550–555.

Greenberg, Paul. *Four Fish: The Future of the Last Wild Food*. New York: The Penguin Press, 2010.

Greenpeace International and FOEI. "Consideration of the Draft International Convention for the Safe and Environmentally Sound Recycling of Ships." Agenda item 6, International Conference on the Safe and Environmentally Sound Recycling of Ships, International Maritime Organization, February 9, 2009. http://www.shipbreaking-platform.org/shipbrea_wp2011/wp-content/uploads/2011/11/Platform-submission-to-IMO-Diplomatic-Conference-May-2009-1.pdf.

Greenstone, Michael and B. Kelsey Jack. "Envirodevonomics: A Research Agenda for an Emerging Field." *Journal of Economic Literature* LIII (2015): pp. 5–43.

Grimes, Sue, John Donaldson, and Gabriel Cebrian Gomez. *Report on the Environmental Benefits of Recycling*. Brussels: Bureau of International Recycling, 2008. http://www.bir.org/assets/Documents/publications/brochures/BIR_CO2_report.pdf.

Gu, Lianhong, et al. "Response of a Deciduous Forest to the Mount Pinatubo Eruption: Enhanced Photosynthesis." *Science* 299, no. 5615 (2003): pp. 2035–8.

Guardian. "Women to Blame for Earthquakes, Says Iran Cleric." April 19, 2010. http://www.theguardian.com/world/2010/apr/19/women-blame-earthquakes-iran-cleric.

———. "Price of Ivory in China Triples." July 3, 2014. http://www.theguardian.com/environment/2014/jul/03/price-ivory-china-triples-elephant.

———. "UK Electric Car Sales Surge in 2014." October 7, 2014. http://www.theguardian.com/environment/2014/oct/07/uk-electric-car-sales-surge-in-2014.

Guilford, Gwynn. "Why Does a Rhino Horn Cost $300,000? Because Vietnam Thinks It Cures Cancer." *The Atlantic*, May 15, 2013.

Guinnane, Timothy W. "The Historical Fertility Transition: A Guide for Economists." *Journal of Economic Literature* 49, no. 4 (2011): pp. 589–614.

Gullone, Eleonora. "The Biophilia Hypothesis and Life in the 21st Century: Increasing Mental Health or Increasing Pathology?" *Journal of Happiness Studies* 1 (2000): pp. 293–321.

Gupta, Aarti. "Transparency as Contested Political Terrain: Who Knows What about the Global GMO Trade and Why Does It Matter?" *Global Environmental Politics* 10, no. 3 (2010): pp. 32–52.

Haener, M.K., and M.K. Luckert. "Forest Certification: Economic Issues and Welfare Implications." *Canadian Public Policy* 24, supplement 2 (1998): pp. S83–S94.

Haglund, David. "The New Geopolitics of Minerals: An Inquiry into the Changing International Significance of Strategic Minerals." *Political Geography Quarterly* 5, no. 3 (1986): pp. 221–240.

Hanning, Christopher D., and Alun Evans. "Wind Turbine Noise. Seems to Affect Health Adversely and an Independent Review of Evidence Is Needed." *BMJ*, March 8, 2012.

Hardin, Garrett. "The Tragedy of the Commons." *Science* 162, no. 3859 (1968): pp. 1243–8.

Hardner, Jared, and Bruce McKenney. *The US National Park System: An Economic Asset at Risk*. A study commissioned by the National Parks Conservation Association, 2006. http://www.npca.org/assets/pdf/NPCA_Economic_Significance_Report.pdf.

Harris, Nancy, Rachel Petersen, and Susan Minnemayer. "8 Percent of the World's Remaining Pristine Forests Degraded since 2000." *World Resources Institute* (blog), September 4, 2014. http://www.wri.org/blog/2014/09/8-percent-worlds-remaining-pristine-forests-degraded-2000.

Harrison, John P. "Wind Turbines Noise." *Bulletin of Science, Technology and Society* 31 (2011): pp. 256–261.

Harrison, Robert Pogue. *Forests: The Shadow of Civilization*. Chicago: University of Chicago Press, 1992.

Harrower, Michael J. "Hydrology, Ideology, and the Origins of Irrigation in Ancient Southwest Arabia." *Current Anthropology* 49, no. 3 (2008): pp. 497–510.

Hartwick, John M. "Intergenerational Equity and the Investment of Rents from Exhaustible Resources." *American Economic Review* 67 (1977): pp. 972–974.

Harvey, Fiona and Arthur Neslen. "Fishing Quotas Defy Scientists' Advice". *The Guardian*, December 16, 2014.

Haszeldine, R. Stuart. "Carbon Capture and Storage: How Green Can Black Be?" *Science* 325, no. 5948 (2009): pp. 1645–52.

Hayes, Tanya M. "Parks, People, and Forest Protection: An Institutional Assessment of the Effectiveness of Protected Areas." *World Development* 34 no. 12 (2006): pp. 2064–75.

Heal, Geoffrey. *The Economics of Renewable Energy*. NBER Working Paper No. 15081, National Bureau of Economic Research, Cambridge, Mass. 2009. http://www.nber.org/papers/w15081.

Heap, Alan. *China: The Engine of a Commodities Super Cycle*. New York: Citigroup, 2005.

Heckenberger, M.J., et al. "The Legacy of Cultural Landscapes in the Brazilian Amazon: Implications for Biodiversity." *Philosophical Transactions of the Royal Society, Biological Sciences* 362, no. 1478 (2007): pp. 197–208.

Hegerl, Gabriele C., and Susan Solomon. "Risks of Climate Engineering." *Science* 325 (2009): p. 955.

Hensel, Nayantara D. "Economic Challenges in the Clean Energy Supply Chain." *Business Economics* 46, no. 3 (2011): pp. 171–184.

Hernandez, R.R. "Environmental Impacts of Utility-Scale Solar Energy". *Renewable and Sustainable Energy Reviews* 29 (2014): pp. 766–779.

Highfield, Roger. "25 Years after Chernobyl, We Don't Know How Many Died." *New Scientist* 21, April 21, 2011.

Hilburn, Ray, et al. "State of the World's Fisheries." *Annual Review of Environment and Resources* 28 (2003): pp. 359–399.

Hillel, Daniel. *Negev: Land, Water and Life in a Desert Environment*. New York: Praeger, 1982.

Hixon, Mark A., and Brian N. Tissot. "Comparison of Trawled vs. Untrawled Mud Seafloor Assemblages of Fishes and Macro Invertebrates at Coqville Bank, Oregon." *Journal of Experimental Marine Biology and Ecology* 344 (2006): pp. 23–35.

Hoare, Philip. *The Whale: In Search of the Giants of the Sea*. New York: HarperCollins, 2010.

Hochschild, Adam. *King Leopold's Ghost: A Story of Greed, Terror and Heroism in Colonial Africa*. Houghton Mifflin Co., 1998.

Hodge, A. Trevor. *Roman Aqueducts and Water Supply*. 2nd ed. London: Gerald Duckworth & Co., 2002.

Hoffman, Richard C. "A Brief History of Aquatic Resource Use in Medieval Europe." *Helgoland Marine Research* 59 (2005): pp. 22–30.

Homeland Security News Wire. "Mexico City's Sinking Is Worsening," January 21, 2011. http://homelandsecuritynewswire.com/mexico-citys-sinking-worsening.

Homer-Dixon, Thomas. *The Ingenuity Gap: Can We Solve the Problems of the Future?* Toronto: Vintage Canada, 2002.

Hosonuma, Noriko, et al. "An Assessment of Deforestation and Forest Degradation Drivers in Developing Countries." *Environmental Research Letters* 7, no. 4 (2012).

Hubbert, M. King. "Techniques of Prediction as Applied to the Production of Oil and Gas." In *Oil and Gas Supply Modeling*, edited by S.I. Gass. National Bureau of Standards Special Publication 631 (1982): pp. 16–141.

Huete-Pérez, Jorge Alberto, et al. "Scientists Raise Alarm About Fast Tracking of Transoceanic Canal through Nicaragua". *Environmental Science and Technology* (2015, forthcoming).

Humphries, David. "The Great Metals Boom." *Resources Policy* 35 (2010): pp. 1–13.

Hurd, Ian. "Almost Saving Whales: The Ambiguity of Success at the International Whaling Commission." *Ethics and International Affairs* 26 (2012): pp. 1–10.

Hurst, Cindy. *China's Rare Earth Elements Industry: What Can the West Learn?* Institute for the Analysis of Global Security, Potomac, MD., March 2010. http://www.iags. org/rareearth0310hurst.pdf.

Ingraffea, Anthony R., et al. "Assessment and Risk Analysis of Casing and Cement Impairments in Oil and Gas Wells in Pennsylvania." *PNAS* 111, no. 30 (2014): pp. 10955–60.

Inhofe, James. *The Greatest Hoax: How the Global Warming Conspiracy Threatens Your Future*. Washington, DC: WND Books, 2012.

Innis, Harold A. *The Fur Trade in Canada*. Yale, New Haven: Yale University Press, 1930.

Intact Forest Landscapes. http://www.intactforests.org/.

InterAcademy Council. *Review of the IPCC*. http://reviewipcc.interacademycouncil.net/.

Intergovernmental Panel on Climate Change. *First Assessment Report, 1990, Overview*. http:// www.ipcc.ch/ipccreports/1992%20IPCC%20Supplement/IPCC_1990_and_1992_ Assessments/English/ipcc_90_92_assessments_far_overview.pdf.

———. *Fourth Assessment Report, Climate Change 2007: Synthesis Report*. http://ipcc.ch/ publications_and_data/ar4/wg2/en/contents.html.

———. *Summary for Policymakers*. In *IPCC Special Report on Renewable Energy Sources and Climate Change Mitigation*. New York: Cambridge University Press, 2012.

———. *Fifth Assessment Report, Climate Change 2013: The Physical Science Basis* . http:// www.ipcc.ch/report/ar5/wg1/.

———. "Decisions Taken with Respect to the Review of IPCC Processes and Procedures, Governance and Management." IPCC 33rd Session, Abu Dhabi, UAE, May 10–13, 2011. http://www.ipcc.ch/pdf/tor/TOR_ExComm.pdf.

International Air Transport Association. *Technology Roadmap, June 2013*. http://www.iata. org/whatwedo/environment/Documents/technology-roadmap-2013.pdf.

———. *Alternative Fuels Report, 2014*. http://www.iata.org/publications/Documents/2014- report-alternative-fuels.pdf.

International Atomic Energy Agency. *Energy, Electricity and Nuclear Power Estimates for the Period up to 2050*. Reference Data Series No. 1. Vienna: IAEA, 2014. http://www-pub.iaea.org/MTCD/Publications/PDF/rds-1-34-web-57882020.pdf.

———. *The Long Term Storage of Radioactive Waste: Safety and Sustainability. A Position Paper of International Experts*. Vienna: IAEA, June 2003. http://www.iaea.org/sites/ default/files/LTS-RW_web.pdf.

International Commission for the Conservation of Atlantic Tunas. *Report for Biennial Period 2012–13: Part II (2013) – Vol 2*. Madrid: ICCAT, 2014. http://www.iccat.int/ Documents/BienRep/REP_EN_12-13_II_2.pdf.

International Commission on Irrigation and Drainage. www.icid.org/sprinkler.html.

International Commission on Stratigraphy. "Subcommission on Quaternary Stratigraphy." Working Group on the Anthropocene. Last modified December 8, 2014. http:// quaternary.stratigraphy.org/workinggroups/anthropocene/.

International Council on Mining and Metals. The Role of Mining in National Economies. 2014. www.icmm.com/document/7950.

International Cyanide Management Code. www.cyanidecode.org.

International Development Research Centre. "Growing Better Cities: Urban Agriculture for Sustainable Development." www.idrc.ca/in_focus_cities/.

International Energy Agency. Carbon Capture and Storage. http://www.iea.org/topics/ccs/.

———. "Nuclear Power." Brief. Energy Technology Essentials No. 04, OECD / IEA, 2007. http://www.iea.org/techno/essentials4.pdf.

———. "IEA Hails Historic Launch of Carbon Capture and Storage Project." Press release. October 1, 2014. http://www.iea.org/newsroomandevents/pressreleases/2014/october/iea-hails-historic-launch-of-carbon-capture-and-storage-project.html.

———. Key World Energy Statistics. Various years. www.iea.org.

———. Medium-Term Oil and Gas Markets: Overview. Paris: OECD / IEA, 2011. http://www.iea.org/publications/freepublications/publication/mtogm2011_unsecured.pdf.

———. Renewable Energy: Medium-Term Market Report, 2014. Paris: OECD / IEA, 2014. http://www.iea.org/Textbase/npsum/MTrenew2014sum.pdf.

———. World Energy Outlook 2014 Fact Sheet. http://www.worldenergyoutlook.org/media/weowebsite/2014/141112_WEO_FactSheets.pdf .

International Maritime Organization. "Convention on the Prevention of Marine Pollution by Dumping of Wastes and Other Matter." Adopted November 13, 1972. http://www.imo.org/about/conventions/listofconventions/pages/convention-on-the-prevention-of-marine-pollution-by-dumping-of-wastes-and-other-matter.aspx.

———. "The Hong Kong International Convention for the Safe and Environmentally Sound Recycling of Ships." Adopted May 5, 2009. http://www.imo.org/about/conventions/listofconventions/pages/the-hong-kong-international-convention-for-the-safe-and-environmentally-sound-recycling-of-ships.aspx.

International Monetary Fund. "IMF Executive Board Considers Use of Windfall Gold Sale Profits." Public Information Notice No. 11/121, September 16, 2011. http://www.imf.org/external/np/sec/pn/2011/pn11121.htm.

———. Energy Subsidy Reform: Lessons and Implications. January 28, 2013. http://www.imf.org/external/np/pp/eng/2013/012813.pdf.

International Tropical Timber Organization. www.itto.int.

International Union for Conservation of Nature. www.iucn.org.

———. "Mangrove forests in worldwide decline." Press release. April 9, 2010. https://www.iucn.org/news_homepage/?5025/Mangrove-forests-in-worldwide-decline

Jaccard, Mark. Sustainable Fossil Fuels: The Unusual Suspect in the Quest for Clean and Enduring Energy. New York: Cambridge University Press, 2006.

Jackson, Robert B., et al. "The Environmental Costs and Benefits of Fracking." Annual Review of Environment and Resources 39 (2014): pp. 327–362.

Jackson, Tim. Prosperity without Growth: Economics for a Finite Planet. London and Sterling, VA: Earthscan, 2009.

Jacobsen, Mark R., and Arthur A. van Benthem. "Vehicle Scrappage and Gasoline Policy." American Economic Review 105 (2015): pp. 1312–1338.

Jacobson, Mark Z., and Mark A. Delucchi. "Providing All Global Energy with Wind, Water, and Solar Power, Part I: Technologies, Energy Resources, Quantities and Areas of Infrastructure and Materials." Energy Policy 39 (2011): pp. 1154–69.

Jacquet, Jennifer, et al. "Seafood Stewardship in Crisis." Nature 476 (2010): pp. 28–29.

Jahara, Yahaya, Ahmad Sabri, and Scott W. Kennedy. "Impacts of Biodiesel Development on the Palm Oil Industry." Malaysian Journal of Economic Studies 43 (2006): pp. 113–140.

James, Clive. "Global Status of Commercialized Biotech / GM Crops." Brief No. 39. International Service for the Acquisition of Agri-biotech Applications, Ithaca, NY, 2008. http://isaaa.org/resources/publications/briefs/39/download/isaaa-brief-39-2008.pdf.

Jefferies, Duncan. "50m Tonnes of e-Waste Generated Every Year—and It Is Increasing." *The Guardian*, April 2, 2014. http://www.theguardian.com/sustainable-business/50m-tonnes-ewaste-designers-manufacturers-recyclers-electronic-junk.

———. "Back to the Future: Are We About to Crack Energy Fusion?" *The Guardian*, May 7, 2014. http://www.theguardian.com/big-energy-debate/nuclear-fusion-energy-research.

Jevons, W. Stanley. *The Coal Question: An Inquiry Concerning the Progress of the Nation and the Probable Exhaustion of Our Coal Mines.* 2nd ed. London: MacMillan and Co., 1866. Reprinted in Cornish, et al. (eds.). *The Study of the Future.* Washington, DC: World Future Society, 1977.

Johnson, Eric. "Goodbye to Carbon Neutral: Getting Biomass Footprints Right." *Environmental Impact Assessment Review* 29 (2009): pp. 165–168.

Joye, Yannick, and Andreas de Block. "'Nature and I Are Two': A Critical Examination of the Biophilia Hypothesis." *Environmental Values* 20 (2011): pp. 189–215.

Juffe-Bignoli, D. et al. *Protected Planet Report, 2014.* UNEP-WCMC: Cambridge, UK: 2014.

Kahneman, Daniel. *Thinking, Fast and Slow.* New York: Farrar, Straus and Giroux, 2011.

Kaiman, Johnathan. "China's Water Diversion Project Starts to Flow to Beijing". *The Guardian*, December 12, 2014. http://www.theguardian.com/world/2014/dec/12/china-water-diversion-project-beijing-displaced-farmers .

Kalron, Nir, and Andrea Crosta. "Africa's White Gold of Jihad: Al-Shabaab and Conflict Ivory." Elephant Action League. 2013. http://elephantleague.org/project/africas-white-gold-of-jihad-al-shabaab-and-conflict-ivory/.

Kammen, Daniel M., Kamal Kapadia, and Matthias Fripp. *Putting Renewables to Work: How Many Jobs Can the Clean Energy Industry Generate?* Report of the Renewable and Appropriate Energy Laboratory, University of California, Berkeley, 2004.

Kanellos, Michael. "Sail-Powered Cargo Ship Test Results In: It Cut Fuel by 20 Percent." CNET News, March 19, 2008. http://www.cnet.com/news/sail-powered-cargo-ship-test-results-in-it-cut-fuel-by-20-percent/.

Karam, Souhail. "Saudi Arabia Scraps Wheat Growing to Save Water." Reuters, January 8, 2008. http://www.reuters.com/article/2008/01/08/idUSL08699206.

Kareiva, Peter, and Michelle Marvier. "What is Conservation Science?" *Bioscience* 62 (2012): pp. 962–961.

Kathage, Jonas, and Matin Qaim. "Economic Impacts and Impact Dynamics of Bt (*Bacillus thuringiensis*) Cotton in India." *PNAS* 109 (2012): pp. 11652–6.

Kea, John. *The Spice Route: A History.* London: John Murray, 2005.

Keating, Joshua. "Bolivia's Lithium-Powered Future." *Foreign Policy*, October 21, 2009. http://foreignpolicy.com/slideshow/bolivias-lithium-powered-future/.

Keith, David W. "Photophoretic Levitation of Engineered Aerosols for Geoengineering." *PNAS* 107 (2010): pp. 16428–31.

Keller, David P., Ellias Y. Feng, and Andreas Oschlies. "Potential Climate Engineering Effectiveness and Side Effects during a High Carbon Dioxide-Emission Scenario." *Nature Communications* 5 (February 2014). http://www.nature.com/ncomms/2014/140225/ncomms4304/full/ncomms4304.html.

Kelley, Colin P. et al. "Climate Change in the Fertile Crescent and Implications of the Recent Syrian Drought." *PNAS* 112, no 11 (2015): pp. 3241–3246.

Kelly, Erin, et al. "Oil Sands Development Contributes Elements Toxic at Low Concentrations to the Athabasca River and Its Tributaries." *PNAS* 107, no. 37 (2010): pp. 16178–83.

Kelly, Erin, et al. "Oil Sands Development Contributes Polycyclic Aromatic Compounds to the Athabasca River and Its Tributaries." *PNAS* 106, no. 52 (2009): pp. 22346–51.

Kew Royal Botanical Gardens. "Kew's Millennium Seed Bank Partnership." Accessed December 14, 2014. http://www.kew.org/science-conservation/millennium-seed-bank.

Keynes, John Maynard. *Essays in Persuasion: The Collected Writings of John Maynard Keynes.* Vol. 9. Cambridge: Cambridge University Press, 1978.

Khalilian, Setareh, et al. "Designed for Failure: A Critique of the Common Fisheries Policy of the European Union." *Marine Policy* 34, no. 6 (2010): pp. 1178–1182.

Khon, V.C., et al. "Perspectives of Northern Sea Route and Northwest Passage in the Twenty-First Century." *Climatic Change* 100 (2010): pp.757–768.

Kim, Lucian and Maria Levitor. "Russia Heat May Cost 15,000 lives, $15 Billion of GDP". Bloomberg News, August 10, 2010.

Kimberly Process. www.kimberlyprocess.com.

Kiple, Kenneth F., and Kriemhild Coneè Omelas, eds. *The Cambridge World History of Food.* Cambridge: Cambridge University Press, 2000.

Klare, Michael T. *Resource Wars: The New Landscape of Global Conflict.* New York: Metropolitan Books, 2001.

———. *The Race for What's Left. The Global Scramble for the World's Last Resources.* New York: Picador, 2012.

Klein, Naomi. *This Changes Everything: Capitalism vs the Climate.* Toronto: Random House of Canada Ltd., 2014.

Klein-Marcuschamer, Daniel, et al. "Technoeconomic Analysis of Renewable Aviation Fuel from Microalgae, *Pongamia Pinnata* and Sugar Cane." *Biofuels, Bioproducts and Biorefining* 7 (2013): pp. 416–428.

Klink, Carlos A. and Ricardo B. Machado. "Conservation of the Brazilian Cerrado." *Conservation Biology* 19 (2005): pp. 707–713.

Klinkenborg, Verlyn. "The Folly of Big Agriculture: Why Nature Always Wins." *Yale Environment 360,* April 9, 2012. http://e360.yale.edu/feature/the_folly_of_big_agriculture_why_nature_always_wins/2514/.

Kolbert, Elizabeth. *The Sixth Extinction: An Unnatural History.* New York: Henry Holt and Company, 2014.

Komendantova, Nadejda, et al. "Perception of Risks in Renewable Energy Projects: The Case of Concentrated Solar Power in North Africa." *Energy Policy* 40 (2012): pp. 103–109.

Kosaka, Yu, and Shang-Ping Xie. "Recent Global-Warming Hiatus Tied to Equatorial Pacific Surface Cooling." *Nature* 501 (2013): pp. 403–407.

Kovarik, Bill. "Henry Ford, Charles Kettering and the Fuel of the Future." *Automotive History Review* 32 (Spring 1998): pp. 7–27.

Koven, Peter. "Investors Eager for Barrick Dividend Hike." *National Post,* May 2, 2012. http://business.financialpost.com/2012/05/01/investors-eager-for-barrick-dividend-hike/.

Krautkraemer, Jeffrey A. "The Economics of Scarcity: The State of the Debate." In *Scarcity and Growth Revisited: Natural Resources and the Environment in the New Millennium,* edited by R. David Simpson, Michael A. Toman, and Robert U. Ayres, pp. 54–78. Washington, DC: Resources for the Future, 2005.

Kurlansky, Mark. *Cod: A Biography of the Fish that Changed the World.* New York: Walker and Company, 1997.

———. *Salt: A World History.* Toronto: Vintage Canada, 2002.

Kyoto Protocol. http://unfccc.int/kyoto_protocol/items/2830.php.

Lake, Karry W., et al. "A Primer on the Economics of Shale Gas Production. Just How Cheap is Shale Gas?" *Journal of Applied Corporate Finance* 251 (2013): pp. 87–95.

Landes, David S. *The Wealth and Poverty of Nations: Why Some Are So Rich and Some So Poor*. New York: W.W. Norton & Co., 1998.

Lang, Chris. "Deforestation in Indonesia Continues, despite the Moratorium." REDD-monitor.org, May 4, 2012. http://www.redd-monitor.org/2012/05/04/deforestation-in-indonesia-continues-despite-the-moratorium/.

Lawson, Sam, and Larry MacFaul. *Illegal Logging and Related Trade: Indicators of the Global Response*. London: The Royal Institute of International Affairs, July 2010.

Lebreton, Laurent C.-M., and Jose C. Borrero. "Modeling the Transport and Accumulation Floating Debris Generated by the 11 March 2011 Tohoku Tsunami." *Marine Pollution Bulletin* 66 (2013): pp. 53–58.

Leigh Haag, Amanda. "Pond-Powered Biofuels: Turning Algae into America's New Energy." *Popular Mechanics*, March 29, 2007. http://www.popularmechanics.com/science/energy/biofuel/4213775.

Leiserowitz, A., et al. *Climate Change in the American Mind: Americans' Global Warming Beliefs and Attitudes in March 2012*. New Haven, CT: Yale Project on Climate Change Communication, 2012. http://environment.yale.edu/climate/files/Climate-Beliefs-March-2012.pdf.

Lenton, Timothy, et al. "Tipping Elements in the Earthly Climate Systems." *Nature* 105 (2008): pp. 1786–1793.

Lenzen, M., et al. "International Trade Drives Biodiversity Threats in Developing Nations." *Nature* 486 (June 7, 2012): pp. 109–112.

Leonard, Andrew. "When Guano Imperialists Ruled the Earth." *Salon*, February 29, 2008. http://www.salon.com/2008/02/29/guano_imperialism/.

Lewis, Simon L. and Mark A. Maslin. "Defining the Anthropocene." *Nature* 519 (2015): pp. 174–180.

Leroux, Nicolas, and Makane Moïse Mbengue. "Deep Sea Marine Bioprospecting under UNCLOS and the CBD." Unpublished paper, 2010. http://www.gmat.unsw.edu.au/ablos/ABLOS10Folder/S3P1-P.pdf.

Linton, Jamie. *What Is Water? The History of a Modern Abstraction*. Vancouver: UBC Press, 2010.

Little, Jane Braxton. "The Ogallala Aquifer: Saving a Vital U.S. Water Resource." *Scientific American*, March 1, 2009. www.scientificamerican.com/article.cfm?id=the-ogallala-aquifer.

Liu, Jianguo and Wu Yang. "Water Sustainability for China and Beyond." *Science* 327 (2013): pp. 649–650.

Lobo, Aaron Savio, et al. "Commercializing Bycatch Can Push a Fishery beyond Economic Extinction." *Conservation Letters* 3 (2010): pp. 277–285.

Lomborg, Bjorn. *The Skeptical Environmentalist: Measuring the Real State of the World*. New York: Cambridge University Press, 2001.

Louv, Richard. *Last Child in the Woods: Saving Our Children from Nature-Deficit Disorder*. Chapel Hill, NC: Algonquin Books, 2005.

Lovelock, James E. "A Physical Basis for Life Detection Experiments." *Nature* 207, no. 7 (1965): pp. 568–570.

———. *Gaia: A New Look at Life on Earth*. Oxford: Oxford University Press, 1979.

———. *The Vanishing Face of Gaia: A Final Warning*. New York: Basic Books, 2009.

Lukacs, Martin. "World's Biggest Geoengineering Experiments 'Violates' UN Rules". *The Guardian*, October 15, 2012. http://www.theguardian.com/environment/2012/oct/15/pacific-iron-fertilisation-geoengineering.

Lujala, Päivi. "The Spoils of Nature: Armed Civil Conflict and Rebel Access to Natural Resources." *Journal of Peace Research* 47, no. 1 (2010): pp. 15–28.

Lüthi, Dieter, et al. "High-Resolution Carbon Dioxide Concentration Record 650,000–800,000 Years before Present." *Nature* 453 (2008): pp. 379–382.

Lynn, Richard, and John Harvey. "The Decline of the World's IQ." *Intelligence* 36 (2008): pp. 112–120.

Macalister, Terry. "Nuclear Disposal Put in Doubt by Recovered Swedish Galleon." *The Guardian*, November 14, 2009. http://www.theguardian.com/environment/2009/nov/14/copper-nuclear-containment-vasa-sweden.

MacDonald, Alistair, and Edward Welsch. "Next Frontier: Mining the Ocean Floor." *Wall Street Journal*, June 4, 2012.

MacKay, David. *Sustainable Energy without the Hot Air*. Cambridge: UIT Cambridge, 2009. www.withouthotair.com.

MacKerron, George, and Susana Mourato. "Happiness Is Greater in Natural Environments." *Global Environmental Change* 23 (2013): pp. 992–1000.

Magurran, Anne E., et al. "Long-Term Datasets in Biodiversity Research and Monitoring: Assessing Change in Ecological Communities through Time." *Trends in Ecology and Evolution* 25, no. 10 (2010): pp. 574–582.

Maisels, F., et al. "Devastating Decline of Forest Elephants in Central Africa." *PLOS ONE* 8, no. 3 (2013). http://www.plosone.org/article/info%3Adoi%2F10.1371%2Fjournal.pone.0059469.

Makower, Joel, et al. "Two Steps Forward: The State of Green Business 2014." *GreenBiz*, January 21, 2014. http://www.greenbiz.com/blog/2014/01/21/state-green-business-2014.

Malatesta, M., et al. "A Long-Term Study on Female Mice Fed on a Genetically Modified Soybean: Effects on Liver Aging." *Histochemical Cell Biology* 130 (2008): pp. 967–977.

Malthus, T. *An Essay on the Principle of Population*. 1798. Reprint, London: Penguin Books, 1983.

Mann, Charles C. *1491: New Revelations of the Americas Before Columbus*. New York: Alfred A. Knopf, 2005.

———. *1493: Uncovering the New World Columbus Created*. New York: Alfred A. Knopf, 2011.

Mann, Michael E., et al. "Global Signatures and Dynamical Origins of the Little Ice Age and Medieval Climate Anomaly." *Science* 326, no. 5957 (2009): pp. 1256–60.

Marine Stewardship Council. Annual Report, 2013–2014. http://www.slideshare.net/MSCecolabel/msc-annual-reportsummary201314.

Margono, Belinda Arumarwati, et al. "Primary Forest Cover Loss in Indonesia over 2000–2012". *Nature Climate Change* 4 (2014): pp. 730–735.

Markandya, Anil., et al. *The Economics of Ecosystems and Biodiversity—Phase 1 (Scoping) Economic Analysis and Synthesis*. Final report for the European Commission, Venice, 2008. http://ec.europa.eu/environment/nature/biodiversity/economics/pdf/scoping.pdf.

Marris, Emma. *Rambunctious Garden: Saving Nature in a Post-Wild World*. New York: Bloomsbury, 2011.

Martin, John, et al. "A Primer on the Economics of Shale Gas Production: Just How Cheap Is Shale Gas?" Social Science Research Network working paper, April 3, 2012. http://ssrn.com/abstract=2033238.

Martín-López, Berta, Carlos Montes, and Javier Benayas. "Economic Valuation of Biodiversity Conservation: The Meaning of Numbers." *Conservation Biology* 22 (2008): pp. 624–635.

Massari, Stefania, and Marcello Ruberti. "Rare Earth Elements as Critical Raw Materials: Focus on International Markets and Future Strategies." *Resources Policy* 38 (2013): pp. 36–43.

Mathiesen, Brian Vad, Henrik Lund, and Kenneth Karlsson. "100% Renewable Energy Systems, Climate Mitigation and Economic Growth." *Applied Energy* 88 (2011): pp. 488–501.

Maxwell, Daniel, et al. "Fit for Purpose? Rethinking Food Security Responses in Protracted Humanitarian Crises." *Food Policy* 35 (2010): pp. 91–97.

McArthur, Greg. "SNC Division Created Web of Illicit Payments." *The Globe and Mail*, May 15, 2013.

McCaffrey, Stephen. "The Contribution of the UN Convention on the Law of the Non-Navigational Uses of International Water Courses." *International Journal of Global Environmental Issues* 1, no. 3/4 (2001): pp. 250–263.

McCarthy, D.P., et al. "Financial Costs of Meeting Global Diversity Conservation Targets: Current Spending and Unmet Needs." *Science* 338 (2012): pp. 946–949.

McCord, Edward. *The Value of Species.* New Haven: Yale University Press, 2012.

McCormick, K., et al. "Advancing Sustainable Urban Transformation." *Journal of Cleaner Production* 50 (2013): pp. 1–11.

McGlade, Christophe E. "A Review of the Uncertainties in Estimates of Global Oil Resources." *Energy* 47 (2012): pp. 262–270.

———, and Paul Ekins. "The Geographical Distribution of Fossil Fuels Unused When Limiting Global Warming to 2° C". *Nature* 517 (2015): pp. 287–190.

McIntyre, Steven, and Ross McKitrick. "Corrections to the Mann et al. (1998) Proxy Data Base and Northern Hemisphere Average Temperature Series." *Environment and Energy* 14, no. 6 (2003): pp. 751–771.

McKie, Robin. "Marine Treasure Trove Could Bring Revolution in Medicine and History." *The Observer*, November 10, 2012.

McQuaig, Linda. *War, Big Oil, and the Fight for the Planet: It's the Crude, Dude.* Revised ed. Toronto: Anchor Canada, 2006.

Meadows, D., et al. *The Limits to Growth.* New York: Universe Books, 1972.

Medjibe, Vincente, and Francies E. Putz. "Cost Comparisons of Reduced Impact and Conventional Logging in the Tropics." *Journal of Forest Economics* 18 (2012): pp. 242–256.

Mellars, Paul. "Why Did Modern Human Populations Disperse from Africa ca. 60,000 Years Ago? A New Model." *PNAS* 103, no. 25 (2006): pp. 9381–6.

Mendenhall, Chase D., Gretchen C. Daily, and Paul R. Ehrlich. "Improving Estimates of Biodiversity." *Biological Conservation* 151 (2012): pp. 22–34.

Mengewein, Julia. "Merkel Facing Power Dilemma as Coal Plants Open: Energy Markets." *Bloomberg News*, November 4, 2013. http://www.bloomberg.com/news/2013-11-04/merkel-facing-power-dilemma-as-coal-plants-open-energy-markets.html.

Menzie, W. David, Donald A. Singer and John H. DeYoung, Jr. "Mineral Resources and Consumption in the Twenty-First Century." In *Scarcity and Growth Revisited: Natural Resources and the Environment in the New Millennium*, edited by R. David Simpson, Michael A. Toman, and Robert U. Ayres, pp. 33–54. Washington: Resources for the Future, 2005.

Menzies, Gavin. *1421: The Year China Discovered North America.* New York: Harper-Collins, 2003.

Mesarovic, Mihajlo D., and Eduard Pestel. *Mankind at the Turning Point: The Second Report to the Club of Rome.* New York: E.P. Dutton, 1974.

Met Office (UK). *Latest Decadal Forecast 2014–2018.* Devon, UK: Met Office, January 2014. http://www.metoffice.gov.uk/media/pdf/1/8/decadal_forecast_2014-2018_jan2014.pdf.

Micklin, Philip. "The Aral Sea Disaster." *The Annual Review of Earth and Planetary Science* 35 (2007): pp. 47–72.

Miedema, Jan H., and Henri C. Moll. "Lithium Availability in the EU27 for Battery-Driven Vehicles: The Impact of Recycling and Substitution on the Confrontation between Supply and Demand until 2050." *Resources Policy* 38, no. 2 (2013): pp. 204–211.

Millennium Ecosystem Assessment. *Ecosystems and Human Well-Being: Synthesis*. Washington, DC: Island Press, 2005.

———. *Ecosystems and Human Well-Being: Desertification Synthesis*. Washington, DC: World Resources Institute, 2005. http://www.unep.org/maweb/documents/document.355.aspx.pdf.

Milman, Oliver. "Rhinohorn Demand in Vietnam Drops by More Than 33 % in One Year". *The Guardian*, October 16, 2014.

Minteer, Ben A., and Thaddeus Miller. "The New Conservation Debate: Ethical Foundations, Strategic Trade-Offs and Policy Opportunities." *Biological Conservation* 144 (2011): pp. 945–947.

Mohan, Sushil. "Market-Based Price-Risk Management for Coffee Producers." *Development Policy Review* 25 (May 2007): pp. 333–354.

Molden, David, ed. *Water for Food, Water for Life: A Comprehensive Assessment of Water Management in Agriculture*. London, UK: Earthscan / International Water Management Institute, 2007. http://www.iwmi.cgiar.org/assessment/files_new/synthesis/Summary_SynthesisBook.pdf.

Monastersky, Richard. "Anthropocene: The Human Age". *Nature News* 519(2015): pp. 144–147.

Monbiot, George. "Put a Price on Nature? We Must Stop This Neoliberal Road to Ruin". *The Guardian*, July 24, 2014. http://www.theguardian.com/environment/georgemonbiot/2014/jul/24/price-nature-neoliberal-capital-road-ruin .

Montgomery, David R. *Dirt: The Erosion of Civilizations*. Berkeley: University of California Press, 2007.

Mora, Camilo., et al. "How Many Species Are There on Earth and in the Ocean?." *PLOS Biology* 9, no. 8 (2011).

Mora, Camilo, and Peter Sale. "Ongoing Global Biodiversity Loss and the Need to Move Beyond Protected Areas: A Review of the Technical and Practical Shortcomings of Protected Areas of Land and Sea." *Marine Ecology Progress Series* 434 (2011): pp. 251–266.

Morgan, Geoffrey. "Forget Carbon Capture and Storage: Carbon Marketing Is the Future." *Alberta Oil*, February 18, 2014. http://www.albertaoilmagazine.com/2014/02/ingenuity-lab-carbon-capture/.

Morse-Jones, Sian, et al. "Stated Preferences for Tropical Wildlife Conservation amongst Distant Beneficiaries: Charisma, Endemism, Scope and Substitution Effects." *Ecological Economics* 78 (2012): pp. 9–18.

Mueller, Nathaniel D., et al. "Closing Yield Gaps through Nutrient and Water Management." *Nature* 490 (October 2012): pp. 254–257.

Muttitt, Greg. *Fuel on the Fire: Oil and Politics in Occupied Iraq*. London: Bodley Head, 2011.

Myers, Norman. *The Sinking Ark: A New Look at the Problem of Disappearing Species*. Oxford: Pergamon Press, 1979.

———. *The Primary Source: Tropical Forests and Our Future*. New York and London: W.W. Norton and Company, 1985.

Myers, Norman, et al. "Biodiversity Hot Spots for Conservation Priorities." *Nature* 403 (2000): pp. 853–858.

Myers, Ransom A., and Boris Worm. "Rapid Worldwide Depletion of Predatory Fish Communities." *Nature* 423 (2003): pp. 280–283.

Nace, Raymond L. "Pierre Perrault: The Man and His Contribution to Modern Hydrology." *Journal of the American Water Resources Association* 10 (1974): pp. 633–647.

Nash, Madeleine. "How Did Life Begin?" *Time*, June 24, 2001. http://www.time.com/time/magazine/article/0,9171,162476,00.html.

National Geographic Daily News. "New Species Found in Lost World: Pinocchio Frog, More." May 17, 2010. http://news.nationalgeographic.com/news/2010/05/photogalleries/100517-new-species-lost-world-foja-science-pictures/.

National Mining Association. *Minerals, Critical Minerals, and the U.S. Economy.* Prepublication version. Washington, DC: The National Academies Press, 2007. http://www.nma.org/pdf/101606_nrc_study.pdf.

National Oceanic and Atmospheric Administration. http://www.noaa.gov/.

National Research Council. *The Impact of Genetically Engineered Crops on Farm Sustainability in the United States.* Washington, DC: The National Academies Press, 2010.

Natural Resource Charter. www.naturalresourcecharter.org.

Nepstad, Daniel., et al. "The End of Deforestation in the Brazilian Amazon." *Science* 326 (Dec. 4, 2009): pp. 1350–1351.

New Scientist. "Hydroelectric Power's Dirty Secret Revealed." February 24, 2005. http://www.newscientist.com/article/dn7046-hydroelectric-powers-dirty-secret-revealed.html#.VFZffI1oypo.

New York Times. "Tar Sands and the Carbon Numbers." Editorial. August 21, 2011. http://www.nytimes.com/2011/08/22/opinion/tar-sands-and-the-carbon-numbers.html?_r=1.

Newman, D.J., and G. Cragg. "Natural Products as Sources of New Drugs over the Last 29 Years." *Journal of Natural Products* 70, no. 3 (2007): pp. 461–477.

Nguyen, Tuan C. "This Tower Pulls Drinking Water Out of Thin Air". *Smithsonian.com*, April 14, 2014. http://www.smithsonianmag.com/innovation/this-tower-pulls-drinking-water-out-of-thin-air-180950399/.

Nicolia, Alessandro, et al. "An Overview of the Last 10 Years of Genetically Engineered Crop Safety Research." *Critical Reviews in Biotechnology* 34, no. 1 (March 2014): pp. 77–88. http://informahealthcare.com/doi/abs/10.3109/07388551.2013.823595.

Nikiforuk, Andrew. *Tar Sands, Dirty Oil and the Future of a Continent.* Vancouver, BC: Greystone Books, 2008.

Nordhaus, William. "A Review of the Stern Review on the Economics of Climate Change." *Journal of Economic Literature* XLV (2007): pp. 686–702.

———. *A Question of Balance: Weighing the Options on Global Warming Policies.* New Haven, CT.: Yale University Press, 2008.

———. *The Climate Casino: Risk, Uncertainty, and Economics for a Warming World.* New Haven, CT.: Yale University Press, 2013.

———. "Climate Clubs: Overcoming Free-Riding in International Climate Policy." *American Economic Review* 105 (2015): pp. 1339–1370.

Norse, Elliot A., et al. "Sustainability of Deep Sea Fisheries." *Marine Policy* 36, no. 2 (2012): pp. 307–320.

Nriago, Jerome O. "The Rise and Fall of Leaded Gas." *Science of the Total Environment* 92 (1990): pp.13–28.

Núñez, Montserrat, et al. "Assessing Potential Desertification Environmental Impact in Life Cycle Assessment." *International Journal of Life Cycle Assessment* 15, no. 1 (2010): pp. 67–78.

Off, Carol. *Bitter Chocolate: Investigating the Dark Side of the World's Most Seductive Sweet.* Toronto: Random House Canada, 2006.

Ogungbuyi, Olatikan, et al. "e-Waste Country Assessment Nigeria." e-Waste Africa Project of the Secretariat Basel Convention. Chatelain, Switzerland, May 2012. http://www.basel.int/Portals/4/Basel%20Convention/docs/eWaste/EwasteAfrica_Nigeria-Assessment.pdf

Olmstead, Alan L. and Paul W. Rhode. "Biological Globalization: The Other Grain Invasion." In *The New Comparative Economic History: Essays in Honor of Jeffrey Williamson*, edited by Timothy J. Hatton, Kevin H. O'Rourke, and Alan M. Taylor, pp. 115–141. Cambridge, MA: MIT Press, 2007.

Organization of the Petroleum Exporting Countries. "A Brief History." http://www.opec.org/opec_web/en/about_us/24.htm.

———. "Statute". http://www.opec.org/opec_web/static_files_project/media/downloads/publications/OPEC_Statute.pdf

O'Rourke, F., F. Boyle, and A. Reynolds. "Tidal Energy Update 2009." *Applied Energy* 87 (2009): pp. 398–409.

Orr, James C., et al. "Anthropogenic Ocean Acidification over the Twenty-First Century and Its Impact on Calcifying Organisms." *Nature* 437 (2005): pp. 681–686.

Ostrom, Elinor. "Beyond Markets and States: Polycentric Governance of Complex Economic Systems." *The American Economic Review* 100, no. 3 (2010): pp. 641–673.

Overdevest, Christine. "Comparing Forest Certification Schemes: The Case of Ratcheting Standards in the Forest Sector." *Socio-Economic Review* 8, no. 1 (2010): pp. 47–76.

Oxford Martin School. "'Oxford Principles' Vital for Geoengineering Research." Press release. September 14, 2011. http://www.oxfordmartin.ox.ac.uk/news/201109-oxfordprinciples.

Paine, Robert T. "Food Web Complexity and Species Diversity." *The American Naturalist* 100 (1966): pp. 65–75.

Palaniappan, Meena, et al. "Water Privatization Principles and Practices." In *The World's Water 2004–2005: The Biennial Report on Freshwater Resources*, edited by Peter Gleick, pp. 45–79. Washington: Island Press / Pacific Institute for Studies in Development, 2004.

Paquette, A. and C. Messier. "The Role of Plantations in Managing the World's Forests in the Anthropocene." *Frontiers in Ecology and Environment* 8 (2010): pp. 27–39.

Parajulee, Abha and Frank Wania. "Evaluating Officially Reported Polycyclic Aromatic Hydrocarbon Emissions in the Athabasca Oil Sands Region with a Multimedia Fate Model." *PNAS* 11(2014): pp. 3344–3349.

Parker, A.R., and C.R. Lawrence. "Water Capture by a Desert Beetle." *Nature* 414 (2001): pp. 33–34.

Pauly, Daniel. "Fishing Down Marine Food Webs." *Science* 279 (1998): pp. 860–863.

———. "Major Trends in Small-Scale Marine Fisheries, with Emphasis on Developing Countries, and Some Implications for the Social Sciences." *Maritime Studies (MAST)* 4, no. 2 (2006): pp. 7–22.

———. "Fishing More, Catching Less." *The New York Times*, March 26, 2014. http://www.nytimes.com/2014/03/27/opinion/fishing-more-catching-less.html?_r=0.

Pear, Robert. "After Three Decades, Tax Credit for Ethanol Expires." *The New York Times*, January 1, 2012. http://www.nytimes.com/2012/01/02/business/energy-environment/after-three-decades-federal-tax-credit-for-ethanol-expires.html.

Pearce, David. "Do We Really Care about Biodiversity?" *Environmental and Resource Economics* 37 (2007): pp. 313–333.

Peepoople. www.peepoople.com.

Peiser, Benny. "From Genocide to Ecocide: The Rape of Rapa Nui." *Energy & Environment* 16 (2005): pp. 513–539.

Pembina Institute. *Oilsands, Heavy Crudes, and the EU Fuel-Quality Directive*. Briefing note. March 20, 2012. http://www.pembina.org/reports/heavy-crude-comparison.pdf .

Pergams, Oliver R.W., and Patricia A. Zaradic. "Videophilia Implications for Childhood Development and Conservation." *The Journal of Developmental Processes* 2 (2007): pp. 130–144.

———. "Evidence for a Fundamental and Pervasive Shift Away from Nature-Based Recreation." *PNAS* 105 (2007): pp. 2295–300.

Perrings, Charles. "Pests, Pathogens and Poverty: Biological Invasions and Agricultural Dependence." In *Biodiversity Economics*, edited by Andreas Kontoleon, Unai Pascual, and Timothy Swanson, pp. 133–165. New York: Cambridge University Press, 2007.

Peskett, Leo, and Gernot Brodnig. *Carbon Rights in REDD+: Exploring the Implications for Poor and Vulnerable People*. World Bank and REDD-net, 2011. http://documents. worldbank.org/curated/en/2010/10/15525368/carbon-rights-redd-plus-exploring-implications-poor-vulnerable-people .

Pew Charitable Trust. "ICCAT Ignores Science and Increases Quota for Atlantic Bluefin Tuna". November 20, 2014. http://www.pewtrusts.org/en/about/news-room/ news/2014/11/20/iccat-ignores-science-and-increases-quota-for-atlantic-bluefin-tuna .

Pew Environment Group. *A Forest of Blue: Canada's Boreal*. Seattle: Pew Environment Group, International Boreal Conservation Campaign, 2012. http://borealscience.org/ wp-content/uploads/2012/06/report-forestofblue.pdf.

Pezzey, John. C.V., and Michael A. Toman. "Progress and Problems in the Economics of Sustainability." In *The International Yearbook of Environmental and Resource Economics 2002/2003: A Survey of Current Issues*, edited by Tom Tietenberg and Henk Folmer, pp. 165–232. Cheltenham, UK: Edward Elgar Publishing, 2002.

Phrampus, Benjamin J., and Matthew J. Hornback. "Recent Changes to the Gulf Stream Causing Widespread Gas Hydrate Destabilization." *Nature* 490, no. 7421 (2012): pp. 527–530.

Picketty, Thomas. *Capital in the Twenty-First Century*. Cambridge, Mass.: The Belknap Press of Harvard University Press, 2014.

Pieters, Rik. "Bidirectional Dynamics of Materialism and Loneliness: Not Just a Vicious Cycle." *Journal of Consumer Research* 40 (2013): pp. 615–631.

Pimental, David, et al. "Environmental, Energetic and Economic Comparisons of Organic and Conventional Farming Systems." *Bioscience* 55, no. 7 (2005): pp. 573–582.

Pimm, Stuart, et al. "The Biodiversity of Species and Their Rates of Extinction Distribution and Protection". *Science* 344 (May 30, 2014): p. 987.

Pindyck, Robert S. "Climate Change Policy: What Do the Models Tell Us?" *Journal of Economic Literature* 51, no. 3 (2013): pp. 860–872.

Pomeranz, Kenneth, and Steven Topik. *The World That Trade Created: Society, Culture, and the World Economy, 1400 to the Present*. Armonk, NY: M.E. Sharpe, 1999.

Ponting, Clive. *A Green History of the World*. New York: Penguin Books, 2007.

Porter-Bolland, L. et al. "Community Managed Forests and Forest Protected Areas: An Assessment of Their Conservation Effectiveness Across the Tropics." *Forest Ecology and Management* 268 (2012): pp. 6–17.

Postel, Sandra. *Pillar of Sand: Can the Irrigation Miracle Last?* New York: Worldwatch Institute / Norton & Co., 1999.

———. *Water: Adapting to a New Normal*. Santa Rosa, CA: Post Carbon Institute, 2010.

Powell, Devin. "Rare Earth Elements Plentiful in Ocean Sediments." *Science News*, July 3, 2011. https://www.sciencenews.org/article/rare-earth-elements-plentiful-ocean-sediments.

Prado, Larry. "Opportunities Remain Despite Conventional Oil, Gas Discoveries Slump." *E&P Magazine*, June 16, 2014. http://www.epmag.com/opportunities-remain-despite-conventional-oil-gas-discoveries-slump-717901#p=full.

Prebisch, Raul. *The Economic Development of Latin America and Its Principal Problems.* New York: Economic Commission for Latin America, 1950. http://archivo.cepal.org/pdfs/cdPrebisch/002.pdf.

President's Material Policy Commission. *Resources for Freedom: A Report to the President.* Washington, DC: US Government Printing Office, 1952.

Preston, Peter. "Wanted: An Eco Prophet." *The Guardian*, March 7, 2010. http://www.theguardian.com/commentisfree/2010/mar/07/climate-change-inertia-prophet.

Prüss-Üstün, Annette, et al. *Safer Water, Better Health: Costs, Benefits and Sustainability of Interventions to Protect and Promote Health.* Geneva: WHO, 2008. www.who.int/quantifying_ehimpacts/publications/saferwater/en/index.html.

Publish What You Pay. www.publishwhatyoupay.org.

Putz, Francis E., et al. "Reduced-Impact Logging: Challenges and Opportunities." *Forest Ecology and Management* 256 (2008): pp. 1427–33.

Qaim, Matin. "The Economics of Genetically Modified Crops." *Annual Review of Resource Economics* 1 (2009): pp. 665–693.

Quammen, David. *The Song of the Dodo: Island Biogeography in an Age of Extinctions.* New York: Touchstone, 1996.

Radetzki, Marian. *A Handbook of Primary Commodities in the Global Economy.* Cambridge: Cambridge University Press, 2008.

———. "Seven Thousand Years in the Service of Humanity: The History of Copper, the Red Metal." *Resources Policy* 34 (2009): pp. 176–184.

———. "Peak Oil and Other Threatening Peaks: Chimera without Substance." *Energy Policy* 38 (2010): pp. 6566–9.

———. "Price Formation and Price Trends in Exhaustible Resource Markets." In *Trade, Competition and the Pricing of Commodities*, edited by Simon J. Everett, and Frederic Jemmy, pp. 31–69. London: Centre for Economic Policy Research, 2012.

Ramirez-Llodra, Eva, et al. "Man and the Last Great Wilderness: Human Impact on the Deep Sea." *PLOS ONE* 6, no. 7 (2011): pp. 1–25.

Ranganathan, Jai, et al. "Sustaining Biodiversity in Ancient Tropical Countryside." *PNAS*, 105 (2008): pp. 17852–4.

Ray, Deepak K., et al. "Yield Trends Are Insufficient to Double Global Crop Production by 2050." *PLOS ONE* 8, no. 6 (2013).

Reardon, Arthur C., ed. *Metallurgy for the Non-Metallurgist.* 2nd ed. Materials Park, OH: ASM International, 2011.

Reguly, Eric. "No Mining Company Is Too Big to Swallow." *The Globe and Mail Report on Business*, May 8, 2007. http://www.theglobeandmail.com/report-on-business/rob-commentary/no-mining-company-is-too-big-to-swallow/article18138522/.

Reilly, John, and Sergey Paltsev. "Biomass Energy and Competition for Land." Report No. 145, MIT Joint Program on the Science and Policy of Global Change, Cambridge, MA, April 2007. http://globalchange.mit.edu/files/document/MITJPSPGC_Rpt145.pdf.

Reimer, Jeffrey. "Virtual Water Trade Means 'Trade in Water Services.'" GWF Discussion Paper 1229, presented at the Global Water Forum, Canberra, Australia, August 2012. http://www.globalwaterforum.org/2012/08/07/virtual-water-trade-means-trade-in-water-services/.

Relyea, Rick A. "Amphibians Are Not Ready for Roundup." *Wildlife Ecotoxicology* 3 (2011): pp. 267–300.

Renewable Energy Policy Network for the 21st Century. *Renewables 2014: Global Status Report*. Paris: REN21, 2014. http://www.ren21.net/ren21activities/globalstatusreport. aspx.

Reuters. "Two Dead after Yemenis Clash over Water Rights." World Preservation Foundation, May 17, 2010. http://www.worldpreservationfoundation.org/blog/news/two-dead-after-yemenis-clash-over-water-rights/#.VFZitY1oypo.

———. "China to Resume Electric Car Subsidies." March 25, 2013. http://www.reuters. com/article/2013/03/25/byd-subsidies-idUSL3N0CH19F20130325.

Reynolds, Jesse. "The Regulation of Climate Engineering." *Law, Innovation and Technology* 3 (2011): pp. 113–136.

Ribeiro, Jeferson. "Brazil's Amazon Fund Bogs Down, Donors Frustrated." Reuters, January 14, 2012.

Richter, Burton. "Nuclear Energy." In *Climate Change Science and Policy*, edited by Stephen H. Schneider, Armin Rosencranz, Michael D. Mastrandrea, and Kristin Kuntz-Duriseti, pp. 467–475. Washington, DC: Island Press, 2010.

Rifkin, Jeremy. *The Hydrogen Economy*. New York: Jeremy P. Tarcher/Penguin, 2002.

Rijsberman, Frank R. "Sanitation and Access to Clean Water." In *Global Crises, Global Solutions*, edited by Bjorn Lomborg, pp. 498–521. Cambridge: Cambridge University Press, 2004.

———. "Water Scarcity: Fact or Fiction." In *New Directions for a Diverse Planet*, proceedings of the 4th International Crop Science Congress, September 26–October 1, 2004. http://www.cropscience.org.au/icsc2004/.

Robb, Carolyn, et al. "Commercial Fisheries Closures in Marine Protected Areas: The Exception, Not the Rule." *Marine Policy* 35, no. 3 (2011): pp. 309–316.

Robbins, James S. "How Capitalism Saved the Whales." *The Freeman*. Foundation for Economic Education, August 1, 1992. http://fee.org/freeman/detail/how-capitalism-saved-the-whales.

Robinson, Warren C., and John E. Ross, eds. *The Global Family Planning Revolution: Three Decades of Population Policies and Programs*. Washington: World Bank, 2007.

Rockström, Johan, et al. "Planetary Boundaries: Exploring the Safe Operating Space for Humanity." *Ecology and Society* 14, no. 2 (2009): pp. 1–33.

Rodrik, Dani. "Where Did All the Growth Go? External Shocks, Social Conflict, and Growth Collapses." *Journal of Economic Growth* 4, no. 4 (1999): pp. 385–412.

Romaniuk, Anatole. "Persistence of High Fertility in Tropical Africa: the Case of the Democratic Republic of the Congo." *Population and Development Review* 37, no. 1 (2011): pp. 1–28.

Ronald, Pamela. "Plant Genetics, Sustainable Agriculture and Global Food Security." *Genetics* 188 (2011): pp. 11–20.

Rooney, Rebecca C., Suzanne E. Bayley, and David D. Schindler. "Oil Sands Mining and Reclamation Cause Massive Loss of Peatland and Stored Carbon." *PNAS* 109 (2012): pp. 4933–7.

Root, Terry L., and Elizabeth S. Goldsmith. "Wild Species and Extinction". In *Climate Change Science and Policy*, edited by Stephen H. Schneider et al., pp. 44–55. Washington, DC: Island Press, 2010.

Rosnick, David. "Reduced Work Hours as a Means of Slowing Climate Change." Washington, DC: Centre for Economics and Policy Research, February 2013.

Ross, Michael. "Blood Barrels: Why Oil Wealth Fuels Conflict." *Foreign Affairs* 87, no. 3 (2008). http://www.foreignaffairs.com/articles/63396/michael-l-ross/blood-barrels.

Roundtable on Sustainable Palm Oil. www.rspo.org.

Royal Society. *Geoengineering the Climate: Science, Climate and Uncertainty.* London: The Royal Society, 2009.

Royal Society of Canada Expert Panel. *Environmental and Health Impacts of Canada's Oil Sands Industry.* Ottawa: Royal Society of Canada, December 2010. https://rsc-src.ca/en/expert-panels/rsc-reports/environmental-and-health-impacts-canadas-oil-sands-industry.

Rubin, Jeff. *Why Your World Is about to Get a Whole Lot Smaller.* Toronto: Random House, 2009.

Runge, C. Ford, and Benjamin Senauer. "How Biofuels Could Starve the Poor." *Foreign Affairs* 86 (May–June 2007).

Sachs, Jeffrey D., and A.M. Warner. "Natural Resource Abundance and Economic Growth." NBER Working Paper No. 5398, National Bureau of Economic Research, Washington, DC, 1997.

Sachs, Jeffrey. "A Big Chance for Small Farmers." *Project Syndicate,* July 20, 2009. www.project-syndicate.org/commentary/sachs155.

Salman, M.A. "The Helsinki Rules, the UN Watercourses Convention and the Berlin Rules: Perspectives on International Water Law." *Water Resources Development* 23 (2007): pp. 625–640.

Sambasivan Swaminathan, Monkombu. "An Evergreen Revolution." *Crop Science* 46 (2006): pp. 2293–303.

Sample, Ian. "DNA Kit to Fight Trade in Endangered Animals." *The Guardian,* June 12, 2007. http://www.theguardian.com/uk/2007/jun/12/animalwelfare.science.

Samset, Ingrid. "Natural Resource Wealth, Conflict, and Peacebuilding." Ralph Bunche Institute for International Studies, Program on States and Security, City University of New York, 2009. http://www.cmi.no/publications/publication/?3283=natural-resource-wealth-conflict.

Sax, Dov, Steven Gaines, and James Brown. "Species Invasions Exceed Extinctions on Islands Worldwide: A Comparative Study of Plants and Birds." *American Naturalist* 160 (2002): pp. 766–783.

Scarborough, Vernon L., and Lisa J. Lucero. "The Non-Hierarchical Development of Complexity in the Semitropics: Water and Cooperation." *Water History* 2 (2010): pp. 185–205.

Schenk, C.J. *An Estimate of Undiscovered Conventional Oil and Gas Resources of the World,* 2012. U.S. Geological Survey Fact Sheet 2012–3042.

Schipani, Andres. "Bolivia: The Saudi Arabia of Lithium?" *beyondbrics* (blog), January 7, 2013. http://blogs.ft.com/beyond-brics/2013/01/07/bolivia-the-saudi-arabia-of-lithium/?#axzz2dkSMSZey.

Schivelbusch, Wolfgang. *Tastes of Paradise: A Social History of Spices, Stimulants, and Intoxicants.* New York: Vintage Books, 1993.

Schmidt, Gavin A., Drew T. Shindell, and Kostas Tsigaridis. "Reconciling Warming Trends." *Nature Geoscience* 7 (2014): pp. 158–160.

Schneider, Howard. "World Bank Rethinks Stance on Large-Scale Hydropower Projects." *Guardian Weekly,* May 14, 2013. http://www.theguardian.com/environment/2013/may/14/world-bank-hydropower-dam-rethink.

Seams, Clayton. "Here's Why Norway Is an Electric Car Utopia." *National Post,* October 10, 2014.

Searchinger, Timothy, et al. "Use of U.S. Croplands for Biofuels Increases Greenhouse Gases through Emissions from Land-Use Change." *Science* 319, no. 5867 (February 2008): pp. 1238–40.

Secretariat of the Convention on Biological Diversity. *Global Diversity Outlook 3*. Montreal: Secretariat of the Convention on Biological Diversity, 2010. http://www.cbd.int/doc/publications/gbo/gbo3-final-en.pdf.

Sedjo, Roger A. "Adaptation of Forests to Climate Change: Some Estimates." Discussion Paper No. 10-06, Resources for the Future, Washington, DC, January 2010. www.rff.org/Documents/RFF-DP-10-06.pdf.

———. "The Future of Trees: Climate Change and the Timber Industry." *Resources* 174 (2009): pp. 29–33.

Segerfeldt, Fredrik. *Water for Sale: How Business and the Market Can Resolve the World's Water Crisis*. Washington, DC: Cato Institute, 2005.

Seitz, Russell. "Bright Water: Hydrosols, Water Conservation and Climate Change." *Climatic Change* 105 (2011): pp. 365–381.

Seufert, Verena, Navin Ramankutty, and Jonathan Foley. "Comparing the Yields of Organic and Conventional Agriculture." *Nature* 485 (2012): pp. 229–232.

Shafiee, Sharif, and Erken Topal. "When Will Fossil Fuel Reserves Be Diminished." *Energy Policy* 37 (2009): pp. 181–189.

Sharma, Rahul. "Deep-Sea Mining: Economic, Technical, Technological and Environmental Considerations for Sustained Development." *Marine Technology Society Journal* 45, no. 5 (2011): pp. 28–41.

Shaw, D. John. *World Food Security: A History since 1945*. Houndmills, Basingstoke: Palgrave Macmillan, 2007.

Shepherd, Daniel, et al. "Evaluating the Impact of Wind Turbine Noise on Health-Related Quality of Life." *Noise & Health* 13 (2011): pp. 333–339.

Shift Project. http://www.tsp-data-portal.org/Energy-Production-Statistics.

Shleifer, Andrei. "Psychologists at the Gate: A Review of Daniel Kahneman's *Thinking Fast and Slow*." *Journal of Economic Literature* 50 (2012): pp. 1080–92.

Sicotte, Richard, Catalina Vizcarra, and Kirsten Wandschneider. "The Fiscal Impact of the War of the Pacific". *Cliometrica* 3 (2009): pp. 97–121.

Sillitoe, Richard H. "Exploration and Discovery of Base- and Precious-Metal Deposits in the Circum-Pacific Region during the Last 25 Years." Special issue, *Resource Geology* 19 (1995): 119 pp.

Simandl, George J. "World Fluorspar Resources, Market and Deposit Examples from British Columbia, Canada." Information Circular 2009-4, British Columbia Geological Survey, Victoria, 2009.

Simmons, Matthew R. *Twilight in the Desert: The Coming Saudi Oil Shock and the World Economy*. Hoboken, NJ: John Wiley and Sons, 2005.

Simula, Markku. *The Pros and Cons of Procurement: Developments and Progress in Timber-Procurement Policies as Tools for Promoting the Sustainable Management of Tropical Forests*. ITTO Technical Series No. 34. Yokohama: International Tropical Timber Organization, April 2010.

Singer, Hans W. "The Distribution of Gains between Investing and Borrowing Countries." *American Economic Review* 40 (May 1950): pp. 473–485.

Siry, Jacek P., Frederick W. Cubbage, and David H. Newman. "Global Forest Ownership: Implications for Forest Production, Management, and Protection." In Proceedings of XIII World Forestry Congress, Buenos Aires, Argentina, October 18–23, 2009. http://www.pefc.org/images/stories/documents/external/global_forest_ownership_FD.pdf.

Skidelsky, Robert, and Edward Skidelsky. *How Much Is Enough? The Love of Money and the Case for the Good Life*. London: Penguin Books, 2012.

Slackman, Michael. "Belatedly Egypt Spots Flaws in Wiping Out Pigs." *The New York Times*, September 19, 2009.

Smedema, Lambert, and Karim Shiati. "Irrigation and Salinity: A Perspective Review of the Salinity Hazards of Irrigation Development in the Arid Zones." *Irrigation and Drainage Systems* 16 (2003): pp. 161–172.

Smil, Vaclav. *Energy in World History*. Boulder, CO: Westview Press, 1994.

Smith, Allan H., et al. "Contamination of Drinking Water by Arsenic in Bangladesh: A Public Health Emergency." *Bulletin of the World Health Organization* 78 (2000): pp. 1093–1103.

Smithsonian Science. "Smithsonian Scientists Discover New Carnivore: the Olinguito". August 15, 2013. http://smithsonianscience.org/2013/08/olinguito/ .

Snell, Chelsea, et al. "Assessment of the Health Impact of GM Plant Diets in Long-Term and Multigenerational Animal Feeding Trials: A Literature Review." *Food and Chemical Toxicology* 50, nos. 3–4 (2012): pp. 1134–48.

Sokoloff, Kenneth L., and Stanley L. Engerman. "Institutions, Factor Endowments, and Paths of Development in the New World." *Journal of Economic Perspectives* 14, no. 3 (2000): pp. 217–232.

Sokolov, A.P., et al. "Probabilistic Forecast for 21st Century Climate Based on Uncertainties in Emissions (without Policy) and Climate Parameters." Report No. 169, MIT Joint Program on the Science and Policy of Global Change, Cambridge, MA, January 2009. http://globalchange.mit.edu/files/document/MITJPSPGC_Rpt169.pdf.

Solberg, Birger, et al. "Forest Sector Market Impacts of Changed Roundwood Export tariffs and Investment Climate in Russia." *Forest Policy and Economics* 12 (2010): pp. 17–23.

Solecki, Ralph S., Rose L. Solecki, and Anagnostis P. Agelarakis. *The Proto-Neolitihic Cemetry in Shanidar Cave*. College Station, TE: Texas A&M University press, 2004: p. 256.

Solomon, Lawrence. "Warmed-Over Nukes: The Climate Scare Revives the Biggest Business Flop Ever." *The Financial Post*, March 8, 2008. http://energyquest4nanticoke.ca/flop.htm.

Solomon, Susan, et al., eds. *Climate Change 2007: The Physical Science Basis*. Contribution of Working Group I to the Fourth Assessment Report of the Intergovernmental Panel on Climate Change. Cambridge: Cambridge University Press, 2007.

Solow, Robert M. "Intergenerational Equity and Exhaustible Resources." *The Review of Economic Studies* 41 (1974): pp. 29–46.

Sorrell, Steve, John Dimitropoulos, and Matt Sommerville. "Empirical Estimates of the Direct Rebound Effect: A Review." *Energy Policy* 37, no. 4 (2009): pp. 1356–1371.

Specter, Michael. "The Climate Fixers: Is There a Technological Solution to Global Warming?" *New Yorker*, May 14, 2012.

Spiegel Online International. "Europe's 'Human Zoos': Remains of Indigenous Abductees Back Home after 130 Years." January 13, 2010. http://www.spiegel.de/international/zeitgeist/europe-s-human-zoos-remains-of-indigenous-abductees-back-home-after-130-years-a-671759.html.

Stedje, Jörgen. "Ytterby gruva—ett industriminnesmärke." *Teknik 360*, June 30, 2009. http://t360.idg.se/2.8229/1.86905/ytterby-gruva...ett-industriminnesmärke.

Steinfeld, Henning, et al. *Livestock's Long Shadow: Environmental Issues and Options*. Rome: FAO, 2006.

Stern, Nicholas. *The Economics of Climate Change: The Stern Review*. Cambridge: Cambridge University Press, 2007.

———. "The Structure of Economic Modeling of the Potential Impacts of Climate Change: Grafting Gross Underestimation of Risk onto Already Narrow Science Models." *Journal of Economic Literature* 51, no. 3 (2013): pp. 838–859.

Stevenson, Betsey, and Justin Wolfers. "Economic Growth and Subjective Well-Being: Reassessing the Easterlin Paradox." *Brookings Papers on Economic Activity* (Spring 2008): 1–87.

Stiglitz, Joseph E. "New Agenda for Global Warming." *Economists' Voice*, July 2006. https://wwwo.gsb.columbia.edu/faculty/jstiglitz/download/papers/2008_New_Agenda_for_Global_Warming.pdf .

Stockholm International Water Institute. www.siwi.org.

Streeter, A.K. "Hybrid Containership Wind-Driven with Automatic Sails." Treehugger. com. November 26, 2012. http://www.treehugger.com/wind-technology/hybrid-container-ship-wind-driven-with-automatic-sails.html.

Strong, Aaron, John Cullen, and Sallie W. Chisholm. "Ocean Fertilization, Science, Policy, and Commerce." *Oceanography* 22 (2009): pp. 236–269.

Stueck, Wendy. "Copper Called Critical in World Gone Green." *The Globe and Mail Report on Business*, October 2, 2007.

Sumaila, U. Rashid, et al. "A Bottom-Up Re-estimation of Global Fisheries Subsidies." *Journal of Bioeconomics* 12 (2010): pp. 201–225.

Sumaila, Ussif Rashid, and D. Pauly, eds. *Catching More Bait: A Bottom-Up Re-estimation of Global Fisheries Subsidies*. UBC Fisheries Centre Research Reports 14, no. 6. Vancouver: The Fisheries Centre, UBC, 2006. http://www.fisheries.ubc.ca/webfm_send/126.

Sunstein, Cass R. "Beyond the Precautionary Principle." Public Law and Legal Theory Working Paper No. 38, University of Chicago Law School, 2003. http://www.law.uchicago.edu/files/files/38.crs_.precautionary.pl-lt.pdf.

Suttle, Curtis A. "Viruses in the Sea." *Nature* 437 (September 2005): pp. 356–361.

Tabuchi, Hiroko. "Japan Recycles Minerals from Used Electronics." *The New York Times*, October 4, 2010. http://www.nytimes.com/2010/10/05/business/global/05recycle.html?pagewanted=all.

Tagliabue, John. "A City that Turns Garbage into Energy Copes with a Shortage." *The New York Times*, April 29, 2013. http://www.nytimes.com/2013/04/30/world/europe/oslo-copes-with-shortage-of-garbage-it-turns-into-energy.html.

Tanji, Kenneth K., and Neeltje C. Kielen. "Agricultural Drainage Water Management in Arid and Semi-Arid Areas." FAO Irrigation and Drainage Paper No.61, Food and Agriculture Organization of the United Nations, Rome, 2002.

Taussig, Michael. "Culture of Terror—Space of Death: Roger Casement's Putumayo Report and the Explanation of Torture." *Comparative Studies in Society and History* 26, no. 3 (1984): pp. 467–497.

TEEB. *Mainstreaming the Economics of Nature: A Synthesis of the Approach. Conclusions and Recommendations of TEEB*. Geneva: The Economics of Ecosystems and Biodiversity, 2010. http://www.unep.org/pdf/LinkClick.pdf.

ter Steege, Hans, et al. "Hyperdominance in the Amazonian Tree Flora." *Science* 342, no. 6156 (2013): p. 325.

Tertzakian, Peter. *A Thousand Barrels a Second: The Coming Oil Break Point and the Challenges Facing an Energy Dependent World*. New York: McGraw Hill, 2006.

Thaler, Richard, and Cass R. Sunstein. *Nudge: Improving Decisions about Health, Wealth, and Happiness*. Revised ed. New York: Penguin Books, 2009.

Themnér, Lotta, and Peter Wallensteen. "Armed Conflicts, 1946–2013." *Journal of Peace Research* 51 (2014.): pp. 541–554.

Tilman, D. "Biodiversity and Environmental Sustainability amid Human Domination of Global Ecosystems." *Daedalus* 141 (2012): pp. 108–120.

——— et al. "Global Food Demand and the Sustainable Intensification of Agriculture." *PNAS* 101 (2011): pp. 20260–4.

Times of India. "Traditional Medicine a Threat to Tigers, Rare Plants." July 2, 2008. http://www.highbeam.com/doc/1P3-1504311201.html .

Tol, Richard S.J. "The Economic Effects of Climate Change." *Journal of Economic Perspectives* 23, no. 2 (2009): pp. 29–53.

Toropova, Caitlyn., et al., eds. *Global Ocean Protection: Present Status and Future Possibilities.* Brest, France: Agence des aires marines protégées; Gland, Switzerland, Washington, DC, and New York: IUCN WCPA; Cambridge, UK: UNEP-WCMC; Arlington, TX: TNC; Tokyo: UNU, New York: WCS: IUCN, 2010. https://portals.iucn.org/library/efiles/documents/2010-053.pdf.

Toronto Star. "Canada First Nation to Withdraw from Kyoto Protocol." December 12, 2011. http://www.thestar.com/news/canada/2011/12/12/canada_first_nation_to_withdraw_from_kyoto_protocol.html.

Tuinhof, Albert, et al. *Appropriate Groundwater Management Policy for Sub-Saharan Africa.* World Bank Strategic Overview Series No 5. Washington, DC: The World Bank, 2011. http://www.un-igrac.org/dynamics/modules/SFIL0100/view.php?fil_Id=205.

Turley, Carol, and H.S. Findlay. "Ocean Acidification as an Indicator for Climate Change." In *Climate Change: Observed Impacts on Planet Earth*, edited by T.M. Letcher, pp. 367–390. Oxford: Elsevier, 2009.

Turner, B.L. and Jeremy A. Sabloff. "Classic Period Collapse of the Central Maya Lowlands: Insights about human-environmenta relationships for sustainability". *PNAS* 109 (2012): pp. 13908–13914.

Turner, John, et al. "Antarctic Climate Change during the Last 50 Years." *International Journal of Climatology* 25 (2005): pp. 279–294.

Udry, Christopher. "Esther Duflo: 2010 John Bates Clark Medalist." *Journal of Economic Perspectives* 25, no. 3 (2011): pp. 197–216.

Ulrich, Roger S. "View through a Window May Influence Recovery from Surgery." *Science* 224 (April 1984): pp. 420–421.

UNCLOS. "The United Nations Convention on the Law of the Sea of 10 December 1982." Oceans and Law of the Sea, United Nations. Last updated August 22, 2013. http://www.un.org/depts/los/convention_agreements/convention_overview_convention.htm.

———. The United Nations Convention on the Law of the Sea of 10 December 1982. Provision Relating to the Conservation and Management of Straddling Fish Stocks and Highly Migratory Fish Stocks, United Nations Conference of Straddling Fish Stocks and Highly Migratory Fish Stocks. August 4, 1995. *The United Nations Convention on the Law of the Sea (A Historical Perspective).* http://www.un.org/depts/los/convention_agreements/convention_historical_perspective.htm.

UNCTAD. *The Biofuels Market: The Current Situation and Alternative Scenarios.* Geneva: United Nations, 2009. http://unctad.org/en/Docs/ditcbcc20091_en.pdf.

UNDESA. International Decade for Action "Water for Life" 2005–2015 (website). http://www.un.org/waterforlifedecade/index.shtml.

UNDP. Millennium Development Goals: Eight Goals for 2015 (website). December 2000. http://www.undp.org/content/undp/en/home/mdgoverview.html.

———. The Human Development Index. http://hdr.undp.org/en/statistics/hdi/.

———. *World Energy Assessment and the Challenge of Sustainability.* New York: UNDP/UNDESA/WEC, 2000. http://www.undp.org/content/undp/en/home/librarypage/environment-energy/sustainable_energy/world_energy_assessmentenergyandthechallengeofsustainability.html.

UNECE/FAO. *Forest Products Annual Market Review, 2010–2011.* Geneva: United Nations, 2011. http://www.unece.org/fpamr2011.html.

────. *Forest Products Annual Market Review, 2012–2013.* Geneva: United Nations, 2013. http://www.unece.org/fileadmin/DAM/timber/publications/FPAMR2013.pdf .

UNEP. *Decoupling Natural Resource Use and Environmental Impacts from Economic Growth.* A Report of the Working Group on Decoupling to the International Resource Panel. Geneva: United Nations Environment Programme, 2011. http://www.unep.org/resourcepanel/decoupling/files/pdf/Decoupling_Report_English.pdf.

────. *The Environmental Food Crisis: The Environment's Role in Averting Future Food Crises.* Nairobi: United Nations Environment Programme, February 2009. http://www.grida.no/files/publications/FoodCrisis_lores.pdf.

────. Ozone Secretariat: Treaties and Decisions (website). http://ozone.unep.org/en/treaties.php.

────. *Protected Planet Report: Tracking Progress toward Global Targets for Protected Areas.* Cambridge, UK: United Nations Environment Programme, 2012. http://cmsdata.iucn.org/downloads/protected_planet_report.pdf.

────. *Recycling Rates of Metals: A Status Report.* Paris: United Nations Environment Programme, 2011. http://www.unep.org/resourcepanel/Portals/24102/PDFs/Metals_Recycling_Rates_110412-1.pdf.

────. Report of the United Nations Conference on Environment and Development. Rio Declaration on Environment and Development, 1992. Rio de Janeiro, 1992. http://www.unep.org/Documents.multilingual/Default.asp?DocumentID=78&ArticleID=1163.

UNEP-WCMC. "Background to Forest Mapping and Data Harmonisation." 2007. http://wayback.archive.org/web/20070110002936/http://www.unep-wcmc.org/forest/fp_background.htm.

United Nations. Climate Summit. New York Declaration on Forests. September 23, 2014. http://www.un.org/climatechange/summit/wp-content/uploads/sites/2/2014/09/FORESTS-New-York-Declaration-on-Forests.pdf.

World Water Assessment Programme. *World Water Development Report 3: Water in a Changing World.* Paris: UNESCO / London: Earthscan, 2009. http://webworld.unesco.org/water/wwap/wwdr/wwdr3/pdf/WWDR3_Water_in_a_Changing_World.pdf .

Union of Concerned Scientists. *A Climate of Corporate Control: How Corporations Have Influenced the US Dialogue on Climate Science and Policy.* May 2012. http://www.ucsusa.org/sites/default/files/legacy/assets/documents/scientific_integrity/a-climate-of-corporate-control-summary.pdf.

United Nations. Convention to Combat Desertification. http://www.unccd.int/en/Pages/default.aspx.

────. Convention on the Law of Non-Navigable Uses of International Water Courses, 2014. http://legal.un.org/ilc/texts/instruments/english/conventions/8_3_1997.pdf.

────. Framework Convention on Climate Change. The Copenhagen Accord, 2009. http://unfccc.int/resource/docs/2009/cop15/eng/11a01.pdf.

────. Framework Convention on Climate Change. Decision 11/Cp 7. Land Use, Land-Use Change and Forestry. http://unfccc.int/resource/docs/cop7/13a01.pdf#page=54.

────. Framework Convention on Climate Change. Key Documents, 1992. http://unfccc.int/resource/docs/convkp/conveng.pdf.

────. Framework Convention on Climate Change. Kyoto Protocol, 1998. http://unfccc.int/resource/docs/convkp/kpeng.pdf.

────. "General Assembly Adopts Resolution Recognizing Access to Clean Water and Sanitation as Right." Meeting Coverage and Press Releases, 2010. http://www.un.org/press/en/2010/ga10967.doc.htm.

————.Minamata Convention on Mercury. http://www.mercuryconvention.org/Portals/11/documents/conventionText/Minamata%20Convention%20on%20Mercury_e.pdf.

————. *Report of the United Nations Conference on Environment and Development, Annex III, 2b*. Rio de Janeiro, June 1992. http://www.un.org/documents/ga/conf151/aconf15126-3annex3.htm.

————. "World Population Prospects. The 2012 Revision, Key Findings and Advance Tables." Working Paper No. EA/P/WP.227. Dept. of Economic and Social Affairs, Population Division, New York, 2013. http://esa.un.org/unpd/wpp/Documentation/pdf/WPP2012_%20KEY%20FINDINGS.pdf .

US Department of Agriculture. "Adoption of Genetically Engineered Crops in the US". July 2014. http://www.ers.usda.gov/data-products/adoption-of-genetically-engineered-crops-in-the-us/recent-trends-in-ge-adoption.aspx.

US Energy Information Administration. International Energy Statistics. Various years. http://www.eia.gov/cfapps/ipdbproject/IEDIndex3.cfm.

————. Residential Energy Consumption Survey. March 7, 2013. http://www.eia.gov/consumption/residential/ .

————. International Energy Outlook, 2012 and 2014. www.eia.doe.gov/oiaf/ieo/index.html.

————. "Tight Oil Production Pushes US Crude Supply to over 10 Percent of World Total." Today in Energy, March 26, 2014. http://www.eia.gov/todayinenergy/detail.cfm?id=15571.

————. *Annual Energy Outlook, 2014, with Projections to 2040*. Washington, DC: DOE/EIA-0383, April 2014. http://www.eia.gov/forecasts/aeo/pdf/0383(2014).pdf.

US Geological Survey. "Gas (Methane) Hydrates: A New Frontier." Marine and Coastal Geology Program, September 1992. http://web.calstatela.edu/academic/natsci/zzstuff/Transfer/Urban_Geology/357_Lectures/357_Lecture14/meth_hydrates_story.htm.

————. Mineral Commodity Summaries, various years. http://minerals.usgs.gov/minerals/pubs/commodity.

US Securities and Exchange Commission. "SEC Adopts Rule for Disclosing Use of Conflict Minerals." Press Release, August 22, 2012. http://www.sec.gov/News/PressRelease/Detail/PressRelease/1365171484002#.Uh-tbmxzapo.

Vanderklippe, Nathan, and Richard Blackwell. "How Lower Oil Prices Are Hampering Growth: Oil Patch Saddled with Discount for Canadian Crude; Lost Revenue Holding Economy Back." *The Globe and Mail*, April 18, 2012.

Van Dover, Cindy Lee. "Mining Seafloor Massive Sulphides and Biodiversity: What Is at Risk?" *ICES Journal of Marine Science* 68 (2011): pp. 341–348.

van Kooten, G. Cornelis, Harry W. Nelson, and Ilan Vertinsky. "Certification of Sustainable Forest Management Practices: A Global Perspective on Why Countries Certify." *Forest Policy and Economics* 7 (2005): pp. 857–867.

Vassiliou, M.S. *The A to Z of the Petroleum Industry*. Plymouth, UK: The Scarecrow Press, 2009.

Vaughn, Naomi E., and Timothy M. Lenton. "A Review of Climate Engineering Proposals." *Climatic Change* 109 (2011): pp. 745–790.

Verne, Jules. *The Mysterious Island*. France: Hetzel, 1874. Republished in 2008 by www.forgottenbooks.org.

Vicente, Pedro C. "Does Oil Corrupt? Evidence from a Natural Experiment in West Africa." *Journal of Development Economics* 92 (2010): pp. 28–38.

Vitsouek, P., et al. "Human Appropriation of the Product of Photosynthesis." *Bioscience* 36, no. 3 (1986): pp. 368–373.

Voigtländer, Nico, and Hans-Joachim Voth. "How the West 'Invented' Fertility Restriction." *The American Economic Review* 103, no. 6 (2013): pp. 2227–64.

Vörösmarty, Charles J., et al. "Global Threats to Human Water Security and River Biodiversity." *Nature* 467 (2010): pp. 555–561.

Wackernagel, Mathis, and W. Rees. *Our Ecological Footprint: Reducing Human Impact on the Earth.* Gabriola Island, BC: New Society Publishers, 1996.

Wagener, Amy. "Endangered Species: Traded to Death." In *EarthTrends.* Washington, DC: The World Resources Institute, August 2001.

Walls, Margaret. *Parks and Recreation in the United States: The National Parks System.* Washington, DC: Resources for the Future, 2007.

Wall Street Journal. "Rhino Horns Can Make You Sick, Vietnamese Moms to Be Warned." September 16, 2013. http://blogs.wsj.com/searealtime/2013/09/16/rhino-horns-can-make-you-sick-vietnamese-moms-to-be-warned/.

Wang, Yunshi, Jacob Teter, and Daniel Sperling. "China's soaring vehicle production: Even greater than forecasted?" *Energy Policy* 39 (2011): pp. 3296–306.

Ward, Frank, and Manuel Pulido-Velazquez. "Water Conservation Irrigation Can Increase Water Use." *PNAS* 105 (2008): pp. 18215–20.

Ward, Peter. *The Medea Hypothesis: Is Life on Earth Ultimately Self-Destructive.* Princeton: Princeton University Press, 1979.

Watson, J.E., and James E. Lovelock. "Biological Homeostasis: The Parable of Daisyworld." *Tellus B* 35, no. 4 (1983): pp. 286–289.

Watson, Reg and Daniel Pauly. "Systematic Distortion in World Fisheries Catch Trends." *Nature* 41 (2001): pp. 534–536.

Watts, Johnathan. "Land of Opportunity—and Fear—Along Route of Nicaragua's Giant New Canal". *The Guardian,* January 20, 2015.

Weart, Spencer R. *The Discovery of Global Warming.* Cambridge, MA: Harvard University Press, 2003.

Weinstein, Barbara. *The Amazon Rubber Boom 1850–1920.* Stanford: Stanford University Press, 1983.

Weizman, Martin L. "On Modeling and Interpreting the Economics of Catastrophic Climate Change." *The Review of Economics and Statistics* 91 (2009): pp.1–19.

———. "Book Review—A Review of William Nordhaus' *The Climate Casino: Risk, Uncertainty, and Economics for a Modern World".* *Review of Environmental Economics and Policy* 9 (2015): pp. 145–156.

Westing, Arthur. *Global Resources and International Conflict: Environmental Factors in Strategic Policy and Action.* Oxford: Oxford University Press, 1986.

Whisson, M. "Two Proposals for Unlimited Fresh Water." *International Journal of Global Environmental Issues* 8 (2008): pp. 224–232.

White, Andy, and Alejandra Martin. *Who Owns the World's Forests? Forest Tenure and Public Forests in Transition.* Washington, DC: Forest Trends Association, 2002. http://www.forest-trends.org/documents/files/doc_159.pdf.

White House. *U.S. - China Joint Announcement on Climate Change.* November 12, 2014. http://www.whitehouse.gov/the-press-office/2014/11/11/us-china-joint-announcement-climate-change.

WHO. *Guidelines for Drinking-Water Quality,* 3rd ed. Geneva: World Health Organization, 2008. www.who.int/water_sanitation_health/dwq/fulltext.pdf.

———. *Burden of Disease from Household Air Pollution for 2012.* Geneva: World Health Organization. 2014.

WHO and UNICEF. *Progress on Water and Sanitation, 2014 Update*. New York, UNICEF / WHO, 2014. http://www.wssinfo.org/fileadmin/user_upload/resources/JMP_report_2014_webEng.pdf.

Wiens, Kyle. "A Visit to the Only American Mine for Rare Earth Metals." *The Atlantic*, February 21, 2012.

Wilen, James E., José Cancino, and Hirotsugu Uchida. "The Economics of Territorial Use Rights Fisheries, or TURFs." *Review of Environmental Economics and Policy* 6, no. 2 (2012): pp. 237–257.

Wilkinson, Richard, and Kate Pickett. *The Spirit Level: Why More Equal Societies Almost Always Do Better*. London: Allen Lane, 2009.

Williams, Michael. *Deforesting the Earth: From Prehistory to Global Crisis, an Abridgment*. Chicago: University of Chicago Press, 2006.

Wilson, Edward O. *Biophilia*. Cambridge, MA: Harvard University Press, 1984.

———. *The Future of Life*. New York: Alfred A. Knopf, 2003.

Wiseman, John, T., Taegen Edwards, and Kate Luckins. *Post Carbon Pathways. Towards a Just and Resilient Post Carbon Future*. Melbourne Sustainable Society Institute. CPP Discussion Paper. April, 2013.

Wisser, D., et al. "The Significance of Local Water Resources Captured in Small Reservoirs for Crop Production: A Global Scale Analysis." *Journal of Hydrology* 384, nos. 3–4 (2009): pp. 264–275.

Wittfogel, K. *Oriental Despotism: A Comparative Study of Total Power*. New Haven: Yale University Press, 1957.

Wood, R., et al. *Shale Gas: A Provisional Assessment of Climate Change and Environmental Impacts*. A report commissioned by the Cooperative and undertaken by researchers at the Tyndall Centre for Climate Change Research, University of Manchester, 2011.

World Agroforestry Centre. *Creating an Evergreen Agriculture in Africa for Food Security and Environmental Resilience*. Nairobi, 2009. http://www.worldagroforestry.org/downloads/publications/PDFS/b09008.pdf.

World Bank. *The Cost of Pollution in China: Economic Estimates of Physical Damages: A Brief Status Report*. November 14, 2007. http://siteresources.worldbank.org/EXTUNITFESSD/Resources/1633787-1196098351543/CoPC_presentation.pdf.

———. Motor Vehicles (per 1,000 People). http://data.worldbank.org/indicator/IS.VEH.NVEH.P3.

———. *World Development Report*. Washington, DC: World Bank, 2003.

———. *World Development Report*. Washington, DC: World Bank, 2008. http://siteresources.worldbank.org/INTWDR2008/Resources/WDR_00_book.pdf.

———. Gross Domestic Product 2014. http://databank.worldbank.org/data/download/GDP.pdf.

World Commission on Environment and Development. *Our Common Future*. Oxford: Oxford University Press, 1987.

World Energy Council. *Global Transport Scenarios, 2050*. London, UK: WEC, 2011. http://www.worldenergy.org/publications/2011/global-transport-scenarios-2050/.

World Meteorological Association. "The Dublin Statement on Water and Sustainable Development." Paper presented at the International Conference on Water and the Environment, Dublin, January 1992. https://www.wmo.int/pages/prog/hwrp/documents/english/icwedece.html.

World Meteorological Association/UNEP. Global Ozone Research and Monitoring Project. *Scientific Assessment of Ozone Depletion: 2010*. Report No 53. National Oceanic and

Atmospheric Administration, National Aeronautics and Space Administration, United Nations Environmental Programme, World Meteorological Association, European Commission, 2011. http://ozone.unep.org/Assessment_Panels/SAP/ExecutiveSummary_SAP_2010.pdf.

World Nuclear Association. *The New Economics of Nuclear Power.* London, UK, 2005. http://pbadupws.nrc.gov/docs/ML1000/ML100050089.pdf.

World Nuclear News. "China Looks at Nuclear-Powered Cargo Ships." December 4, 2009. http://www.world-nuclear-news.org/IT-China_looks_at_nuclear_powered_cargo_ships-0412095.html.

World Nuclear Organization. *Decommissioning Nuclear Facilities.* Updated March 2014. http://www.world-nuclear.org/info/Nuclear-Fuel-Cycle/Nuclear-Wastes/Decommissioning-Nuclear-Facilities/#.Ui808Wxzapo.

World Resources Institute. *World Resources 2000–2001: People and Ecosystems: The Fraying Web of Life.* Washington, DC: World Resources Institute, 2000.

———. "Ok Tedi Mine: Unearthing Controversy." In *World Resources 2002–2004: Decisions for the Earth: Balance, Voice, and Power,* pp. 188–197. Washington, DC: World Resources Institute, 2003. http://pdf.wri.org/wr2002_case_oktedi_papua.pdf.

World Trade Organization. *World Merchandise Exports by Major Product Group and Region.* Table II.2, 2011. wto.org/english/res_e/statis_e/its2011_e/its11_merch_trade_product_e.htm,

———. *WTO Dispute Settlement: One-Page Case Summaries, 1995–2012.* Geneva: World Trade Organization, 2013. http://www.wto.org/english/res_e/booksp_e/dispu_settl_1995_2012_e.pdf.

World Wildlife Fund for Nature and Roundtable on Sustainable Palm Oil. www.wwf.org.au/our_work/saving_the_natural_world/forests/palm_oil/what_wwf_is_doing/roundtable_on_sustainable_palm_oil/.

World Wildlife Fund for Nature. *The Living Planet Report,* 2014. http://wwf.panda.org/about_our_earth/all_publications/living_planet_report/.

World Wildlife Fund for Nature and Dalberg. *Fighting Illicit Wildlife Trafficking: A Consultation with Governments.* Gland, Switzerland, 2012. http://www.dalberg.com/documents/WWF_Wildlife_Trafficking.pdf.

Worm, Boris, and Trevor A. Branch. "The Future of Fish." *Trends in Ecological Evolution* 27 (2012): pp. 594–598.

Worm, Boris, et al. "Impacts of Biodiversity Loss on Ocean Ecosystem Services." *Science* 314 (2006): pp. 787–790.

Wright, Gavin, and Jesse Czelusta. "Why Economies Slow: The Myth of the Resource Curse." *Challenge* 47, no. 2 (2004): pp. 6–38.

Yang, Shujun, et al. "Narrowing Down the Targets: Towards Successful Genetic Engineering of Drought-Tolerant Crops." *Molecular Plant* 3 (2010): pp. 469–490.

Yergin, Daniel. *The Quest: Energy, Security, and the Remaking of the Modern World.* New York: The Penguin Press, 2011.

———. "The Global Shakeout from Plunging Oil". *The Wall Street Journal,* November 30, 2014.

Young, Emma. "China Approves Colossal River Diversion Plan." *New Scientist,* November 2002. http://www.newscientist.com/article/dn3107-china-approves-colossal-river-diversion-plan.html#.VJPR914Ag.

Zalasiewicz, Jan, et al. "The New World of the Anthropocene." *Environmental Science and Technology* 44 (2010): pp. 2228–31.

Zand, Bernard. "Zero Hour in the Middle East: What the Arab World's Past Can Tell Us about Its Future." *Spiegel Online International*, March 8, 2011. www.spiegel.de/international/world/0,1518,749537,00.html.

Zartman, I. William. "Need, Creed, and Greed in Intrastate Conflict." In *Rethinking the Economics of War: The Intersection of Need, Creed, and Greed*, edited by Cynthia J. Arnson and I. William Zartman, pp. 256–284. Washington, DC: Woodrow Wilson Centre Press / Baltimore: The Johns Hopkins University Press, 2005.

Zettler, Erik R., Tracy Mincer, and Linda Amaral-Zettler. "Life in the 'Plastisphere': Microbial Communities on Plastic Marine Debris." *Environmental Science and Technology* 47 (2013): pp. 7137–46.

Zhang, Lijia. "Edinburgh Zoo's Pandas Are a Big Cuddly Waste of Money." *The Guardian*, December 7, 2011. http://www.theguardian.com/commentisfree/2011/dec/07/edinburgh-zoo-pandas-big-waste-money.

Ziv, Guy, et al. "Trading-off Fish Biodiversity, Food Security and Hydropower in the Mekong River Basin." *PNAS* 109, no. 15 (2012): pp. 5609–14.

Endnotes

1. Most resources can be turned into commodities. For example, agricultural resources can be used to produce grain, petroleum resources to produce crude oil, and copper deposits to produce copper ore. Grain, crude oil, and copper ore can be traded, which is a feature of commodities. A resource such as biodiversity cannot be turned into a commodity, which creates a problem in a market economy because it does not have a price. Similarly, beautiful scenery can be economically exploited through tourism but cannot be turned into a commodity. Nevertheless, a tale of resources is to some extent a tale of commodities.

2. Kurlansky, 2002.

3. Alexander, 1982.

4. Chazelas, 1968.

5. Kurlansky, 2002.

6. Kurlansky, 2002, pp. 349–353.

7. Kea, 2005.

8. Schivelbusch, 1993.

9. From a book first published in 1309; de Joinville, 1963.

10. Schivelbusch, 1993, p. 6.

11. Ibid., 11.

12. Pomeranz and Topik, 1999.

13. See the classic *The Fur Trade in Canada* by Innis, 1930.

14. There are exceptions. For example, the region around the Putumayo River in Peru was under control of the infamous rubber baron Julio Cesar Arana, who managed to enslave the local Huitoto Indians. Death by torture, disease, and flight from the area is reputed to have decimated the Huitoto population by thirty thousand. See Taussig, 1984.

15. For a chilling account, see Hochschild, 1998.

16. Ibid., pp. 119–121. See also Weinstein, 1983.

17. Pomeranz and Topik, 1999, pp. 126–129.

18. Craig, Vaughan, and Skinner, 1988. The Incas knew of the deposits and apparently controlled the harvesting so as not to endanger the seabirds.

19. See *Wikipedia* entry for Charles Townshend, http://en.wikipedia.org/wiki/

Charles_Townshend,_2nd_Viscount_Townshend.

20. Leonard, 2008.

21. For estimates of the value of the deposits, see Sicotte, Vizcarra and Wandschneider, 2009.

22. In 2015 Bolivia requested a ruling by the International Court of Justice that Chile grant Bolivia sovereign access to the sea. See *The Economist*, May 9, 2015.

23. He received the Nobel Prize for his discovery in 1918. The process became known as the Haber Process.

24. Off, 2006.

25. This hypothesis is referred to as the Prebisch-Singer hypothesis, after Prebisch, 1950, and Singer, 1950.

26. The long-term decline appears to have reversed itself in the first decade of the 21st century, caused by the rapidly expanding economies of India and China. This is discussed in Chapter 2.

27. In Canada, the high-tariff policy, implemented in 1879, was known as the National Policy, the last remnants of which did not disappear until 1988 with a free-trade agreement with the United States.

28. The main reason for price instability is that supply in the short run is fairly fixed (inelastic), which means any changes in demand will have a large impact on prices. Similarly, demand is relatively insensitive to price changes in the short run. For example, it takes time for people to change their behaviour in response to high oil prices; therefore, short-run supply disruptions—e.g., strikes—will also have a large effect on prices.

29. Examples included the International Coffee Agreement, International Cocoa Agreement, International Natural Rubber Agreement, International Tin Agreement, International Sugar Agreement, and the United Nations–sponsored Common Fund for Commodities.

30. Sachs and Warner, 1997.

31. For further evidence and discussion, see Barbier, 2011, Chapter 9, and Frankel, 2010.

32. There is now a substantial body of literature. See Deacon, 2011.

33. McArthur, 2013.

34. Vicente, 2010.

35. Amoore and Arbuthnott, 2013.

36. For a discussion, see Deacon, 2011.

37. See Sokoloff and Engerman, 2000.

38. A recent book by Acemoglu and Robinson, *Why Nations Fail: The Origins of Power, Prosperity and Poverty* (2012), explores the role of institutions in economic development, arguing that only countries with inclusive institutions that protect individual rights and encourage investments and effort have prospered and will prosper.

39. This view is associated with Barbier, 2011.

40. World Bank, *World Development Report,* 2003, pp. 59–82.

41. Barbier, 2011, p. 633.

42. Wright and Czelusta, 2004.

43. The Human Development Index, compiled by the United Nations, is a weighted average of measures of life expectancy, education levels, and purchasing power adjusted gross national income per capita. See http://hdr.undp.org/en/statistics/hdi/.

44. www.publishwhatyoupay.org.

45. See Extractive Industries Transparency Initiative, www.eiti.org.

46. See Beattie, 2009, pp. 124–125.

47. www.naturalresourcecharter.org.

48. Malthus, 1798.

49. Clark, 2007.

50. Ehrlich, 1968, p. 3.

51. Ibid., p. xi.

52. Jevons. 1866. The President's Material Policy Commission, 1952.

53. Meadows et al., 1972.

54. A second report by the Club of Rome was published in 1974 and was less gloomy. More comprehensive, it included variables for technological change in the models. The main constraint in the model was now waste generation, which could, of course, be minimized with appropriate policies. Mesarovic and Pestel, 1974.

55. See Lomborg, 2001, p. 137.

56. World Commission on Environment and Development, 1987.

57. Ibid., p. 43.

58. There are now many attempts to measure the value of ecosystem services. These are discussed in Chapter 6.

59. For a discussion of alternative measures of economic activity, see Constanza et al., 2009.

60. See Solow, 1974. Solow's analysis was expanded by Hartwick, 1977, who showed that society's consumption is sustainable if investments in each year are equal to the value of resource rents. This is known as the *Hartwick Rule.*

61. Pezzey and Toman, 2002.

62. This view is associated with Herman Daly. See Daly, 1990.

63. See Homer-Dixon, 2002.

64. Kurlansky, 1997.

65. The Hanseatic League was an alliance of merchant guilds and towns that controlled much of the trade in Northern Europe during the late Middle Ages.

66. Ponting, 2007.

67. See Krautkraemer, 2005, and World Resources Institute, 2000.

68. Rockström et al., 2009.

69. Interest in collapse of civilizations goes back a long time. See, for example, *The History of the Decline and Fall of the Roman Empire,* written by E. Gibbon in the latter part of the 18th century, and O. Spengler's *The Decline of the West,* published in the early 1920s.

70. Diamond, 2005.

71. Peiser, 2005.

72. Turner and Sabloff, 2012. Deforestation also exacerbated the drought through its impact on solar radiation.

73. Klare, 2001 and Klare, 2012.

74. Gat, 2000. See also Clark, 2007, pp. 124–128.

75. See Landes, 1998, pp. 422–441.

76. See Haglund, 1986.

77. For these and other examples, see Westing, 1986.

78. See Muttitt, 2011.

79. Beaumont and Walters, 2007.

80. See Ross, 2008.

81. See Lujala, 2010.

82. Ross, 2008.

83. Themnér and Wallensteen, 2014.

84. Summarized in Collier, 2009.

85. For a summary, see Samset, 2010, and Blattman and Miguel, 2010.

86. For a model and empirical evidence, see Boix, 2008.

87. Collier et al., 2003, and Rodrik, 1999.

88. See Ernst and Young, 2012.

89. http://www.foei.org/news/friends-of-the-earth-nigeria-era-launches-publish-what-you-pump-campaign/.

90. See Zartman, 2005.

91. Acemoglu et al, 2012.

92. Dyer, 2008, pp. 1–2.

93. Kelley et al, 2015.

94. For a more detailed discussion, see Chapter 9.

95. These issues, mainly involving ocean resources, are discussed in Chapter 10.

96. Solecki, Solecki, and Agelarakis, 2004.

97. See Reardon, ed., 2011, Chapter 4.

98. Bowles, Bowker, and Samsonoff, 2011.

99. Reardon, 2011.

100. Arsenic and antimony are metalloids, intermediate between metals and solid non-metals.

101. For an account of coltan as a conflict mineral, see Bleischwitz, Dittrich, and Pierdicca, 2012.

102. See US Geological Survey, *Mineral Commodities Summaries*, various years.

103. European Commission, Critical Raw Materials for the EU 2010.

104. http://en.wikipedia.org/wiki/Portland_cement.

105. World Trade Organization, World Merchandise Exports, 2011.

106. International Council on Mining and Metals, 2014.

107. This is known as the *Hartwick Rule*. See Hartwick, 1977.

108. The World Bank, 2011.

109. Radetzki, 2009.

110. Menzie, Singer, and DeYoung, Jr., 2005.

111. *The Economist*, February 16, 2013.

112. The EU is considering the introduction of some rules. See Angel and Farge, 2013.

113. Christian, 2006.

114. Sillitoe, 1995, p. 119.

115. Humphries, 2010.

116. Heap, 2005.

117. Cuddington and Jarrett, 2008, using statistical analysis, agree that the recent cycle was a supercycle, and find three previous cycles covering the same period as Heap.

118. See Radetzki, 2012. A newspaper report in 2012 claimed that "a mine that would have cost US$2 billion a few years ago is now US$5 billion." (Koven, 2012).

119. The giant nickel company INCO was taken over by Xstrata of Switzerland and Falconbridge by the Brazilian mining giant CVRD. Alcan was taken over by Rio Tinto, apparently because Rio Tinto did not believe that China's aluminum production could keep up with demand. The

other heavyweights in the base-metals industry are BHP and Anglo-American. BHP-Billiton is the world's largest diversified mining company, created through a merger between an Australian mining company (Broken Hill) and the Dutch company Billiton. See Reguly, 2007.

120. Strictly speaking, silicon is not a metal but a metalloid. However, it is commonly referred to as silicon metal. (See, for example, the annual Mineral Commodities Summaries by the US Geological Survey.)

121. US Geological Survey, *Mineral Commodities Summaries*, 2014.

122. Antonioli, 2011.

123. US Geological Survey, 2014.

124. Blackwell, 2007.

125. See US Securities and Exchange Commission, 2012.

126. US Geological Survey, 2014.

127. Bonel and Chapman, 2005.

128. Stueck, 2007.

129. Ibid.

130. Barouski, 2007.

131. For a summary of the impacts of mercury, see Flannery, 2010, pp. 183–188.

132. Note, however, that according to Table 2.2, the price of mercury has more than doubled in the last few years, indicating that a substantial demand for mercury still exists. The USGS identified gold mining as one of the sources of demand.

133. Minamata Convention on Mercury, http://www.mercuryconvention.org/ .

134. In Japan, where widespread poisoning occurred because of contamination of a river, the poisoning was referred to as the *itai-itai* or the "ouch-ouch" disease.

135. US Geological Survey, 2011.

136. See, for example, Miedema and Moll, 2013.

137. Keating, 2009.

138. Schipani, 2013.

139. Bonel and Chapman, 2005.

140. US Geological Survey, 2014.

141. See Stedje, 2009.

142. Massari and Ruberti, 2013.

143. US Geological Survey, 2009.

144. Massari and Ruberti, 2013

145. US Geological Survey, 2014.

146. Wiens, 2012.

147. Hensel, 2011.

148. Hensel, 2011. However, it should be noted that the use of export controls has a long history. See Radetzki, 2008, p. 16.

149. Barrett and Whittaker, 2010.

150. Gholz, 2014.

151. See Bernstein, 2000.

152. Berton, 1972, pp. 354–355.

153. Chancellor, 1999, p. 189.

154. Bogoslaw, 2009.

155. The gold sales stopped in 2010. See IMF, 2011.

156. Flynn and Giraldez, 1995.

157. Ibid., p. 184.

158. Chancellor, 1999, p. 252.

159. See *Wikipedia* entry for "Silver Thursday." http://en.wikipedia.org/wiki/Silver_Thursday.

160. Graphite, a soft form of carbon, has traditionally been used in refractories and for steel making and brake linings but has found new uses in batteries, composites, and electronics. The largest producer by far is China, followed by India.

161. The Kimberly Process, www.kimberly-process.com .

162. The complaint was launched in 2009 by the United States, Mexico, and the European Union and involved Chinese export restrictions on bauxite, coke, fluorspar, magnesium, manganese, silica carbide, silicon metals, yellow phosphorus, and zink. See WTO, 2013.

163. Behrman, 2014.

164. BBC News, January 7, 2014.

165. For a survey, see Bridge, 2004.

166. Dudka and Adriano, 1997.

167. UNEP, 2011.

168. The world's largest tailings dam and the world's largest man-made structure is a settling pond associated with tar-sands mining in Alberta, Canada.

169. See Coumans, 2002.

170. World Resources Institute, 2002.

171. Coumans, 2002.

172. Butler, 2012.

173. The International Cyanide Management Code, www.cyanidecode.org .

174. The International Council on Mining and Metals, www.icmm.com .

175. UNEP, 2011.

176. Greenpeace International and FOEI, 2009.

177. For a detailed analysis of the problems, see Chang, Wang, and Durak, 2010.

178. European Commission, An EU Strategy for Better Ship Dismantling, 2008.

179. Jefferies, 2014.

180. Ogunbuyi et al., 2012.

181. Ibid.

182. Tabuchi, 2010.

183. European Commission, Waste Electrical and Electronic Equipment, 2014.

184. For a summary of the report, see National Mining Association, 2007.

185. European Commission, Critical Raw Materials for the EU, 2010.

186. As part of the accession rules to the WTO, countries cannot restrict trade through the use of duties, quotas, export taxes, and other measures.

187. Smil, 1994, p. 246.

188. British Petroleum, 2013.

189. International Energy Agency, Key World Energy Statistics, 2014.

190. Smil, 1994, p. 117.

191. Ibid., p. 107.

192. Ibid., p. 103.

193. Ibid., p. 159.

194. Clay and Troesken, 2010.

195. Ibid.

196. Bell, Davis, and Fletcher, 2004, pp. 6–8.

197. See Tertzakian, 2006, p. 11.

198. Tertzakian, 2006.

199. For an excellent account of whaling, see Hoare, 2010.

200. See Robbins, 1992.

201. Ibid.

202. Davis et al., 1997.

203. Kovarik, 1998.

204. Tertzakian, 2006, p. 17.

205. See Tertzakian, 2006, Chapters 2 and 3.

206. Vassiliou, 2009.

207. Tertzakian, 2006, Chapter 2.

208. The last decades saw further consolidation in the oil industry. Chevron bought Gulf Oil in 1984, Chevron and Texaco merged under the name of Chevron in 2000, and Exxon and Mobil merged into ExxonMobil in 1998.

209. Tertzakian, 2006, p. 70.

210. Ibid., 2006. p. 72.

211. Organization of the Petroleum Exporting Countries: A Brief History, www.opec.org .

212. See the Statute, Article 2B published on its website.

213. A spot market is a commodity or asset market where the products are sold for cash and delivered immediately.

214. See the International Energy Agency, www.iea.org .

215. In its thirty years of existence, the strategic reserves have only been used three times: during the Gulf Crisis 1990–1991; in the aftermath

of the Hurricanes Katrina and Rita in 2005; and in 2011 as a response to the Libyan civil war.

216. Yergin, 2011, pp. 119–140.

217. A major factor in explaining the severity of the recession was the financial crisis caused by the collapse of the mortgage credit bubble in the United States, which rapidly spread to other countries. However, most indicators show the recession started before the collapse.

218. Yergin, 2014.

219. US Energy Information Administration, 2014.

220. Shafiee and Topal, 2009.

221. There is some doubt that the estimates of the reserves left in Saudi Arabia are correct—they may be overstated. See Simmons, 2005, pp. 69–100.

222. McGlade, 2012.

223. Yergin, 2011, p. 17.

224. Alarmists embraced the Notion of *Hubbert's Peak* named after the US geologist M.King Hubbert (Hubbert, 1982) who showed with the aid of a mathematical model that the discoveries of oil in an area could be described by a bell-shaped curve where discoveries would first keep up with exploration, then hit a peak and decline. Production would also follow a bell curve, with a ten-year lag behind the discoveries curve. It was argued that if this model is applied to world reserves and production, it would prove that the end of oil is near. It became known as the *Peak Oil Hypothesis* and has now been widely discredited (Radetzki, 2010).

225. Prado, 2013.

226. Yergen, 2011, p. 163.

227. Ibid., p. 164.

228. Schenk, 2012.

229. Bird, et al, 2008.

230. *The Economist*, August 3, 2013.

231. *The Economist*, March 3, 2012.

232. Alberta Energy, Facts and Statistics.

233. Figure quoted in Rubin, 2009, p. 46.

234. Gault, 2014.

235. Nikiforuk, 2008, p. 105.

236. Kelly et al., 2009.

237. Kelly et al., 2010.

238. The Royal Society of Canada, Expert Panel, 2010.

239. Parajulee and Wania, 2014.

240. *The New York Times*, August 22, 2011.

241. Vanderklippe and Blackwell, 2012.

242. European Commission, Transport and Environment, "Fuel Quality Monitoring."

243. Pembina Institute, 2012. The figures were based on a commissioned study by the European Union (Brandt, 2011).

244. The release of carbon into the atmosphere is estimated to be between 11.4 and 47.3 million tonnes. See Rooney, Bayley, and Schindler, 2012.

245. Alberta has a carbon tax of \$15/tonne. Most analysts argue that this is too low to have an impact.

246. For these and other energy-related statistics, see the annual report *Key World Energy Statistics* published by the International Energy Agency.

247. Baker and Hyvonen, 2011.

248. World Bank, 2013, Motor Vehicles per 1,000 People.

249. Wang, Teter, and Sperling, 2011. Economic studies have shown that when per-capita income reaches \$5,000, car ownership rapidly expands (Chamon, Mauro, and Okawa, 2012).

250. The International Energy Agency, 2014.

251. Yergen, 2011, p. 326.

252. *The Economist*, August 13, 2009.

253. Deffeyes, 2005, p. 78.

254. International Energy Agency, 2011.

255. R. Wood et al., 2011.

256. Ingraffea et al., 2014.

257. For a recent survey of the scientific literature, see Jackson et al., 2014.

258. US Energy Information Administration, 2014. www.eia.doe.gov/forecasts/aeo/.

259. Lake et al, 2013.

260. *The Economist*, November 26, 2011.

261. World Bank, 2007.

262. Goodell, 2006, p. xx.

263. *The Economist*, May 22, 2003.

264. Wright and Czelusta, 2004.

265. *The Economist*, February 24, 2011.

266. See Auty, 2005, pp. 193–207.

267. *The Economist*, April 24, 2008.

268. Ibid., July 23, 2009.

269. Zand, 2011.

270. Wright and Czelusta, 2004.

271. Inhofe, 2012.

272. The former Czech President Václav Havel was a prominent doubter, arguing that the global warming claim is an attack on freedom and democracy and reminds him of a communist conspiracy.

273. Union of Concerned Scientists, 2012.

274. Mellars, 2006.

275. See Behringer, 2010.

276. The Black Death, or Bubonic Plague, is believed to have originated in central Asia and spread to Europe from fleas carried by rats.

277. Behringer, 2010, pp. 125–127.

278. Dwyer, 2010.

279. *The Guardian*, April 19, 2010.

280. The history draws from Weart, 2003.

281. Behringer, 2010, p. 189.

282. Despite being located near a volcanic crater, the Mauna Loa Observatory's distance from industries apparently makes it ideally situated for carbon dioxide measurements, and the surrounding area has little vegetation, which is important as vegetation both emits and absorbs carbon dioxide. If the winds change direction, sweeping over the crater, the models can easily handle anomalies in the data. See earthobservatory.nasa.gov/IOTD/view.php?id=43182.

283. Intergovernmental Panel on Climate Change, 1990.

284. Ibid., 2007

285. Ibid., 2013.

286. United Nations Framework Convention on Climate Change, 1992.

287. See United Nations Framework Convention on Climate Change, The Kyoto Protocol, 1998.

288. *The Economist*, December 19, 2007.

289. Ibid.

290. United Nations Framework Convention on Climate Change, The Copenhagen Accord, 2009.

291. Preston, 2010.

292. InterAcademy Council, 2010.

293. The White House, 2014.

294. Despite claims to the contrary, 97–98 percent of climate scientists agree with the IPCC conclusions (based on a survey of 1,372 climate scientists). William R.L. Anderegg et al., 2010.

295. Solomon et al., eds., 2007, p. 685f.

296. See A.P. Sokolov et al., 2009.

297. Timothy Lenton et al., 2008.

298. These new models—energy-balance models—are simpler than the general circulation models used by the IPCC, using actual temperature data to estimate the sensitivity of the climate system, but they may not pick up some of the dynamic effects at play, such as the impact of volcanoes on circulation patterns.

See Amundsen, 2013 and Met Office, 2014.

299. Turner et al., 2005.

300. Cowtan and Way, 2014.

301. Schmidt, Shindell, and Tsigaridis, 2014.

302. Kosaka and Xie, 2013.

303. Chen and Tung, 2014.

304. Orr, 2005, and Turley and Findlay, 2009.

305. Arctic Council, Arctic Monitoring and Assessment Program, 2013.

306. UNEP, 1992. The Rio Declaration was adopted by the 1992 United Nations Conference on Environment and Development.

307. The best and most thorough treatment of cost-benefit analysis applied to climate change is Nordhaus, 2013.

308. Weitzman, 2015.

309. See Table 1 in Tol, 2009.

310. Pindyck, 2013.

311. Stern, 2007.

312. William Nordhaus estimates the damage per unit of CO_2 at only $7 per ton. See Nordhaus, 2008.

313. Stern, 2007, p. ii.

314. See, for example, Nordhaus, 2007, and Arrow, 2007.

315. Stern, 2013.

316. This is known as the "dismal theorem." See Weizman, 2009.

317. A. Leiserowitz et al., 2012.

318. Coady et al, 2015.

319. Nordhaus, 2013.

320. *The Economist*, April 16, 2013.

321. Ibid., January 5, 2013.

322. See Goodell, 2006.

323. Jaccard, 2006.

324. There are three capture technologies: pre-combustion, post-combustion, and oxyfuel combustion, and as of 2009 there were twenty experimental plants in operation. See Haszeldine, 2009.

325. *The Economist*, May 31, 2007

326. Haszeldine, 2009.

327. International Energy Agency, Carbon Capture and Storage.

328. International Energy Agency, "IEA Hails Historic Launch of Carbon Capture and Storage", 2014.

329. Ibid.

330. Finkenrath, 2010.

331. Black, 2005.

332. Morgan, 2014.

333. McQuaig, 2006.

334. GATT (The General Agreement on Tariffs and Trade) was the precursor of the World Trade Organization.

335. Ibid. p. 177

336. Ibid. p. 186

337. For a discussion, see Sorrell et al., 2009.

338. Jacobsen and van Benthem, 2015.

339. Examples quoted by Pascal Lamy, president of the World Trade Organization, in a speech to the Bali Conference on Climate Change.

340. White House, 2014.

341. Stiglitz, 2006.

342. For a thorough discussion of this issue, see Frankel, 2009.

343. Nordhaus also shows that such a tariff combined with carbon prices would provide an incentive for any miscreant country to follow with its own carbon price (Nordhaus, 2015).

344. UNEP, Ozone Secretariat.

345. World Meteorological Association, 2011.

346. McGlade and Ekins, 2015.

347. Carrington, 2014.

348. The Royal Society, 2009, and Vaughn and Lenton, 2011. The Vaughn and Lenton survey also mentions artificial upwelling of oceans and ocean alkalization as potential geoengineering techniques.

349. For a full discussion, see the Royal Society, 2009, pp. 13–15.

350. Strong, Cullen, and Chisholm, 2009.

351. The Economist, March 17, 2012.

352. American Physical Society, 2011.

353. Ibid.

354. Seitz, 2011.

355. Fleming, 2010.

356. Crutzen, 2006.

357. Barrett, 2008.

358. Keith, 2010.

359. Barrett et al, 2014.

360. See, for example, Hegerl and Solomon, 2009; Gu et al., 2003; and Braesicke, Morgenstern and Pile, 2011.

361. See Specter, 2012.

362. For a discussion, see Barrett, 2008.

363. For a discussion of the regulatory issues, see Reynolds, 2011.

364. Royal Society, 2009, p. xi.

365. Keller, Feng, and Oschlies, 2014.

366. International Maritime Organization, 1972.

367. See Convention on Biological Biodiversity, http://www.cbd.int/convention/ .

368. Lukacs, 2012.

369. The Climate Response Fund, 2009.

370. Oxford Martin School, 2011.

371. The International Atomic Energy Agency, 2014, Table 12.

372. U.S. Energy Information Administration, 2013.

373. Heal, 2009, p. 3.

374. Ibid.

375. Another European group is working on an experiment using magnetic fields and hot hydrogen (magnetic confinement fusion). See Jefferies, "Back to the Future", 2014.

376. Quoted in Lomborg, 2001, p. 129.

377. Jaccard, 2006, pp. 101–112.

378. It is claimed, however, that the necessary plutonium came from an Indian-designed facility. See Albright and Hibbs, 1992.

379. The Economist, April 26, 2011.

380. Highfield, 2011.

381. Cardis et al., 2006.

382. So far (2014), one hundred commercial reactors have been decommissioned, some of which were fully dismantled. See World Nuclear Organization, 2014.

383. See World Nuclear Association, 2005.

384. International Energy Agency, Nuclear Power, 2007.

385. Richter, 2010.

386. The International Atomic Energy Agency, 2003.

387. Macalister, 2009.

388. For a discussion, see The Economist, October 22, 2007.

389. See the International Atomic Energy Agency (https://www.iaea.org/) for a brief history.

390. In recognition of their dedicated efforts to prevent nuclear energy from being used for military purposes, the IAEA and its director general, Mohamed ElBaradei, were jointly awarded the Nobel Peace Prize in 2005.

391. See Albright, 2010.

392. See Richter, 2010.

393. The Economist, April 15, 2010.

394. See US Energy Information Administration, International Energy Statistics.

395. Solomon, 2008.

396. The Economist, March 10–16, 2012.

397. Rifkin, 2002.

398. Verne, 1874, p. 301.

399. See Jaccard, 2006, pp. 64–60 and Deffeyes, 2005, pp. 152–166.

400. MacKay, 2007.

401. See Jaccard, 2006, pp. 113–117.

402. Kenneth E. Boulding in Farvar and Milton, 1973.

403. Duflo and Pande, 2007

404. Graham-Rowe, 2005.

405. Demarty and Bastien, 2011.

406. *The Economist*, February 19, 2008.

407. Ziv et al., 2012.

408. Schneider, 2013.

409. *The Economist*, April 26, 2007.

410. MacKay, 2006, p. 73.

411. For a survey, see O'Rourke, Boyle, and Reynolds, 2009.

412. Allen et al., 2011.

413. See the International Energy Agency, Medium-Term Renewable Energy Market, 2014.

414. Delucchi and Jacobson, 2011.

415. Mengewein, 2013.

416. A recent study demonstrated that if the total amount of energy used in battery manufacturing is included in estimating the amount of energy produced by wind farms, battery technology does not make sense, but for solar technology it does. It is more energy efficient to shut down power generation in periods of excessive generation, or to use the surplus energy to pump water into dams. See Barnhart et al., 2013.

417. Erickson et al, 2014.

418. Colby et al., 2009.

419. Harrison (John), 2011.

420. Ibid. As a comparison, the typical night decibel level for rural areas is 25 dBA.

421. Shepherd et al., 2011.

422. Hanning and Evans, 2012.

423. Komendantova et al., 2012.

424. BBC News, November 2, 2009.

425. A 2012 newspaper article reported that on a sunny day Germany produced a record twenty-two gigawatts of electricity, which was 50 percent of total electricity production. Recent additions to capacity have made Germany the site for 50 percent of world photovoltaic solar capacity. *The Guardian*, May 28, 2012.

426. Hernandez et al, 2014.

427. Kovarik, 1998.

428. Yergen, 2011, pp. 647–650.

429. Searchinger et al., 2008.

430. See Bruinsma, 2003, pp. 98–106.

431. Ibid.

432. Bruinsma, 2003, p. 102.

433. See Brown and Jacobson, 2005.

434. Roundtable on Sustainable Palm Oil, http://www.rspo.org/ .

435. Reilly and Paltsev, 2007.

436. UNCTAD, 2009, p. 31.

437. Eisentraut, 2010, p. 21.

438. Ibid.

439. Leigh Haag, 2010.

440. See Chisti and Yan, 2011.

441. Jacobson, 2011, p. 1156.

442. World Energy Council, 2011.

443. MacKay, 2009.

444. http://whokilledtheelectriccar.com/.

445. See Bullis, 2008.

446. Reuters, March 25, 2013.

447. Seams, 2014.

448. *The Economist*, March 1, 2014, and *The Guardian*, October 7, 2014.

449. World Nuclear Association, 2014.

450. *World Nuclear News*, December 4, 2009.

451. Kanellos, 2008.

452. Streeter, 2012.

453. Jacobson and Delucchi, 2011.

454. The airline industry has been at the forefront of promoting carbon offsets. They have been criticized for not being effective.

455. Coenen, 2009.

456. See the website for the International Air Transport Association.

457. IATA, 2014.

458. Klein-Marcuschamer et al., 2013.

459. IPCC, 2012.

460. For a survey of studies, see Wiseman, Edwards, and Lucking, 2013.

461. MacKay, 2009.

462. Mathiesen, Lund, and Karlsson, 2011.

463. Jacobson and Delucchi, 2011, and Delucchi and Jacobson, 2011.

464. Delucchi and Jacobson, 2011, p. 1171.

465. World GDP was approximately US$76 trillion in 2013. See World Bank, 2014.

466. The following figures are based on Renewable Policy Network for the 21st Century, 2014.

467. Ibid.

468. European Commission, Climate Action.

469. Renewable Policy Network, Framework for Climate and Energy Policies.

470. European Commission, Climate Action, 2015.

471. For a full discussion, see Fischer and Preonas, 2010.

472. Kammen, Kapadia, and Fripp, 2004.

473. CNN, November 3, 2013.

474. Tilman, 2012.

475. Wilson, 2003.

476. The following is based on "Zoological gardens" in *Encyclopedia Britannica*, 15th edition.

477. Glavin, 2007, p. 47.

478. *Spiegel Online International,* January 13, 2010.

479. See Dowie, 2009.

480. See UNEP, 2012.

481. Dudley, 2008. There are six categories of protected areas: strict nature reserves and wilderness areas, national parks, natural monument or features, habitat species management areas, protected landscapes, protected areas with sustainable use of natural resources.

482. For a review of the success and failures of protected areas, see Mora and Sale, 2011.

483. Balmford et al., 2009.

484. CBC News, January 15, 2012.

485. *The Economist,* July 12, 2008. See also the study by Walls, 2007, for Resources for the Future, showing that total visits to national parks peaked in 1987 and have remained stable since then, while the number of camping visits have declined considerably. On a per-capita basis, the visits have declined.

486. Pergams and Zaradic, 2007, "Evidence . . . ."

487. Ibid.

488. See Louv, 2005 and Pergams and Zaradic, 2007, "Videophilia . . .".

489. Caley, Fisher, and Mengersen, 2014.

490. Mora et al, 2011.

491. The following is based on Wilson, 2003, Chapter 1.

492. *Smithsonian Science,* August 15, 2013.

493. *National Geographic Daily News,* May 17, 2010.

494. ter Steege et al., 2013.

495. Myers et al., 2000.

496. Wilson, 2003, p. 92

497. For a fascinating account of how the European settlement of the Americas shaped the world ecologically and economically, see Mann, 2011.

498. de Vos, et al, 2015.

499. For an excellent explanation of the role of extinctions and how their presence was discovered, see Kolbert, 2014.

500. Pimm, et al., 2014.

501. Vitsouek et al., 1986.

502. See the website of the IUCN, http://www.iucn.org/ .

503. McCord, 2012.

504. Paine, 1966.

505. For a critical assessment, see Cottee-Jones and Whittaker, 2012.

506. The study linked twenty-five thousand of the animal species listed under threat on the Red List to fifteen thousand export-related commodities produced in 187 countries. M. Lenzen et al., 2012.

507. Wilson, 2003, p. 58.

508. Beketov et al., 2013.

509. Brühl et al., 2013.

510. Goulson, 2013.

511. Mendenhall, Daily, and Ehrlich, 2012.

512. Ranganathan et al., 2008.

513. Perrings, 2007.

514. See Quammen, 1996.

515. For an interesting discussion of new trends in thinking about conservation, see Marris, 2011.

516. Sax, Gaines, and Brown, 2002.

517. Root and Goldsmith, 2010.

518. Ibid.

519. For an excellent discussion, see Kolbert, 2014.

520. World Wildlife Fund for Nature, 2014.

521. The numbers are associated with 95 percent confidence intervals with the 1970 interval set at zero and with the ensuing intervals becoming wider.

522. For a discussion, see Magurran et al., 2010.

523. Wackernagel and Rees, 1996.

524. World Wildlife Fund for Nature, 2014, p. 12

525. For these and other criticisms, see Fiala, 2008.

526. See the Millennium Ecosystem Assessment, 2005.

527. The Millennium Development Goals was agreed on at the Millennium Summit of the United Nations in 2000. The goals commit nations to achieve targets ranging from eradication of extreme poverty to reducing child mortality by 2015.

528. Wilson, 1984.

529. Gullone, 2000.

530. Ulrich, 1984.

531. For a full discussion, see Joye and de Block, 2011.

532. For a summary of evidence, see Frumkin, 2001.

533. The individuals who took part were contacted twice a day on their smart phones and were asked to report the extent to which they felt happy. This information was coordinated with satellite information on their location when they were contacted (MacKerron and Mourato, 2013).

534. For a discussion, see TEEB, 2010. For a survey, see Markandya et al., 2008.

535. Gallai et al., 2009.

536. Markandaya, 2008, p. 106.

537. Millennium Ecosystem Assessment, 2005, p. 70.

538. Eliasch, 2008.

539. Newman and Cragg, 2007.

540. Costello and Ward, 2006.

541. Gowdy, 1997.

542. Hardner and McKenney, 2006.

543. For a discussion of the most appropriate estimates of the economic value of various ecosystem services, see de Groot, Wilson, and Boumans, 2002.

544. Alternatively, the question can be one of how much people are willing to accept as a payment for the loss of a resource or a service.

545. Pearce, 2007.

546. Constanza et al., 1997.

547. Pearce, 2007.

548. McCarthy et al., 2012.

549. For a survey of the literature, see Martín-López, Montes, and Benayas, 2008.

550. See, for example, Morse-Jones et al., 2012.

551. Monbiot, 2014.

552. For a discussion, see Engel, Pagiola, and Wunder, 2008.

553. Bulte et al., 2008.

554. For a discussion, see the special issue of *Biological Conservation* in 2011, summarized in Minteer and Miller, 2011.

555. Secretariat of the Convention on Biological Diversity, 2010.

556. Convention on Biological Diversity, 2010.

557. Ibid., 2012.

558. Ibid., 2014.

559. Hurd, 2012.

560. Ibid.

561. Wagener, 2001.

562. World Wildlife Fund for Nature, 2012.

563. *The Times of India*, July 2, 2008.

564. Guilford, 2013.

565. See *The Wall Street Journal*, September 16, 2013.

566. Milman, 2014.

567. Sample, 2007.

568. Wagener, 2001.

569. *The Economist*, March 6, 2008.

570. Maisels et al., 2013.

571. Ibid.

572. Kalron, 2013.

573. *The Economist*, March 18, 2010.

574. Kareiva and Marvier, 2012.

575. Marriss, 2011.

576. Gammage, 2011.

577. Mann, 2005.

578. DeFries et al., 2012.

579. These so called *biodiversity offsets* are highly contentious as they will not protect critically important habitats from being destroyed.

580. Zhang, 2011.

581. Kew Royal Botanic Gardens.

582. Ibid.

583. *The Economist*, July 23, 2010.

584. See Williams, 2006.

585. Ibid. p. 45.

586. Ibid. p. 59.

587. It is estimated that 50 million died 1570–1620. Data from Antarctic ice-cores show that the resulting increase in forest cover led to a decrease in CO_2 concentrations (Lewis and Maslin, 2015).

588. Williams, 2006, p. 32. See also Heckenberger et al., 2007.

589. Harrison, 1992, pp. 13–18.

590. Williams, 2006, p. 92.

591. Ibid. p. 174.

592. Ibid. p. 296.

593. Ibid. p. 261.

594. Ibid. p. 394.

595. In general, forest classification is a controversial issue with little agreement on a uniform standard. UNESCO classifies forests into twenty-six categories, while UNEP has adopted a simplified system of six categories consisting of temperate needleleaf forests, temperate broadleaf and mixed, tropical moist, tropical dry, sparse trees and parkland, and forest plantations. See UNEP-WCMC.

596. FAO, 2011.

597. Sedjo, 2010.

598. Kim and Levitor, 2010.

599. See FAO, 2011, Table 4.

600. FAO, 2014.

601. UNECE/FAO.

602. Drouin, 2015.

603. Johnson, 2009.

604. Solberg et al., 2010.

605. Sedjo, 2010, p. 22.

606. FAO, 2014, Table 31.

607. Hosonuma et al., 2012.

608. Williams, 2006, pp. 437–464.

609. *The Economist*, April 12, 2007.

610. Ibid.

611. Amazon Fund, http://www.amazonfund.gov.br/FundoAmazonia/fam/site_en .

612. Ribeiro, 2012.

613. Margono et al, 2014.

614. Lang, 2012.

615. Ibid.

616. Lawson and MacFaul, 2010.

617. UNECE/FAO, 2011.

618. IUCN, 2010.

619. Asner et al., 2013.

620. Hosonuma et al, 2012.

621. A joint satellite mapping by the World Resources Institute and Global Forest Watch compared the degradation of intact forests between 2000 and 2013. Harris, Petersen, and Minnemayer, 2014.

622. The Pew Environmental Group, 2012.

623. The Canadian Boreal Forest Agreement, http://cbfa-efbc.ca/ .

624. FAO, 2011.

625. Ibid., p. 98.

626. See Myers, 1985, pp. 116–119.

627. World Health Organization, 2014.

628. Global Alliance for Clean Cookstoves, http://cleancookstoves.org/ .

629. United Nations, 1992.

630. International Tropical Timber Organization, www.itto.int .

631. Ibid. http://www.itto.int/sustainable_forest_management/ .

632. Blaser et al., 2011.

633. Asner et al., 2006.

634. The Economist, May 10, 2001.

635. Putz et al., 2008.

636. Ibid. See also Medjibe and Putz, 2012. Out of ten case studies, three found reduced impact logging to be less expensive than conventional logging, one showed the same cost, and the remaining six showed less cost for conventional logging.

637. Forest Stewardship Council, https://ca.fsc.org/ .

638. See van Kooten, Nelson, and Vertinsky, 2005.

639. Overdevest, 2010.

640. UNECE/FAO, 2013.

641. The Economist, September 25, 2010.

642. See Haener and Luckert, 1998.

643. van Kooten, Nelson, and Vertinsky, 2005.

644. Simula, 2010.

645. Ibid.

646. The most productive plantation trees are, in descending order, eucalyptus, tropical acacias, pines, hybrid poplars, and exotic larches. Eucalyptus can yield at a maximum of forty cu.

m/ha/year compared with a certified natural forest, which yields less than one. (Paquette and Messier, 2010).

647. Sedjo, 2009.

648. FAO, Planted Forests, 2012.

649. See Evans, ed., 2009.

650. For a survey, see Paquette and Messier, 2010.

651. The statistic is from Siry et al., 2009.

652. For a discussion, see White and Martin, 2001.

653. Hardin, 1968.

654. For a survey of her work, see Ostrom, 2010.

655. Porter-Bolland et al., 2012.

656. Berry, 2009.

657. Chatre and Agrawal, 2008.

658. For a good summary, see FAO, 2011.

659. Intergovernmental Panel on Climate Change, 2007.

660. United Nations Framework Convention on Climate Change. The Kyoto Protocol to the United Nations Framework Convention on Climate Change.

661. United Nations Framework Convention on Climate Change. Decision 11/Cp 7: Land Use, Land-Use Change and Forestry.

662. Creed and Makood, 2011.

663. For a discussion of the carbon markets, see UNECE/FAO.

664. Peskett and Brodnig, 2011.

665. For a review of existing legal frameworks, see FAO, 2011, Chapter 3.

666. Blaser et al., 2011, p. 39.

667. The Economist, September 25, 2010.

668. United Nations, Climate Summit, 2014.

669. See Chapter 2 in Montgomery, 2007.

670. Darwin, 1881.

671. Montgomery, 2007, p. 174.

672. Ibid., Chapter 3.

673. However, it is important to note that manure does not return all the nitrogen that the plants get from the soil; some ends up in the atmosphere as nitrous oxide. Therefore, soil fertility cannot be maintained in the long run unless additional manure from somewhere else is brought in.

674. Ibid., p. 44.

675. Branigan, 2008.

676. Montgomery, 2007, Chapter 4.

677. Ibid., p. 146.

678. Ibid., p. 164.

679. Ibid.

680. Ibid., p. 198.

681. See Bruinsma, ed., 2003.

682. Federico, 2005, p. 85.

683. For a fascinating account of the theories behind the development of maize, see Mann, 2005, pp. 220–224.

684. Carter and Miller, 2012.

685. See Olmstead and Rhode, 2007.

686. Table 8.1 shows that 23 percent of wheat production is traded compared with 13 percent of coarse grains and 8 percent of rice.

687. Kiple and Ornelas, ed., 2000.

688. *The Economist*, December 19, 2009.

689. See Jahara, Sabri, and Kennedy, 2006.

690. Bruinsma, ed., 2003, p. 102.

691. See Brown and Jacobson, 2005.

692. The following is based on Runge and Senauer, 2007. However, the by-product from bioethanol production from maize can be used for cattle feed.

693. Pear, 2012.

694. For a survey of the evidence, see Auld, 2012.

695. Reilly and Paltsev, 2007.

696. UNCTAD, 2009.

697. FAO, 2002.

698. See the Millennium Ecosystem Assessment, *Desertification Synthesis*, 2005.

699. Núñez et al., 2010.

700. United Nations Convention to Combat Desertification, http://www.unccd.int .

701. World Agroforestry Centre, http://www.worldagroforestry.org/ .

702. Quoted in Gassman et al., 2003.

703. Intergovernmental Panel on Climate Change, 2007.

704. Evans, 2009, p. 22.

705. For a discussion, see Cassman et al., 2003.

706. *The Economist*, August 26, 2010.

707. Klink and Machado, 2005.

708. FAO, 2009.

709. Ibid.

710. Mueller et al., 2012.

711. Pimental et al., 2005.

712. Seufert, Ramankutty, and Foley, 2012.

713. Evans, 2009.

714. Montgomery, 2007, p. 211.

715. Evans, 2009.

716. An article in *Science* modelled and compared the impact on wildlife of wildlife-friendly, low-intensity, low-yield farming with land-sparing farming, which minimizes demand for farmland by increasing yields. It found that the latter was more beneficial in saving wild nature in general (Green et al., 2005).

717. Garrity et al., 2010.

718. Sambasivan Swaminathan, 2006.

719. This section is based on Ronald, 2011.

720. US Department of Agriculture, 2014.

721. James, 2008, p. iv.

722. Kathage and Qaim, 2012.

723. For a summary of the evidence, see Qaim, 2009.

724. Board of Agriculture and Natural Resources, 2010.

725. Qaim, 2009.

726. Benbrook, 2012.

727. Relyea, 2011.

728. Klinkenborg, 2012.

729. The American Academy of Environmental Medicine, 2009.

730. See, for example, A. Finamore et al., 2008, and Malatesta et al., 2008.

731. Shaw, 2007.

732. However, several cases have been reported of transgenic seeds spreading into the countryside—which is hardly surprising. One case was discovered in North Dakota, where GM canola had interbred in the wild to form a new plant with different traits. Gilbert, 2010.

733. European Commission, 2010.

734. Snell et al., 2012. On the other hand, in a much-criticized 2012 study, researchers in Europe compared the impact over two years on rats consuming Roundup-resistant GM maize and rats drinking water contaminated with Roundup with rats eating non-GM maize and drinking non-contaminated water. The rats fed GM maize or Roundup had mortality rates two to three times more than the control rats and died quickly. Researchers also noted an increased incidence of tumours and impacts on the hormonal balance and on the functions of liver and kidneys. They attributed these effects to the endocrine disruption of Roundup and the exposure to the transgene in GM maize and its metabolic consequences. See Gilles-Eric Séralini et al., "Long-Term Toxicity of Roundup Herbicide and a Roundup-Tolerant Genetically Modified Maize," *Food and Chemical Toxicology* 50 (2012): pp. 4221–31. However, the study is more an indictment of Roundup than of genetic engineering itself and has been widely criticized because of its use of statistics and its small control group. The paper was subsequently withdrawn.

735. Alessandro Nicolia et al., 2014.

736. The Cartagena Protocol on Biosafety.

737. Gupta, 2010.

738. For a survey of research into second-generation genetic engineering, see Cressey, 2013.

739. Bruinsma, 2009, p. 4.

740. Steinfeld et al., 2006.

741. FAO, Tackling Climate Change through Livestock, 2012.

742. Campbell, 2010.

743. For a good discussion, see Garnett, 2009.

744. UNEP, 2009.

745. Ibid. Each ton of cereal contains approximately three million calories; 1.45 million tonnes contain 4,350 billion calories. Grain-fed cattle would provide 787 billion calories (each 1,500 calories of grain provides 500 calories' worth of meat, using a three-to-one ratio), which means the net addition to calories available for humans would be 4,350 − 787 = 3,563 billion calories. Each human with a diet of 3,000 calories requires approximately one million calories per year. The additional calories could therefore feed 3.563 billion people.

746. Gerber et al., 2013.

747. Slackman, 2009.

748. Evans, 2009.

749. For summary of evidence, see FAO, The State of Food Insecurity in the World, 2011.

750. Ibid.

751. FAO, WFP, and IFAD, 2014.

752. Alexandratos and Bruinsma, 2012.

753. World Bank, 2008.

754. The study that estimates a 100 percent increase uses the statistical link between GDP per capita and food demand to project what food demand will be in 2050. Tilman et al., 2011.

755. Alexandratos and Bruinsma, 2012.

756. Bruinsma, 2009.

757. Estimates for current- and future-yield growth may be overoptimistic. See Ray et al., 2013.

758. Ibid., p. 23.

759. The Economist, November 21, 2009.

760. Duflo, Kremer, and Robinson, 2009.

761. Goyal, 2010.

762. Sachs, 2009.

763. With both inelastic (unresponsive) demand and supply in the short run, relatively small shifts in either lead to large changes in prices.

764. Banerjee and Duflo, 2007.

765. See Demeke, Pangrazio, and Maetz, 2009.

766. Dawe, ed., 2010.

767. The Economist, November 21, 2009.

768. FAO, 2011.

769. For a good discussion, see Mohan, 2007.

770. FAO, 1996.

771. The Economist, May 3, 2007.

772. For a summary of the debate, see The Economist, May 29, 2008.

773. Godfray et al., 2010.

774. The Economist, November 21, 2009.

775. Maxwell et al., 2010.

776. See IDRC.

777. The two-litre number comes from the World Health Organization. The WHO also defines reasonable access to water to a minimum of twenty litres per person per day within one kilometre of the place of residence. This figure takes into account the water needed for cooking and for hygiene. See World Health Organization, 2008.

778. See Chapter 5 in Linton, 2010.

779. Nace, 1974.

780. The Economist, May 20, 2010.

781. UNDESA.

782. United Nations, Meeting Coverage and Press Releases, General Assembly Adopts Resolution . . . , 2010.

783. New scientific thinking has moved away from the Darwin hypothesis. For a good summary, see Nash, 2001.

784. Hodge, 2002.

785. Wittfogel,1957.

786. Scarborough and Lucero, 2010.

787. See Postel, 1999.

788. Harrower, 2008.

789. See Hillel, 1982.

790. Postel, 1999, p. 41.

791. Gordon, Finlayson, and Falkenmark, 2010.

792. Postel, 1999, p. 92.

793. Estimates vary from 10 percent of irrigated lands to 25 percent of irrigated areas in arid and semi-arid regions. Smedana and Shiati, 2003.

794. Prüss-Üstün et al., 2008.

795. Goal number 7, Target 10. UNDP Millennium Development Goals.

796. WHO and UNICEF, 2014.

797. Buxton and Kolpin, 2002.

798. Lomborg, 2001, p. 152.

799. The Economist, October 12, 2013.

800. Liu and Yang, 2013.

801. Rijsberman, 2004.

802. A study on river basins integrating climate models, hydrological models, and

socio-economic data predicts that by 2050 increased domestic water use in developing regions because of increased incomes will in general have a greater impact on water scarcity than climate change or population changes. A secondary influence on future water scarcity is increased water use by industry and agriculture. Alcamo, Flörke, and Märker, 2007.

803. These figures are quoted in the press release following the publication of the *Third World Water Development Report*. See http://webworld.unesco.org/water/wwap/wwdr/wwdr3/tableofcontents.shtml.

804. Alcamo, Flörke, and Märker, 2007.

805. Dr. Allen was awarded the International Water Prize in 2008 by the Swedish International Water Institute. For a summary of his contributions, see http://www.siwi.org/prizes/stockholmwaterprize/laureates/.

806. Council of Canadians, 2013.

807. The virtual water trade is based on a notion of absolute advantage rather than the accepted theory of comparative advantage. For a discussion from an economist's viewpoint, see Reimer, 2012.

808. Karam, 2008.

809. Little, 2009.

810. *The Economist*, July 17, 2003.

811. Biswas and Bozer, 2014.

812. *Homeland Security News Wire*, January 21, 2011.

813. Micklin, 2007.

814. This is based on de Villiers, 2000.

815. The most comprehensive account is in Micklin, 2007.

816. Postel, 1999, pp. 100–101.

817. Smith et al., 2000.

818. Vörösmarty et al., 2010.

819. The concept of water security is widely used, but no agreement has been reached on what it means. Most would probably subscribe to the idea that we have water security if an accepted level of risks to humans and to ecosystems both in terms of availability of water and water quality can be agreed on. For a survey of the literature, see Cook and Bakker, 2012.

820. Young, 2002.

821. Kaiman, 2014.

822. *The Economist*, July 17, 2003.

823. Tuinhof et al., 2011.

824. Comprehensive Assessment, 2007, p. 398

825. GMR (Great Man-Made River) Water Supply Project, Libya.

826. See Gleick, Cooley, and Wolff, 2006.

827. Whisson, 2008.

828. Parker and Lawrence, 2001.

829. Nguyen, 2014.

830. Fields, 2009.

831. Rijsberman, 2004, p. 499.

832. See Peepoople.

833. *The Economist*, October 12, 2013.

834. See Comprehensive Assessment of Water Management in Agriculture, 2007.

835. Wisser et al., 2009.

836. Postel, 1999, pp. 173–174.

837. Calculated from data in Table "Sprinkler and Micro Irrigated Area", International Commission on Irrigation and Drainage, http://www.icid.org/sprin_micro_11.pdf .

838. Rijsberman, "Sanitation and Access to Clean Water," 2004,

839. Ward and Velazquez, 2008.

840. Tanji and Kielen, 2002.

841. For a survey, see Yang et al., 2010.

842. The Dublin Statement on Water and Sustainable Development, http://www.wmo.int/pages/prog/hwrp/documents/english/icwedece.html ,1992.

843. Global Water Partnership.

844. *The Economist*, July 17, 2003.

845. Segerfeldt, 2005, p. 22.

846. Brichieri-Colombi, 2009, p. 6.

847. Segerfeldt, 2005, p. 45.

848. Palaniappan et al., 2004.

849. Segerfeldt, 2005, p. 31.

850. Ibid., pp. 84–88.

851. Ostrom, 2010.

852. *The Economist*, May 20, 2010.

853. Delli Priscoli and Wolf, 2009, p. 16.

854. Reuters, May 7, 2010.

855. Brichieri-Colombi, 2009.

856. Convention on the Law of Non-Navigational Uses of International Water Courses.

857. See McCaffrey, 2001.

858. A similar convention is being prepared for international aquifers.

859. Salman, 2007.

860. See Gleick, ed., 2004, pp. 234–255.

861. Pacific Institute, Water Conflict, 2014. http://worldwater.org/water-conflict/.

862. See FAO, 2008.

863. Davidson, 2012.

864. Postel, 2010.

865. Glover, 2006, pp. 1–2.

866. Finn, September 30, 2013.

867. Arnason, Kelleher, and Willmann, 2009.

868. For a readable but controversial account, see Menzies, 2003.

869. Watts, 2015.

870. Huete-Pérez, et al, 2015.

871. The search for the Northwest Passage led to numerous expeditions during the nineteenth century. The first successful expedition to navigate a passage was led by Roald Amundsen in 1906.

872. Khon et al., 2010.

873. Borgeson, 2008.

874. In the summer of 2013, the nineteen-thousand-ton ship *Yong Sheng* travelled from China to Europe via the Northeast Passage in thirty-five days compared with forty-eight days for the Suez Canal route. The same summer, the Danish-owned Nordic bulk carrier *Orion* carried a seventy-three-thousand-ton cargo of metallurgical coal through the Northwest Passage from Vancouver to Finland, saving five days and US$80,000 in fuel costs. See Binkley, 2013.

875. The first descent into the Mariana Trench was in 1960, when an American and a Frenchman reached the bottom in *Trieste*, a submersible operated by the US Navy.

876. Ramirez-Llodra et al., 2011.

877. Suttle, 2005.

878. McKie, 2012.

879. Fenical et al., 2013.

880. One of the results of the treaty is that Portuguese is spoken in Brazil, parts of which lie east of the demarcation line, while the rest of South America is Spanish speaking. The treaty has also been used recently as a justification for the Argentinian claim of the Falkland Islands (the Malvinas). For an interesting account, see Brown, 2011.

881. This is based on UNCLOS, 1998.

882. UNCLOS, 1982. One hundred and sixty countries have ratified the convention.

883. See the website of the National Oceanic and Atmospheric Administration.

884. Churchill, 2012.

885. BBC News, May 13, 2009.

886. Ibid., June 27, 2011.

887. Leroux and Mbengue, 2010.

888. Powell, 2011.

889. Sharma, 2011.

890. MacDonald and Welsch, 2012.

891. Ramirez-Llodra, 2011, p. 11.

892. Van Dover, 2011.

893. See US Geological Survey, Fact Sheet, *Gas (Methane) Hydrates*, 1992.

894. Ramirez-Llodra et al., 2011, p. 6.

895. International Maritime Organization, 1972.

896. Bialik, 2009.

897. Erikson et al., 2014.

898. See Allsopp et al., 2006.

899. Ramirez-Llodra et al., 2011, p. 5.

900. Zettler, Mincer, and Amaral-Zettler, 2013.

901. Erikson et al., 2014.

902. Lebreton and Borrero, 2013.

903. The high figure often quoted does not seem to be based on fact. See Geoghegan, 2013.

904. Orr et al., 2005.

905. Fish migration caused by climate change is already taking place. See Cheung et al., 2013.

906. Ramirez-Llodra et al., p. 15.

907. Phrampus and Hornback, 2012.

908. Hoffman, 2005.

909. Goldman, 2013.

910. Hoffman, 2005.

911. Ibid.

912. See Kurlansky, 1997.

913. Kurlansky, 1997, p. 49.

914. Ibid., p. 132.

915. Ibid., p. 109. The fecundity of codfish was well known: "The codfish lays 10,000 eggs, the homely hen lays one. The codfish never cackles, to tell you what she's done. And so we scorn the codfish, while the humble hen we prize. Which only goes to show you, that it pays to advertise." Anonymous.

916. Emery, 2010.

917. Greenberg, 2010.

918. BBC Asia News, January 5, 2013.

919. Pew Charitable Trust, 2014.

920. This is equivalent to high-grading in forestry and has been shown to have an adverse impact on the gene pool.

921. Pauly, 1998. More recent research argues that fishing down the food web does not happen everywhere; instead, fishing *through* the web is prevalent, which means increasing numbers of smaller target fish are added to the catches. See Essington, Beaudreau, and Wiedenman, 2005.

922. See Clover, 2008, p. 88.

923. Ibid., p. 92.

924. Norse et al., 2012.

925. Watson and Pauly, 2001.

926. Myers and Worm, 2003.

927. Worm et al., 2006.

928. FAO, *The State of World Fisheries and Aquaculture*, 2012.

929. Ibid.

930. Worm and Branch, 2012.

931. Fiedler et al., 2012.

932. Hixon and Tissot, 2006.

933. Davis et al., 2009.

934. Lobo et al., 2010.

935. Condie, Grant, and Catchpole, 2014.

936. The *Economist*, January 24, 2015.

937. FAO, 2009, Agreement on Port State Measures to Prevent, Deter and Eliminate Illegal, Unreported and Unregulated Fishing.

938. Flothman et al., 2010.

939. For an analysis, see Khalilian et al., 2010.

940. The *Economist*, December 13, 2007.

941. European Commission, 2009.

942. Ibid.

943. European Commission, 2014.

944. Harvey and Neslen, 2014.

945. See Wilen et al., 2012; Arnason, 2012; Deacon, 2012.

946. Costello et al., 2008.

947. Hilburn et al., 2003.

948. For a good discussion, see Clover, 2008, Chapter 14.

949. For a discussion, see Deacon, 2009.

950. UNCLOS, 1995.

951. For a full list, see Cullis-Suzuki and Pauly, 2010.

952. Ibid.

953. The following is based on Sumaila et al., 2010.

954. Ibid.

955. FAO, 2014, The State of World Fisheries and Aquaculture.

956. Ibid.

957. Greenberg, 2010, pp. 40–43.

958. The *Economist*, December 30, 2008.

959. Greenberg, 2010, pp. 228–230.

960. Ibid., pp. 122–123.

961. Toropova et al., eds., 2010.

962. Juffe-Bignoli, et al., 2014.

963. For a discussion of the ecosystem services of the deep sea, see Armstrong et al., 2012.

964. See, for example, Robb et al., 2011.

965. For a discussion of the problems, see Corrigan and Kershaw, 2008.

966. Pauly, 2014.

967. The study estimated that for the major bottom-trawling countries, subsidies made up 25 percent of landed values, while profit per unit of landed value was only 10 percent. See Sumaila and Pauly, eds., 2007.

968. Pauly, D., 2006.

969. FAO, 2005.

970. See the annual report of the Marine Stewardship Council.

971. Jacquet et al., 2010.

972. Rockström et al., 2009. The other six planetary boundaries are ocean acidification, the concentration of stratospheric ozone, global freshwater use, land system change, chemical pollution, and atmospheric aerosol loading.

973. See Clark, 2007.

974. For a survey of the literature on the causes of the fertility declines, see Guinnane, 2011.

975. The Central Intelligence Agency, 2013.

976. United Nations, 2013.

977. Ibid.

978. See Guinnane, 2011, p. 599.

979. Voigtländer and Voth, 2013.

980. Guinnane, 2011, p. 601.

981. See, for example, Chowdhury, Ohno, and Axemo, 2010, and the earlier 2007 study by the World Bank, edited by Robinson and Ross, 2007.

982. For a different view about family planning and population control, see Connelly, 2008. Connelly argues that family planning was a misguided attempt to control world population, in many cases through coercive methods on par with eugenics.

983. Romaniuk, 2011.

984. Romaniuk, 2011, p. 11.

985. Dearing et al., 2012.

986. Crutzen, 2002, Zalasiewicz, Steffen, and Crutzen, 2010, and *The Economist*, May 28, 2011.

987. The previously quoted study (Dearing et al., 2012) of sediments in the Yangtze basin indicates that human activity has already left markers.

988. Subcommission on Quaternary Stratigraphy.

989. Monastersky, 2015

990. Lovelock, 1965.

991. Lovelock, 1979.

992. Watson and Lovelock, 1983.

993. Lovelock, 2009.

994. Ward, 1979.

995. See Flannery, 2010.

996. See, for example, Clutton-Brock et al., 1999.

997. Dawkins, 1976.

998. Kahneman, 2011. See also Shleifer, 2012.

999. Kahneman, 2011, p. 367.

1000. Thaler and Sunstein, 2009.

1001. Flannery, 2010, p. 20.

1002. Ibid.

1003. For a thorough discussion of the reasons, see Greenstone and Kelsey Jack, 2015.

1004. There is a discussion in the literature of the difference between happiness and well-being.

1005. Easterlin, 1974.

1006. For a survey of the literature, see Blanchflower and Oswald, 2011. See also Stevenson and Wolfers, 2008.

1007. Sacks, Stevenson and Wolfers, 2012.

1008. Skidelsky and Skidelsky, 2012.

1009. Keynes, 1978.

1010. Pieters, 2013.

1011. For a survey of the literature, see Jackson, 2009.

1012. Skidelsky and Skidelsky, 2012, p. 192.

1013. This issue has been thoroughly explored in Jackson, 2009.

1014. According to a study sponsored by Globe International, 2013.

1015. Flannery, 2010, p. 126.

1016. Flynn, 1987.

1017. Lynn and Harvey, 2008.

1018. Flannery, 2010, p. 122.

1019. Barrett, 2010.

1020. See Frankel, 2009.

1021. See Frankel, 2009, for a thorough discussion.

1022. Nriago, 1990.

1023. Barrett, 2011.

1024. Naomi Klein in her book *This Changes Everything: Capitalism vs the Climate* demonstrates how social movements can become catalysts for change (Klein, 2014).

1025. Easterly, 2006.

1026. For a survey of her pioneering work, see Udry, 2011.

1027. This could be achieved by the introduction of a guaranteed annual income, which is an old idea in economics. Another suggestion is to replace income taxes with progressive consumption taxes. This would directly target excessive consumption. See Frank, 2000, pp. 211–216.

1028. Piketty, 2014. He showed with the help of two simple equations that if the rate of return on capital (wealth) is consistently greater than the economic growth rates, capital's share of national income will keep increasing at the expense of labour. This is what is currently happening.

1029. See Wilkinson and Pickett, 2009.

1030. One study by Rosnick, 2013, estimates that a 0.5% yearly cut in working hours in the United States would result in one-quarter to one-half of the global warming projected to arise from the additional emissions if things continue as they are.

1031. There is a vast literature on sustainable cities. For a good summary, see McCormick et al., 2013.

1032. Tagliabue, 2013.

1033. United Nations Global Compact. http://www.unglobalcompact.org/AboutTheGC/index.html.

1034. Makower et al., 2014.

1035. Boyd and Richerson, 2009.

Index

About the author

Dr. Ingrid Bryan
Professor Emerita
Department of Economics
Ryerson University

INGRID BRYAN is professor emerita in the Department of Economics at Ryerson University. Born in Sweden, she emigrated to Canada in 1967 after undergraduate studies in Sweden, the United States, and England. She received her Ph. D. from the University of Alberta, Edmonton and spent most of her academic career at Ryerson University, Toronto where she served as chair of the department and dean of arts. Initially specializing in international trade and transportation, she has authored two previous books: *Economic Policies in Canada* and *Canada in the New Global Economy*, as well as academic articles on transportation and trade. However, more recently her research has concentrated on problems of global resource use, stimulated by first-hand observation of many critical issues during extensive travels on every continent. *Are We Running Out?* is the result. She lives near Toronto, Canada.

12799690R00294

Printed in Great Britain
by Amazon.co.uk, Ltd.,
Marston Gate.